THERMODYNAMICS OF HEAT POWER

THE MACMILLAN COMPANY
NEW YORK · CHICAGO
DALLAS · ATLANTA · SAN FRANCISCO
LONDON · MANILA

BRETT-MACMILLAN LTD.
TORONTO

Branca's Impulse Turbine (1629)

Thermodynamics
of Heat Power

VIRGIL MORING FAIRES

Professor of Mechanical Engineering
North Carolina State College

A revised edition of THEORY AND
PRACTICE OF HEAT ENGINES

The Macmillan Company · New York

© The Macmillan Company 1958

Printed in the United States of America

First Printing

Previous edition, under the title *Theory and Practice of Heat Engines*, © The Macmillan Company 1948

Library of Congress catalog card number: 57-10291

PREFACE

The first edition of this book, under the title of *Theory and Practice of Heat Engines,* was intended as a reappraisal of the contents of a short course. Inasmuch as this edition has the same objective and since the contents have been changed sufficiently to warrant another title, we might call it a reappraisal of the reappraisal. The modern concept of thermodynamics as a logical and unified discipline has been adopted: and while this book contains adequate descriptive material, the major emphasis has been shifted toward the development and application of theory, especially as applied to steady flow systems.

In the writing, I had students other than mechanical engineering majors in mind and I have tried to be interesting as well as instructive to these students. While the book is designed to appeal to those who wish to use a short book for a short course, some material must be omitted in the shortest courses, unless a survey type of coverage is used. The length, I feel sure, is such that the teacher has an opportunity in most cases to make some choice of topics.

There is a set of problems at the end of each chapter, with the answers to nearly all of them. The answers to the problems with steam as the system are based on the Combustion Engineering Company tables. This company may be willing to furnish their tables for loan to students; these same tables are reproduced completely in *Problems on Thermodynamics* (Faires, Brewer, and Simmang), which some teachers may care to use for a supplementary source of problems and for the convenience of the tables and charts in it.

I am grateful to the manufacturers who have supplied information and illustrations, favors which are individually acknowledged in the text. I have drawn without inhibition from my *Thermodynamics.*

Comments, suggestions, and notification of errors are always gratefully received.

V. M. F.

Raleigh, N. C.

SYMBOLS

With few exceptions, the ASA standard symbols have been used, but the choice of symbols has been influenced by those used in the ASHAE *Guide* and in Keenan and Kaye *Gas Tables*.

A area; mass number; availability; A_n, availability, nonflow process; A_f, availability, steady flow.

a acceleration; temperature coefficient.

B volumetric percentage of a component in a mixture.

C a constant.

C_p, C_v molar specific heats at constant pressure and at constant volume.

c clearance ratio in engines and compressors; specific heat, Btu/lb-°F; c_p, specific heat at constant pressure; c_v, specific heat at constant volume; c_n, polytropic specific heat.

D diameter.

d a dimension; distance.

E general symbol for energy; total stored energy of a system; E_e, electrical energy; E_c, chemical energy and energy chargeable against an engine in obtaining the thermal efficiency; E_f, energy dissipated in friction (not a different kind of energy); E_a, available energy; E_u, unavailable energy; E_t, total stored energy.

e thermal efficiency; e_b, brake thermal efficiency; e_i, indicated thermal efficiency; e_k, combined or overall thermal efficiency; e_n, nozzle efficiency.

F force or total load.

g acceleration of gravity; g_o, standard acceleration of gravity.

H total enthalpy of w lb. of substance; head; H_m, enthalpy of a mixture; H_p, enthalpy of products of combustion; H_r, enthalpy of reactants; $H°$, enthalpy in standard state.

h specific enthalpy; h_f, specific enthalpy of saturated liquid; h_g, specific enthalpy of saturated vapor; h_{fg}, change of specific enthalpy during evaporation; h_{g2}, enthalpy of saturated vapor at state 2, etc.; $\bar{h}$, enthalpy of 1 mol of substance; $h°$, enthalpy in standard state (77°F).

I	correction factor for initial velocity in nozzles.
J	Joule's constant (≈ 778).
K	kinetic energy.
k	the ratio c_p/c_v.
L	distance; length; stroke of piston; L'', stroke in inches.
M	Mach number
M	molecular weight; lb./mol; M_x, molecular weight of gas X, etc.
m	mass in slugs; percentage steam bled in regenerative cycles; exponent in $pV^m = C$, which defines the pV relation at the end points of an irreversible process.
N	number of anything; number of mols of a gas; number of power cycles per minute completed by an engine.
n	revolutions per minute (rpm); polytropic exponent.
P	potential energy; represents the unit of a pound.
p	unit pressure (psi or psf); p_m, mean effective pressure (mep); p_{mI}, indicated mep; p_{mB}, brake mep; p_o, stagnation or impact pressure; p_r, relative pressure.
Q	heat; Q_A, heat added; Q_R, heat rejected; Q_r, radiated heat; etc.
q	heating value; q_l, lower heating value; q_h, higher heating value; q_v, heating value at constant volume; $\bar{q}$, heating value per mol of fuel.
R	specific gas constant, pv/T; $\bar{R}$, universal gas constant.
r	radius; ratios; reheat factor; r, compression ratio; r_c, cutoff ratio; r_p, pressure ratio; r_e, expansion ratio.
S	total entropy.
s	specific entropy; s_f, specific entropy of saturated liquid; s_g, specific entropy of saturated vapor; s_{fg}, change of specific entropy during vaporization; s_{g2}, specific entropy of saturated vapor in state 2; etc.
T	absolute temperature, usually degrees Rankine; T_o, stagnation temperature.
t	temperature, usually in degrees Fahrenheit; time; t_o, stagnation temperature.
U	total internal energy; U_p, internal energy of products, etc.; $U°$, internal energy at standard state.
u	specific internal energy; u_f, for saturated liquid; u_g, for saturated vapor; u_{fg}, change during vaporization; u_{f2}, for a saturated liquid in state 2, etc.

$\bar{u}$ internal energy of 1 mol of substance.

V total volume; V_D, displacement volume.

v specific volume; v_r, relative volume.

$\bar{v}$ volume of one mol.

υ velocity; speed.

W work; W_n, nonflow work; W_I, indicated work; W_B, brake work; W_K, combined work; W_f, flow work; W_p, pump work.

w mass in pounds; mass flow per unit time; w_f, specific fuel consumption; w_b, brake steam rate; w_i, indicated steam rate; w_k, combined steam rate.

x quality of a two-phase system.

y percentage (or fraction) of liquid (moisture) in a two-phase system.

z altitude; potential energy of 1 pound, ft-lb./lb.

Z atomic number.

α (alpha)   constant in specific heat equation.

β (beta)   constant in specific heat equation.

γ (gamma)   constant in specific heat equation; coefficient of performance; specific weight; angle.

δ (delta)   angle.

ϵ (epsilon)   effectiveness.

η (eta)   efficiency ratios; engine efficiency; combustion efficiency; η_b, brake engine efficiency; η_c, compression efficiency (adiabatic if not qualified); η_d, discharge coefficient; η_i, indicated engine efficiency; η_k, combined engine efficiency; η_m, mechanical efficiency; η_n, nozzle velocity coefficient; η_p, propulsive efficiency, pump efficiency; η_r, effectiveness of regenerative process; η_v, volumetric efficiency.

θ (theta)   represents unit of temperature; angle.

μ (mu)   degree of saturation; absolute viscosity.

π (pi)   3.1416 . . .

ρ (rho)   density.

ϕ (phi)   relative humidity; angle; used to mean *function of*.

ω (omega)   humidity ratio; angle.

Δ (delta)   indicates a difference or a change of value, $\Delta t =$ change of temperature or difference in temperatures, in accordance with the context.

ABBREVIATIONS

A/F	air/fuel ratio.	HP	high pressure.
ASA	American Standards Association.	hp	horsepower.
		ICE	internal combustion engine.
ASME	American Society of Mechanical Engineers.	ID	inside diameter.
ASHAE	American Society of Heating and Air Conditioning Engineers.	ihp	indicated horsepower.
		imep	indicated mean effective pressure.
atm	atmospheres, a unit of pressure.	kg.	kilogram.
		kw	kilowatt.
BDC	bottom dead center.	ln	natural logarithm (base e).
bhp	brake horsepower.		
bmep	brake mean effective pressure.	log	logarithm to the base 10.
		LP	low pressure.
Btu	British thermal unit.	mep	mean effective pressure.
cfm	cubic feet per minute.	mev	million electron volts.
cgs	centimeter-gram-second system.	mph	miles per hour.
		OD	outside diameter.
cm.	centimeter.	psf	pounds per square foot.
COP	coefficient of performance.	psi	pounds per square inch.
		psia	pounds per square inch absolute.
cpm	cycles per minute.		
cps	cycles per second.	psig	pounds per square inch gage.
da.	dry air.		
dg.	dry gas.	rpm	revolutions per minute.
ev	electron volt.	rps	revolutions per second.
F/A	fuel/air ratio.	TDC	top dead center.
fhp	friction horsepower.	TEL	tetraethyl lead.
fpm	feet per minute.	SAE	Society of Automotive Engineers.
fps	feet per second.		
fps^2	feet per second-second	v.	vapor.
gpm	gallons per minute.	wg.	water, gage pressure.

CONTENTS

THERMODYNAMICS OF HEAT POWER

1

PROPERTIES OF SUBSTANCES

1. Introduction. *Thermodynamics is that branch of physics which treats of various phenomena of energy, and especially of the laws of transformations of heat into other forms of energy, and vice versa.* Examples of such transformations are: the process of converting heat into work, the process of converting electricity into heat (because of a resistance), and any chemical reaction (heat of reaction). In engineering, the science is conventionally divided into two parts: chemical thermodynamics, which is devoted largely to reactions and solutions, and the thermodynamics concerned with the production and use of work and power. However, this division is fortuitous, as the areas merge at many points. Moreover, there are aspects of the science which may not be included in either of the foregoing parts, notably the thermodynamics of atomic processes, those processes in which the structure of the atom is changed.

This book deals with the heat-power phase of thermodynamics. Using the basic principles, we shall study the theory of gas turbines, air compressors, steam turbines, refrigeration, etc.

The principal sources of power are:

1. Steam engines,
   (a) reciprocating engines,
   (b) turbines.
2. Hydraulic turbines (not a heat engine).
3. Internal combustion engines,
   (a) gasoline engines,
   (b) gas engines,
   (c) oil (Diesel) engines,
   (d) gas turbines, jet propulsion, turbo-jet engines.

Minor quantities of power are generated in air engines using compressed air, by windmills, in so-called hot-air engines, and in engines operated by heat obtained directly from the sun's rays. The present plan of adapting atomic energy is to use an atomic reactor as a source of energy to generate steam for use in turbines. By far the largest amount of electrical energy is developed

in steam power plants, and considering the evidence at hand, this will continue to be true in the indefinite future.   About 2% of the electrical energy
in this country is produced from internal combustion engines, about 23%
from hydraulic turbines, and about 75% (about 100 million kw in 1957)
from steam power plants.   It is estimated that by 1980, about 9% of central
station electric power will be produced from hydroelectric installations,
about 68% from the combustion of coal and oil, and about 23% from nuclear
energy.*   Although a rapid growth of electrical power from nuclear energy
is predicted, the total growth of power needs (which double about every ten
years) is so large that the amount of conventional fuel-fired power in 1980
will be about four times what it is today.

The topics selected for inclusion cover principles which will be of most use
and interest to engineers in general.   While the basic laws are widely
applicable, we shall consider them particularly from the viewpoint of
machines which are producing power or consuming it.   Since power-
generating machinery and power-consuming machinery are common elements in modern civilization, no student of engineering can afford to consider
this subject of minor importance.   No matter what your major engineering
interest is, some of the principles that you learn in this study will almost
surely be of use.

2. The System and the Working Substance.   A *system* is that portion of
the universe, usually some certain quantity of matter or some particular
space, which we specifically wish to study.   It is enclosed by specified
boundaries or by boundaries which the mind constructs.   The *free body* of
mechanics is a system.   The difference between a free body and a thermodynamic system is in the mode of analysis.   In mechanics, one studies the
effects of forces on the system; in thermodynamics, one studies the system
from the viewpoint of the passage of energy either with or without the
passage of matter into and/or out of the system.

*The **working substance** in thermodynamics is a fluid in which energy can
be stored and from which energy can be removed.*   The purpose of storing and
removing energy is to bring about desired energy transformations, such as
transforming heat into work.   Examples of working substances are: *steam*
in a steam turbine, *air* in an air compressor, *air-fuel mixture* in an internal
combustion engine, and *water* in a hydraulic turbine.

A working substance or a certain mass of working substance may be
taken as the system.   However, the word *system* has a more general conno-
tation.   The system which the mind has surrounded with imaginary bound-

---

* McClure and Mellor, *Electric-power generation—past, present, and future*, Mech.
Eng., Vol. 78, p. 521.

aries may be an electric motor, a storage battery, or a shaft and propeller combination on an airplane. The mind can place the boundaries of the system wherever desired, as easily in one position as another, the choice being appropriate to the requirements of the problem (situation).

In a closed system, matter does not cross the boundaries. Energy may, however, flow into or out of this system. *An open system is one in which matter passes across its boundaries.* Energy may also pass across the boundaries either with the flow of mass or separately.

3. Phases of Substances. In general, a substance may exist in any of three *phases:* the solid phase, the liquid phase, or the gaseous phase. Under certain conditions, all three phases may coexist. *Melting* is the change of phase from solid to liquid. Heat must be added to cause melting. The change in the reversed direction, liquid to solid, is *freezing* or *solidifying.* The change from the liquid to the gaseous phase is called *vaporization,* and the liquid is said to *vaporize* (or boil). The change from vapor (gaseous phase) to liquid is *condensation,* and during the process the vapor is said to be *condensing.*

Not all substances pass through these three phases; some normally pass directly from the solid to the gaseous phase, a change of phase called *sublimation.* Moreover, many substances which ordinarily pass through the three phases may sublimate under certain conditions. For example, a piece of ice exposed to the atmosphere at temperatures below 32°F will sublimate, and given time (in certain climates), will pass entirely into the atmosphere as water vapor (steam). Dry ice, which is solid carbon dioxide, sublimates while it receives heat as you would ordinarily use it.

4. Properties and State. In order to compute changes of energy which have occurred in a system or a working substance, we must be able to express the behavior of the system in terms of descriptive characteristics which are called *properties.* Familiar properties include pressure p, temperature t, T, density ρ, and specific volume v.

The condition (state) of a substance in liquid or gaseous form is defined by two independent properties. If these two properties are stipulated, the *state* of the substance is set. By this, we mean that all other properties of the substance have certain particular values whenever the substance is in this particular state. There are a number of properties of interest and utility, but the working list for the heat-power engineer includes those mentioned above together with internal energy, enthalpy, and entropy. (These terms are studied later.) Now repeating the idea of the first sentence of this paragraph, we may say that if the pressure and specific volume of a certain pure substance are stipulated, the temperature will be a certain value, as will the specific values of internal energy, enthalpy, and entropy.

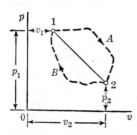

No matter what happens to the substance (no chemical change, though)—be it compressed, heated, expanded, or cooled—if it is returned to the stipulated pressure and volume, the other properties also return to values identical, respectively, with their original values. See Fig. 1.

Fig. 1. A substance whose state is represented by point 1 has a temperature T_1. If the pressure and volume are varied as defined by the path 1-A-2-B-1, returning to their original values, the temperature also returns to its original value T_1.

From your study of mathematics, you have learned that two coordinates (the values of x and y) locate (or define) a point which is known to lie in a given plane (the xy plane). Three coordinates locate a point in space. So it is with the properties of a pure substance. We look upon these properties as being coordinates, locating a point (*defining a state*), and we may picture this point, or any number of state points, on various planes; for example, the pressure-volume plane, Fig. 1, the temperature-en-

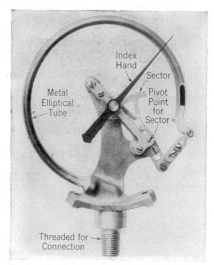

Courtesy Crosby Steam Gage and Valve Co., Boston

(a) Movement for a Bourdon Pressure Gage.

Courtesy United States Gauge, Sellersville, Pa.

(b) Pressure Gage.

Fig. 2. *Pressure gage.* The picture in (a) shows the mechanism in one type of pressure gage, known as the single-tube gage. The fluid enters the tube through the threaded connection. As the pressure increases, the tube with an elliptical section tends to straighten, the end that is nearest the linkage moving toward the right. The linkage causes the sector to rotate. The sector engages a small pinion gear. The index hand moves with the pinion gear. The whole mechanism is of course enclosed in a case, and a graduated dial, from which the pressure is read, is placed under the index hand, as seen in (b).

tropy plane, etc.   Any two properties may be used.   Because, as described, two properties locate a point in a plane, these properties are called *point functions.*

5. Pressure. Pressure, which is the force per unit area, is one of the most useful thermodynamic properties be‑ cause it is measured directly.   In terms of the kinetic theory of matter, the pres‑ sure of a fluid is due to the change of momentum of the molecules when they strike the boundaries of the system (walls of the container).

In practice, pressures above and below atmospheric pressure are deter‑ mined by means of a pressure gage (Fig. 2) or a manometer.   The dial of a pres‑ sure gage is marked to read the *gage pressure,* usually in pounds per square inch.   The gage pressure is the differ‑ ence between the pressure inside a vessel and the atmospheric pressure outside. Thus, to find the *absolute pressure* when this pressure is *above* atmospheric pres‑ sure, one must add the atmospheric pressure to the gage reading; that is,

Courtesy Taylor Instrument Co., Rochester, N. Y.

Fig. 3.   Aneroid Barometer. In this type of barometer, there is a flat cylindrical vacuum chamber. As the pressure on the chamber changes, the flat surface, acting as a diaphragm, moves in or out.   The movement of a point on this surface is magnified many times through a suitable arrangement of links into a movement of the pointer on the dial.   The reader is doubtless familiar with the inverted mercury tube barometer.

(a)   Absolute pressure (psia) = Atmospheric pressure + Gage pressure (psig).

The units of pressure in each of the foregoing terms must of course be the same.   Hence it will be convenient to recall the relations of the various units of pressure in common use by the engineer.   Barometers, Fig. 3, for measur‑ ing atmospheric pressure,* and vacuum gages, for measuring pressures below

---

* After Evangelista Torricelli (1608–1647) discovered the pressure of the atmosphere. Otto von Guericke (1602–1686) invented the air pump and set about producing a vacuum, He finally succeeded after having made two hemispheres, known as the Madgeburg hemispheres, which were capable of withstanding atmospheric pressure. Before a large audience of notables, von Guericke placed his hemispheres together and soon had most of the air pumped from the inside. A horse was hitched to each hemisphere, and try as they might, the two of them could not pull the hemispheres apart. Additional horses were hitched until there were thirty in all and still the hemispheres could not be pulled apart. The people, who knew nothing of the pressure of the atmosphere, were astounded when von Guericke broke the vacuum and the hemispheres *fell* apart. If von Guericke had not been a public official, renowned for his wisdom and kindness, his magic might have resulted in no good for him. Other scientists of the time were persecuted, even killed, for less.

atmospheric pressure, usually give the pressure in inches of mercury. Manometers may give the pressure in inches of mercury, in inches of water, or in terms of the height of the column of any fluid that may be used. The pressure in inches of mercury when multiplied by 0.491 psi/in. Hg gives the pressure in pounds per square inch. For example, let $p = 29.92$ in. Hg, which is **standard atmospheric pressure** (14.696 psia). Then

$$\text{(b)} \quad 29.92 \text{ in. Hg} = (29.92 \text{ in. Hg})\left(0.491 \frac{\text{psi}}{\text{in. Hg}}\right) = 14.696 \text{ psia};$$

use 14.7 psia on the slide rule. It is important to observe that in the equations of this book, the unit of pressure should in general be pounds per square foot.

$$\text{(c)} \quad \left(p \frac{\text{lb.}}{\text{in.}^2}\right)\left(144 \frac{\text{in.}^2}{\text{ft.}^2}\right) \longrightarrow \frac{\text{lb.}}{\text{ft.}^2}.$$

In some cases, the unit cancels out, so that it does not matter what unit is used as long as consistency is observed; this is true, for instance, in equation (a) above. However, in order to be sure of having the correct unit when it really matters, the student should get the habit of reducing all pressures before use in equations to pounds per square foot, or at least of showing the conversion. Thus, it may be convenient to write 50 psi as (144)(50) psf; then, if the unit does not affect the answer, the conversion factor 144 will cancel.

If the absolute pressure is less than atmospheric pressure, the gage reading is sometimes spoken of as the **vacuum** or **vacuum pressure.** In this instance, the absolute pressure is

(d)   Absolute pressure = Atmospheric pressure − Gage pressure.

The gage still measures the *difference* between the pressure inside the system and the pressure of the atmosphere.

6. Specific Volume and Density. The density ρ (rho) of any substance is its mass per unit volume,

$$\text{(e)} \quad \text{Density} = \frac{\text{Mass}}{\text{Volume}} \longrightarrow \frac{\text{lb.}}{\text{ft.}^3} \quad \text{or} \quad \frac{\text{slugs}}{\text{ft.}^3}.$$

If the mass w is measured in pounds and the total volume V in cubic feet, then the density is $\rho = w/V$ lb./cu. ft. The specific volume v is the volume of a unit mass, say in cubic feet per pound, and is the reciprocal of the density, $v = V/w = 1/\rho$. Unless otherwise stated, the density will be in pounds per cubic foot.

7. Temperature. "The temperature of a body is its thermal state considered with reference to its power of communicating heat to other bodies."* Temperature is a measure of the kinetic energy of the molecules; it tells of the *intensity* of energy, but by itself, it reveals nothing of the quantity of energy. In a sense, it is analogous to pressure in that pressure reveals the intensity of force but not the total force itself. Methods of using temperature to determine energy quantities will be considered later.

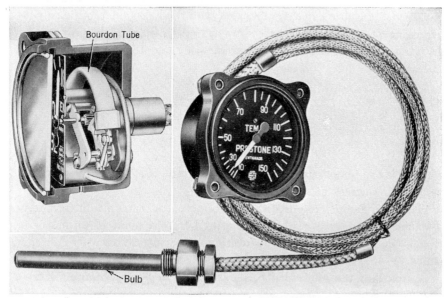

Courtesy United States Gauge, Sellersville, Pa.

Fig. 4. Aircraft Thermometer. The system, including the bourdon tube, is filled with a fluid which vaporizes at temperatures below the range of the instrument. The bulb is located at the point where the temperature is desired, for example, for oil, coolant, or air temperatures. If the temperature increases, more of the liquid in the bulb vaporizes, increasing the internal pressure. This increase in pressure actuates the bourdon tube, as described for Fig. 2, and the temperature is shown on the dial. The internal construction, as shown by the insert in the upper left-hand corner, is similar to that of the pressure gage.

Since there is some relation between the properties pressure and temperature, and volume and temperature, various substances may be used for thermometers. Mercury thermometers measure temperature because mercury expands and contracts in volume as the temperature increases or decreases. Constant volume gas thermometers measure temperature because the pressure of the gas increases and decreases with the temperature. Also, see Fig. 4. There are other means of measuring temperature, however. Electrical pyrometers are suited for accurate measurements in general and

* James Clerk Maxwell, *Theory of Heat.*

for high temperatures (say, above 500°F) in particular. Electrical pyrometers show temperature changes because the electrical resistance of metals varies with the temperature or because a measurable electric voltage, proportional to the temperature, is generated when the junction of two different metals is heated (thermocouple). Optical pyrometers, which measure the intensity of a particular light wave, have uses in industry for measuring temperatures of hot substances, such as molten metal.

There are two temperature scales in common use in this country, the centigrade, or Celsius, in scientific work, and the Fahrenheit, ordinarily used by engineers.* Recalling that between the freezing and boiling points of water, there are 100° on the centigrade scale and 180° on the Fahrenheit scale, we note that ($^{100}\!/_{180} = \frac{5}{9}$)

(f)
$$t_c = \left(\frac{5}{9}\right)(t_f - 32),$$

(g)
$$t_f = \left(\frac{9}{5}\right)t_c + 32,$$

where t_c is the temperature in degrees centigrade (Celsius) and t_f is the temperature in degrees Fahrenheit.

Thermodynamics requires the use of absolute temperature (or thermodynamic temperature) which is measured from a point of absolute zero. At this time, we shall accept the location of absolute zero on the Fahrenheit scale as −459.69° (below 0°F). Use 460 in slide rule work. Absolute temperatures T on the Fahrenheit scale are called *degrees Rankine* (°R);

(h)
$$T°R = t°F + 459.69 \approx t°F + 460.$$

For example, 60°F is the same temperature as 520°R, approximately. Absolute temperatures on the centigrade scale are called *degrees Kelvin,* written °K, and absolute zero is −273.16°C. Thus

(i)
$$T°K = t°C + 273.16.$$

For example, 40°C is the same temperature as 313°K, approximately. Notice the symbolization; lower case t for Fahrenheit (or centigrade) and upper case T for Rankine (or Kelvin). Engineers in this country use Fahrenheit and Rankine degrees. Temperatures below 0.01°R have been attained in the laboratory.

---

* Galileo invented a thermometer in 1592, but it did not have a well-founded scale. Gabriel Fahrenheit of Amsterdam, Holland, was the first (in 1720) to devise an instrument that indicated temperature in degrees, choosing the ice and boiling points of water as 32° and 212°, respectively. The centigrade scale was introduced in 1742 by Anders Celsius (1701–1744), a Swedish astronomer and professor at Uppsala.

8. Closure. Do not be lulled into complacency by the fact that you have previously covered many if not all of the concepts of this chapter, because it is necessary now to have these things on the tip of your tongue. So study diligently all of the material which may be reviewed for you in the first three chapters. It will pay off handsomely in a better understanding of subsequent chapters.

PROBLEMS

NOTE. *Where the atmospheric pressure is not given, it is understood that standard atmospheric pressure is to be used. This statement applies to all problems in this book.*

1. Atmospheric pressure is 24 in. Hg. (a) Gas in a tank is at a pressure of 20 in. Hg gage. What is its absolute pressure in in. Hg, in psf, in psi? (b) A pressure gage on a condenser reads 20 in. Hg vacuum. What is the corresponding absolute pressure in in. Hg, in psf, in psi?
    Ans. (a) 21.6 psia, (b) 283 psfa.

2. The same as **1** except that the barometer reads 30 in. Hg.
    Ans. (a) 3530 psia, (b) 4.91 psia.

3. The temperature of steam in a boiler is 405°F. What is its temperature in °R, °K, °C?   *Ans.* 208°C.

4. If the atmospheric temperature is 20°C, what is it in °F, °R, and °K?
    Ans. 67°F.

5. Suppose pressure is being measured by a column of water whose density is 62 lb./cu. ft. Explain how to convert a column height z in feet to psi and determine the conversion constant.
    Ans. 0.431 psi/ft.

6. A 51-cu. ft. tank contains 3 lb. of a gas at 80°F and a vacuum pressure of 24 in. Hg. (a) What is the absolute pressure in psia and psfa? (b) What is the gas's specific volume and density? (c) What is its temperature in °C, °R, and °K?
    Ans. (a) 418 psfa, (b) 0.0588 lb. per cu. ft., (c) 299.7°K.

7. Steam at a pressure of 150 psia and a temperature of 400°F occupies 3.223 cu. ft./lb. (a) What is its density in lb./cu. ft. and in slugs/cu. ft.? (b) Convert the pressure to inches Hg and feet of water (60°F). (c) Convert the temperature to °R, °C, and °K.
    Ans. (a) 0.31, 0.00965, (b) 5085 ft. H_2O, (c) 478°K.

8. Recall Newton's law from mechanics that force is proportional to acceleration (force on a particular mass, $F = ma$). Since this is so, the force of gravity, which is called *weight*, is proportional to the acceleration of gravity. A mass of 10 lb. weighs 10 lb. at standard gravity (32.174 fps²). What does this mass weigh on top of Pikes Peak where $g \approx 32.12$ fps²? at the equator at sea level where $g \approx 32.26$ fps²? (Note that quantities of matter in thermodynamics are absolute quantities, usually in pounds, not weights—although the quantity is often spoken of as a "weight" of substance.)

9-10. Note to the instructor. Numbers left blank at the end of each chapter will be advantageous for extra problems. Additional problems suitable for use with this text, together with a convenient group of useful tables and charts, are to be found in *Problems on Thermodynamics* by Faires, Brewer, and Simmang.

CONSERVATION OF ENERGY

9. Introduction. Energy E is inherent in all matter. Indeed, there is scientific evidence which suggests that matter and energy are fundamentally the same, or at least that mass may be converted into energy and energy into mass. The relationship between mass and energy defined by Einstein, whose hypothesis (1905) was one step in the development of atomic power, is (energy) = (mass)(velocity of light)^2, in which a consistent system of units is used. Since the velocity of light squared is a very large number, the energy corresponding to a particular mass is very large. For example, 1 lb. of matter is equivalent to nearly 39×10^{12} Btu—but this is not to say that it will *ever* be possible to convert a particular mass of any substance entirely into energy.

By *energy,* we mean a certain something which appears in many different forms, forms which are related to each other insofar as conversion can be made from one form of energy to another. This is admittedly not a definition. We are unable to define the general term *energy E* in a simple way, but we can define with precision the various forms in which it appears. This chapter considers the forms of energy with which we shall be concerned in this study, and it names some of the other forms.

10. Measuring Energy. Since the total amount of energy that a system possesses cannot be determined, we are accustomed to measure energy above some arbitrary datum. This practice is quite satisfactory, since in engineering we need know only the change in energy. Thus, we consider the potential energy of 1 lb. of water to be the *change* in potential energy that this pound of water would undergo in falling from the reservoir to the power plant. The level of the power plant is the datum level. We may think of this potential energy as being stored in the water. In a similar manner, other forms of stored energy are measured above some so-called datum state.

Energy is a *scalar* quantity, not a *vector* quantity. Velocity, a vector quantity, has direction and sense as well as magnitude. Energy has only magnitude. The energy of a system of bodies is simply the sum of the energies of the individual bodies. The total energy of a single system or substance is the sum of the magnitudes of the various forms of energy, such as kinetic energy and chemical energy, which the system or substance possesses.

During your study of physics, you became familiar with many of the units used to measure energy. Some of these units were established before the equivalence of the various kinds of energy was known. When this equivalence was at last realized, much experimental effort went toward trying to find the relations between the various energy units. The present tendency is to *define* these relations; for example,

1 Btu is equivalent to 778.172 ft-lb. = *J*.

Because of Joule's* contributions in establishing the relation between heat and work, we call this conversion constant Joule's constant and designate it by J; use $J = 778$ in slide rule work. See the Appendix for other conversion constants.

11. Mechanical Potential Energy. The mechanical potential energy P or gravitational energy of a body is the work which would be done by the force of gravity on the body as the body moves through a vertical distance z to some arbitrarily chosen datum level. The force of gravity on a mass of 1 lb. varies somewhat with geographic location and altitude, but it does not vary much unless the location is some distance from the earth. Thus, for locations close to the earth's surface, either Pikes Peak or Death Valley, we may assume with little error that the force of gravity on 1 lb. of mass is 1 lb.; for w_o lb. of mass, the force of gravity is approximately w_o lb. (exactly $w_o g/g_o$, where w_o is the mass in pounds, say, g is the acceleration of gravity at

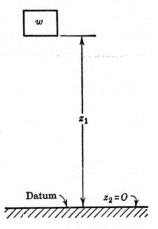

Fig. 5. Potential Energy. The body of weight w lb. undergoes a change of potential energy of $\Delta P = w(z_2 - z_1) = -wz_1$ ft-lb in falling through the distance z_1 ft.

the location where the force of gravity is desired, and g_o is the standard acceleration of gravity, 32.174 fps²—use 32.2 in slide rule work). With the approximation then of constant gravity, we have $P = wz$, or

(1) $\Delta P = w\Delta z = w(z_2 - z_1)$ ft-lb   and $\Delta P = \dfrac{w(z_2 - z_1)}{J}$ Btu,

* James Prescott Joule (1818–1889), an English scientist, was educated privately by a tutor, being at one time a student assistant to Dalton (§ 253). His researches were significant in the budding science of electricity as well as in the science of thermodynamics, in which he established two important fundamental principles: the equivalence of heat and work and the dependence of the internal energy change of a perfect gas upon temperature change (§ 45). As a result of this work, the modern kinetic theory of heat superseded the caloric theory of heat. Joule once remarked, "I believe I have done two or three little things, but nothing to make a fuss about."

where Δ means *change of*, and the change here and in subsequent equations is to be the second value minus the first, as $\Delta z = z_2 - z_1$; where w is in pounds and z ft. is the vertical distance of the body's center of gravity from the datum level. The value of ΔP is negative if the body or system undergoes a decrease in gravitational energy. See Fig. 5. Potential energy is energy *stored* in the system.

12. Mechanical Kinetic Energy. As you recall from your mechanics, a mass w lb. of a substance moving with a speed v fps possesses a certain amount of kinetic energy (with the earth as the reference body) equal to

$$(2) \qquad K = \frac{wv^2}{2g_o} \text{ ft-lb.} \qquad \text{or} \qquad K = \frac{wv^2}{2g_oJ} \text{ Btu,}$$

in which w lb. (and w/g_o slugs) is the mass of the body, v fps is its speed, and g_o fps² is the standard acceleration of gravity. (If you care to remember it, $2g_oJ \approx 50,000.$) Equation (2) is applicable to moving fluids, liquids, or gases as well as to rigid bodies. If a body undergoes a change of speed, the change of kinetic energy is

$$(\mathbf{a}) \qquad \Delta K = K_2 - K_1 = \frac{wv_2{}^2}{2g_o} - \frac{wv_1{}^2}{2g_o} = \frac{w}{2g_o}(v_2{}^2 - v_1{}^2) \text{ ft-lb.}$$

Kinetic energy is *stored* in the system. Divide the value from (a) by J to convert to Btu.

13. Internal Energy. Matter is composed of an aggregation of molecules which are moving continuously but haphazardly. According to the kinetic theory of gases, it is the impact of these moving molecules on a surface which accounts for the pressure exerted by a gas on the surface. Since the molecules have mass, we conceive of them as having kinetic energy analogous to that of any more tangible body or mass in motion. The motions involved in internal energy are the translational and rotational motions of the molecule, and the vibrational motions of the atoms which make up the molecule. In addition to this internal kinetic energy, substances have an internal potential energy, that is, an internal energy due to the relative positions of its molecules. We know that a change in the gravitational energy of a body occurs when the elevation of the body relative to the earth as a datum is changed, because the force of gravity is acting to aid or hinder this motion; that is, the change of potential energy results from a force of attraction between at least two bodies which change position with respect to one another. Now since there is an attractive force between molecules, we see by analogy that if anything happens to increase or decrease the average distance between molecules, there will be a change in the **internal potential**

energy, that portion of the internal energy due to the configuration of the molecules.

Summarizing from the foregoing discussion, we may define **internal energy** as that energy *stored* in a substance in the form of molecular energy that is due to the configuration of the molecules and to the motions of the molecules and their parts.

We do not know how to find the absolute quantity of internal energy in any substance. What must be known in engineering is not the absolute quantity but the change of internal energy. Above any convenient datum,

u　Btu/lb. represents the specific internal energy (1 lb.),
$U = wu$ Btu represents the internal energy of w lb.,
$\Delta u = u_2 - u_1$ and $\Delta U = U_2 - U_1$, the change of internal energy.

In thermodynamic practice, w is often a rate of flow, in which case the time unit is made clear by the context.

14. Work. For work W to be done, there must be a force acting on a body which moves. The **work** of a force F may be defined as *the displacement dx of a body* (considered as a rigid particle) *multiplied by the component F_x of the force in the direction of the displacement*, $dW = F_x \, dx$ ft-lb. This definition provides a basic unit of energy, the foot-pound, when the force is measured in pounds and the displacement in feet.

It is important to observe that work is energy *in transition;* that is, it exists only when a force is overcoming a resistance (which may be inertia only in an ideal system), and it is being done only when a force is "moving through a distance." When the point of application of the force ceases to move, there is no work. Contrast the concept of work with that of internal energy. The internal energy is energy which the body contains. On the other hand, a body never contains work. Work flows into a system; but after it is "in," it is not work; it may have been converted into internal energy. (We will study what happens in detail later.) Also, as you know from mechanics, work done on a body may be converted into kinetic energy and vice versa.

Work is a form of energy which can be converted 100% into other forms in the absence of friction of any kind, and for that reason, it is the most valuable form. For example, it can all be converted into electricity or kinetic energy, and electricity and kinetic energy can be fully converted into work in ideal frictionless systems. In fact, we could with logic take electricity as a form of work. It too can be converted 100% into other forms of energy in ideal systems; it is fully *available energy in transition;* but not so with kinetic energy, which is comparable in kind to internal energy in that it is *stored* in a body or system. Work can always be converted 100% into heat (§ 15). We say that work is not a point function (as contrasted with internal energy and pressure which are), because it has no relation to the state of a substance, which is represented by a point on a plane with properties as coordinates.

Since work can be measured at various points in a machine, adjectives must be applied in order to say what work is intended. Many thermodynamic computations give the **ideal work** W of the fluid, that is, the shaft work which the fluid would do (or have done on it) if there were no friction or other losses during the process. It is work done *by* or *on* the fluid. In a reciprocating engine, such as a Diesel engine, the actual work of the fluid in the cylinder, system (1), Fig. 6, is called the **indicated work** W_I when it is taken for a complete cycle of events in the cylinder, because it may be determined with an indicator (§ 82). Note that energy W_I is crossing the boundary of system (1). The actual work which passes a boundary at C is less

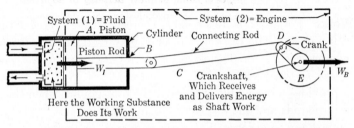

Fig. 6. Work in a Reciprocating Engine. Observe that shaft work (or any kind of work) is energy *in transition* in the sense that it exists by virtue of the movement of an element of a machine against a resistance or, in general, of the movement of a force through a distance. Shaft work may be transformed into kinetic energy and *stored* in the attached rotating parts to a limited extent. System (2) is outlined by the large dotted rectangle.

than W_I because of friction at the piston rings and cylinder walls, at the packing glands at B, and at the pin near C. In system (2), the engine, the work W_B which crosses the boundary (that is, delivered by the shaft) is smaller than W_I not only because of the losses up to C but also because of friction at the crank pin and at the crankshaft bearings (and other miscellaneous frictional losses; for example, the fanning of the air by the flywheel and crank). This work which is delivered by the shaft is commonly called **brake work** W_B, because it was first measured by a brake which absorbed all of the output of the engine via friction. Other names for brake work include **shaft work** and **delivered work.**

Since work may be done either by or on the system, it is convenient to use plus and minus signs to designate the direction of "flow." Let

Work done *by* the system be positive (as a steam turbine); an outflow of energy;
Work done *on* the system be negative (as an air compressor); an inflow of energy.

The symbol W stands for work done by or on one pound or any number of pounds of substance; the mass involved is defined by the context.

15. Heat. We shall use the word **heat** Q to mean *energy in transition (moving) from one body or system to another because of a temperature difference between the bodies or systems.** This transfer of energy occurs by conduction, by radiation, and by convection. We have confidence on the basis of personal experience that heat flows from a "hot" body to a "cold" body. Also, it is easy to accept the notion that if two bodies are at the same temperature, heat does not "flow." Thus when two bodies are in thermal equilibrium with the same environment, they are in equilibrium with each other and there will be no net interchange of heat between them (the heat from A to B is equal to the heat from B to A).

Conduction of heat occurs because the faster moving molecules in the hotter part of a body transfer by impacts some of their activity to adjacent molecules. Since temperature is a measure of the molecular activity, we are reminded that heat flows from the hotter to the cooler portion of a body, that the more active molecules lose some of their activity upon contact with the less active molecules. Heat is conducted through solids, liquids, and gases.

Radiant heat consists of electromatic waves, waves of the same nature as light and radio waves. Typical wave lengths of radiant energy in meters are as given in parentheses:† cosmic rays (10^{-14} and shorter), gamma rays (10^{-13}—10^{-11}), X-rays (10^{-11}—10^{-9}), ultra-violet (10^{-9}—10^{-7}), visible light (4×10^{-7}—7×10^{-7}), infrared or *heat* (10^{-6}—10^{-4}), microwaves, radar (10^{-2}—10^{-1}), television and FM radio (1—10), short wave radio (10—10^2), AM radio (10^2—10^3), maritime communications (10^3—10^4).

All bodies radiate heat; so a transfer of heat by radiation occurs because a hot body emits more heat than it receives and a cold body receives more heat than it emits.

Convection occurs because a moving fluid picks up energy from a warm body and delivers energy to a colder body. For example, the air surrounding the furnace of a hot-air heating system receives heat by radiation and conduction. This heated air, being lighter, will rise and circulate through the house, giving up energy by radiation and conduction to keep the house and contents warm. When this series of events happens, we say that heat has been convected, although the energy is not classified as heat while it is being transported but only while it is being received or discharged. In the systems which we shall study, the convected energy will generally not be

---

* In some physics books, *heat* is used to mean molecular energy, that which we here call *internal energy*. If you are accustomed to this notion of heat, you must make an effort to replace it with the foregoing definition.

† Shortley and Williams, *Elements of Physics*, Prentice-Hall.

considered as heat. This energy quantity will be cared for by energies carried by the stream.

Observe that heat, like work, is energy in transit, that it is a concept of that something which moves across a boundary into or out of a system by virtue of a driving potential which we call temperature. Heat Q which flows into a system may result in an increase of internal energy of the system or in work being done by the system, but after it enters the system, it is no longer heat. Like work, heat is not a point function; that is, it is not a property and cannot be represented by a point on a plane. Work is 100% available for conversion into other forms of energy, whereas heat cannot continuously be converted 100% into work even in the most perfect engine imaginable; this is a significant distinction between these two kinds of energy in transition.

16. Flow Work. If a substance is flowing into or out of a system being studied, a certain energy quantity is involved as the substance crosses the boundaries of the system. This quantity is called the *flow work* or *flow energy.* Imagine a fluid, liquid or gas, flowing in a pipe, Fig. 7. Let some small quantity G of this substance be on the point of crossing the boundary BB, entering the system. In order for G to get into the system, work must be done on it in an amount sufficient to move it against the resistance (pressure p) at the boundary. If the length L of G is small, the pressure on G at section C is virtually the same as at B, namely p. Thus the force F at C is pA, and the work is $FL = pAL = pV$, where $V = AL$ is the volume of fluid G pushed across the boundary BB. An energy quantity equal to pV thus crosses the boundary and enters the system. This idea is generalized for a movement of any volume V across any boundary against constant resistance when we say that the energy of flow crossing such boundary is pV, where p and V *are values at the boundary.*

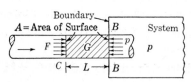

Fig. 7. Flow Work.

The flow work $W_f = pV$ is a point function because it depends on particular values of p and V at some boundary; therefore for boundaries 1 and 2, we may say

(3A) $$\Delta W_f = W_{f2} - W_{f1} = p_2 V_2 - p_1 V_1 \text{ ft-lb.,}$$

(3B) $$\Delta W_f = W_{f2} - W_{f1} = p_2 v_2 - p_1 v_1 \text{ ft-lb./lb.,}$$

where p is the absolute pressure in *pounds per square foot*, $V = wv$ is the volume of the total mass of substance crossing a boundary (usually during a particular time, as cfm), and v is the specific volume (for unit mass per unit time).

Since the energy to cause flow in a pipe does not create itself, we may think of the flow work W_f as originating, for example, in a pump which is located upstream, or in the potential energy of a reservoir. However, it is *not* pump work (but it may be); it exists because energy is being expended somewhere, somehow to cause a movement of a fluid across a boundary.

17. Other Forms of Energy. Manifestations of energy occur in many forms in which we shall have little or no concern in this book. However, the laws of thermodynamics apply to all forms of energy and are often useful in specialized fields of study. Other energies, which are to be considered as irrelevant unless specifically included, are: electricity (which we shall call combined work W_K on occasion), chemical energy (resulting from a change in molecular structure—as in combustion), electromagnetic emanations (light, radio, etc.), acoustic energy (sound waves), electrochemical energy— a source of electricity (storage battery), nuclear energy (resulting from a change in the structure of the atom's nucleus and a conversion of mass into energy), energy stored due to surface tension, and others.

18. Conservation of Energy. The law of the conservation of energy states that *energy can be neither created nor destroyed.** It is a law based on physical observations and is not subject to mathematical proof. In its application to energy transformations on this earth, there is no known exception, except as mass is converted into energy, and vice versa, and it is therefore an accepted principle and a reliable guide.

Historically, the ***first law of thermodynamics*** states that work and heat

---

* This law is not an idea which burst unexpectedly upon the scientific world. After scientists began working with energy, it was years before the law was comprehended. Benjamin Thompson (Count Rumford) (1753–1814), who has been called an arrogant and insufferable genius, really discovered the equivalence of work and heat in the course of manufacturing cannon (1797) by boring solid metal submerged in water. He was intrigued by the water boiling because of the mechanical work of boring, yet no heat had been added to the water. He convinced himself, but not the world, that the then accepted caloric theory of heat (a theory which supposed heat to be a substance without mass) did not explain all known phenomena of heat, and that work and heat were in some manner related phenomena. In his words, "Is it possible that such a quantity of heat as would have caused five pounds of ice cold water to boil could have been furnished by so inconsiderable a quantity of metallic dust merely in consequence of a change in its capacity for heat?" Other experimenters later discovered more evidence, until some fifty years after Rumford's cannon experiments, Joule, with assistance from Lord Kelvin, showed conclusively that mechanical work and heat are equivalent. (We are now just a few years from Joule. See the footnote on p. 11. Considering the age of the earth in billions of years and the age of man as about 1,000,000 years, thermodynamics is a new science—as is all science.) Rumford was teaching school in Rumford, Mass. (now Concord, N. H.) when he met, wooed, and won a wealthy widow. He was sympathetic with the "other" side at the time of the Revolutionary War and decided that it would be smart to leave Boston with the British, which he did, deserting his wife and daughter. Though he wanted to, he never returned to America, but he gained fame and honors in Europe and England.

are mutually convertible, but the tendency now is to broaden the statement to include all forms of energy: *one form of energy may be converted into another.*

19. Energy Equations for Closed Systems. The law of conservation of energy may be stated in several different working forms. For example, for any kind of a system, it should be evident if energy is neither created nor destroyed that

(4A) $\begin{bmatrix} \text{Energy} \\ \text{entering} \\ \text{system} \end{bmatrix} = \begin{bmatrix} \text{Increase (or decrease—negative)} \\ \text{of energy stored within the system} \\ (U \text{ for nonflow, } E \text{ for general case}) \end{bmatrix} + \begin{bmatrix} \text{Energy} \\ \text{leaving} \\ \text{system} \end{bmatrix}$,

(4B) $\begin{bmatrix} \text{Initial} \\ \text{stored} \\ \text{energy} \end{bmatrix} + \begin{bmatrix} \text{Energy} \\ \text{entering} \\ \text{system} \end{bmatrix} - \begin{bmatrix} \text{Energy} \\ \text{leaving} \\ \text{system} \end{bmatrix} = \begin{bmatrix} \text{Final} \\ \text{stored} \\ \text{energy} \end{bmatrix}$.

[ANY KIND OF SYSTEM]

The energy quantities are usually evaluated during a particular time interval.

A **closed system** is one in which mass does not cross its boundaries. Consider equation (4) with respect to the nonflow system of the fluid in

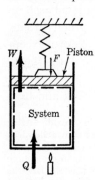

Fig. 8. Let heat Q flow into this system, which causes the fluid to expand, pushing the movable piston against any kind of resistance, say a weight and a spring which exerts a variable force F depending on the type and amount of compression of the spring. Thus, work W is done by the fluid in lifting the weight and compressing the spring. In the absence of turbulence within the nonflow system, the stored energy is entirely internal energy U, § 13; hence, we may write, after Equation (4A), the equation called the **nonflow energy equation** or the **simple energy equation:**

Fig. 8. Nonflow System. The surroundings are at p_0.

(5A) $Q = U_2 - U_1 + W = \Delta U + W,$

(5B) $dQ = dU + dW,$ or $dQ = du + dW,$

[NONFLOW ENERGY EQUATION]

where equation (5B) expresses the relation for infinitesimal energy quantities;

$\Delta U = U_2 - U_1 = \int dU$ is the change of internal energy which may be either positive (an increase) or negative (a decrease);

$Q = \int dQ = Q_{in} - Q_{out} = Q_{net}$, where it is seen that Q in equation (5) is the net heat when heat flows both into and out of the system; Q is *positive* when heat is *added*, *negative* when heat is *rejected* (flows out of the system);

$W = \int dW = W_{out} - W_{in} = W_{net}$, where we see that W in (5) is the net work done by the system and that energy in the form of work may flow out (system does work) and/or work may flow in (work is done *on* the system); W is *positive* when net work is done *by* the system; W is *negative* when net work is done *on* the system.

The meanings given to the algebraic signs are arbitrary but conventional. If the conservation of energy statement (4A) is applied to a closed system in which the substance is in motion, as the water and steam in a power plant, or in which chemical energy is stored, as fuel and air mixtures, we have

$$(5C) \qquad Q = E_2 - E_1 + W \qquad \text{or} \qquad dQ = dE + dW,$$
$$\text{[ANY CLOSED SYSTEM]}$$

where E is the total energy *stored* in the system and includes all appropriate kinds of stored energies (kinetic, potential, internal, chemical, etc.).

20. Steady Flow System. The most common system in engineering practice is a steady flow system, or one which is assumed to be steady flow. A steady flow system is one in which (1) the rate of mass flow is constant; the mass entering is equal to the mass leaving during any time interval; there is no increase or diminution of mass within the system; (2) the rate of energy flow is constant; the energy entering is equal to the energy leaving; there is no change of stored energy, $\Delta E = 0$; (3) the state of the working substance at any point in the system remains constant. For most practical purposes, a reciprocating machine can be assumed to be steady flow when the state at any point in the system varies cyclically through the same series of states; for example, an internal combustion engine at a constant load in a fixed environment.

In applying condition (1), we presume the truth of the law of **continuity of mass** (also called **conservation of mass**), which says that *mass is indestructible* (except, we know now, as mass is converted into energy in nuclear processes). Substitute the word *mass* for *energy* in equation (4) and you have other statements of this law. To put the law into a useful equation, consider Fig. 7 and let the average velocity of the fluid at section C in the pipe
line be v fps, then the quantity of fluid flowing is Av cu. ft./sec. where A sq. ft. is the
cross-sectional area. If the specific volume is v cu. ft./lb., then the mass rate of
flow is $w = Av/v$ lb./sec. If the area of

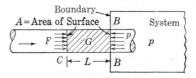

Fig. 7. Repeated.

the cross section changes, the law of the continuity of mass shows that

$$(6) \qquad w = \frac{A_1 v_1}{v_1} = \frac{A_2 v_2}{v_2} \qquad \text{and} \qquad w = A_1 v_1 \rho_1 = A_2 v_2 \rho_2 \text{ lb./sec.,}$$

for v fps, A sq. ft., v cu. ft./lb., and ρ lb./cu. ft. Equation (6) says that the mass of flow past boundary 1 is equal to the mass passing boundary 2— assuming no accumulation or diminution of mass between sections 1 and 2.

21. Steady Flow Energy Equation. From the foregoing discussion, we see that in a steady flow system the law of conservation of energy, statement (4), p. 18, reduces to

$$\text{Energy entering system} = \text{Energy leaving system.}$$

Thus, the problem reduces to one of accounting for the energy forms crossing the boundary. Of the various forms which have been previously mentioned, the ones which we use in this course are potential energy P, kinetic energy K, internal energy U, flow work W_f, heat Q, and mechanical work W. In Fig. 9, all of these forms are accounted for; P_1, K_1, and U_1 enter the system

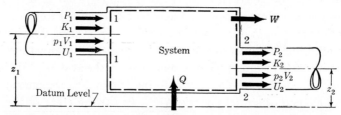

Fig. 9. *Energy Diagram of a Steady Flow System.* At section **1**, the pressure, specific volume, and velocity of the fluid are p_1, v_1, and υ_1, respectively; at section **2**, they are p_2, v_2, and υ_2. An *energy diagram* is a representation of a system with an indication thereon of all energy quantities passing in or out. This diagram represents the general case and includes all energy quantities, except chemical energy, with which we shall be concerned. In a particular application, one or several of the energy terms may be zero or negligible. Observe that W = the *net* work and Q = the *net* transferred heat.

as energy stored in the entering fluid, $p_1V_1 = W_{f1}$ is the flow work entering the system because of the work done at boundary 1 against a pressure p_1 to force the fluid into the system. Similarly, the flow work at exit, $W_{f2} = p_2V_2$, is that necessary to force the fluid out against the pressure p_2 just outside of the system. Since Q is shown as heat *in* and W as work *out*, Q will be positive when heat is added and negative when heat is rejected; W is positive when the system does the work (energy out) and negative when work is done on the system. The energy equation is then written, energy entering equal to energy leaving, Fig. 9,

(7A) $\qquad P_1 + K_1 + W_{f1} + U_1 + Q = P_2 + K_2 + W_{f2} + U_2 + W,$

or solving for Q,

(7B) $\qquad\qquad Q = \Delta U + \Delta W_f + \Delta K + \Delta P + W,$
$$\text{[STEADY FLOW ENERGY EQUATION]}$$

where all terms are in the same units and all Δ values are the second state property minus the first state property. Since the foot-pound is a relatively small unit for most engineering purposes, we use the British thermal unit (Btu) more often and Joule's constant J to show the conversion where necessary. Also, (7A) may represent one pound or any number of pounds of fluid flowing during some elapsed time. You should fix in mind the meaning of (7) and the method of determining the value of each term. We know that the change of potential energy ΔP is expressed by equation (1), $P_2 - P_1 = w(z_2 - z_1)/J$ Btu; that the kinetic energy $K = wv^2/(2g_oJ)$ Btu, equation (2), and $\Delta K = w(v_2{}^2 - v_1{}^2)/2g_oJ)$; that the flow work, equation (3), is $W_f = pV/J$ Btu and $\Delta W_f = (p_2V_2 - p_1V_1)/J$ Btu. Further details on finding Q, W, and ΔU are given later. There is no change in the convention of signs as previously given for the nonflow equation (5), p. 18.

22. Enthalpy. A *property* which is found to be frequently useful to engineers and scientists is one called **enthalpy** (H, h), pronounced en-thal'-py. It is a composite property applicable to all fluids and defined by

$$(8) \qquad h = u + \frac{pv}{J} \text{ Btu/lb.}, \qquad \text{and} \qquad H = U + \frac{pV}{J} \text{ Btu for } w \text{ lb.,}$$

where $H = wh$. It is seen to be a point function (or property) because it is defined in terms of properties only. The change in specific enthalpy is

$$(9A) \qquad \Delta h = \Delta u + \frac{\Delta pv}{J},$$

$$h_2 - h_1 = u_2 - u_1 + \frac{p_2v_2}{J} - \frac{p_1v_1}{J},$$

and in terms of differentials,

$$(9B) \qquad dh = du + \frac{d(pv)}{J} = du + \frac{p\,dv}{J} + \frac{v\,dp}{J}.$$

Enthalpy* being a point function, we have $\int dh = h_2 - h_1$ from state 1 to state 2. Since the absolute quantity of internal energy is not known, the absolute value of enthalpy is unknown. However, it usually matters little, because what we wish to know is the *change* of enthalpy. Enthalpy may be measured above any convenient datum.

23. Steady Flow Equation with Enthalpy. Inasmuch as the steady flow equation (7) includes the terms $u + W_f = u + pv/J$ and $U + W_f = U + pV/J$, we may replace these two terms with their equivalents, h and H. As we shall learn later, it will be as easy or easier to determine the change in enthalpy as it is to find the change in internal energy (not to mention Δpv). It is also true that we shall seldom be concerned with the

---

* Other names in use for this property are *total heat* and *heat content*, both of which should be avoided.

change in potential energy ΔP; it is not to be considered unless specifically included or unless it obviously should be included. The change of potential energy in a hydraulic power plant is the significant change, but in heat engines, elevation differences are relatively minor or $P_1 \approx P_2$. With these two revisions, the steady flow equation can be written in several forms as follows:

(10A) $$K_1 + H_1 + Q = K_2 + H_2 + W \text{ Btu,}$$

for any mass w lb.,

(10B) $$K_1 + h_1 + Q = K_2 + h_2 + W \text{ Btu/lb.,}$$
(10C) $$Q = h_2 - h_1 + K_2 - K_1 + W = \Delta h + \Delta K + W,$$
(10D) $$dQ = dh + dK + dW,$$

(10E) $$Q = \Delta u + \frac{\Delta pv}{J} + \Delta K + W \text{ Btu/lb.}$$

[ANY STEADY FLOW PROCESS]

Note that we can expect enthalpy to be a most helpful property. The form set out in equation (10C) will perhaps be most useful.

24. Applications of the Steady Flow Equation. In order to apply any energy equation to a device, *it is necessary to know what the device does* and more or less how it does it. One reason for this is that not all of the energy terms in an energy equation, (5) or (10), are applicable to all devices and machines. One or more terms usually drop out because they are irrelevant or inconsequential. Thus, the first step in the solution of a thermodynamic problem is to determine, by whatever means possible, the operation of the thing with which the problem is concerned. With this knowledge, you are in a position to decide, or tentatively decide, what energies are to be considered.

(a) Conventional Energy Flow.   (b) Actual Directions of Energy Flow.

Fig. 10.   Turbine as a System.

Consider a turbine, gas or steam. It receives a stream of fluid, more or less steadily, at high pressure which then expands to a low pressure, doing work. In stationary practice, this turbine will be fairly well insulated; that is, $Q \approx 0$. From a practical point of view, the speed at which the fluid approaches the turbine is not very different from the speed at which it departs, which is to say that there is not much change in kinetic energy. Thus, the change of kinetic energy may be negligible, $\Delta K \approx 0$. Now draw an energy diagram, Fig. **10**, *considering all forms of energy* but omitting those which are not apropos; or using the full steady flow equation, write the energy equation for this particular application. It is best to do both. Thus, from the energy equation (10C), we may write

(b) $W = -\Delta h - \Delta K,$ or $W = -\Delta h = h_1 - h_2$ Btu/lb.
                [Q = 0]   [Q = 0, ΔK = 0]

The same results are obtained from energy diagrams.

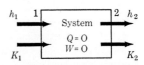

For another illustration, consider a nozzle on a jet engine (see Fig. 67, § 106). A nozzle is a device which receives a fluid and guides its expansion to some lower pressure, converting some of the entering energy into kinetic energy at exit, Fig. 11. No shafts are turned so that $W = 0$. Also, $Q \approx 0$ because the time of passage of a particular particle

Fig. 11. Energy Diagram for Nozzle. The system is bounded by the internal surface of the nozzle and imaginary planes at its extremities, sections 1 and 2.

of mass through the nozzle is so short (a fraction of a second) that there is not enough time for the heat loss Q to be significant as compared to other energy quantities. From the energy diagram, Fig. 11, or from (10C), we get

(c) $\Delta K = -\Delta h = -(h_2 - h_1) = h_1 - h_2$ Btu/lb.,   [Q = 0, W = 0]

which says that the increase in kinetic energy in the nozzle is equal to the decrease of that useful property enthalpy. In many nozzles, the entering kinetic energy is negligible, $K_1 \approx 0$ and $\Delta K \approx K_2$. If this is so, (c) becomes

(d) $K_2 = \dfrac{v_2{}^2}{2g_oJ} = h_1 - h_2$ Btu/lb.   [K₁ = 0, Q = 0, W = 0]

The reader probably observes that, even in these two simplest applications, one must have some engineering knowledge in order to judge the appropriateness of the various energies. Such elementary knowledge (and much more) is the working knowledge of the engineer. Other applications will be made here and there throughout the book. The student should make an energy diagram for each problem solved.

25. Example. An air compressor takes in air at 15 psia and discharges it at 100 psia; $v_1 = 2$ cu. ft./lb. and $v_2 = 0.5$ cu. ft./lb. The increase of internal energy is 40 Btu/lb. and the work is 70 Btu/lb.; $\Delta P = 0$ and $\Delta K = 0$. How much heat is transferred?

SOLUTION. The forms of energy to be considered are flow work, internal energy, work, and of course heat. For 1 lb. of substance,

$$W_{f1} = \frac{p_1 v_1}{J} = \frac{(15)(144)(2)}{778} = 5.55 \text{ Btu/lb.,}$$

$$W_{f2} = \frac{p_2 v_2}{J} = \frac{(100)(144)(0.5)}{778} = 9.25 \text{ Btu/lb.,}$$

$$\Delta W_f = W_{f2} - W_{f1} = 9.25 - 5.55 = +3.7 \text{ Btu/lb.}$$

Since work must be done *on* the air to compress it, the work is negative, $W = -70$ Btu/lb.; and since the internal energy increases, $\Delta u = u_2 - u_1 = +40$ Btu/lb. Using these various values in (10E), we solve for Q and find

$$Q = \Delta u + \Delta W_f + W$$
$$= (+40) + (+3.7) + (-70) = -26.3 \text{ Btu/lb.,}$$

where the negative sign indicates that heat is rejected by the system. Some air compressors have water jackets for the purpose of cooling the air during compression, so the negative sign would be expected.

Since it is important to be able to utilize energy diagrams, we shall repeat the solution from this viewpoint. The procedure is to decide upon what the system is, say the air on its way through the compressor. Figure 12 sets the boundaries and shows what is known. The internal energy may be measured above the datum of the entering air which gives $u_1 = 0$ and $u_2 = 40$, because $u_2 - u_1 = +40$. At this stage, it may not be known whether heat flows in or out. If we choose to show heat Q as transferred in, as in Fig. 12, a plus sign for the answer would say that

The direction of energy flow as shown is correct,

and a negative sign would say that

The direction of energy flow as shown is not correct;

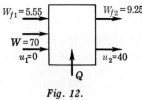

Fig. 12.

hence, it does not matter if the decision is correct at this point. (This statement applies only to the unknown energy quantity. As in mechanics, if an unknown force is assumed in the wrong direction, its value as solved for is negative.) Now setting up the energy equation to agree with Fig. 12, we get

$$\text{Energy in} = \text{Energy out}$$
$$5.55 + 70 + 0 + Q = 9.25 + 40,$$

from which $Q = -26.3$ Btu/lb., heat abstracted as before.

26. Power. Power is the *rate* at which energy is transformed into work; it is work per unit of time. The common units of power used in this country are the *horsepower* (hp) and the *kilowatt* (kw). By definition and the relation between units, we have the conversion constants given in the Appendix, Table XVI. A horsepower generated for a particular duration of time represents a certain amount of work; that is, for example, a horsepower-hour (hp-hr.), which is 1 horsepower for 1 hr, is a unit of energy equivalent to 2544 Btu; a horsepower-minute (hp-min.) is equivalent to 33,000 ft-lb. Referring to the previous example, suppose that 20 lb./sec. of air are compressed; the work is

$$W = \left(70 \; \frac{\text{Btu}}{\text{lb.}}\right)\left(20 \; \frac{\text{lb.}}{\text{sec.}}\right) = 1400 \text{ Btu/sec.} = 83,000 \text{ Btu/min.}$$

In the Appendix, Table XVI, we find 42.4 Btu/hp-min. Thus, the horsepower needed to drive the compressor is $84,000/42.4 = 1980$ hp.   Since the negative sign serves only to designate the direction of the flow of energy, we ignore it in speaking of the power required.

27. Closure.   As in Chapter 1, the reader is no doubt more or less familiar with many of the concepts treated in this chapter.   However, this is all foundation material and must be reviewed in detail.   In its most general aspects, *the law of the conservation of energy is one of the most useful discoveries ever made.*   Fix in mind the kinds of energy with which we shall deal:

P, potential energy; *stored;* change is $P_2 - P_1$;
K, kinetic energy; *stored;* change is $K_2 - K_1$;
U, u, internal energy; *stored;* change is $U_2 - U_1$ or $u_2 - u_1$;
W_f, flow work; in *transition;* change between boundaries 1 and 2 is $W_{f2} - W_{f1}$;
W, work; in *transition;* change is a path function;
Q, heat; in *transition;* change is a path function.

Incidentally, it is necessary to learn thermodynamic theory for an understanding of the subject; therefore, it would save time to learn the theory reasonably well first and *then* work the problems.

PROBLEMS

NOTE.   *Consider all energy problems from two viewpoints, the energy equation and the energy diagram.   Use the full energy equation in each solution, except that ΔP may be omitted if it does not apply.   The index may help in locating pictures of the equipment involved.*

11. Water leaves a nozzle with a velocity of 50 mph.   (a) If the jet is directed vertically upward, how far above the nozzle will the water go? Consider the heating and frictional effects as zero.   Solve by using the law of conservation of energy.   (b) If the exit section of the nozzle has a sectional area of 0.25 sq. in., what is the flow work at this boundary?
   Ans.   (a) 83.6 ft., (b) 16,180 ft-lb. per min.

12. (a) A 64,400-lb. airplane is traveling at 1000 fps (682 mph).   How much is its kinetic energy in hp-hr?   (b) If it noses vertically upward at this speed with power off and in a vacuum (no friction) at standard gravity, through what vertical distance would it move?
   Ans.   (a) 50.5 hp-hr., (b) 2.94 mi.
   505.0

13. During a steady flow process, the pressure of the working substance drops from 100 to 20 psia, the velocity increases from 200 to 1200 fps, the internal energy decreases 25 Btu/lb., and the volume increases from 1 to 6 cu. ft./lb.   If the heat transferred is zero, what is the work of 1 lb. of the substance?   *Ans.* -6.7 Btu/lb.

14. The same as **12** except that heat in the amount of 3 Btu/lb. is rejected.
   Ans. -9.7 Btu/lb.

15. Let a boiler be operating in steady flow. Usually, $\Delta K \approx 0, \Delta P \approx 0$, and no shaft work is done by it. Set up the energy diagram and the energy equation. The water enters with $u + pv/J$ = 168 Btu/lb. The departing steam has an internal energy of 1115.8 Btu/lb. The heat transferred to the system, which is the H_2O en route through the boiler, is 1033.1 Btu/lb. Compute the flow work at the exit boundary.

Ans. 85.3 Btu/lb.

16. An air compressor receives 50 lb./min. of air for which $h_1 = 20$ Btu/lb. and delivers it when $h_2 = 70$ Btu/lb. While the air passes through the compressor, it rejects 10 Btu/lb. of heat. (a) Neglecting the change of kinetic energy, determine the work in horsepower. (b) The same as (a) except the kinetic energy decreases 200 Btu/min. (c) The same as (a) except that the kinetic energy increases 200 Btu/min.

Ans. (a) 70.7 hp, (b) 66 hp, (c) 75.5 hp.

17. (a) A centrifugal compressor takes in 10 lb./min. of air at 14.5 psia. As the air crosses the boundary of the system (enters the compressor), the flow work is 277,000 ft-lb./min.; at the exit boundary, the flow work is 388,500 ft-lb./min. The increase of internal energy during passage is 19.55 Btu/lb. No heat is transferred and there is no change of kinetic energy. What work is done? Is it done on or by the system? (b) The same as (a) except that the heat rejected is 2 Btu/lb. during compression. *−339 Btu/min*

Ans. (a) −274.5 Btu/min., (b) 294.5 Btu/min.
−359 Btu/min

18. (a) Steam enters the blades of a single-stage impulse turbine (Fig. 152) with an absolute velocity of 3667 fps and leaves at 1405 fps. The rate of

flow is 2 lb./sec. For ideal, frictionless flow, there is no change in enthalpy and no heat. What is the ideal horsepower delivered by the blades? (b) There is friction during the actual flow with a resulting increase in enthalpy. Let the other data be as in (a), but let the increase in enthalpy be 35 Btu/lb. What is the horsepower?

Ans. (a) 635 hp, (b) 551 hp.
628 hp

19. (a) A substance flows through a turbine at the rate of 100 lb./min. with $\Delta K = 0$ and $Q = 0$. At entry, its pressure is 175 psia, its volume is 3.16 cu. ft./lb., and its internal energy is 1166.7 Btu/lb. At exit, its pressure is 0.813 psia, its volume is 328 cu. ft./lb., and its internal energy is 854.6 Btu/lb. What horsepower is developed? (b) The same as (a) except that the heat loss from the turbine is 10 Btu/lb. of steam. *Ans.* (a) 861 hp, (b) 838 hp.

20. Steam enters a turbine at the rate of 2 lb./sec. with a velocity of 50 fps and $h_1 = 1292$ Btu/lb. The exit velocity is 117 fps and $h_2 = 1098$ Btu/lb. The loss by radiation is 13 Btu/lb. (a) What horsepower is delivered? (b) The change of kinetic energy (Btu/lb.) is what percentage of Δh?

Ans. (a) 512 hp.

21. A turbine is supplied with 22,500 lb./hr. of steam at 166 psia and 480°F with an initial speed of 6000 fpm at an elevation of 5 ft. above the exhaust outlet. Radiation and frictional losses are 140,000 Btu/hr. At the entrance, $h_1 = 1261.8$ Btu/lb. At the exit, p_2 = 3 in. Hg abs., $v_2 = 24,000$ fpm, and $h_2 = 1001.5$ Btu/lb. Compute the work in Btu/hr. and in horsepower. Does the change of potential energy significantly affect the result? What is the percentage error if the change of kinetic energy is neglected?

Ans. 2220 hp.

22. A steam condenser, Fig. 129, § 168, is a heat exchanger which receives exhaust steam from an engine and cooling water from the surroundings. The steam condenses by virtue of the flow of heat from the steam to the cooling water. Thus, there is no shaft work and the changes of kinetic energy are negligible. The incoming 20,000 lb./hr. of exhaust steam have an enthalpy of 1120 Btu/lb. The condensate (water) leaves with $h_2 = 75$ Btu/lb. If 1 lb. of cooling water carries away 1 Btu for each degree of temperature rise and if the temperature rise of the cooling water is from 60 to 80°F, how much cooling water must be circulated?   *Ans.* 1,035,300 lb./hr.

23. A nozzle is a system which converts some of the entering energy into kinetic energy. No shafts are turned within this system ($W = 0$) and $Q \approx 0$. Let a nozzle receive 2400 lb./hr. of steam at $p_1 = 200$ psia, $v_1 = 2.29$ cu. ft./lb., $u_1 = 1113.7$ Btu/lb., and negligible speed. At the exit, $p_2 = 14.7$ psia, $v_2 = 26.77$ cu. ft./lb., and $u_2 = 1077.5$ Btu/lb. (a) What is the exit speed in mph? (b) If all of the exit kinetic energy were later converted into work, what would be the horsepower?   *Ans.* (a) 1056 mph, (b) 45.6 hp.

24. The same as **23** except that the initial speed is 600 fpm at entrance.
        Ans. $K_1 = 0.002$ Btu/lb.

25. A combustor on a gas turbine, Fig. 56, § 97, receives air with an enthalpy of 208 Btu/lb. and, at the same time, fuel which carries with it 323 Btu/lb. of air, mostly chemical energy which is released by combustion. The

heat loss is 14 Btu/lb. of air passing through, and the amount of energy in the exit stream in the form of unburned fuel is 16 Btu/lb. of air. What is the enthalpy of the departing gases?
        Ans. 501 Btu.

26. Jet engines on a plane moving at 500 mph provide a thrust of 10,000 lb. What is the rate at which work is being expended on the plane in Btu/sec., in hp, in kw, and in hp-hr./sec?
        Ans. 13,350 hp.

27. A hydraulic turbine receives 10,000 lb./min. of water from a reservoir which is 778 ft. above the tail race (discharge) of the turbine. Let the flow be frictionless and consider that the kinetic energy at discharge is negligible. Use the law of conservation of energy and find (a) the approximate speed of the water at the turbine entrance, (b) the work in Btu/min. and horsepower.
        Ans. (a) 224 fps, (b) 236 hp.

28. Bernoulli's equation for the frictionless flow of a liquid is derived from mechanics considerations and can be placed in the form

$$\frac{p_1}{\rho_1} + \frac{v_1^2}{2g_o} + z_1 = \frac{p_2}{\rho_2} + \frac{v_2^2}{2g_o} + z_2,$$

where ρ stands for the density in lb./cu. ft. In this equation p/ρ is called the pressure head, $v^2/(2g_o)$ is called the velocity head, and z the gravity head. Find the Bernoulli equation from the steady flow energy equation (7) and summarize the thermal conditions under which Bernoulli's equation applies.

29–40. These numbers may be used for other problems.

3

WORK AND HEAT

28. Introduction. We have already discussed work and heat in a general way, but we may now find more specific expressions for evaluating them. Having found these expressions, we may modify the energy equations advantageously.

29. Work of the Nonflow Process and the $\int p\,dV$. Let the system be a quantity of an expansible fluid, such as a gas or vapor, enclosed within a cylinder and piston, Fig. 13. This is a

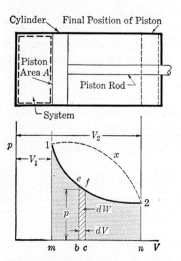

Fig. 13. *Closed System—Work of Expansion.* The boundaries of the system expand and contract with the movement of the piston. The different paths may be brought about by adding or abstracting different quantities of heat.

closed system in which **nonflow processes** may occur. The volume of the fluid is V_1 and its pressure is p_1. If we consider the state of the fluid on the pV plane (meaning that the coordinates are p and V), the particular coordinates p_1 and V_1 locate the point 1, Fig. 13. If the working substance expands and moves the piston against a variable resistance, work will be done by the fluid. In a typical practical process of this sort, the pressure drops and the state of the substance changes as suggested by the curve 1-*e*-*f*-2, which curve is called the **path of the state point.** Since the pressure and therefore the force on the piston is varying, it is necessary to integrate $\int F_x\,dx$ in order to find the work. Consider a change of state from *e* to *f*, Fig. 13, so small that the pressure is essentially constant during the change. The force acting on the piston will be the pressure times the area of the piston, $F_x = pA$. The distance that the piston moves is a differential quantity dL, and the work for this infinitesimal motion of the piston is force times distance,

(a)
$$dW = (pA)\,dL = p(A\,dL) = p\,dV,$$

28

where $A\, dL$ is the differential volume dV.   The total work of the nonflow process is (use W_n for nonflow work)

(11) $$W_n = \int p\, dV \text{ ft-lb.} \quad \text{ or } \quad W_n = \int p\, dv \text{ ft-lb./lb.,}$$
[REVERSIBLE NONFLOW PROCESS]

where the units must be p lb./sq. ft. (psf), V cu. ft., and v cu. ft./lb. to give work in foot-pounds.   We shall go into the matter of a reversible process later so let it suffice here to say that in a *reversible process*, there is no-friction, mechanical or fluid; everything is on an ideal basis and the work of the fluid on the face of the piston, $\int p\, dV$, appears as shaft work.

Notice the differential area *befc*, Fig. 13, whose width is dV and whose height is p.   The magnitude of this area is $p\, dV$ and the sum of all of these differential areas is the total area under the curve 1-*e*-*f*-2 when the integration is made from state 1 to state 2.   Thus we have the area equal to $\int p\, dV$ and $W = \int p\, dV$; therefore, *the area "under" the curve of the process on the pV plane represents the work done during a nonflow reversible process.*

The work done and the area under the curve on the pV plane depend upon the location of the path 1-*e*-*f*-2, Fig. 13, that is, upon the relation between p and V $[p = \phi(V)]$.   Although states 1 and 2 are particular points and p_1, p_2, V_1, and V_2 have particular values, the change of state may occur along any other path 1-*x*-2.   Thus the work done has changed because the path of the state point has changed—*the work depends upon the process.* It is not a property.   While it is correct to say that the change of volume $\Delta V = V_2 - V_1$, it is not correct to say that the work done is $W_2 - W_1$; W is not a *point* function.

When the function $p = \phi(V)$ is known or assumed, the integration can be made.   For example, if $pV = C$, where C is a constant, we substitute $p = C/V$ into (11) and get the work during a frictionless process as

(b) $$W = \int_1^2 p\, dV = C \int_{V_1}^{V_2} \frac{dV}{V} = C \ln \frac{V_2}{V_1} \text{ ft-lb.}$$

for p psf and V cu. ft., where $C = p_1 V_1 = p_2 V_2 = pV$.   This integration can be made for any kind of expansible substance, given the pV relation. The convention of signs agrees with that defined for equation (5); namely,

> $\int p\, dV$ is *positive* when nonflow work is done *by* the system,
> $\int p\, dV$ is *negative* when nonflow work is done *on* the system.

Now the energy equation may be written in the important form

(12) $$dQ = dU + \frac{p\, dV}{J} \text{ Btu,} \quad \text{ or } \quad dQ = du + \frac{p\, dv}{J} \text{ Btu/lb.}$$
[ANY REVERSIBLE PROCESS]

Compare this equation with the steady flow equation in differential form; that is, after (7B),

(7C) $$dQ = dU + dW_f + dK + dP + dW.$$

Since U is a thermodynamic property, its value depends only on the state of the substance, and its change ΔU depends only upon the properties at the initial and final states, not upon whether the change of state occurs during steady flow or nonflow. The heat Q does not depend upon whether a certain kind of process is nonflow or steady flow, but it does depend upon the path between states 1 and 2 which is defined by the relation between p and V during the process. Thus, for a particular substance with a given pV relation, we see that, between states 1 and 2, Q is the same for nonflow and steady flow, ΔU is the same for nonflow and steady flow, and that therefore, by comparison of equations (12) and (7C), $p\,dV/J$ Btu must be equal to the sum of the various mechanical energy terms in (7C); or

(13) $$\int p\,dV = \Delta W_f + \Delta K + \Delta P + W \text{ ft-lb.} \qquad \text{[REVERSIBLE]}$$

Note particularly that the $\int p\,dV$ is *not* equal to the work in a steady flow process. It is often true that $\Delta K = 0$ and $\Delta P = 0$, but the change of flow work $\Delta W_f = \Delta pV$ is equal to zero only under special circumstances. It also follows from the foregoing discussion that equation (12), $dQ = dU + p\,dV/J$, *applies to any reversible process,* flow or nonflow.

30. Meaning of $-\int V\,dp$. Writing equation (13) in differential form and using

(c) $$dW_f = d(pV) = p\,dV + V\,dp,$$

we get

$$p\,dV = p\,dV + V\,dp + dK + dP + dW;$$

whence, for reversible processes,

(14) $$-\int V\,dp = \Delta K + \Delta P + W \text{ ft-lb.}$$

In our applications, ΔP is nearly always negligible, so that the working form of (14) may be taken as

(d) $$-\int V\,dp = \Delta K + W. \qquad \text{[REVERSIBLE STEADY FLOW AND } \Delta P = 0]$$

Moreover, it often happens that either ΔK or W is zero or negligible. If it should be true that ΔK is negligible, we have the work of a steady flow process as

(15) $$W = -\int V\,dp \text{ ft-lb.} \qquad \text{or} \qquad W = -\int v\,dp \text{ ft-lb./lb.}$$

$$\text{[REVERSIBLE STEADY FLOW; } \Delta K = 0 \text{ and } \Delta P = 0]$$

Perhaps, a more important energy equation is obtained by differentiating the defining equation of enthalpy, $H = U + pV/J$. This gives

(e) $$dH = dU + \frac{p\,dV}{J} + \frac{V\,dp}{J}.$$

Now using $dQ = dU + p\,dV/J$, which is equation (12), in (e) and solving for dQ, we have

(16A) $\quad dQ = dH - \dfrac{V\,dp}{J}$ Btu, $\quad$ or $\quad dQ = dh - \dfrac{v\,dp}{J}$ Btu/lb.

(16B) $$Q = \Delta h - \int \frac{v\,dp}{J}.$$

[ANY REVERSIBLE PROCESS]

Equation (16), like equation (12), is an energy equation which applies to any reversible process, nonflow or steady flow (it must be reversible in order for the $-\int V\,dp$ to have its assigned meanings). Compare and contrast it with equation (12). The integral $-\int V\,dp$ represents an area, Fig. 14, the area "behind" the curve. Consequently this area, Fig. 14, represents:

W, the steady flow work when $\Delta K = 0$—see equation (d);
ΔK, the change of kinetic energy when $W = 0$—see equation (d);
$-\Delta H$, the change of enthalpy when $Q = 0$—see equation (16).

Observe that $-\int V\,dp$ is a positive number when integrated from 1 to 2, Fig. 14, the work being done *by* the substance. In order to make the integration, one must know the relation between p and V. For example, let $pV = C$; then we have $V = C/p$ and $-\int V\,dp = -C\int dp/p = -C \ln p_2/p_1$ between the limits of states 1 to 2. If $pV = C$, it follows that $p_1V_1 = p_2V_2$ or that $p_2/p_1 = V_1/V_2$. Substituting the volume ratio for the pressure ratio in the foregoing integration, we have $-\int V\,dp = +C \ln V_2/V_1$, which is seen to be the same as $\int p\,dV$, equation (b). This is true only for the particular relation $pV = C$.

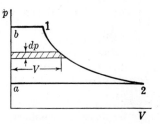

Fig. 14. Area for $\int V\,dp$. Area 1-2-a-b represents the work of a reversible steady flow process when $\Delta K = 0$ and $\Delta P = 0$.

31. Specific Heat. The specific heat of a substance is defined as the amount of heat required to change the temperature of unit mass through one degree. In dimensional form,

(f) $$c \rightarrow \frac{\text{Heat (energy units)}}{\text{Mass} \times \text{Change of temperature}}.$$

The unit for heat may be any energy unit. In this country, engineers ordinarily use Btu. Since a change in temperature on the Fahrenheit and

Rankine scales is one and the same thing, the change in temperature may be in either °F or °R. With the mass in pounds, we have the specific heat in terms of differential quantities as

(17A) $$c = \frac{dQ}{w\,dT}\frac{\text{Btu}}{\text{lb-°R}}, \quad\text{or}\quad dQ = wc\,dT \text{ Btu},$$

and for a particular mass w,

(17B) $$Q = w\int c\,dT = wc(T_2 - T_1) \text{ Btu}.$$
$$[c = \text{A CONSTANT}]$$

This is the *specific heat equation*. It was previously pointed out that heat is a path function, that the heat would be different between any two state points 1 and 2 for different processes between the states. For example, the specific heat of a constant volume process is different from that of a constant pressure process. Even in a particular process, the specific heat is not constant (§ 34), but luckily it can usually be expressed as a function of temperature so that (17B) may be integrated readily. For small variations of temperature, the specific heat may be considered constant. Thus, in the integrated form of (17B), the specific heat should be the average or mean value of c between the temperatures T_1 and T_2.

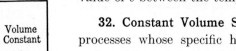

Volume
Constant

Q_v

Fig. 15. Constant Volume System.

32. Constant Volume Specific Heat. There are two processes whose specific heats are especially important and useful—constant volume c_v and constant pressure c_p. Consider first a nonflow constant volume system, Fig. 15. Since $W = 0$, the heat transferred into the system must go into internal energy and the nonflow equation for unit mass gives $Q_v = \Delta u$, where the subscript v suggests that the volume remains constant. Thus, we have

(g) $$Q_v = \Delta U = wc_v(T_2 - T_1) \text{ Btu} \quad\text{and}$$
$$Q_v = \Delta u = c_v(T_2 - T_1) \text{ Btu/lb.} \qquad [\text{CONSTANT } c_v]$$
$$[\text{CONSTANT } c_v]$$

See Table V, in the Appendix, for some values of c_v. (NOTE. Working tables are placed together in the Appendix for convenient reference.)

33. Constant Pressure Specific Heat. Let the system be a nonflow system as before, and add heat while the pressure is maintained constant, Fig. 16. The pressure is balanced by a constant load F, Fig. 16, on a frictionless, movable piston. From equation (16), p. 31, we have $Q = \Delta H$ for constant pressure. Then for an average value of c_p, the heat is

(h) $$Q_p = \Delta H = wc_p\Delta T \text{ Btu} \quad\text{or}\quad Q_p = \Delta h = c_p\Delta T \text{ Btu/lb.};$$

this heat goes into internal energy, into work being done in raising the weight F, and in overcoming the pressure of the surroundings on the piston. For 1 lb., the nonflow work is, § 29,

(i) $\qquad W_n = \dfrac{1}{J} \displaystyle\int p\,dv = \dfrac{p}{J} \displaystyle\int dv = \dfrac{p(v_2 - v_1)}{J} = \dfrac{p_2 v_2}{J} - \dfrac{p_1 v_1}{J}$ Btu/lb.

[PRESSURE CONSTANT ONLY, NONFLOW]

Then the equation, $dQ = du + p\,dv$ for 1 lb., applied to a reversible constant pressure process gives

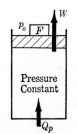

Fig. 16. Constant Pressure System.

(j) $\qquad Q_p = u_2 - u_1 + \dfrac{p_2 v_2}{J} - \dfrac{p_1 v_1}{J} = h_2 - h_1 = \Delta h$ Btu/lb.,

where $u + pv/J$ has been replaced by h, the specific enthalpy. See Table V in the Appendix for values of c_p for a few common substances.

Air is so often the working substance that the student should memorize its specific heats at normal atmospheric ‘temperatures:

$c_p = 0.24$ and $c_v = 0.1715$ Btu/lb-°R, or Btu/lb-°F. [AIR ONLY]

The ratio of these specific heats appears so often in thermodynamic equations that it is given a symbol k;

(k) $\qquad\qquad\qquad\qquad k = \dfrac{c_p}{c_v} > 1.$

The value of k is always greater than unity because the heat in the constant pressure process not only increases the internal energy but does work.

34. Variable Specific Heats. Although in general, specific heats are not constant, in most practical applications they fortunately are closely represented as functions of temperature only. However, substances in a state near which they would condense upon heat extraction and substances under high pressure may have specific heats which vary markedly with pressure. Considering only the situations in which the specific heats vary with temperature, we can easily integrate equation (17A), given the function (see the example below), though sometimes this approach may be tedious. Equations expressing the variation of the constant volume and constant pressure specific heats are found in more complete studies.*

Also useful are *mean* or average specific heats for a certain temperature range of a substance. When these are available, the integrated form in (17B), $Q = wc\Delta T$, applies.

* Including the author's *Thermodynamics*, Macmillan.

35. Example. The specific heat at constant volume for a certain substance is expressed closely by the equation $c_v = 0.2 + 0.00005T$ Btu/lb-°R. How much heat is added to 10 lb. of the substance confined in a closed vessel in order to raise its temperature from 500°R to 2000°R? What are the change of internal energy and the mean specific heat for this temperature range?

SOLUTION. This is a nonflow constant volume system. From equation (17), we have

$$Q = w \int c_v \, dT = w \int_{500}^{2000} (0.2 + 0.00005T) \, dT$$
$$= 10 \left[0.2T + \frac{0.00005T^2}{2} \right]_{500}^{2000} = 3945 \text{ Btu.}$$

Since the work $W = \int p \, dV = 0$ because $dV = 0$, we have from equation (5), $Q = \Delta U + W$,

change of internal energy, $\Delta U = Q = 3945$ Btu.

The mean specific heat for the temperature range of $2000 - 500 = 1500$ is [see equation(f)]

$$c = \frac{Q}{w\Delta T} = \frac{3945}{(10)(1500)} = 0.263 \text{ Btu/lb-°R.}$$

36. Reversibility. It has been stated that for the $\int p \, dV$ and $-\int V \, dp$ to have the meanings assigned to them, the process should be reversible, which is to say that the process is idealized. While all actual processes and events are inherently irreversible, it is simpler to learn first how to handle reversible processes and then to introduce experience factors. At least this is the engineering approach. So let us consider briefly the meaning of *reversibility*.

(*a*) *External irreversibility* is some irreversibility external to the system when the system is the working substance; it includes friction at the bearings, between a piston and cylinder, and between the atmosphere and the rotating members; all absorb some of the W output of the system. Instinctively you know that you cannot use the "frictional energy" to recompress the fluid to its original state (which is one of the things said by the second law of thermodynamics—see Chapter 9).

Another and significant form of external irreversibility is the flow of heat because of a temperature difference. Since heat is that energy which is transferred because of a temperature difference, heat is necessarily transferred if a temperature difference exists, and such an event is irreversible. We say it is irreversible because all experience suggests the improbability of heat flowing in the other direction. As Clausius* said in 1850, "It is

---

* Rudolf Julius Emmanuel Clausius (1822–1888), born in northern Germany, a professor of physics, was a genius in mathematical investigations of natural phenomena. He elaborated and restated the work of Carnot, deducing the principle of the second law of thermodynamics. His mathematical work in optics, electricity, and electrolysis was significant. James Clerk Maxwell credits him with being the founder of the kinetic

impossible for a self-acting machine unaided by external agency to move heat from one body to another at a higher temperature." (This is a statement of the second law of thermodynamics, Chapter 9.) We see then that heat can be transferred reversibly only when $\Delta T = 0$ and that the transfer approaches reversibility as ΔT approaches zero.

(b) *Internal irreversibility* is illustrated by fluid friction and turbulence. As a fluid flows through a turbine, for instance, there are bound to be eddies and crosscurrents which "absorb" energies that otherwise might have been delivered as shaft work. Also, for another example, imagine an expansible fluid in a cylinder with a piston (say, compressed air). If the piston moves rapidly, that portion of the fluid adjacent to the piston expands first, rushing in to fill the void left by the movement of the piston. This initial rush results in some differences of temperature and pressure in the various parts of the fluid and numerous whirlpools and eddies. The consequent fluid friction accounts for some energy which might otherwise have been delivered as work. In order for this sort of an expansion to be reversible, the piston would have to move very slowly (at an infinitesimal speed in the limit); the substance must pass through a series of equilibrium states, which is to say that there is no fluid turbulence of any degree. At any instant, all parts of the system must be at the same temperature and pressure. While internal reversibility cannot be achieved, actual processes can approach it closely. It is internal reversibility that we most often assume in this study. For example, the work of a fluid in a nonflow process is $W = \int p \, dV$ when the process is *internally* reversible (p is the instantaneous pressure in all parts of the system), whether there is or is not external reversibility.

To summarize: *If, after a process consisting of a continuous series of equilibrium states is completed, the substance can be made to retrace in the reverse order the various states of the original process, if all energy quantities to or from the surroundings can be returned to their original states (everything as it was before the process), then the **process is externally and internally reversible.*** The conditions for reversibility are: (1) processes controlled through a series of equilibrium states (no fluid friction), (2) no mechanical friction, and (3) no temperature difference during transfer of heat. In engineering, we usually care for irreversibilities or convert ideal results into actual results by the use of ratios and efficiency numbers which are based on experience.

37. Entropy. The time has come to introduce another property, entropy (en'-tro-py), one which we define in terms of a change. For an internally

theory of gases, on the basis of which Clausius made many important calculations, one of which was the mean free path of a molecule. He is the author of an exhaustive treatise on the steam engine, wherein he emphasized the then new conception of entropy.

reversible process, the change of entropy of a substance receiving (or delivering) heat is defined by

$$(18) \quad \Delta S = \int dS = \int \frac{dQ}{T} \text{ Btu/°R} \quad \text{or} \quad \Delta s = \int \frac{dQ}{T} \text{ Btu/lb-°R.}$$

[REVERSIBLE PROCESS]

where dQ is the heat transferred at the temperature T; ΔS is the total change of entropy for w lb.; Δs is the change of specific entropy. If the integrations are made from 1 to 2, the signs of the answers obtained will always accord with the conventions set up in Chapter 2; an increase is positive, a decrease negative.

In processes where the specific heat is a known finite value, we may use $dQ = wc\, dT$ and evaluate the change in entropy as

$$(1) \quad \Delta S = w \int \frac{c\, dT}{T} \text{ Btu/°R}; \quad \text{or} \quad \Delta S = wc \int \frac{dT}{T} = wc \ln \frac{T_2}{T_1} \text{ Btu/°R,}$$

[CONSTANT SPECIFIC HEAT]

between the limits of states 1 and 2, where in the integraded form, the specific heat is the proper average value for the kind of process involved; for example, for a reversible constant pressure process, $\Delta s = c_p \ln (T_2/T_1)$ Btu/lb-°R.*

38. Temperature-Entropy Coordinates. If equation (18) is rewritten as

$$(\mathbf{m}) \quad Q = \int T\, dS \text{ Btu} \quad \text{or} \quad Q = \int T\, ds \text{ Btu/lb.}$$

and compared with $W = \int p\, dV$, we observe that T, like p is an intensity factor and s, S like v, V is an extensive factor. We see that the product of T and dS, during a reversible process, gives heat and that this product repre-

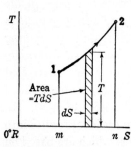

Fig. 17. TS Plane. A differential area is $T\, ds$ recognized as dQ.

sents an area on the TS plane, Fig. 17. The integration of $T\, dS$ from 1 to 2, Fig. 17, gives the area "under" the curve down to absolute zero temperature, area m-1-2-n, which represents the amount of heat transferred during the process 1-2. This is a useful attribute of entropy and makes the TS or Ts plane a favorite one for depicting processes and cycles. Since $dQ = dU + p\, dV/J = T\, dS$, we can write

$$(\mathbf{n}) \quad dS = \frac{dU}{T} + \frac{p\, dV}{JT},$$

which can be integrated for certain circumstances (§ 50).

* Recall that the logarithm of a number less than one is negative. Therefore, if $T_2 < T_1$, ΔS is negative. Also if $T_2 < T_1$, it will be convenient to recall that $\ln (T_2/T_1) = -\ln (T_1/T_2)$. Students without a log log type of slide rule should remember that $\ln N = \log_e N = 2.3 \log_{10} N$.

The process must be reversible for the area $\int T\,dS$ to have significance. Irreversible processes will be shown dotted as a reminder that areas under curves on pV and TS planes do not represent work or heat.

39. Example. What is the change of entropy of air which is heated at constant pressure from $t_1 = 40°F$ to $t_2 = 1540°F$ if its specific heat is given by

(o) $$c_p = \alpha + \beta T + \gamma T^2 \text{ Btu/lb-°R}$$

where $\alpha = 0.219$, $\beta = 0.342 \times 10^{-4}$, and $\gamma = -0.293 \times 10^{-8}$?

SOLUTION. From $\Delta s = \int dQ/T$, we have

$$\Delta s = \int \frac{c\,dT}{T} = \int_{500}^{2000} \left(\frac{\alpha\,dT}{T} + \beta\,dT + \gamma T\,dT \right)$$

$$= \left[\alpha \ln T + \beta T + \gamma \frac{T^2}{2} \right]_{500}^{2000}$$

$$= \alpha \ln \frac{2000}{500} + \beta(2000 - 500) + \frac{\gamma}{2}(2000^2 - 500^2),$$

from which $\Delta s = 0.35$ Btu/lb-°R.

40. Closure. This chapter covers some basic energy relations which will be useful throughout this study (and throughout the practice of engineering, for that matter). If the reader will review this chapter several times within the next few weeks, he will no doubt find meanings which were missed on first study, meanings which will enlighten the subsequent study (and improve your grade).

At this stage, you have learned how to evaluate separately the change of kinetic and potential energies, how to obtain the work from the $\int p\,dV$ or $-\int V\,dp$, given a relation between p and V, and how to find the heat if the specific heat is known. However, the methods of making an independent evaluation of the change in the properties enthalpy and internal energy have not been discussed because the way in which these changes are handled depends upon the substance. The first substance to be studied, in the next chapter, is the ideal gas.

PROBLEMS

NOTE. *Where an equation of a curve is given, it will be good practice to sketch the curve freehand (just its general trend is usually satisfactory for thermodynamics problems). Be careful of units.*

41. A gas undergoes a change of state in accordance with Boyle's law, $pV = C$ and $T = C$. At state 1, $p = 235.3$ psig, $V_1 = 3.25$ cu. ft., $t_1 = 75°F$; at 2, $V_2 = 13$ cu. ft. Compute (a) the $\int p\,dV/J$, (b) the work of a nonflow process, and (c) the work of a steady flow process if $\Delta K = 0$ and $\Delta P = 0$. *Ans.* (a) 208 Btu.

42. In a certain process, the pressure remains constant at $p = 778$ psia while the volume changes from 5 to 10 cu. ft. Determine (a) the $\int p\,dV/J$, (b) the nonflow work. (c) If the process is steady flow in which no work is done, what is the change of kinetic energy ($\Delta P = 0$)? (d) Is $-\int V\,dp = \int p\,dV - \Delta W_f$?

Ans. (a) 720 Btu, (d) Yes.

43. During a process $p = 28.8\,V + 90$ psia (V in cu. ft.) and the volume changes from $V_1 = 10$ cu. ft. to $V_2 = 25$ cu. ft. Compute (a) the $\int p\,dV/J$, (b) $-\int V\,dp/J$. (c) Is $-\int V\,dp = \int p\,dV - \Delta(pV)$?

Ans. (a) 1650 Btu, (b) −1400 Btu.

44. The pV relation for a certain process is $p = V^2 + 8/V$ psia, when V is in cu. ft. The volume changes from 5 cu. ft. to 15 cu. ft. (a) What is the $\int p\,dV/J$? (b) How much work is done if the process is nonflow? (c) If the process is steady flow with $\Delta K = 0$ and $\Delta P = 0$, what is the work?

Ans. (a) 203 Btu, (c) −398.4 Btu.

45. The relation between p and V for a certain process is $V = -0.1p + 300$ cu. ft. when p is psfa. (a) If the pressure changes from 1000 psfa to 100 psfa, what is $-\int V\,dp/J$? (b) Sketch the curve on pV coordinates. Note that it is a straight line and that therefore the area "behind" the curve is the average abscissa times the change of ordinate. Find this area and check against $-\int V\,dp$. (c) If the increase in kinetic energy is 25 Btu, what work is done?

Ans. (a) 283.4 Btu, (c) 258.4 Btu.

46. A process follows the relation $pV^n = C$, where n and C are constants. Show that

$$\int_1^2 p\,dV = \frac{p_2V_2 - p_1V_1}{1 - n}$$

and

$$-\int_1^2 V\,dp = \frac{n(p_2V_2 - p_1V_1)}{1 - n}.$$

47. The heat rejected by 10 lb. of each of the following gases is 200 Btu: nitrogen, helium, argon. For each gas

at 80°F, what is the change of temperature and the final temperature (a) if the pressure remains constant, (b) if the volume remains constant?

Ans. (a) $t_2 = 160.5$°F for N_2; (b) $t_2 = 346$°F for A.

48. (a) If 1400 Btu are transferred to a certain mass of nitrogen in order to change its temperature 100°F at constant pressure, how much heat is necessary for the same temperature change at constant volume? (b) The same as (a) except that the substance is helium. (c) The same as (a) except that the substance is acetylene.

Ans. (c) = 1138 Btu.

49. (a) The change of enthalpy of a certain amount of oxygen is 2800 Btu. What is its change of internal energy? (b) The change of internal energy of a certain amount of argon is 1000 Btu. What is its change of enthalpy?

Ans. (b) 1668 Btu.

50. The constant pressure specific heat of a certain gas is $c_p = 0.3 + 0.003T$ Btu/lb., where T is °R, applicable from 0°F to 600°F. The corresponding $c_v = -0.3 + 0.003T$ Btu/lb. Determine the heat to raise the temperature of 3 lb. from 40°F to 540°F (a) at constant pressure, (b) at constant volume. (c) Compute the average specific heats for the process.

Ans. (a) 3825 Btu, (c) $c_v = 1.95$ Btu/lb-°R.

51. The heat required to change 1 lb. of a gas 1°F at constant volume is $Q = 0.21 + 0.336T \times 10^{-3} + 0.166T^2 \times 10^{-7}$ Btu/lb-°R. (a) What is its constant volume specific heat at 340°F? at 100°F? (b) Using the average of these two values, compute the decrease of internal energy of 1 lb. of gas for constant c_v. Ans. (b) −107 Btu/lb.

52. While the pressure remains constant, 3 lb. of a gas are reversibly cooled from 340°F to 60°F. Assuming constant c_p, determine the gas's change of entropy if the gas is (a) air, (b) argon, and (c) helium.

Ans. (a) −0.31, (b) −0.161, (c) −1.61 Btu/°R.

53. During cooling from 502°F at constant volume, the entropy of 1.446 lb. of air decreases 0.134 Btu/°R. What is the final temperature? *Ans.* 100°F.

54. The heat to a substance is 1000 Btu during a reversible process for which the temperature remains constant at 200°F. What is ΔS if the substance is (a) air, (b) argon?

Ans. (b) 1.515 Btu/°R.

55. The specific heat of a certain gas during a certain internally reversible process is $c = -0.0919$ Btu/lb-°R. If 3 lb./sec. undergo change of temperature from 500°R to 426°R, what is the change of entropy?

Ans. 0.0442 Btu/sec-°R.

56. A reversible process occurs such that $T = 100 + 300S^2$. What is the heat if the entropy changes from 0.6 to 0.5 Btu/°R? *Ans.* −19.1 Btu.

57. The constant pressure specific heat of a gas is represented by $c_p = 0.4 - 5/T^{1/2}$ Btu/lb-°R for a temperature change from 640°F to 840°F. If 10 lb. undergo a constant pressure process between these temperatures, what is ΔS? *Ans.* 0.414 Btu/°R.

58–70. These numbers may be used for other problems.

THE IDEAL GAS

41. Introduction. Since the mathematics of an ideal or perfect gas is relatively simple, it is fitting that we study this substance (or group of substances) first. Early experiments on air resulted in laws which we now recognize as being characteristic of an ideal gas (§§ 42, 43). That is, air is almost an ideal gas in its most common states, as are all the monatomic and diatomic gases, which is one practical reason for studying this hypothetical substance. While no actual gas conforms exactly to the tenets of an ideal gas, many of them are so close that ideal gas calculations give good engineering answers. Hence, this substance is not entirely visionary.

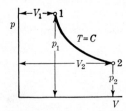

Fig. 18. *Boyle's Law.* A point such as 1 is a *state point*. The curve joing 1 and 2 is the *path of the state point* as the state of the substance changes and is spoken of as a *process*.

42. Boyle's Law. Robert Boyle (1627–1691), during the course of experiments with air, observed the following relation between the pressure and volume: *If the temperature of a given quantity of gas is held constant, the volume of gas varies inversely with the absolute pressure during a change of state* (***Boyles' law***).* In mathematical form, if a gas is in a condition represented by state 1, Fig. 18, and undergoes a change of state at constant temperature (***isothermal process***) to state 2, then

$$(19) \qquad \frac{p_1}{p_2} = \frac{V_2}{V_1}, \qquad \text{or} \qquad p_1 V_1 = p_2 V_2, \qquad \text{or} \qquad pV = C.$$

[BOYLE'S LAW, $T = C$]

The equation of the curve 1-2, Fig. 18, is thus $pV = C$, where C has some particular positive value. This curve is seen to be an equilateral hyperbola ($xy = C$), and since C may have any one of an infinite number of values, it is one of a family of curves.

Observe that we shall use C in a generic sense to mean a constant, but it will be a different constant in different equations; that is, for example, in

---

* Edme Mariotte, a Frenchman, independently discovered this same principle at approximately the same time that Boyle did. Although Mariotte therefore is due fully as much credit for the discovery, the law is more commonly called Boyle's in this country.

stating Boyle's law mathematically, we write $t = C$ and $pV = C$, in which the two C's are different constants; t is not equal to pV.

The experiments of Boyle were not as precise as modern sicence can make them. More accurate observations reveal that no actual gas follows this law exactly. Hence, we consider Boyle's law as being a defining character- istic of an ideal gas.

43. Charles' Law. About a hundred years after the discovery of Boyle's law, two Frenchmen, Jacques A. Charles (1746–1823) and Joseph L. Gay-Lussac (1778–1850), each without knowledge of the other's work, dis- covered the law which we usually call **Charles' law.** This law is in two parts:

1. *If the pressure on a particular quantity of gas is held constant, then, with any change of state, the volume will vary directly as the absolute temperature.*
2. *If the volume of a particular quantity of gas is held constant, then, with any change of state, the pressure will vary directly as the absolute temperature.*

The equations (20) and (21) below, which are mathematical expressions of Charles' law, may be considered as other characteristics of the *perfect gas*, usable however for gases which are nearly perfect. As before, consider a change of state for some gas, state 1 to state 2 [Fig. 19(a)], this time using

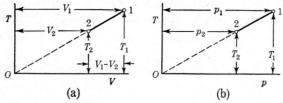

Fig. 19. *Charles' Law.* In (a), the line 1-2 represents a constant pressure process for an *ideal gas* as it appears on the TV plane. In (b), the line 1-2 represents a constant volume process as it appears on the Tp plane.

the absolute temperature T and volume V as coordinates, and letting the pressure at 1 equal the pressure at 2, $p_1 = p_2$. Then we may write

$$(20) \qquad \frac{V_1}{V_2} = \frac{T_1}{T_2}, \quad \text{or} \quad \frac{T_1}{V_1} = \frac{T_2}{V_2}, \quad \text{or} \quad \frac{T}{V} = C.$$
$$[\text{CHARLES' LAW, } p = C]$$

The volume V in this law is any volume, including specific volume v, of a constant mass of gas. Next, using the coordinates T and p [Fig. 19(b)], letting $V_1 = V_2$, we have

$$(21) \qquad \frac{p_1}{p_2} = \frac{T_1}{T_2}, \quad \text{or} \quad \frac{T_1}{p_1} = \frac{T_2}{p_2}, \quad \text{or} \quad \frac{T}{p} = C.$$
$$[\text{CHARLES' LAW, } V = C]$$

The equations (20) and (21) are seen to be straight lines ($y = Cx$) which pass through the origin with slopes C. However, since all actual gases undergo changes of phase at low temperatures, this law does not hold down to absolute zero. Charles' law is applicable to gases through only a limited range of temperature.

Each of the parts of Charles' law is used as a basis for measuring temperature. If the most nearly ideal gases are used, accurate temperature indications may be obtained from a constant-volume gas thermometer, in which $T_1/T_2 = p_1/p_2$, or from a constant-pressure gas thermometer, in which $T_1/T_2 = V_1/V_2$.

44. Equation of State of an Ideal Gas. An equation of state of a substance is one which relates three properties of the substance; for example, pressure as a function of volume and temperature, $p = \phi(V, T)$. Satisfactory equations of state for the more imperfect gases or "vapors" are complicated, but the one for an ideal gas is simple. What we wish is a relation between p, v, and T that applies to any two states whatsoever. Such a relation may be obtained by combining Boyle's law with either part of Charles' law, or by combining the two parts of Charles' law.

Let an ideal gas be in state 1, Fig. 20, and let the state be changed *at random*, 1-b-2, until it is represented by point 2. Let the mass of gas be 1 lb., for convenience; so the corresponding volume is the specific volume v.

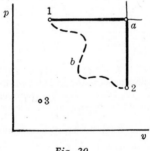

Fig. 20.

Now through point 1, draw a horizontal line of indefinite extent representing a constant pressure process on the pV plane; through point 2, draw a vertical line of indefinite extent representing a constant volume process. The lines representing these processes intersect at point a. Applying Charles' law and noting that $v_a = v_2$ and $p_a = p_1$, we find from the constant pressure process 1-a,

(a) $$\frac{v_1}{v_a} = \frac{T_1}{T_a}, \quad \text{or} \quad T_a = T_1\left(\frac{v_a}{v_1}\right) = T_1\left(\frac{v_2}{v_1}\right);$$

and from the constant volume process a-2,

(b)　　　　　$\dfrac{p_a}{p_2} = \dfrac{T_a}{T_2}$,　　or　　$T_a = T_2\left(\dfrac{p_a}{p_2}\right) = T_2\left(\dfrac{p_1}{p_2}\right)$.

From (a) and (b), we find

(c)　　　　　$T_a = T_2\left(\dfrac{p_1}{p_2}\right) = T_1\left(\dfrac{v_2}{v_1}\right)$,

or, by transposing terms,

(d)　　　　　$\dfrac{p_1 v_1}{T_1} = \dfrac{p_2 v_2}{T_2} = R$, a constant.

Since points 1 and 2 were selected at random, it follows that the same relation could be derived for any other pair of points, say, 1 and 3; thus $p_1 v_1 / T_1 = p_3 v_3 / T_3$. Consequently, this expression pv/T must be constant for a particular gas. Since the constant R is associated with a unit mass of substance, it is designated as the *specific gas constant,* ordinarily shortened, however, to the *gas constant.* It is expressed in general terms as $pv/T = R$ or

(22)　　　　　$pv = RT$　　and　　$pV = wRT$,
　　　　　　　[1 LB.]　　　　　　　　[w LB.]

where $V = wv$. Equation (22) is the *equation of state* or the *characteristic equation of a perfect gas.* From it may be obtained Boyle's and Charles' laws by letting T, p, and V be successively constant.

A few values of the gas constant R are given in Table V in the Appendix. For the values of R in this table always use p in pounds per square foot (psf), V in cubic feet, and T in degrees Rankine.

The value of R for any gas may be determined from experimental observations of simultaneous values of p, v, and T. Thus at 32°F and standard atmospheric pressure, the specific volume of *air* is 12.39 cu. ft. Hence,

(e)　　　　　$R = \dfrac{pv}{T} = \dfrac{(14.7)(144)(12.39)}{(460 + 32)} = 53.3$ ft-lb./lb-°R,　　　[AIR]

the approximate gas constant for air only. Air is so frequently used that the student should memorize this number. Gas constants for other gases are given in Table V in the Appendix. In § 251, it is shown that for ideal gases, the gas constant is

$$R = \dfrac{1545}{M},$$

where M is the molecular weight of the gas.

45. Joule's Law. Joule arranged two copper containers, as shown diagrammatically in Fig. 21, in a bath of water. The water was in an insu-

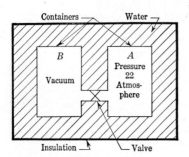

Fig. 21. *Joule's Experiment.*

lated vessel, so that the whole apparatus could be considered as an isolated system, without thermal contact with outside bodies. One of the containers held air at a pressure of 22 atm [(22)(14.7) psia], and the other container was evacuated as nearly as possible. After all parts had reached thermal equilibrium, the valve was opened. The air rushed into the evacuated container, and the whole mass of air finally came to rest at a pressure of 11 atm. Joule observed that there was no change in the temperature of the water surrounding the containers, a simple observation that leads to an important deduction.

There are several facts to be noted. First, although there is a momentary flow of air, giving rise to energy terms characteristic of flow, the net effect due to flow is zero, since, in the initial and final states, the gas is at rest. Consequently, the experiment is considered in relation to the simple energy equation. Second, inasmuch as there is no connection by which energy may leave the system as work, $W = 0$. Third, because the temperature of the water did not change, there must have been no flow of heat from the air in the containers to the water or from the water to the air, $Q = 0$. Fourth, the temperature of the air in the containers did not change, since otherwise, due to the temperature difference, there would have been a transfer of heat.*

Now from the energy equation, $\Delta U = Q - W = 0$. The pressure changed, the volume changed, but the internal energy did *not* change. Consequently, we conclude that the internal energy of this gas is not a function of the pressure or volume. However, since the temperature did not change, Joule deduced that *the change of internal energy is a function of the temperature change.* The italicized statement is known as **Joule's law.** While the evidence from Joule's experiment leading to this deduction is not conclusive,

---

* More precise experiments conducted later by Joule and William Thomson (Lord Kelvin) showed a change of temperature of the air. A porous plug was used at the valve, and extreme care was taken to prevent heat transfer to or from an external source. Thus, real gases do have a change of temperature with a change in pressure. The rate of change of temperature with pressure under the conditions of this experiment is called the Joule-Thomson coefficient. Mathematically, the Joule-Thomson coefficient = $(dT/dp)_h$, where the subscript h means that the enthalpy is constant. In a perfect gas, this coefficient is zero. Thus, Joule's law is true only for ideal gases, is nearly true for nearly ideal gases, is decidedly in error for "vapors." The magnitude of the Joule-Thomson coefficient measures the degree of departure of the gas from the ideal.

the law is true for an ideal gas and can be proved mathematically for a gas conforming to the characteristic equation, $pv = RT$.

46. Internal Energy of an Ideal Gas. The absolute amount of internal energy in any body cannot be determined, but the change of internal energy can be computed. Since the change of internal energy depends only on the temperature change, we may select any convenient process, evaluate the change between any two temperatures, and rest assured that this change is the same between these same temperatures no matter what process is used. The constant volume process is a convenient one. In a constant volume process, since there is no change of volume, $dV = 0$, and $\int p \, dV = 0$. The energy equation then becomes $Q = U_2 - U_1$. But as we have already learned, § 32, the heat transferred in a constant volume process is $Q = w \int c_v \, dT$. Therefore

$$(23) \qquad Q = \Delta U = U_2 - U_1 = w \int_{T_1}^{T_2} c_v \, dT,$$

which, for constant c_v becomes

$$(f) \qquad \Delta U = wc_v(T_2 - T_1),$$

an equation which is applicable when the specific heat of an ideal gas is constant, and with this limitation, it gives ΔU for *all* processes of *an ideal gas* during which the temperature changes from T_1 to T_2; it is approximately true for many real gases through a limited range of temperature.

47. Enthalpy of an Ideal Gas. In equation (j), § 33, it is shown that during a constant pressure process of any fluid $Q = \Delta H$ Btu. But also, equation (h), § 33, gives $Q = wc_p\Delta T$; or from the differential form, we get

$$(24) \qquad H_2 - H_1 = \int dH = w \int c_p \, dT = wc_p(T_2 - T_1).$$
$$\text{[CONSTANT } c_p]$$

Now if the fluid is an ideal gas, (24) gives the change of enthalpy whether the pressure is constant or not. The reason for this is that in $\Delta H = \Delta U + \Delta pV$, ΔU for an ideal gas is a function of the temperature only (Joule's law) and ΔpV is a function of temperature also ($pV = wRT$), from which we conclude that ΔH is a function of the temperature only *for an ideal gas.*

48. Example. A gas in the initial state of $p_1 = 75$ psia and $V_1 = 5$ cu. ft. undergoes a process to $p_2 = 25$ psia and $V_2 = 9.68$ cu. ft. during which the enthalpy decreases 62 Btu. The specific heat at constant volume is $c_v = 0.745$ Btu/lb-°R. Determine (a) the change of internal energy, (b) the specific heat at constant pressure, (c) the gas constant R.

SOLUTION. In general, if a method of solution is not immediately apparent, it is a good idea to write down on your work sheet all that you can think of which might have a bearing, including the most fundamental relations. If this is done for this problem, the work sheet should have on it $\Delta U = wc_v(T_2 - T_1)$ and $pV = wRT$; with these two equations there to look at, it might occur to you to use $pV = wRT$ in order to eliminate the temperatures in the equation for ΔU. [See part (c).] However, the gas constant R is unknown and this solution cannot be made. If you have written the fundamental definition of enthalpy change, $\Delta H = \Delta U + \Delta(pV)$, a solution for (a) is evident.

(a) Substitute $\Delta H = -62$ Btu because the change is a decrease. Then

$$-62 = \Delta U + \frac{[(25)(9.68) - (75)(5)]144}{778} = \Delta U - 24.6,$$

or $\Delta U = -62 + 24.6 = -37.4$ Btu, a decrease of U as indicated by the negative sign. Be sure to remember to convert psi to psf (144) and to have all energy terms in the same units (778).

(b) We notice from the fundamental equations (23) and (24) that, for constant k,

$$k = \frac{\Delta u}{\Delta h} = \frac{c_p}{c_v} = \frac{-62}{-37.4} = 1.655,$$

$$c_p = 1.655 c_v = (1.655)(0.754) = 1.25 \text{ Btu/lb-}^\circ\text{R.}$$

(c) Now we may use $T_1 = p_1 V_1/(wR)$ and $T_2 = p_2 V_2/(wR)$ in the internal energy equation and find

(g)
$$\Delta U = wc_v(T_2 - T_1) = \frac{c_v}{R}(p_2 V_2 - p_1 V_1) \text{ Btu,}$$

$$-37.4 = \frac{0.754}{R}[(25)(9.68) - (75)(5)]144,$$

$$R = 386 \text{ ft-lb./lb-}^\circ\text{R.}$$

Equation (26) below could also be used to compute R.

NOTE. If the substance is known, these constants c_p and R can be found in the literature, as in Table V. Comparing the answers found with the values in Table V, we see that the gas in this problem is helium, if it is a single gas. However, such a problem as this might be a mixture of gases with constants different from those of any single gas. ANOTHER NOTE. The way to study examples is with pencil and paper. You solve or try to solve the example before or after reading the solution.

49. Relation Between c_p and c_v, Ideal Gas. The relations derived below will be repeatedly useful. Starting with the definition $dH = dU + d(pV)/J$, we substitute $dH = wc_p\,dT$, $dU = wc_v\,dT$, and $pV = wRT$ [or $d(pV) = wR\,dT$], and find

$$wc_p\,dT = wc_v\,dT + \frac{wR\,dT}{J},$$

(25) $$c_p = c_v + \frac{R}{J} \quad \text{or} \quad c_p - c_v = \frac{R}{J} \text{ Btu/lb-}^\circ\text{R.}$$

This equation says that the difference between the specific heats is equal to the gas constant in Btu; it is not only true for ideal gases but is also substantially true for real gases. Now, using $k = c_p/c_v$ or $c_p = kc_v$, we get

$kc_v - c_v = R/J$ from (25); or

$$(26) \qquad c_v = \frac{R}{J(k-1)} \quad \text{and} \quad c_p = kc_v = \frac{kR}{J(k-1)}.$$

Recall that k varies with the temperature.

50. Entropy Change of an Ideal Gas. From equation (18), § 37, we have $dQ = T \, dS$ which may be used in the energy equations (12) and (16). Considering (12), $dQ = dU + p \, dV/J$, we also use $dU = wc_v \, dT$, § 46, and get

$$(\mathbf{h}) \qquad T \, dS = wc_v \, dT + \frac{p \, dV}{J}.$$

Divide each term of this equation by T, use $p/T = wR/V$ from $pV = wRT$, which restricts the results to ideal gases, and get

$$(\mathbf{i}) \qquad \int dS = w \int \frac{c_v \, dT}{T} + \frac{wR}{J} \int \frac{dV}{V}.$$

If the specific heat is constant, we integrate from state 1 to 2 and get

$$(\mathbf{j}) \qquad \Delta S = S_2 - S_1 = wc_v \ln \frac{T_2}{T_1} + \frac{wR}{J} \ln \frac{V_2}{V_1} \text{ Btu/°R.}$$
$$[\text{IDEAL GAS, CONSTANT } c_v]$$

This equation gives the change of entropy in terms of point functions only and is applicable to any process, reversible or irreversible, of an ideal or nearly ideal gas. Since pressure and temperature are the properties most easily measured, we may wish to obtain an equation similar to (**j**) but in terms of T and p. To do this, use the energy equation in the form of (16), $dQ = dH - V \, dp/J$, use $dQ = T \, dS$, $dH = wc_p \, dT$, and find

$$(\mathbf{k}) \qquad T \, dS = wc_p \, dT - \frac{V \, dp}{J}.$$

Divide through by T, use $V/T = wR/p$, and get

$$(\mathbf{l}) \qquad \int dS = w \int \frac{c_p \, dT}{T} - \frac{wR}{J} \int \frac{dp}{p}.$$

If the specific heat is constant, integration from 1 to 2 yields

$$(27) \qquad \Delta S = S_2 - S_1 = wc_p \ln \frac{T_2}{T_1} - \frac{wR}{J} \ln \frac{p_2}{p_1} \text{ Btu/°R.}$$
$$[\text{IDEAL GAS, CONSTANT } c_p]$$

It may be useful to recall that

$$-\log \frac{A}{B} = +\log \frac{B}{A} \quad \text{and} \quad \ln N = 2.3 \log_{10} N.$$

Using various known relations, $pV = wRT$, $c_p - c_v = R/J$, etc., with the equations (j) and (27), many different equations for ΔS can be obtained.

51. Closure. The various relations evolved in this chapter apply to ideal gases only. When you think of Boyle, think $T = C$ and $pV = C$; when you think of Charles, think $p = C$ and $V/T = C$, and also $V = C$ and $p/T = C$. Apply $pV = wRT$ to monatomic (He, A) or diatomic (H_2, O_2, etc.) gases; to other gases when more accurate properties are unavailable. Other gases are definitely imperfect, except at low pressures. Joule's law, $\Delta U = wc_v\Delta T$, and also $\Delta H = wc_p\Delta T$, applies only to an ideal gas (or for all practical purposes a nearly ideal gas).

If a gas follows the ideal gas laws closely enough so that computations from these laws yield results of satisfactory engineering value, then for this purpose the gas is an ideal gas. In one situation, a certain gas may be considered as ideal, but it may behave very differently in another situation (greater pressure or higher temperature or both). With the advent of jet engines and gas turbines, accurate properties of gases at high temperature, that is, allowing for the variation of specific heats, have become desirable. Such properties are now available for several gases in tabular form. The air table, Table VI, Appendix, is discussed in Chapter 6 on Compressors. See also Table VII, Appendix.

PROBLEMS

NOTE. *If not stated, the atmospheric pressure is standard.*

71. Hydrogen at 400°R occupies 30 cu. ft. (a) If the volume is increased to 90 cu. ft. at constant pressure, what is the final temperature in °K and °C? (b) If the pressure is tripled from state 2 in (a) while the volume remains constant, what is the temperature? (c) An ideal gas occupying 0.308 cu. ft. expands from 100 psig to standard atmospheric pressure while the temperature remains constant. What is the final volume?

Ans. (a) 667°K, (b) 3140°F, (c) 2.4 cu. ft.

72. The temperature of an ideal gas remains constant while the pressure changes from 14.7 psia to 100 psig. (a) If $V_1 = 3.2$ cu. ft., what is V_2? (b) If the mass of gas is 0.2 lb., what is the change of density?

Ans. (a) 0.410 cu. ft., (b) 0.425 lb./cu. ft. increase.

73. An automobile tire contains 1.5 cu. ft. of air at 30 psig and 80°F. The barometric pressure is 28 in. Hg. If, due to running conditions, the temperature of the air in the tires rises to 180°F, what is the percentage increase in the gage pressure? Assume that the volume of the tire is unchanged.

Ans. 26.9%.

74. (a) An ideal gas confined within an inflexible tank is at 85.3 psig and 240°F. If the gas is cooled until $p_2 = 25.3$ psig, what will be the temperature in °R? in °F? in °C? (b) While the pressure remains constant at 98 psig, the temperature of an ideal gas changes from 140°F to 240°F. For an original volume of 18 cu. ft., what is the final volume?

Ans. (a) −118°C, (b) 21 cu. ft.

75. An engineer estimates that for proper ventilation of an industrial plant, 40,000 cfm are needed when the atmosphere is at 100°F and 14.3 psia. What volume of air as measured under standard conditions of 60°F and 14.7 psia is being handled by the fans?

Ans. 36,100 cfm.

76. Compute the density of the following gases in lb./cu. ft. and slugs/cu. ft.: (a) air at 1 atm and 80°F; (b) carbon monoxide at 85 psia and 270°C; (c) hydrogen at a vacuum pressure of 22 in. Hg and 200°F.

Ans. (a) 0.0735 lb./cu. ft., (b) 0.00706 slugs/cu. ft.

77. A gas has a density of 0.0892 lb./cu. ft. at 14.7 psia and 32°F. (a) What is its specific volume at 150 psia and 100°F? (b) Calculate its gas constant and molecular weight.

Ans. (a) 1.25 cu. ft./lb., (b) 48.2, 32.1.

78. A balloon is to have a gross lifting force of 2 tons when the atmosphere is at 50°F and 14.7 psia and when the gas in the balloon is at atmospheric pressure and 65°F. How many cubic feet of gas are needed if the gas is (a) hydrogen, (b) helium? (c) What size spheres would contain these volumes?

Ans. (b) 59,250 cu. ft., (c) D = 47.2 ft. for H_2.

79. The volume of a certain automobile tire is 1.5 cu. ft. The air in it is at 25 psig and 80°F. Barometer is 30.6 in. Hg. (a) What is the mass of air? (b) Suppose the tire does not stretch while the temperature rises to 160°F. How much air must be re-

moved to bring the pressure back to 25 psig at 160°F? (c) What volume would the bled air occupy at atmospheric conditions?

Ans. (a) 0.3 lb., (b) 0.038 lb. (c) 0.506 cu. ft.

80. A 76-cu. ft. tank containing helium at 500°F and standard atmospheric pressure is evacuated until the vacuum is 29 in. Hg, the temperature remaining constant. (a) How much air was removed? (b) If the air left in the tank is cooled to 40°F, what is its pressure?

Ans. (a) 0.421 lb., (b) 0.479 in. Hg abs.

81. A tank, 6 in. in diameter by 48 in. long, contained acetylene at 250 psia and 80°F. After some was used, the acetylene was at 200 psia and 70°F. (a) What percentage of the contents of the tank was used? (b) What volume would the used acetylene occupy at 14.7 psia and 60°F?

Ans. (a) 18.5%, (b) 2.38 cu.ft.

82. A closed vessel A contains V_A = 2 cu. ft. of air at 600 psia and 100°F. This vessel connects with another vessel B which contains an unknown volume of air V_B at 20 psia and 40°F. After the valve separating the vessels is opened, internal equilibrium of the mixture is established at 250 psia and 60°F. What is V_B? *Ans.* 2.67 cu. ft.

83. The volume of a 6x12-ft. tank is 339.2 cu. ft. It contains air at 200 psig and 75°F. How many 1-cu. ft. drums can be filled to 50 psig and 65°F if it is assumed that the air temperature in the tank remains at 75°F? The drums have been open to the atmosphere which is at 14.7 psia and 65°F.

Ans. 992.

84. During a process of 4 lb. of air, the temperature increases from 40°F to 340°F. Find (a) ΔU, (b) ΔH. (c) If

$Q = 0$, what are the numerical values of $\int p\, dV/J$ and $-\int V\, dp/J$?

Ans. (a) 205.5 Btu, (c) $-\int V\, dp/J = -288$ Btu.

85. During a certain process of helium, the state changes from $p_1 = 75$ psia and $V_1 = 5$ cu. ft. to $p_2 = 25$ psia and $V_2 = 9.68$ cu. ft. What are ΔU and ΔH? *Ans.* -37.4 Btu, -62 Btu.

86. A certain ideal gas, for which $R = 35$ ft-lb./lb-°R and $k = 1.3$, is at 60 psig and 90°F. (a) What are c_p and c_v? (b) What volume would 5 lb. of this gas occupy? (c) If 20 Btu are added at constant volume, what are the resulting temperature and pressure? *Ans.* (a) 0.195, 0.15, (b) 8.94 cu. ft., (c) 117°F and 63.7 psig.

87. For a certain gas, $R = 400$ ft-lb. per lb-°R, $c_v = 0.8$ Btu/lb., $p_1 = 100$ psia, $V_1 = 40$ cu. ft. This gas is heated at constant pressure to 1000°R. Considering 5 lb. of the gas, find (a) c_p and k, (b) ΔU, (c) ΔH, (d) Q, (e) ΔS, and (f) the $\int p\, dV$. What does this integral represent in nonflow and steady flow processes? Does the nonflow energy equation balance?

Ans. (b) 2848 Btu, (c) 4680 Btu, (e) 1832 Btu.

88. From 80°F and 6 cu. ft., 10 lb. of hydrogen changes state to 150°F and 10 cu. ft. What is the change of entropy? *Ans.* 8.02 Btu/°R.

89. After a series of state changes, the pressure and volume of 5 lb. of nitrogen are each halved. What is ΔS? *Ans.* -1.475 Btu/°R.

90. For a certain gas, $R = 77.8$ ft-lb. per lb-°R and $c_p = 0.2 + 0.0002T$ Btu per lb. It is heated from 40°F to 140°F. For 1 lb., determine (a) the change of internal energy, (b) the change of enthalpy, (c) the change of entropy if the heating is at constant volume, (d) the change of entropy if the heating is at $p = C$, and (e) the value of k at 140°F.

Ans. (a) 21 Btu/lb., (d) 0.0565 Btu/lb-°R, (e) 1.455.

91-100. These numbers may be used for other problems.

$$\mathscr{L} \; 5$$

PROCESSES OF IDEAL GASES

52. Introduction. Knowing the characteristics of one working substance, the ideal gas, we are in a position to study processes of such a substance, after which we shall be able to investigate cycles in detail. _If any property (or all properties) of a substance changes, the substance is said to have undergone a process;_ there has been a change of state.

def: "Process"

Since graphical representations are of inestimable value in the solution of problems, the reader should always sketch the processes on the pV and TS planes.

Area "under" curve on pV plane, $\int p\, dV$, represents the work of a reversible nonflow process,

Area "behind" the curve on the pV plane, $-\int V\, dp$, represents the work of a reversible steady flow process when $\Delta K = 0$.

Area "under" curve on TS plane, $\int T\, dS$, represents heat of any reversible process.

It is worth while to know the energy equation in the forms

$$wc\, dT = wc_v\, dT + \frac{p\, dV}{J} \qquad \text{and} \qquad wc\, dT = wc_p\, dT - \frac{V\, dp}{J}$$

[AFTER EQUATION (12)]   [AFTER EQUATION (16)]

where the specific heat c is chosen in accordance with the kind of process and substance.

For *all* ideal gas processes and constant specific heats:

$$\Delta U = wc_v(T_2 - T_1) \qquad \text{and} \qquad \Delta H = wc_p(T_2 - T_1).$$

For *all* reversible ideal gas processes (constant specific heats):

$$\Delta S = wc \ln \frac{T_2}{T_1} \begin{cases} \text{Except } T = C. \\ c \text{ agrees with process,} \end{cases}$$

$$Q = wc(T_2 - T_1) \begin{cases} \text{Except } T = C. \\ c \text{ agrees with process.} \end{cases}$$

Positive values of ΔU, ΔH, and ΔS mean increases; negative values mean decreases. Positive Q is heat added; negative Q is heat rejected. Positive W is work done by the system; negative W is work done on the system.

You are already familiar with some of the material of this chapter from previous chapters, but it is necessary to organize the knowledge with respect to processes.

53. Constant Volume Process. On the pV plane, this process, which is also called an **isometric process,** is represented by a vertical line 1-2, Fig. 22(a). On the TS plane, a constant volume line of a gas slopes upward toward the right, the equation of the curve being obtained from $\int dS = wc_v \int dT/T$ for constant c_v, or

$$ S = wc_v \ln T + C, $$

where C is a constant of integration. As shown in Fig. 22, the gas is being "heated up"; at least, energy is flowing into the system.

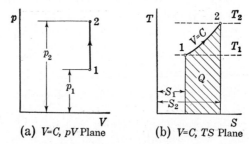

(a) $V=C$, pV Plane   (b) $V=C$, TS Plane

Fig. 22. *Reversible Isometric Process.* On the *pV* plane, there is no area *under* 1-2; $\int p \, dV = 0$.

In the solution of problems on gases it is frequently necessary to recall the p, V, T relations for the process at hand. For $V = C$, we think immediately of Charles' law and have

(a) $$ \frac{p_2}{p_1} = \frac{T_2}{T_1}. $$ [$V = C$, CHARLES]

Since $dV = 0$, the nonflow work $W = \int p \, dV = 0$. Thus, the nonflow energy equation reduces to $Q = \Delta U$ for an internally reversible constant volume process, which is one where the rise in temperature is brought about by heat only:

(b) $$ Q = U_2 - U_1, \quad Q = wc_v(T_2 - T_1). $$ [$V = C$]
              [ANY FLUID]   [IDEAL GAS]

The change of entropy is

(c) $$ \Delta S = wc_v \ln \frac{T_2}{T_1}. $$ [IDEAL GAS]

54. Constant Pressure Process. A *constant pressure process,* also called an **isobaric process,** is a change of state during which the pressure remains constant. It may be reversible or irreversible, nonflow or flow.

In any case for an ideal gas,

(d)
$$\frac{V_2}{V_1} = \frac{v_2}{v_1} = \frac{T_2}{T_1}.$$ $[p = C,$ CHARLES$]$

On the pV plane, Fig. 23, the process is represented by a horizontal line, and on the TS plane, the reversible process is represented by the curve obtained from the indefinite integral of $dS = dQ/T$; or for an ideal gas with constant specific heat,

(e)
$$S = wc_p \ln T + C,$$

where C is the constant of integration. In the reversible process 1-2, Fig. 23, heat is being added to the system and work is being done by it. If the state point should move toward the left, as from 2 to 1, Fig. 23, heat *rejected* and work done *on* a nonflow system would be indicated.

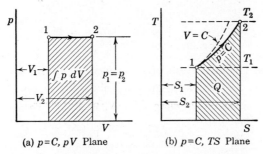

(a) *p=C, pV* Plane   (b) *p=C, TS* Plane

Fig. 23. Reversible Isobaric Process. Observe that the shaded area of figure (a) is equal to $W = p(V_2 - V_1)$, the work for a nonflow process, which is the same as the result obtained from $\int p \, dV$.

Notice the similarity of appearance of the constant volume and constant pressure lines on the TS plane, Fig. 23. The area under the constant pressure line must be larger than the area under the constant volume line for two particular temperatures T_1 and T_2 because c_p is larger than c_v $(dQ = c \, dT)$. Thus, to agree with this fact, it is essential for the constant pressure line to be *less* steep than the constant volume line within a particular temperature range.

(*a*) $\int p \, dV$. For constant pressure,

(f)
$$\int p \, dV = p \int dV = p(V_2 - V_1) = wR(T_2 - T_1) \text{ ft-lb.,}$$
[ANY FLUID]   [IDEAL GAS]

where the last term is obtained by use of $pV = wRT$ and applies to an ideal gas only. Thus, for a nonflow constant pressure process,

$$W_n = \int p \, dV = p(V_2 - V_1) \text{ ft-lb.}$$

For a steady flow process, equation (13), p. 30, shows that with $\Delta P = 0$,

$$\int p \, dV = p(V_2 - V_1) = \Delta W_f + \Delta K + W$$
$$= p(V_2 - V_1) + \Delta K + W.$$

Since the terms $p(V_2 - V_1)$ cancel each other, the shaft work, if any, is $W = -\Delta K$ for any fluid in a reversible steady flow process at constant pressure. The same conclusion is obtained from equation (**d**), § 30, because $dp = 0$ in $-\int V \, dp$.

(**b**) **Heat.** Using a constant c_p in $dQ = wc_p \, dT$, we find for an internally reversible process,

(**g**) $$Q = wc_p \int dT = wc_p(T_2 - T_1) \text{ Btu.}$$

In any reversible process, flow or nonflow, $Q = \Delta U + \int p \, dV/J$; and for $p = C$, this is

(**h**) $$Q = U_2 - U_1 + p_2V_2 - p_1V_1 = H_2 - H_1,$$
[ANY FLUID, FLOW OR NONFLOW, $p = C$]

which shows that the heat transferred in any internally reversible constant pressure process is ΔH, which for an ideal gas is $\Delta H = wc_p\Delta T = Q$ as in (**g**). If the process is steady flow [equation (10) with $\Delta P = 0$],

$$Q = \Delta H + \Delta K + W.$$
[ANY FLUID, ANY PROCESS]

If this flow occurs with little or no change in kinetic energy ($\Delta K = 0$) and with no shaft work ($W = 0$), as it does in all kinds of heat exchangers, then even with the pressure varying,

(**i**) $$Q = \Delta H \qquad\qquad Q = wc_p(T_2 - T_1).$$
[ANY FLUID, STEADY FLOW,   [IDEAL GAS, STEADY FLOW,
$\Delta K = \Delta P = W = 0$] $\Delta K = \Delta P = W = 0$]

This equation holds whether the process is reversible or irreversible when the stated conditions are met. See equation (**h**) again.

55. Example—Constant Pressure. An ideal gas, for which $R = 386$ and $k = 1.659$, undergoes a reversible isobaric process during which 500 Btu are added to 5 lb. of gas. The initial temperature is 100°F. Determine (a) t_2, (b) ΔH, (c) ΔS, (d) ΔU, and (e) W for a nonflow process.

SOLUTION. The specific heats, which will be needed, are found from equations (26). (The gas is not stated.)

$$c_v = \frac{R}{J(k-1)} = \frac{386}{778(1.659 - 1)} = 0.754 \text{ Btu/lb-°R.}$$

$$c_p = \frac{kR}{J(k-1)} = \frac{(1.659)(386)}{778(1.659 - 1)} = 1.25 \text{ Btu/lb-°R.}$$

(a) The heat is $500 = wc_p(T_2 - T_1)$, or

$$T_2 = \frac{500}{wc_p} + T_1 = \frac{500}{(5)(1.25)} + 560 = 640°\text{R};$$

from which $t_2 = 180°\text{F}$.

(b) Since $\Delta H = wc_p\Delta T$, $\Delta H = 500$ Btu. [This is also the heat in any steady flow process—under certain conditions. See equation (i).]

(c) The change of entropy is

$$\Delta S = wc_p \ln \frac{T_2}{T_1} = (5)(1.25) \ln \frac{640}{560} = 0.83 \text{ Btu/°R}.$$

(d) The change in internal energy is

$$\Delta U = wc_v(T_2 - T_1) = (5)(0.754)(640 - 560) = 301.6 \text{ Btu}.$$

(e) The work may be found from $W_n = p(V_2 - V_1) = wR(T_2 - T_1)$ ft-lb., but it is easily found from the nonflow energy equation,

$$W_n = Q - \Delta U = 500 - 301.6 = 199.4 \text{ Btu}.$$

56. Isothermal Process. An *isothermal process* is one carried out at constant temperature, $T = C$. Unless stated otherwise, we shall mean an

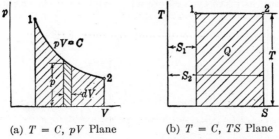

(a) $T = C$, pV Plane   (b) $T = C$, TS Plane

Fig. 24. *Reversible Isothermal Process.* Observe that the differential area in (a), *p dV*, is a differential work quantity *dW* in a nonflow system. When the volume increases, as 1 to 2, the process is called an *expansion.* When the volume decreases, it is said to be a *compression.*

internally *reversible* isothermal process whenever the term is used. Since $T = C$, we think immediately of Boyle's law when the substance is an ideal gas,

$$pV = C, \quad \text{or} \quad p_1V_1 = p_2V_2 = C. \qquad [T = C, \text{ BOYLE}]$$

[ANY REVERSIBLE OR IRREVERSIBLE PROCESS, IDEAL GAS]

The pV and TS curves of this process are shown in Fig. 24, where, on both planes, the state point has a component motion toward the right; heat is added, work is done *by* the system. If the process is run in the opposite direction, the state point has a component motion toward the left; heat is rejected, work is done *on* the system.

Since U and H are functions of temperature only for an ideal gas and since $T = C$, it follows that $U = C$ and $H = C$; or $\Delta U = 0$ and $\Delta H = 0$.

(**a**) $\int p \, dV$. This integration has been made, § 29, using $p = C/V$.

$$\int p \, dV = C \int \frac{dV}{V} = p_1 V_1 \ln \frac{V_2}{V_1} = wRT \ln \frac{p_1}{p_2} \text{ ft-lb.,}$$

where in the last form, we have used $p_1 V_1 = wRT$ and $V_2/V_1 = p_1/p_2$. For the nonflow process, then

(j) $$W_n = p_1 V_1 \ln \frac{V_2}{V_1} \text{ ft-lb.} = \frac{p_1 V_1}{J} \ln \frac{V_2}{V_1} \text{ Btu.}$$

[REVERSIBLE NONFLOW, IDEAL GAS]

For the steady flow process at constant temperature with $\Delta P = 0$ [see equation (14); and also § 30 for the integration],

$$- \int V \, dp = p_1 V_1 \ln \frac{V_2}{V_1} = \Delta K + W \text{ ft-lb.,}$$

from which one may solve for W if the other terms are known. States 1 and 2 are at the boundaries of the system where the substance enters and departs.

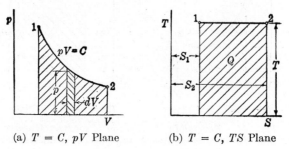

(a) $T = C$, pV Plane   (b) $T = C$, TS Plane

Fig. 24. Repeated.

(**b**) *Heat.* Since heat is transferred but the temperature does not change, the specific heat of the process is infinite, $c = \infty$. With $dT = 0$, we have $Q = c \, dT = (\infty)(0)$, an indeterminate. Therefore to find Q, we must use the energy equation

$$Q = \Delta U + \frac{1}{J} \int p \, dV \quad \text{or} \quad Q = \Delta H - \frac{1}{J} \int V \, dp \text{ Btu.}$$

[REVERSIBLE; ANY FLUID]

(k) $$Q = \frac{1}{J} \int p \, dV = \frac{p_1 V_1}{J} \ln \frac{V_2}{V_1} = wRT \ln \frac{p_1}{p_2} \text{ Btu.}$$

[IDEAL GAS, FLOW OR NONFLOW, $T = C$]

Equation (**k**) says, for example, that the work of a nonflow isothermal process of a gas is exactly compensated by heat—without increase or decrease of internal energy.

The change of entropy is

(1) $$\Delta S = \int \frac{dQ}{T} = \frac{1}{T}\int dQ = \frac{Q}{T} = \frac{wR}{J}\ln\frac{V_2}{V_1}\ \text{Btu/°R.}$$

Compare with the rectangular area under 1-2 on the TS plane, Fig. 24.

57. Adiabatic Processes—Energy Relations. An *adiabatic process* is one in which no heat is transferred, $Q = 0$. Such processes may be reversible or irreversible, flow or nonflow. The reversible adiabatic will be called an *isentropic process* because it is one of constant entropy ($S = C$, $\Delta S = 0$), represented by 1-2, Fig. 25. The processes 1-2′, shown dotted in Fig. 25,

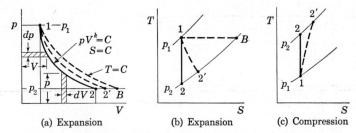

(a) Expansion   (b) Expansion   (c) Compression

Fig. 25. Adiabatic Processes. These curves are not plotted to scale, but the relationship on the pV plane (a) between an isothermal ($T = C$) and an isentropic ($S = C$) is shown qualitatively. Observe that the isentropic line on the pV plane is steeper than the isothermal; also that there is no area under the curve 1-2 on the TS plane, in accordance with $Q = 0$ for $S = C$.

represent irreversible processes. Most of the time, we shall use a prime mark to indicate some actual state point (after an irreversible process—no process is actually reversible), and irreversible processes should be shown dotted in order to remind us that the areas under the curves do not represent nonflow work on the pV plane or heat on the TS plane. The basic energy equations are easily applied. If $Q = 0$, equation (5) shows that the nonflow work is

(28A)　　$W_n = -\Delta U = U_1 - U_2$　or　$W_n = wc_v(T_1 - T_2)$,　[ISENTROPIC
　　　　　[REVERSIBLE, $Q = 0$; ANY FLUID]　　　　　　[IDEAL GAS]　　　　　NONFLOW]

(28B)　　$W'_n = -\Delta U' = U_1 - U_{2'}$　or　$W'_n = wc_v(T_1 - T_{2'})$,　[NONFLOW]
　　　　　[IRREVERSIBLE, $Q = 0$; ANY FLUID]　　　　　[IDEAL GAS]

where it is observed that the only difference in the two sets of equations is in the location of the final point and the use of the prime mark to indicate actual values.

In a steady flow process with $\Delta P = 0$ and $Q = 0$, the work from equation (10) is

$$W = -(\Delta H + \Delta K).$$

If ΔK happens to be negligible, as it often is, we have (see Fig. 25)

(29A)　$W = -\Delta H = H_1 - H_2$　　or　　$W = wc_p(T_1 - T_2)$,　[ISENTROPIC

[REVERSIBLE, ANY FLUID; Q, ΔK, $\Delta P = 0$]　　　　[IDEAL GAS]　　　　FLOW]

(29B)　$W' = -\Delta H' = H_1 - H_{2'}$　　or　　$W' = wc_p(T_1 - T_{2'})$.　　[FLOW]

[IRREVERSIBLE, ANY FLUID; Q, ΔK, $\Delta P = 0$]　　　[IDEAL GAS]

If $W = 0$, as in a nozzle, $\Delta K = -\Delta H$;

(30)　$\dfrac{wv_2^2}{2g_oJ} - \dfrac{wv_1^2}{2g_oJ} = H_1 - H_2$　　or　　$\Delta K = wc_p(T_1 - T_2)$ Btu.

[ANY FLUID; Q, W, $\Delta P = 0$]　　　　　　[IDEAL GAS]

For the corresponding actual adiabatic expansion, the reader may substitute state 2' for state 2 in (30). The irreversible adiabatic is always with increasing entropy, whether the process is an expansion or a compression. See Fig. 25.

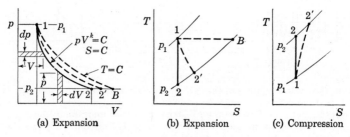

(a) Expansion　　　　(b) Expansion　　　　(c) Compression

Fig. 25. Repeated.

58. Isentropic Process. (a) *Relation between p, V, and T.* During the isentropic process, the pressure, volume, and temperature all vary. Heretofore, one of these properties has been constant. Since by definition of an isentropic the entropy is constant, the change of entropy $\Delta S = 0$. Equating ΔS in equation (j), p. 47, to zero, we find

$$c_v \ln \frac{T_2}{T_1} = \frac{R}{J} \ln \frac{V_1}{V_2},$$

or

$$\ln \left(\frac{T_2}{T_1}\right)^{c_v} = \ln \left(\frac{V_1}{V_2}\right)^{R/J}.$$

Taking antilogarithms, substituting $c_p - c_v$ for R/J (§ 49), and then taking the c_v root of both sides of the equation, we find

(31)　$\dfrac{T_2}{T_1} = \left(\dfrac{V_1}{V_2}\right)^{(c_p-c_v)/c_v} = \left(\dfrac{V_1}{V_2}\right)^{k-1}$,

where $k = c_p/c_v$. This equation (31) is the *TV* relationship for an isentropic process. If the pV relationship is desired, use the characteristic
equation

(m) $$\frac{p_1 V_1}{T_1} = \frac{p_2 V_2}{T_2}$$

to eliminate the temperatures; thus

$$\frac{T_2}{T_1} = \frac{p_2 V_2}{p_1 V_1} = \left(\frac{V_1}{V_2}\right)^{k-1},$$

or

(32A) $$\frac{p_2}{p_1} = \left(\frac{V_1}{V_2}\right)^{k}, \quad \text{or} \quad p_1 V_1{}^k = p_2 V_2{}^k.$$

Since points 1 and 2 are *any* two points on an isentropic curve, we may
write

(32B) $$pV^k = C,$$

which is the equation of the isentropic curve on the pV plane. This curve
is similar in appearance to the equilateral hyperbola, Fig. 25(a).

Then, to get the pT equation for an isentropic process, we may solve
(32A) and (31) simultaneously to eliminate the volumes. From (32A)

$$\frac{V_1}{V_2} = \left(\frac{p_2}{p_1}\right)^{1/k}.$$

Substituting this value of V_1/V_2 into (31), we get

(33) $$\frac{T_2}{T_1} = \left[\left(\frac{p_2}{p_1}\right)^{1/k}\right]^{k-1} = \left(\frac{p_2}{p_1}\right)^{(k-1)/k}.$$

Remember that (31), (32), and (33) represent p, T, V relationships in an
isentropic process of an *ideal gas* only.

(b) *Works.* We have found works from the energy equations (28) and
(29), all of which are very useful, but we must also learn how to obtain the
work from the pV plane. Since $pV^k = C$, Fig. 25(a), we use $p = C/V^k$ in
$p \, dV$ and get

$$\int p \, dV = C \int_{V_1}^{V_2} \frac{dV}{V^k} = \frac{CV^{-k+1}}{-k+1}\bigg]_{V_1}^{V_2} = \frac{CV_2{}^{1-k} - CV_1{}^{1-k}}{1-k}.$$

Setting the first $C = p_2 V_2{}^k$ and the second $C = p_1 V_1{}^k$, we find

(34) $$\int p \, dV = \frac{p_2 V_2 - p_1 V_1}{1-k} \text{ ft-lb.} = \frac{p_2 V_2 - p_1 V_1}{J(1-k)} \text{ Btu.}$$

[NONFLOW WORK, REVERSIBLE PROCESS; $pV^k = C$]

As we recall, this integral, the area under the curve, Fig. 25(a), is the work of a reversible nonflow process, $W_n = \int p\, dV$. The equation can be converted to temperatures by using $pV = wRT$, and it can be shown to be identical to (28A), p. 57, for an ideal gas when both are in the same units.

Next we may determine $-\int V\, dp$ for this process, which is the area behind the curve, Fig. 25(a). Taking the k root of $pV^k = C$ and substituting the resulting value of $V = C/p^{1/k}$, we have*

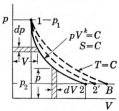

(a) Expansion

Fig. 25.　Repeated.

$$(35) \qquad -\int V\, dp = -C \int_1^2 \frac{dp}{p^{1/k}}$$
$$= \frac{k(p_2 V_2 - p_1 V_1)}{1 - k} \text{ ft-lb.}$$

From previous energy equations, we know from (14) that $-\int V\, dp/J = \Delta K + \Delta P + W$ during a reversible steady flow process. Hence for a steady flow process in which $\Delta K = 0$ and $\Delta P = 0$, we have [see equation (15), p. 30]

$$(\mathbf{n}) \qquad W = \frac{k(p_2 V_2 - p_1 V_1)}{1 - k} \text{ ft-lb.} = \frac{k(p_2 V_2 - p_1 V_1)}{J(1 - k)} \text{ Btu.}$$

[STEADY FLOW WORK; REVERSIBLE; ΔK, $\Delta P = 0$]

If $W = 0$ and $\Delta P = 0$, then $\Delta K = -\int V\, dp$ as found above. The negative sign for the $\int V\, dp$ is there because in integrating with respect to pressure from 1 to 2, the direction of integration is downward (negative) for an expansion and the $\int V\, dp$ turns out to be a negative number. But W done by the system, as in Fig. 25(a), is here taken as positive; hence, we use $-\int V\, dp$ to agree with the convention of signs already defined.

An observation which may sometimes be useful, from equation (16) is that $\Delta H = \int V\, dp/J$ Btu for an isentropic; from which we also see that the area behind the $pV^k = C$ curve represents ΔH to scale.

59. Example. There are compressed 3500 cfm of air from $p_1 = 14.5$ psia and $t_1 = 75°F$ to $p_2 = 29$ psia. Determine the work for each of the following processes: (a) nonflow isentropic, (b) nonflow irreversible adiabatic to a temperature of 190°F (650°R), (c) steady flow isentropic for which $v_1 = 40$ fps and $v_2 = 120$ fps, (d) steady flow adiabatic to a temperature of 190°F, velocities as in (c). (e) What is the change of entropy of the irreversible nonflow; of the irreversible steady flow?

SOLUTION. The temperature after isentropic compression is [Fig. 25(c)]

$$\frac{T_2}{T_1} = \left(\frac{p_2}{p_1}\right)^{(k-1)/k} \qquad \text{or} \qquad T_2 = 535 \left(\frac{25}{14.5}\right)^{(1.4-1)/1.4} = 625°R.$$

* Fill in the details of this integration. Note that this integral is k times the $\int p\, dV$ when $pV^k = C$.

The amount of air involved is

$$w = \frac{p_1 v_1}{RT_1} = \frac{(14.5)(144)(3500)}{(53.3)(535)} = 256 \text{ lb./min.}$$

(a) For a nonflow isentropic,

$$W_n = -\Delta U = wc_v(T_1 - T_2) = (256)(0.1715)(535 - 625) = -3950 \text{ Btu/min.}$$

This work is for the case in which all the air is in a cylinder and the piston compresses it. It does not include work that is necessary to get the air into and out of the cylinder.

(b) For the nonflow irreversible adiabatic,

$$W'_n = -\Delta U' = wc_v(T_1 - T_{2'})$$
$$= (256)(0.1715)(535 - 650) = -5050 \text{ Btu/min.}$$

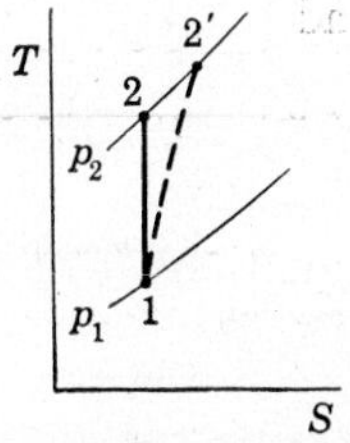

(c) For a steady flow process, $Q = 0$,

$$W = -\Delta K - \Delta H = w\left(\frac{v_1{}^2}{2g_o J} - \frac{v_2{}^2}{2g_o J} + h_1 - h_2\right)$$

$$= 256\left[\frac{40^2}{2g_o J} - \frac{120^2}{2g_o J} + 0.24(535 - 625)\right] = -5600 \text{ Btu/min.}$$

(c) Compression
Fig. 25. Repeated.

This work includes that necessary to get the air into and out of the cylinder.

(d) For the irreversible steady flow adiabatic, $-\Delta H' = wc_p(T_1 - T_{2'})$ and

$$W' = 256\left[\frac{40^2}{2g_o J} - \frac{120^2}{2g_o J} + 0.24(535 - 650)\right] = -7130 \text{ Btu/min.}$$

(e) Since the pressures and temperatures are known at states 1 and 2, use equation (27), § 50;

$$\Delta S = wc_p \ln\frac{T_{2'}}{T_1} - \frac{wR}{J}\ln\frac{p_{2'}}{p_1}$$

$$= (256)(0.24)\ln\frac{650}{535} - \frac{(256)(53.3)}{778}\ln\frac{25}{14.5} = 2.42 \text{ Btu/°R-min.}$$

Since the entropy change of this system is defined by the temperatures and volumes (in general, by thermodynamic properties), it is the same for nonflow and steady flow.

60. Polytropic Process. A *polytropic process,* Fig. 26, is an internally reversible process which conforms to the relation

$$(36) \qquad pV^n = C \qquad \text{or} \qquad p_1 V_1{}^n = p_2 V_2{}^n, \qquad \text{[ANY FLUID]}$$

where n is any constant. Many actual processes follow closely the relation in (36). Inasmuch as $pV^n = C$ is mathematically the same as $pV^k = C$, all of the mathematic consequences of the previous article apply here when $k = n$. Thus, the relations between T and V and between T and p are [see equations (31) and (33), § 58]:

(o)
$$\frac{T_2}{T_1} = \left(\frac{V_2}{V_1}\right)^{1-n} = \left(\frac{V_1}{V_2}\right)^{n-1}.$$
[IDEAL GAS]

(p)
$$\frac{T_2}{T_1} = \left(\frac{p_2}{p_1}\right)^{(n-1)/n}$$
[IDEAL GAS]

If a process is known to be polytropic and if two state points are defined, say pressures and volumes are known, the value of n can be found by use of logarithms. Writing (36) as $p_1/p_2 = (V_2/V_1)^n$ and taking logarithms, we find

(q)
$$n = \frac{\ln (p_1/p_2)}{\ln (V_2/V_1)}.$$

Equations (o) and (p) can be handled similarly.

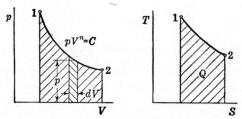

Fig. 26. *Reversible Polytropic Process.* These curves show the general appearance of a polytropic process where the value of n is between 1 and k. Since, in theory, the polytropic exponent may have any value from $n = -\infty$ to $n = +\infty$, curves sloping in any general direction may be obtained (see Fig. 28). In practice, the value of n does not vary greatly from k.

(a) $\int p\, dV$ **and** $\int V\, dp$. Corresponding to equation (34), we have the nonflow work as

(37)
$$W_n = \int p\, dV = \frac{p_2 V_2 - p_1 V_1}{1 - n} = \frac{wR(T_2 - T_1)}{1 - n} \text{ ft-lb.} \quad [pV^n = C]$$
[NONFLOW, ANY FLUID]   [IDEAL GAS]

By inspection of (n) and (36), we find the work of a steady flow polytropic process as

(38)
$$W = -\int V\, dp = \frac{n(p_2 V_2 - p_1 V_1)}{1 - n} \text{ ft-lb.} \quad [pV^n = C]$$
[STEADY FLOW; $\Delta K = 0$]

Equation (38) is also the value of ΔK when $W = 0$ and $\Delta P = 0$.

(b) **Heat.** For any reversible process, nonflow or steady flow, $dQ = dU + p \, dV/J$. For the integral of $p \, dV$, use the value in (37) and use $\Delta U = wc_v(T_2 - T_1) = wc_v \Delta T$ Btu.   Then

$$Q = wc_v(T_2 - T_1) + \frac{wR(T_2 - T_1)}{J(1 - n)} = w\left(\frac{c_v - nc_v + R/J}{1 - n}\right)(T_2 - T_1).$$

Using $c_v + R/J = c_p$ and $k = c_p/c_v$, we find

$$(39) \qquad Q = w\left(\frac{c_p - nc_v}{1 - n}\right)(T_2 - T_1) = wc_v\left(\frac{k - n}{1 - n}\right)(T_2 - T_1) \text{ Btu.}$$

Now suppose we call c_n the specific heat of a polytropic process; that is, it is the amount of heat added or abstracted during the process to change 1 lb. by 1°F.   The heat then becomes $Q = wc_n(T_2 - T_1)$.   Comparing this equation with (39), we can write

$$(40) \qquad\qquad\qquad c_n = c_v\left(\frac{k - n}{1 - n}\right), \qquad\qquad \text{[IDEAL GAS]}$$

the *polytropic specific heat*.   The value of c_n may vary infinitely, inasmuch as n may vary infinitely.   Observe also that c_n is negative when $k > n > 1$. A negative specific heat means that heat is rejected by the substance even though the temperature rises or that heat is added even though the temperature· decreases.   A process of heat rejection with simultaneous temperature increase actually occurs in the usual air compressor.   The work done on the air raises the temperature of the air (stores some internal energy), yet at the same time, in order to obtain a lower final temperature at the end of compression, cooling water is circulated around the cylinder to extract some heat.   The area "under" the curve on the TS plane, Fig. 26(b), represents Q in Btu.

The change of entropy of a reversible polytropic is

$$(\mathbf{r}) \qquad\qquad \Delta S = \int \frac{dQ}{T} = w\int \frac{c_n \, dT}{T} = wc_n \ln \frac{T_2}{T_1},$$

where c_n is the average constant value for the temperature range.   Notice, for example, that by using the values of T_2/T_1 given above by (o) and (p) in (**r**), ΔS may be expressed in terms of other properties.

61. Example—Polytropic Process. See Fig. 27.   Five pounds of an ideal gas are compressed polytropically from a pressure of 15 psia and 40°F to 85.3 psig. The gas constant is $R = 50$, $c_p = 0.25$, and the change of state is according to $pV^{1.3} = C$.   Find (a) the initial volume, (b) the final temperature, (c) the $\int p \, dV$, (d) the change of internal energy, (e) the heat transferred, (f) the change of enthalpy,

(g) the work if the process is steady flow and there is no change of kinetic energy,
(h) the change of entropy.

SOLUTION. (a) From the characteristic equation

$$V_1 = \frac{wRT_1}{p_1} = \frac{(5)(50)(40 + 460)}{(144)(15)} = 57.9 \text{ cu. ft.}$$

(b) From equation (p), $T_2 = T_1(p_2/p_1)^{(n-1)/n}$. Assume standard atmospheric pressure of 14.7 psia. Then $p_2 = 85.3 + 14.7 = 100$ psia, and

$$T_2 = (500)\left(\frac{100}{15}\right)^{(1.3-1)/1.3} = (500)(1.549) = 774°R = 314°F.$$

(c) In the expression $\int p \, dV = (p_2V_2 - p_1V_1)/(1 - n)$, the volume V_2 must be calculated or eliminated. Using $pV = wRT$, we have

$$\int p \, dV = \frac{wR(T_2 - T_1)}{1 - n} = \frac{(5)(50)(774 - 500)}{1 - 1.3} = -228,000 \text{ ft-lb.} = -293 \text{ Btu.}$$

The negative sign indicates mechanical energy entering the substance. If the

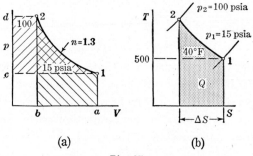

(a)   (b)

Fig. 27.

process is nonflow, the negative sign means that 293 Btu of work are done *on* the substance.

(d) To find c_v, use $c_p - c_v = R/J$, or $c_v = 0.25 - 50/788 = 0.25 - 0.0643 = 0.1857$ Btu/lb-°R. Then

$$\Delta U = wc_v(T_2 - T_1) = (5)(0.1857)(774 - 500) = +254 \text{ Btu.}$$

The positive sign indicates an increase in internal energy.

(e) The value of $k = c_p/c_v = 0.25/0.1857 = 1.346$. The polytropic specific heat is

$$c_n = c_v\left(\frac{k - n}{1 - n}\right) = 0.1857\left(\frac{1.346 - 1.3}{1 - 1.3}\right) = -0.02845 \text{ Btu/lb-°R.}$$
$$Q = wc_n(T_2 - T_1) = (5)(-0.02845)(774 - 500) = -39 \text{ Btu.}$$

The negative sign indicates heat rejected by the substance. As a check on this calculation use the energy equation

$$Q = \Delta U + \frac{1}{J}\int p \, dV = +254 - 293 = -39 \text{ Btu (check).}$$

(f) The change of enthalpy is

$$\Delta H = wc_p(T_2 - T_1) = (5)(0.25)(774 - 500) = 342.5 \text{ Btu.}$$

(g) From the steady flow energy equation, the work is

$$W = H_1 - H_2 + Q = -342.5 + (-39) = -381.5 \text{ Btu,}$$

when $\Delta K = 0$. This value can be checked by $n\int p\, dV = -\int V\, dp = W$, equation (14); thus, $(1.3)(-293) = -381$ Btu. As a precaution against an error, it is usually advisable to check answers by a different approach when possible. A calculating machine would bring the answers closer together.

(h) The change of entropy is

$$\Delta S = wc_n \ln \frac{T_2}{T_1} = (5)(-0.02845) \ln \frac{774}{500} = -0.0624 \text{ units.}$$

The negative sign indicates a decrease of entropy.

62. Effect of Varying n in Polytropic Equations. Polytropic processes are all inclusive in that the equations for the change of state of all the foregoing reversible processes can be obtained from $pV^n = C$ by choosing proper values of n.

Let $n = 0$, then $pV^0 = C$ or $p = C$, a constant pressure process.
Let $n = \infty$, then from $pV^n = C$, we have $p^{1/n}V = C'$, or $p^{1/\infty}V = p^0V = C'$, or $V = C'$, a constant volume process.
Let $n = k$, then $pV^k = C$, which is recognized as the equation for an isentropic process.

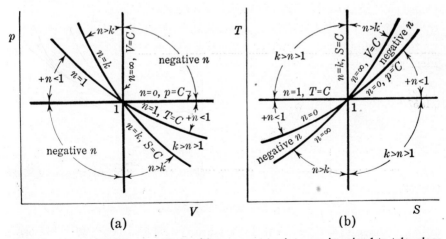

Fig. 28. Effect of Varying n. Expansions or compressions are imagined to take place from some common point 1. Notice that all positive values of n give curves in the second and fourth quadrants on the pV plane (a); that positive values of n may produce curves in all four quadrants on the TS plane (b). Notice, too, that curves with values of n between 1 and k will fall in the second and fourth quadrants on the TS plane and within a very narrow region on the pV plane.

Let $n = 1$, then $pV = C$, which is recognized as Boyle's law and the equation of an isothermal process.

It is important to be able to sketch various curves of thermodynamic processes on the pV and TS planes, and sketch them about as they would appear if they were actually plotted to scale. Figure 28 will be of assistance in learning to make these sketches and it shows also the effect of varying n. Remember that, although they appear much alike, the isentropic curve on the pV plane is *steeper* than the isothermal curve; and that, on the TS plane, the constant volume curve is *steeper* than the constant pressure curve when both are drawn between the same temperature limits.

63. Throttling Process. A throttling process is taken as an adiabatic flow process ($Q = 0$) from one region to another at lower pressure, during which no work is done. It is a free expansion, as in opening the valve on a compressed air tank or the household faucet. It is usually analyzed for a period during which the flow is steady. If $\Delta P = 0$, as well as $W = 0$ and $Q = 0$, the steady flow energy equation becomes

$$H_1 + K_1 = H_2 + K_2.$$

Possibly somewhere in the stage of a throttling expansion, the kinetic energy K might be relatively large. In practical application, however, the end conditions for the substance are virtually stationary or $K_1 \approx K_2$. In either event,

(41) $$H_1 = H_2 \quad \text{or} \quad wc_p(T_2 - T_1) = 0,$$
$$\text{[ANY FLUID]} \qquad\qquad \text{[IDEAL GAS]}$$

represent defining conditions for a throttling process. If the substance is an ideal gas, $T_1 = T_2$ as well as $H_1 = H_2$, but not otherwise. See footnote,

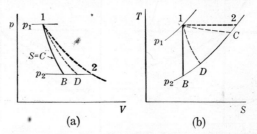

Fig. 29. *Throttling Process.*

p. 44. Since $T = C$, $p_1V_1 = p_2V_2$ for an ideal gas, Fig. 29. Imperfect gases generally undergo a temperature decrease as a result of throttling, corresponding to some end conditions such as 1-C, Fig. 29(b). The process is shown dotted as a reminder that the areas on the pV and TS planes no longer represent work and heat.

The change of entropy, *which will always be an increase*, can be computed from any one of the equations of § 50 (be sure to refer back in order to become oriented), say equation (j) which reduces to

P. 46

(s)
$$\Delta S = \frac{wR}{J} \ln \frac{V_2}{V_1} \text{ Btu/°R},$$

because $T_1 = T_2$ and $\ln 1 = 0$. Compare (s) with the entropy change of a reversible isothermal process, equation (l), § 56.

64. Closure. Thermodynamics is exacting but fascinating. The beginner is prone to depend unduly on memory for details with which to solve problems, whereas it is easier and more profitable to classify the knowledge in such a way as to see the repetitive utility of the more basic laws. For example, in any nonflow process, the law of conservation of energy is expressed by

$$dW = dQ - dU$$

where $dU = wc_v \, dT$ when $pv = RT$; if the process is reversible, $dW = p \, dV/J$ and $dQ = wc \, dT$ where c depends upon the kind of process.

Table I. *IDEAL GAS FORMULAS, CONSTANT SPECIFIC HEATS*

Process →	Constant volume $V = C$	Constant pressure $p = C$	Isothermal $T = C$	Isentropic $S = C$	Polytropic $pV^n = C$
p, V, T relations	$\dfrac{T_2}{T_1} = \dfrac{p_2}{p_1}$	$\dfrac{T_2}{T_1} = \dfrac{V_2}{V_1}$	$p_1V_1 = p_2V_2$	$p_1V_1^k = p_2V_2^k$ $\dfrac{T_2}{T_1} = \left(\dfrac{V_1}{V_2}\right)^{k-1}$ $= \left(\dfrac{p_2}{p_1}\right)^{(k-1)/k}$	$p_1V_1^n = p_2V_2^n$ $\dfrac{T_2}{T_1} = \left(\dfrac{V_1}{V_2}\right)^{n-1}$ $= \left(\dfrac{p_2}{p_1}\right)^{(n-1)/n}$
$\int_1^2 p \, dV$	0	$p(V_2 - V_1)$	$p_1V_1 \ln \dfrac{V_2}{V_1}$	$\dfrac{p_2V_2 - p_1V_1}{1 - k}$	$\dfrac{p_2V_2 - p_1V_1}{1 - n}$
$-\int_1^2 V \, dp$	$V(p_1 - p_2)$	0	$p_1V_1 \ln \dfrac{V_2}{V_1}$	$\dfrac{k(p_2V_2 - p_1V_1)}{1 - k}$	$\dfrac{n(p_2V_2 - p_1V_1)}{1 - n}$
$U_2 - U_1$	$wc_v(T_2 - T_1)$	$wc_v(T_2 - T_1)$	0	$wc_v(T_2 - T_1)$	$wc_v(T_2 - T_1)$
Q	$wc_v(T_2 - T_1)$	$wc_p(T_2 - T_1)$	$\dfrac{p_1V_1}{J} \ln \dfrac{V_2}{V_1}$	0	$wc_n(T_2 - T_1)$
n	∞	0	1	k	$-\infty$ to $+\infty$
Specific heat, c	c_v	c_p	∞	0	$c_n = c_v\left(\dfrac{k - n}{1 - n}\right)$
$H_2 - H_1$	$wc_p(T_2 - T_1)$	$wc_p(T_2 - T_1)$	0	$wc_p(T_2 - T_1)$	$wc_p(T_2 - T_1)$
$S_2 - S_1$	$wc_v \ln \dfrac{T_2}{T_1}$	$wc_p \ln \dfrac{T_2}{T_1}$	$\dfrac{wR}{J} \ln \dfrac{V_2}{V_1}$	0	$wc_n \ln \dfrac{T_2}{T_1}$

All these equations are good for reversible processes

* Only " " " " " any process.

In any steady flow process ($\Delta P = 0$),

$$dW = dQ - dH - \Delta K,$$

where $dH = wc_p \, dT$ when $pv = RT$; dQ is as stated for the nonflow process and $dW = -V \, dp/J = dQ - dH$ when $\Delta K = 0$. ($dW \neq p \, dV/J$.) The tabulation of equations in Table I is for the purpose only of highlighting many similarities and emphasizing differences.

Recall that energy is a scalar quantity, so that should there be two or more successive processes, the total work will be the algebraic sum of the works for the individual processes, and the heat transferred will be the algebraic sum of the heats of the processes.

PROBLEMS

NOTE. *In each of the following problems, indicate clearly whether work is done on or by the substance, whether the heat is transferred to or from the substance, and whether there is an increase or a decrease of internal energy, enthalpy, and entropy. Moreover, a sketch of the process on the pV and TS planes and energy diagrams should be included in all solutions.*

101. Air at 300 psia and 400°F is cooled to 140°F with the volume remaining at 10 cu. ft. Determine (a) the final pressure, (b) the change of internal energy, (c) the transferred heat, (d) the change of entropy, (e) work, (f) the $\int p \, dV$.

Ans. (a) 209 psia, (b) −420 Btu, (d) −0.58 Btu/°R.

102. Nitrogen is heated at a constant volume of 5 cu. ft. until the pressure changes from 40 psia to 200 psig. Find (a) the change of internal energy, (b) the heat, (c) the change of specific entropy, (d) the change of enthalpy, (e) the work.

Ans. (a) 406 Btu, (c) 0.298 Btu/lb-°R, (d) 567 Btu.

103. During a constant pressure process of 5 lb. of air, the temperature drops from 300°F to 40°F. Find (a) $\int p \, dV/J$, (b) the change of enthalpy, (c) the change of internal energy, (d) the heat transferred, (e) the work if the process is nonflow, (f) the change of entropy.

Ans. (a) −89.2 Btu, (b) −312 Btu, (f) −0.5025 Btu/°R.

104. A certain gas, with $c_p = 0.529$ Btu/lb. and $R = 96.2$ ft-lb./lb-°R, expands from 5 cu. ft. and 80°F to 15 cu. ft. while the pressure is constant at $p = 15.5$ psia. Compute (a) T_2, (b) ΔH, (c) ΔU, (d) ΔS. (e) For an internally reversible nonflow process, what is the $\int p \, dV$ and the work? (f) For a steady flow process in which $W = 0$ and $\Delta K = -12$ Btu, what is Q?

Ans. (a) 1160°F, (b) 122.8 Btu, (c) 94 Btu, (d) 0.125 Btu/°R, (e) 28.7 Btu, (f) 122.8 Btu.

105. An isothermal expansion of 8 lb./min. of hydrogen occurs from 80 psia and 80°F to 5 psig. Determine (a) V_2, (b) $\int p \, dV$, (c) ΔU, (d) Q, (e) the work of a nonflow process, (f) the work of a steady flow process during which the kinetic energy decreases 10 Btu/lb., (g) the change of entropy.

Ans. (a) 1185 cfm, (b) 6060 Btu per min., (g) 11.03 Btu/°R-min.

106. A certain gas, for which $c_p =$ 1.25 and $c_v = 0.754$ Btu/lb-°R, expands isothermally from 15 psia and 60°F until the initial volume is doubled. For 2 lb./sec., determine (a) $\int p\,dV/J$, (b) $-\int V\,dp/J$, (c) Q, (d) ΔS, (e) ΔH, (f) the nonflow work, (g) the work of a steady flow in which the kinetic energy increases 10 Btu/sec.

Ans. (a) 358 Btu/sec., (d) 0.687 Btu/°R-sec.

107. Let 3 cu. ft. of carbon dioxide, considered as an ideal gas, be isentropically compressed from 280.85 psia and 25°F to 852.4 psia. Find (a) V_2 and t_2, (b) $\int p\,dV/J$, (c) ΔU, (d) ΔH, (e) Q and ΔS, (f) the nonflow work, (g) the steady flow work if $\Delta K = 0$.

Ans. (a) 1.266 cu. ft., 161°F, (b) 151 Btu, (c) 153 Btu, (g) −197 Btu.

108. An ideal gas, with $c_v = 1$ Btu/lb. and $R = 233.4$ ft-lb./lb-°R, expands isentropically from 75 psia and 1.5 cu. ft. The relation between the temperatures at the initial and final states is $T_1 = 1.6T_2$. Determine (a) the final pressure and volume, (b) $\int p\,dV/J$, (c) ΔU, (d) ΔH, (e) Q and ΔS, (f) the nonflow work, (g) the steady flow work if $\Delta K = 0$.

Ans. (a) 9.81 psia, 7.17 cu. ft., (b) 26 Btu, (d) −33.8 Btu.

109. From a state defined by 300 psia, 100 cfm, 240°F, helium undergoes an adiabatic process to 0.3 psig. If the process is reversible, find (a) V_2 and t_2, (b) ΔU and ΔH, (c) the steady flow work for $\Delta K = +10$ Btu/min. (d) If the efficiency of this process, (ideal work/actual work) is 80%, determine the actual horsepower developed and the final discharge temperature.

Ans. (a) 608 cfm, −247°F, (b) −5870, −9740 Btu/min., (d) 183.5 hp, −149°F.

110. During an isentropic process of 4 lb./sec. of air, the temperature increases from 40°F to 340°F. Compute (a) ΔU and ΔH, (b) $\int p\,dV/J$, (c) $-\int V\,dp/J$, (d) Q and ΔS, (e) the nonflow work, (f) the steady flow work for a kinetic energy change of -10 Btu/sec. (g) For an irreversible adiabatic process from the same initial state to the same final pressure, the final temperature is 400°F. What are the works of the nonflow and steady flow (same ΔK) processes? What is ΔS for this process?

Ans. (a) 205.5, 288 Btu/sec., (f) −278 Btu/sec., (g) $W_{\text{flow}} = -335.6$ Btu/sec., $\Delta S = 0.0695$ Btu/°R-sec.

111. An ideal gas, for which $c_v = 0.2$ Btu/lb-°R and $R = 50$ ft-lb./lb-°R, is compressed from 15 psia, 60°F, and 10 cu. ft. to 105 psia in an internally reversible process $pV^{1.31} = C$. Determine (a) the polytropic specific heat, (b) Q, (c) ΔU and ΔH, (d) ΔS, (e) the nonflow work (without making $\int p\,dV$), (f) the steady flow work (without making $-\int V\,dp$) for $\Delta K = 0$.

Ans. (a) −0.00774 Btu/lb-°R, (b) −1.85 Btu, (c) 50.5, 66.8 Btu, (d) −0.104 Btu/°R.

112. During a polytropic compression, 3 lb. of nitrogen are compressed from 14 psia and 60°F while 75 Btu of heat are rejected. For $pV^{1.32} = C$, find (a) t_2 and p_2, (b) ΔU and ΔH, (c) ΔS, (d) the nonflow work, (e) the steady flow work if $\Delta K = +10$ Btu. (f) Find the $\int p\,dV$ and $-\int V\,dp$ and show energy balances as given in equations (10), (12), and (16).

Ans. (a) 622°F, 289 psia, (b) 299, 419 Btu, (c) 0.0975 Btu/°R, (d) −374 Btu, (e) −504 Btu.

113. An ideal gas undergoes a polytropic process from 20 psia and 40°F to 120 psia and 340°F; use $R = 40$ ft-lb. per lb-°R, $c_p = 0.25$ Btu/lb-°R, and $w = 10$ lb. Find (a) the value of the exponent n, (b) ΔU, (c) ΔH, (d) Q, (e) ΔS, (f) the work of a nonflow process,

(g) the work of a steady flow process with $\Delta K = 0$.

Ans. (a) 1.355, (b) 595 Btu, (c) 750 Btu, (d) 159.5 Btu, (e) 0.25 Btu/°R, (f) −435.5 Btu, (g) −554.5 Btu.

114. During a polytropic expansion, the temperature drops 120°F while 120 Btu of heat are being added to 4 lb. of air. Find (a) ΔU and ΔH, (b) the nonflow work and the magnitude of the $\int p\, dV/J$, (c) the steady flow work for $\Delta K = 0$ and the value of $-\int V\, dp/J$, (d) the value of n in $pV^n = C$.

Ans. (a) −82.4, −115.1 Btu, (b) 202.4 Btu, (c) 235.1 Btu, (d) 1.163.

115. The nonflow work done in compressing helium in accordance with $pV^{1.32} = C$ is 60,000 ft-lb. Calculate ΔU, ΔH, Q, and the steady flow work for $\Delta K = 0$.

Ans. 37.5, 62.2, −39.8, −102 Btu.

116. Air undergoes a throttling process from 60 psig to 12 psia. What is the change of specific entropy? What is the percentage increase in volume?

Ans. 0.1252 Btu/lb-°R, 522.5%.

117. The pressure on 10 lb. of oxygen decreases from 600 to 200 psia while the volume increases from 3 to 9 cu. ft. What is ΔS? Is it an increase or decrease? Ans. +0.68 Btu/°R.

118. Given a system A (see figure) which is 0.1 lb. of air at $p_1 = 14.7$ psia and $t_1 = 80$°F. The movable piston, whose area is 30 sq. in., does not permit the passage of matter or heat. The only heat is Q_A added to system A until the spring has been compressed from its free length (zero force) an amount $L = 6$ in., after which the state of A is

defined by p_2 and t_2. System B includes part of the atmosphere and the spring whose scale is 500 lb./in.; atmospheric conditions of $p_o = 14.7$ psia and $t_o = 80$°F do not change. Make energy diagrams and write the energy equations (a) for system A between states 1 and 2, and (b) for system B while A changes from 1 to 2 in the form of statement

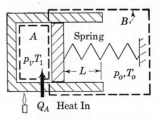

Problem 118.

(4B), § 19. (c) How much energy is stored in the spring (Btu)? (d) What work (Btu) is done in displacing part of the mass in system B across its boundaries? (e) Sketch the pV curve for system A. What work is done by system A? (f) What is the final temperature of system A and its change of internal energy? Let the average specific heat at constant volume be 0.2 Btu/lb-°F. (g) What is the heat added? (h) Determine the internal energy change of the air in system B from the energy balance of system B and from the energy balance of systems A and B taken together. Comment on the difference in your answers.

Ans. (c) 0.964 Btu, (e) 1.249 Btu, (f) 79.8 Btu, (h) −0.0025 Btu.

119–130. These numbers may be used for other problems.

6

COMPRESSORS

65. Introduction. We are now prepared for some detailed applications of the energy equation to particular engines. In this chapter, our discussion will center around the compression of air, although the results obtained apply to any gas and the basic principles apply to the compression of vapors. Compressed air, air at some pressure above atmospheric pressure, has many practical uses: operation of air engines and pneumatic tools such as hammers and drills, spraying paint, cleaning by air blast, operation of air hoists, pumping water by air lift, and many other specialized industrial applications. The compression process is an integral part of gas turbine cycles and refrigeration cycles.

Compressors are also used in maintaining a partial vacuum by pumping gases from some pressure below atmospheric to atmospheric pressure.

66. Classification of Compressors. Compressors may be broadly classified as either rotary compressors, of which there are several types, or reciprocating compressors, in which the flow is intermittent. In any case, however, there is (1) a process of drawing the fluid into the compressor—called the *suction stroke* in a reciprocating machine; (2) a process of compression, which of course is actually irreversible, but which in the ideal case may be an isothermal process, an isentropic process, or a polytropic process; (3) a process of discharging the fluid.

67. Nomenclature. The principal parts of a reciprocating compressor are (Fig. 30): a crank, attached to the crankshaft and rotating with it; a connecting rod; a crosshead which guides the end of the piston rod in a straight line; the piston rod and piston; the cylinder and valves. In internal combustion engines, which are usually single-acting, and in some small single-acting compressors, the crosshead and piston rod are often omitted. In this event, the connecting rod is attached directly to a trunk piston, Fig. 34.

A double-acting engine or compressor is one in which the working substance acts on both sides of the piston. In a single-acting engine, the substance acts on one side of the piston only.

71

When the piston is at the position farthest from the crankshaft, the engine or compressor is said to be on **head-end dead-center position,** Fig. 30. Since it is common to speak of the head end as the top, this position is also called **top dead center,** abbreviated TDC (especially in automotive engineering practice). When the piston is closest to the crankshaft, the engine or compressor is said to be on **crank-end dead-center position,** Fig. 30; this position is also called **bottom dead center,** abbreviated BDC.

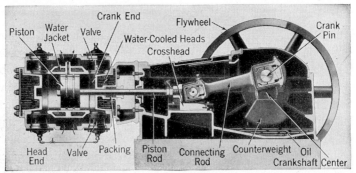

Courtesy Ingersoll-Rand Co., New York

Fig. 30. Belt-Driven, Double-Acting Compressor. An electric motor or other prime mover may be used to drive this compressor with a belt on the flywheel. Observe the names of the parts. The flywheel is mounted on the *crankshaft.* The inertia force of the counterweight balances in part the inertia forces resulting from the movement of the reciprocating parts. The end of the *connecting rod* opposite the crank pin is attached to the *crosshead,* which is a sliding member that guides the outside end of the *piston rod* in the path of a straight line. The *packing* (stuffing box) about the piston rod prevents the leakage of the working substance. Of the two valves at each end of the cylinder, one is the intake valve and the other is the discharge valve. A pump (not shown) circulates the water through the heads and jacket. Cooling water reduces the temperature of the cylinder walls and results in less work being required for a particular compression ratio.

The volume swept out by the piston in one stroke is called the **displacement volume** V_D for one conventional indicator card. Observe that the stroke is twice the crank radius and that the piston makes *two strokes* for *one revolution* of the crank.

The **clearance volume** is the space between the piston and the cylinder head when the engine is on dead-center position. Thus, there is a *head-end clearance* and a *crank-end clearance.*

68. Indicator Card for Reciprocating Compressor. The events which occur in a reciprocating engine, whether a compressor, an automobile engine, or a steam engine, may be conveniently pictured in terms of pV coordinates. Figure 31 shows what we shall call the **conventional indicator card** or *diagram* of a reciprocating compressor without clearance. Although it is impracticable to build a reciprocating compressor without clearance, it is convenient to study this type of indicator card first.

At the outset, the piston is at the end of the stroke with zero volume in the cylinder, point 4, Fig. 31(b). As the piston starts the stroke 4-1, the *inlet* or *intake valve* opens and air (or other gas) is drawn into the cylinder along 4-1. At point 1, the piston starts the return stroke, all valves being closed, and the air is compressed along the curve 1-2. At 2, the *discharge valve* opens and the compressed air is delivered to the receiver, Fig. 32, where it is stored until needed. Two strokes (or one revolution) are necessary to complete an indicator card on one side of the piston. If the compressor is double-acting the usual type, the sequence of events pictured in Fig. 31 is occurring on each side of the piston (at each end of the cylinder as in Fig. 30).

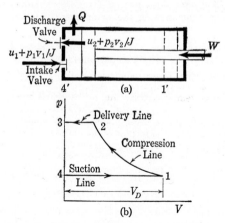

Fig. 31. *Conventional Diagram without Clearance.*   Fig. 32.   *Receiver.*

69. Work of a Compressor. The diagram of Fig. 31(b) may also be taken to represent the happenings in a rotary compressor. The area under the suction line 4-1 represents the flow work p_1v_1/J as the substance enters (crosses the boundary of) the system. Since the substance also possesses internal energy u_1, the energy entering the system is $h_1 = u_1 + p_1v_1/J$ (with $\Delta K = 0$). Process 1-2 is an internally reversible compression in the ideal case. The area under 2-3 represents the outgoing flow work, the work done on the surroundings as the substance leaves the system. Thus, for either the conventional reciprocating compressor or the rotary type, the area "back of" the curve 1-2, area 1-2-3-4 $= -\int v\,dp$, represents the work necessary to receive, compress, and *deliver* the gas or vapor ($\Delta K = 0$). We may consider the steady flow equation with respect to either machine and find from (10), p. 22,

(10) $W = H_1 - H_2 + Q + K_1 - K_2$ Btu.

Either from (10) above or from the energy diagram of Fig. 33(a), we get

(42A) $W = H_1 - H_2 + Q$ Btu,   ($\Delta K = 0$)
                                  [USE CONVENTION OF SIGNS]

in which the numbers are algebraic as obtained from the basic equations previously presented; since the work is done on the system, W as solved for

(a) Conventional Energy Flow.   (b) Actual Directions of Energy Flow.

Fig. 33. Energy Diagrams. Clearance does not affect energy quantities entering or leaving the working substance in the compressor, frictional losses excepted.

is negative. If the work equation is set up from an energy balance of the system, Fig. 33(b), in which the energy quantities are shown in their actual directions of flow, W comes out positive (because it is shown correctly); that is,

(42B) $W = H_2 - H_1 + Q$ Btu.
                                  [W IS POSITIVE; OUTWARD Q IS POSITIVE]

In (42A), Q is likely to be a negative number in accordance with our established sign convention because it is heat rejected in the usual compressor; whereas, in (42B), Q should be substituted as a positive number because it is taken in its actual (not conventional) direction in the energy diagram of Fig. 33(b). Both equations (42A) and (42B) should give the same *numerical* answer; if not, at least one solution is in error.

70. Adiabatic Compression. For an adiabatic compression, reversible or irreversible, $Q = 0$ and the work from (42A) becomes (29), p. 58;

(29) $W = H_1 - H_2,$ $W = -wc_p(T_2 - T_1)$ Btu
                        [ANY FLUID]   [IDEAL GAS]   [$\Delta K = 0$]

or Btu per some unit of time, say a minute or whatever time unit is involved in the mass flow w of gas (as w lb./min.). If the process is a reversible adiabatic (isentropic), the temperature T_2 may be found as stated in § 58,

(a) $$T_2 = T_1 \left(\frac{p_2}{p_1}\right)^{(k-1)/k} = T_1 \left(\frac{V_1}{V_2}\right)^{k-1}.$$

The ratio of the initial volume V_1 divided by the volume at the end of the compression V_2 is called the *ratio of compression* r $(r = V_1/V_2)$. This definition applies to compression processes in general.

71. Example—Isentropic Compression. What work is required to compress and deliver 533 cfm of air at 40°F and 13 psia to 52 psia, if the compression is isentropic?

SOLUTION.   The mass of air w is found from (using 40°F = 500°R and converting the pressure to psf)

$$w = \frac{p_1 V_1}{R T_1} = \frac{(13)(144)(533)}{(53.3)(500)} = 37.4 \text{ lb./min.}$$

The temperature after compression is

$$T_2 = T_1 \left(\frac{p_2}{p_1}\right)^{(k-1)/k} = 500 \left(\frac{52}{13}\right)^{0.4/1.4} = 743°\text{R.}$$

Now using (29), we find

$$W = -w c_p (T_2 - T_1) = -(37.4)(0.24)(743 - 500) = -2180 \text{ Btu/min.}$$

72. Isothermal Compression. If there is no temperature change $(T_1 = T_2)$, the enthalpy change of an ideal gas is equal to zero, and from (42) we get

(b) $$W = Q.$$

Hence for an isothermal process, § 56,

(43) $$W = Q = \frac{p_1 V_1}{J} \ln \frac{V_2}{V_1} = \frac{wRT}{J} \ln \frac{V_2}{V_1} \text{ Btu} = -\frac{wRT}{J} \ln \frac{V_1}{V_2},$$
$$\text{[IDEAL GAS; } \Delta K = 0]$$

where we have used $\ln (V_2/V_1) = -\ln (V_1/V_2)$. Also recall that $V_1/V_2 = p_2/p_1$. The volume V_1 is the volume at p_1 and T_1 corresponding to the mass of gas passing through the compressor. The volume V_2 is for this same mass. The compression ratio is $r = V_1/V_2$.

73. Polytropic Compression. For a polytropic process, the heat is $Q = w c_n (T_2 - T_1)$, where for an ideal gas $c_n = c_v(k - n)/(1 - n)$. Therefore, the work of the compressor for a polytropic compression of a gas is, from (42A),

(44) $$W = -\Delta H + Q = w c_p (T_1 - T_2) + w c_n (T_2 - T_1) \text{ Btu.}$$
$$\text{[IDEAL GAS]}$$

The mass of gas w to be used in computing the work is always that *taken in* *and delivered* by the compressor. Be careful of signs.

74. Example—Polytropic Compression. What work is required to compress and deliver 533 cfm of air at 40°F and 13 psia to 52 psia, if the compression is polytropic with $pV^{1.35} = C$?

SOLUTION. The mass of air is the same as found for the previous example, 37.4 lb./min. The temperature after compression is

$$T_2 = T_1 \left(\frac{p_2}{p_1}\right)^{(n-1)/n} = 500 \left(\frac{52}{13}\right)^{0.35/1.35} = 716°\text{R}.$$

The specific heat of the polytropic process is

$$c_n = c_v \left(\frac{k-n}{1-n}\right) = 0.1715 \left(\frac{1.4 - 1.35}{1 - 1.35}\right) = -0.0245 \text{ Btu/lb}.$$

Using equation (44), we find

$$W = wc_p(T_1 - T_2) + wc_n(T_2 - T_1)$$
$$= (37.4)(0.24)(500 - 716) + (37.4)(-0.0245)(716 - 500) = -2140 \text{ Btu/min}.$$

In an actual compressor, the polytropic process is approached because circulating water in a jacket about the cylinder and heads carries away some heat

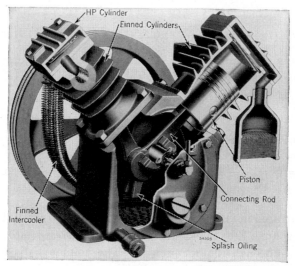

Fig. 34. Air-Cooled Compressor. This is a small two-stage compressor driven by an electric motor via a V-belt drive. A part of the finned intercooler is visible on the left.

(Fig. 30). Observe that this cooling during the compression results in a saving of work (2140 vs. 2180 Btu/min.). The higher the compression pressure, the greater is the possible saving. The compression in small air-cooled compressors, Fig. 34, departs little from an adiabatic. The fins on the cylinder provide a greater surface for heat loss and serve the purpose of preventing overheating of the metal.

75. Preferred Compression Curves. Inasmuch as the isentropic curve 1-2′, Fig. 35, is steeper than the isothermal 1-2, it takes more work to compress and *deliver* the air when the compression is isentropic than when the compression is isothermal, the difference being represented by the shaded area. Compression curves with values of n between 1 and k will fall within the shaded area. Thus we see that the work necessary to drive the compressor decreases as the value of n decreases.

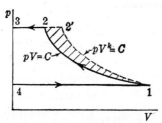

Fig. 35. *Comparison of Work for Isothermal and for Isentropic Compression.*

Polytropic compression and values of n less than k are brought about by circulating cooling water, Fig. 30, or air around the cylinder. In small, cheap compressors, the cooling will be inadequate and the value of n for air will be 1.35 or higher, closely approaching $k = 1.4$. Under favorable circumstances, a value of $n = 1.3$ or less may be expected. Values from 1.25 to 1.3 represent the best results for water-jacketed air compressors.

Observe that in an isothermal compression, all the heat equivalent of the work done on the air is carried away, the air then leaving the compressor with the same internal energy and enthalpy as it had upon entering; that in an isentropic compression, no heat is carried way, so that the air leaves with an increase in enthalpy equal to the work done on it; that in a polytropic compression, there is some heat carried away and there is some increase in internal energy, enthalpy, and temperature.

The air as it leaves the compressor after an adiabatic compression has more stored energy, and therefore it can do more work than when isothermally compressed. In a gas turbine, this extra stored energy is later available to do work in the turbine (Chapter 7). On the other hand, where a gas is compressed and stored for future use, as in ordinary compressed air systems, there is commonly enough elapsed time so that the gas cools nearly to its original temperature. In this event, no advantage is derived from the increase of internal energy and enthalpy during compression.

76. Conventional Diagram with Clearance. The events of a reciprocating compressor with clearance are the same as those for one without clearance, except that the gas in the clearance space must reexpand to the intake pressure, process 3-4, Fig. 36, before intake starts again. Without clearance, the volume of air taken into the cylinder is equal to the displacement volume. As seen from Fig. 36 for the conventional card with clear-

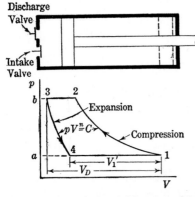

Discharge Valve

Intake Valve

Fig. 36. Conventional Diagram with Clearance. The greater the clearance ($= V_3$), the less air drawn in ($= V_1'$).

ance, the volume of air *drawn into* the cylinder is $V_1 - V_4 = V_1'$, a value less than the displacement volume V_D. Thus, the effect of clearance in the compressor is to decrease the amount of gas that a compressor of a particular size can pump in one revolution.

The clearance volume in all types of reciprocating engines is expressed as a percentage of the displacement volume. Thus, a compressor with a clearance of 6% has a clearance volume of $0.06V_D$, where V_D is the displacement volume of one stroke. Clearances in air compressors vary from about 1% in some very large compressors to 10% or more in others, with common values in the neighborhood of 6% to 8%.

The horsepower required to pump a particular quantity of gas between specified limits is the same in a conventional compressor with clearance as in a conventional compressor without clearance. That is, the clearance has no effect on the necessary power for ideal compressors; and in actual compressors, there is no significant variation in the actual power for small variations in the clearance. Consideration of the energy diagrams of Fig. 33 shows that clearance has no relation to the law of the conservation of energy. Since the displacement of the real compressor with clearance must be greater than that of the compressor without clearance for a particular capacity, the compressor with clearance is a larger machine, costing more and having greater mechanical friction.

77. Displacement. A reciprocating engine, whether consuming or producing power, is said to have displacement, which, for one diagram, is the volume swept out by the piston in one stroke. This volume V_D is the sectional area of the cylinder $\pi D^2/4$ times the stroke L, or

(c) $$V_D = \frac{\pi D^2 L}{4} \text{ cu. ft./diagram,}$$

where D is the bore of the cylinder and L is the stroke, both in feet. If N is the number of diagrams, Fig. 36, that the compressor makes in one minute, then the displacement volume per minute is

(45)
$$V_D = \frac{N\pi D^2 L}{4} \text{ cfm.}$$

In words, we may say for any reciprocating engine

(d) $V_D = \begin{pmatrix} \text{Volume in cu. ft. swept} \\ \text{by piston in one stroke} \end{pmatrix} \times \begin{pmatrix} \text{Number of diagrams} \\ \text{completed per min.} \end{pmatrix}$ cfm.

For a single-acting compressor, N is equal to the number of revolutions per minute n; for a double-acting compressor, N is equal to twice the number of revolutions per minute, $N = 2n$, where $n = $ rpm, because one complete cycle of events occurs on each side of the piston in each revolution.   In specifying the size of reciprocating engines, the practice is to give the bore by the stroke, both in inches; for example, a 20x24-in. engine is one which has a bore of 20 in. and a stroke of 24 in.

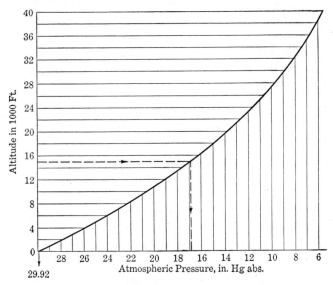

Fig. 37.   *Variation of Atmospheric Pressure with Altitude.*   Useful in estimating the mass of air a compressor will deliver at various altitudes.   Enter chart at the ordinate, which represents altitude.   Move rightward to the curve, as along the dotted line, then downward to the abscissa and read the normal atmospheric pressure at the corresponding altitude.

78. Free Air.   *Free air* is air at normal atmospheric conditions in a particular geographical location.   A given volume of free air at an altitude of 5000 ft. does not have the same mass as the same volume at sea level.   At the higher altitude, the barometric pressure is lower, Fig. 37, and a given mass of air occupies a greater volume. Note also that the volume of free air varies with the temperature. In the absence of a specified temperature, 68°F may be used.

79. Capacity and Volumetric Efficiency. The *capacity of a compressor* is the actual quantity of gas delivered, as measured by an orifice at intake pressure and temperature expressed in cubic feet per minute (cfm).

The actual *volumetric efficiency* of a reciprocating air compressor is the ratio

(e) $$\eta_v' = \frac{\text{Capacity of compressor}}{\text{Displacement in cfm}},$$

where the displacement is computed as given in equation (d). In general, the volumetric efficiency may be defined as follows:

$$\eta_v = \frac{\left[\begin{array}{c}\text{Volume of gas, measured at intake conditions,}\\ \text{entering cylinder per cycle (or per min.)}\end{array}\right]}{\text{Displacement volume per cycle (or per min.)}}$$

$$= \frac{\text{Mass of gas drawn in}}{\text{Mass of gas that at intake conditions would occupy volume } V_D}.$$

The value of the actual volumetric efficiency, which ranges from 65% to 85%, is obtained only from a test of the actual compressor. However, we may calculate a *conventional volumetric efficiency* from the *conventional* diagram of Fig. 38. Using $V_1' = V_1 - V_4$, we have

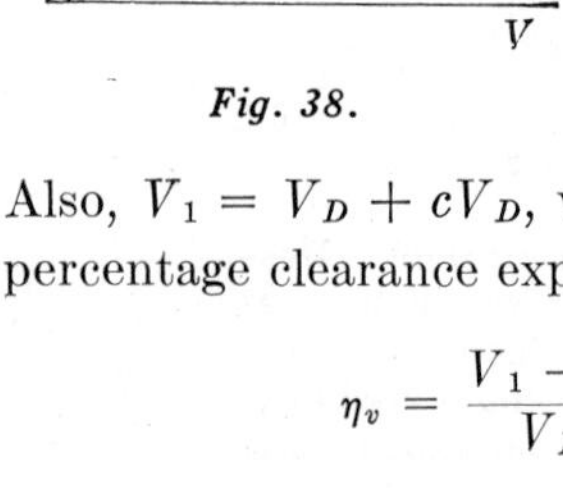

Fig. 38.

(f) $$\eta_v = \frac{V_1'}{V_D} = \frac{V_1 - V_4}{V_D}.$$

From process 3-4.

$$V_4 = V_3\left(\frac{p_3}{p_4}\right)^{1/n} = cV_D\left(\frac{p_2}{p_1}\right)^{1/n}.$$

Also, $V_1 = V_D + cV_D$, where cV_D is the clearance volume V_3 and c is the percentage clearance expressed as a decimal. Therefore we get

$$\eta_v = \frac{V_1 - V_4}{V_D} = \frac{V_D + cV_D - cV_D(p_2/p_1)^{1/n}}{V_D},$$

(46) $$\eta_v = 1 + c - c\left(\frac{p_2}{p_1}\right)^{1/n},$$

which is the **conventional volumetric efficiency.** The actual volumetric efficiency is different from the conventional volumetric efficiency because of fluid friction of flow (the pressure in the cylinder is less than the pressure of free air) and because the cylinder walls, being relatively hot, heat the incoming gas (less mass of hot gas can occupy a given space). Since, in equation (46), p_2 is greater than p_1, the volumetric efficiency decreases as the clearance increases; and as the volumetric efficiency decreases, the capacity decreases. Thus, the clearance may become so large that no gas is discharged by the compressor. This characteristic is sometimes used to control the output of a compressor by increasing the clearance when a reduced output is desired.

Also observe from (46) that the volumetric efficiency goes down as the pressure ratio p_2/p_1 goes up. Neither clearance nor volumetric efficiency is a reliable indicator of quality. The user is most concerned about the actual power consumed for the desired capacity.

80. Example. A double-acting air compressor, operating at 150 rpm, takes in air at 14 psia and 80°F. The size of the cylinder is 14x15 in. and the clearance is 4%. There is a polytropic compression with $n = 1.3$ to 56 psia. Atmospheric pressure and temperature are 14.7 psia and 70°F, respectively.

(a) Estimate the volume of free air from the conventional volumetric efficiency. Because the compressor is double-acting, the *number* of cycles per minute is $N = 2n = (2)(150) = 300$, where $n =$ rpm. The displacement of the cylinder of diameter D and stroke L is

$$V_D = \left(\frac{\pi D^2}{4}\right)(L)(2n) = \frac{\pi(14)^2(15)(2)(150)}{(4)(1728)} = 401 \text{ cfm.}$$

The volume of air drawn in is $\eta_v V_D$, or

$$V_1' = \left[1 + c - c\left(\frac{p_2}{p_1}\right)^{1/n}\right]V_D = \left[1.04 - 0.04\left(\frac{56}{14}\right)^{1/1.3}\right]401$$
$$= (0.924)(401) = 370 \text{ cfm,}$$

measured at $p_1 = 14$ and $t_1 = 80$°F. If the subscript a refers to atmospheric conditions, we have $p_a V_a/T_a = p_1 V_1' T_1$; or the approximate volume of free air is

$$V_a = \frac{p_1 V_1' T_a}{T_1 P_a} = \frac{(14)(370)(530)}{(540)(14.7)} = 346 \text{ cfm.}$$

(b) The temperature at the end of compression is $T_2 = 284$°F [from $T_2/T_1 = (p_2/p_1)^{(n-1)/n}$] and the mass of air pumped is 25.9 lb./min. [from $w = p_1 V_1'/RT_1$]. How much heat is rejected by this air to the circulating water? For the polytropic process,

$$Q = wc_n(T_2 - T_1) = wc_v\left(\frac{k-n}{1-n}\right)(T_2 - T_1)$$
$$= (25.9)(0.1715)\left(\frac{1.4 - 1.3}{1 - 1.3}\right)(744 - 540) = -302 \text{ Btu/min.}$$

81. Actual Indicator Card of Compressor. The actual indicator card differs from the conventional card largely because of the fluid friction of flow and because of the inertia of the valves and the frictional resistance of the valves to motion, Fig. 39. Since the valves are usually operated by a difference in pressure, a relatively large difference is necessary to start their movement. From point 3, Fig. 40, the piston starts a new stroke. The intake valve does not open until some pressure a little below the atmospheric pressure is reached. The intake valve often flutters, an action which produces the wavy portion of the suction line. The intake pressure is below atmospheric pressure. The compression 1-2 continues until a pressure greater than the delivery pressure is reached, at which point the discharge valve opens. Here again, there occurs some fluttering of the valve, so that the discharge line is wavy. Observe that the inertia and friction of the valve increases the area and therefore the work of the diagram. As shown, a polytropic compression line 1-2 falls between the isothermal 1-a and the isentropic 1-b; generally, it is closer to the isentropic.

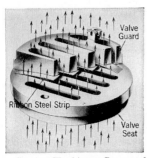

Courtesy Worthington Pump and Machinery Corp., Harrison, N. J.

Fig. 39. Feather Valve for Gas and Vapor Compressors. The strips of ribbon steel are shown pressing against the valve guard in the open position. When the pressure on the valve-seat side of the valve is less than that on the guard side, the strips lie flat on the ground seats, closing the valve. Intake and discharge valves of this type are identical.

82. Indicated Work. The work represented by the indicator card is called indicated work and is the work done on (or by) the working substance in the cylinder. The indicator card is obtained with an *indicator,* Fig. 41. When the indicator is connected to the inside of the cylinder, the drum oscillates in phase with the reciprocation of the piston while the stylus moves up and down as the pressure in the cylinder increases or decreases. The amount of movement of the stylus is also dependent upon the stiffness of the indicator spring. This stiffness is designated by the *scale.* If an indicator spring with a 100-lb. scale

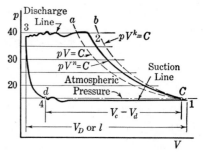

Fig. 40. Actual Indicator Card, Compressor.

is used, the stylus moves vertically 1 in. for a change of pressure of 100 psi.*

After the card has been obtained from the compressor, a planimeter,

---

* The term *scale* in this connection is not the same as the *scale of a spring* in general usage. Also, if an undersized piston is used in the indicator, the scale of the indicator spring used must be modified.

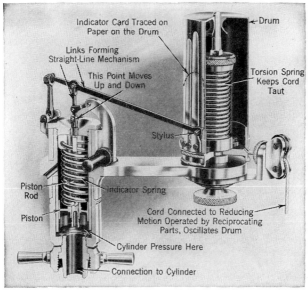

Courtesy Crosby Steam Gage and Valve Co., Boston

Fig. 41. Indicator. Steam enters through the connection to the cylinder and acts on a small piston, whose motion is opposed by the indicator spring. The greater the pressure from the cylinder, the more the piston moves. The piston rod actuates the stylus, through a straight-line linkage, and the indicator card is traced. The cord is attached to the drum, which moves in phase (the motion is reduced in magnitude) with the engine piston (and crosshead). No indicator paper is shown on the drum.

Courtesy Crosby Steam Gage and Valve Co., Boston

Fig. 42. Planimeter. Point *F* is fixed. Point *P* is moved around the boundaries of the area to be measured. Wheel *D* turns with the movement of *P* and, after the complete outline has been traced, the magnitude of the area may be read from the dial *G* and the vernier *E*.

Fig. 42, is used to find its area. This area is converted into work units, usually after finding the mean effective pressure.

83. Mean Effective Pressure and Indicated Horsepower. The mean effective pressure (mep) is that average net pressure which, acting on the piston for one stroke, does the same work as represented by the indicator card. If a rectangle whose length is the length of the indicator card and whose area is the same as the area of the indicator card is drawn, Fig. 43, the height of this rectangle p_{mI} represents to scale the mep, the scale being given by the scale of the indicator spring. Thus, the average height of the indicator card is its area divided by its length. This average height multi-

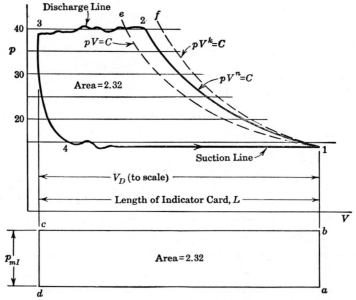

Fig. 43. Mean Effective Pressure. The rectangle *abcd* has the same area as the indicator diagram 1-2-3-4. The height of the rectangle represents to scale that net pressure which, acting through the entire stroke, results in the same work as represented by the indicator card.

plied by the scale of the indicator spring is the average pressure p_{mI}, the indicated mep.

$$(47) \qquad p_{mI} = \frac{(\text{Area of indicator card}) \ (\text{Scale of indicator spring})}{\text{Length of indicator card}}.$$

For an mep of p_{mI} psi, the force acting on the piston is this pressure times the area of the piston A in square inches, or force is equal to $p_{mI}A$. If the piston moves the length of stroke L ft. with this force $p_{mI}A$ acting, the work done is (force × distance) = $p_{mI}AL$ ft-lb. for one cycle of events or one indicator card. If N complete diagrams should be made in one minute, the work per minute is $p_{mI}ALN = p_{mI}LAN$ ft-lb./min. The corresponding horsepower is therefore

$$(\mathbf{g}) \qquad \text{ihp} = \frac{p_{mI}LAN}{33,000},$$

an equation called the mep equation. It may be applied to either ideal or actual machines. In order to distinguish the various kinds of horsepowers and mep's which we shall use, the symbols may be modified. Let hp and p_m represent ideal or conventional horsepower and ideal or conventional mep, respectively. Then

$$(48) \qquad\qquad hp = \frac{p_m LAN}{33{,}000}.$$

Some confusion of units often arises because engineers usually speak of pressures in pounds per square *inch* and volumes in cubic *feet*. In equation (48), if p_m is in pounds per square inch, as is ordinarily the case, A must necessarily be in square inches. However, one could use p_m in psf and A in sq. ft. with identical results. Observe carefully that N is the number of cycles or diagrams that would be completed in a minute—*not* necessarily the revolutions per minute.

In a double-acting engine, the area A on which the pressure acts is less on the crank end (by the amount of the area of the piston rod) than on the head end. Moreover, it is not likely that the mep is the same on both ends. Thus, equations **(g)** and (48) should be applied separately to the head end and to the crank end of double-acting engines.

A more general expression for the mep may also be obtained from Fig. 43. Since the area of the card represents to scale the work done and the length represents the displacement volume, the average height of the card obtained from these quantities is also p_m or p_{mI}; that is,

$$(49) \qquad\qquad p_m = \frac{\text{Work}}{\text{Displacement}} = \frac{W}{V_D} \text{ psf,}$$

where, for consistency in units, the work should be in ft-lb. and the displacement in cu. ft. The mep is then in pounds per square foot, which may be divided by 144 sq. in./sq. ft. to be converted to pounds per square inch. If the work is in ft-lb. per min., for example, the displacement should be in cu. ft. per min. [equation (45)]. If W_I, the indicated work in foot-pounds, is substituted for W in (49), the result is the indicated mep, p_{mI}.

84. Efficiencies. The *mechanical efficiency* η_m of a compressor is defined in two ways by the Compressed Air Institute: (1) when the drive is by steam or internal combustion engine,

$$(\mathbf{h}) \qquad\qquad \eta_m = \frac{ihp \text{ of the compressor}}{ihp \text{ of the driving engine}},$$

an expression which applies to the unit; or (2) when the drive is by electric motor,

(i)
$$\eta_m = \frac{\text{ihp of the compressor}}{\text{bhp of the compressor}},$$

where bhp, the brake horsepower, is the power delivered to the compressor as measured at its crankshaft.

In a general way, the **compression efficiency** is the ideal work divided by the actual work, W/W'. The **adiabatic compression efficiency** η_c, often called *compression efficiency* for short, is the theoretical power required as obtained from a conventional diagram with *isentropic* compression *divided by* the actual indicated power of the compressor,

(j)
$$\eta_c = \frac{\text{Work (or hp) of conventional card, isentropic compression}}{\text{Indicated work (or hp) of compressor}},$$

a value which is likely to fall within the range of 70% to 85%.

The **overall efficiency** η_o is the product of the mechanical efficiency and the compression efficiency, $\eta_o = \eta_m \eta_c$. The **adiabatic overall efficiency** is

(k)
$$\eta_o = [\text{Eq. (h) or (i)}] [\text{Eq. (j)}]$$
$$= \frac{\text{hp corresponding to isentropic compression}}{\text{(ihp of engine) or (bhp of compressor)}}.$$

where the denominator depends on whether the compressor is driven by a steam engine or by an electric motor. The ASME *Test Code* calls the ratio in (k) the **shaft efficiency** when the denominator is the brake power.

85. Multistage Compression. The volumetric efficiency is affected not only by the clearance but also by the ratio of pressures p_2/p_1 [see equation (46)]. Thus, if the compression is carried out in two or more cylinders, Fig. 44, the volumetric efficiency of the multicylinder machine will be greater than that of a single-cylinder machine of the same clearance and the same pressure ratio. Moreover, since the air gets very hot when compressed to high pressures, the temperatures may be so high as to cause trouble with the lubrication of the cylinder and piston. Furthermore, it is possible to save considerable power by using two or more stages, instead of one, if the final pressure is above about 60 to 100 psi, if the installation is permanent, and if the required displacement is greater than about 300 cfm. Study Figs. 45 and 46 for diagrammatic evidence of these statements.

It is common practice to cool the air between the stages of compression in an intercooler, Fig. 44, and it is this cooling that effects the saving in power. The following discussion applies to both Figs. 45 and 46, in which are pictured the events of the conventional indicator cards of a two-stage machine, with the high-pressure (HP) card superposed on the low-pressure (*LP*) card. Suction in the LP cylinder begins at A and the volume V_1' is drawn in: compression 1-2 occurs, and the *LP* cylinder then discharges the air along 2-B. This discharged air passes through an intercooler, being cooled by circulating cold water. The temperature to which the air is cooled is governed by the temperature of the cooling water available. It is

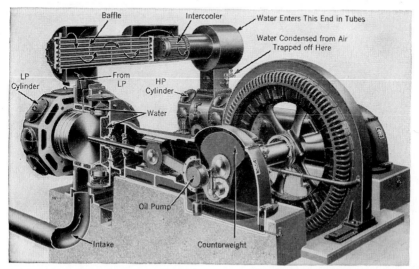

Fig. 44. Two-Stage Compressor, Electric Drive. The synchronous motor is mounted on the compressor shaft and therefore does not have separate shaft and bearings. This drive has a high power factor and efficiency. It is said that about 95% of the output of the motor is utilized in the cylinders. The intercooler is "two-stage." Cold water enters intercooler at HP end, and after circulating through the LP end of the intercooler, goes to the cylinder jackets. Air flows around baffles; see arrows. Two-stage compressors are made with the cylinders at an angle (Fig. **34**), cylinders at right angles (one horizontal and one vertical), and cylinders in a tandem. In sizes over 1000 hp, this compressor is made in twin tandem style, two more cylinders added opposite to those shown, but with a combination of LP and HP cylinders in tandem arrangement. Output is controlled by clearance pockets, two on each end of each cylinder. See Fig. **36**. Compressors are often driven by reciprocating steam engines on the same shaft.

relatively easy to bring the temperature of the air to within 20°F of the temperature of the entering water. In the conventional analysis it is commonly assumed that the air has the same temperature upon entering the HP cylinder as it had upon entering the *LP* cylinder. This assumption places point 3, the end of the suction stroke E-3 in the HP cylinder, on an isothermal line through 1, Figs. 45 and 46. The air is compressed to the final pressure along 3-4 discharged along 4-*F*, after which the clearance air reexpands, *FE*. The same mass of air is involved at points 1, 2, 3, and 4;

also the mass of air discharged is equal to the mass drawn into the LP cylinder, if leakage is neglected and if steady flow has been achieved.

In computing the work of a two-stage (or three-stage) machine, we shall find it convenient for our purposes to find the power required for each

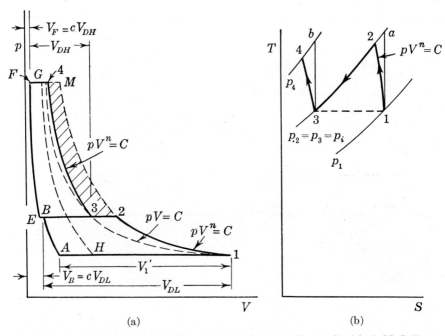

Fig. 45. Conventional Cards, Two-Stage, No Pressure Drop. In (a), 1-M-G-H outlines the conventional card for single-stage compression to p_4 for a given per cent clearance. If the *per cent* clearance is the same in both cylinders, reexpansion in the high-pressure cylinder starts at some point F instead of G. Reexpansion in the low-pressure cylinder starts at B, where $V_B = V_G$. For a two-stage machine, suction starts at A. For a single-stage machine, suction starts at H. The capacity of the two-stage compressor is greater than that of the single-stage by the amount $V_H - V_A$. Observe that it is possible to make the clearance so large that no air would be delivered. The work saved by the two-stage compression is represented by the shaded area 2-M-4-3. Only the thermodynamic processes (not the suction and discharge) are shown on the TS plane in (b). Isentropic compressions should be 1-a and 3-b. If the LP cylinder had an isothermal compression, the state point would follow the dotted line 1-3.

cylinder and add the results. Thus, for the first stage of compression, the work for the case of <u>polytropic compression is given</u> by (44),

$$(44) \qquad W_L = wc_p(T_1 - T_2) + wc_n(T_2 - T_1).$$

Applying the same basic equation to the HP cylinder with points as designated in Figs. 45 and 46,

$$(1) \qquad W_H = wc_p(T_3 - T_4) + wc_n(T_4 - T_3),$$

where all symbols are as previously defined. Notice that equations (I) and (44) are in the basic form for the usual sign convention and the W's will be negative numbers. If the work equation is obtained from an energy diagram with the energy flows shown in their correct directions, the work W would be a positive number. If the adjustment is such that the same amount of work is done in each cylinder, the total work is a minimum for a

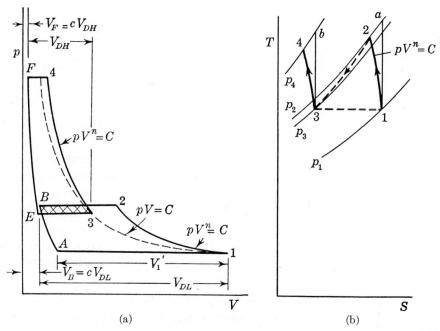

(a)   (b)

Fig. 46.   Conventional Cards, Two-Stage, with Pressure Drop.   The only change from Fig. 45 is the pressure drop from 2 to 3 in the intercooler.   The cards are otherwise conventional in all respects; the compression is taken as polytropic.   The shaded area between B and 3 in (a) represents lost (or repeated) work due to the pressure drop. The process 2-3 through the intercooler is steady flow but irreversible (therefore shown dotted in (b)).

particular capacity.   The equality of work done in each cylinder may be used to find the optimum intermediate pressure $p_i = p_2 = p_3$, Fig. 45. First assume that $T_1 = T_3$.   Then equate W_L to W_H, factor T_1 and T_3 from the parentheses, and change the sign inside and outside of the parentheses of one term on each side of the equation as follows:

$$-wc_p T_1 \left(\frac{T_2}{T_1} - 1\right) + wc_n T_1 \left(\frac{T_2}{T_1} - 1\right)$$
$$= -wc_p T_3 \left(\frac{T_4}{T_3} - 1\right) + wc_n T_3 \left(\frac{T_4}{T_3} - 1\right).$$

Factor again to find

$$\left(\frac{T_2}{T_1} - 1\right)(-wc_pT_1 + wc_nT_1) = \left(\frac{T_4}{T_3} - 1\right)(-wc_pT_3 + wc_nT_3),$$

from which, since $T_1 = T_3$,

$$\frac{T_2}{T_1} = \frac{T_4}{T_3}.$$

But for a polytropic compression

$$\frac{T_2}{T_1} = \left(\frac{p_2}{p_1}\right)^{(n-1)/n} = \left(\frac{p_i}{p_1}\right)^{(n-1)/n}, \quad \text{and} \quad \frac{T_4}{T_3} = \left(\frac{p_4}{p_3}\right)^{(n-1)/n} = \left(\frac{p_4}{p_i}\right)^{(n-1)/n},$$

Therefore,

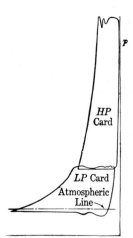

Fig. 47. Actual Cards, Two-Stage Machine.

(m) $\quad \dfrac{p_i}{p_1} = \dfrac{p_4}{p_i} \quad$ or $\quad p_i = (p_1p_4)^{1/2}$

which is the proper value for the intermediate pressure for the conditions assumed. Actual indicator diagrams taken from a two-stage machine are shown in Fig. 47. Three stages may show a net saving in costs when the final pressure is above about 150 psia, the precise transitional pressure being governed of course by local conditions. The reader should be able to use the work equations properly if the compression is other than polytropic.

86. Heat Transferred in Intercooler. If the intercooler is operating steady flow, the energy equation (10) applies:

(10) $$Q = \Delta h + \Delta K + W.$$

But no shaft work is done in connection with the intercooler (a heat exchanger), $W = 0$; and usually the change of kinetic energy is negligible, $\Delta K \approx 0$. Therefore, for reversible or irreversible flow of a particular substance through an intercooler, or any heat exchanger, the heat transferred to or from the substance is ($H = wh$ and $\Delta H = wc_p\Delta T$ for an ideal gas)

(50) $\quad Q = \Delta H = H_2 - H_1 \quad$ or $\quad Q = wc_p(T_2 - T_1)$ Btu,

$\qquad$ [ANY FLUID] $\qquad\qquad\qquad\qquad\qquad$ [IDEAL GAS]

where w is the mass of gas flowing through the intercooler and the subscripts 1 and 2 refer in general to any initial and final states. One of the substances in a heat exchanger loses heat and the other substance (water in the intercooler) receives heat.

87. Example. A two-stage, double-acting air compressor, operating at 150 rpm, takes in air at 14 psia and a temperature of 80°F. The size of the LP cylinder is 14x15 in., the stroke of the HP cylinder is the same as that of the LP cylinder, and the clearance of both cylinders is 4%. The LP cylinder discharges the air at a pressure of 56 psia. The air passes through the intercooler and enters the HP cylinder at 80°F and a pressure of 53.75 psia, after which it is discharged from the compressor at a pressure of 215 psia. The value of n in both cylinders is 1.3. Neglect the effect of the piston rods on the crank end. Atmospheric pressure and temperature are 14.7 psia and 70°F, respectively. See Fig. 48.

(a) How much heat is rejected in the intercooler?

Reference to the example of § 80 shows that the LP cylinder of this example operates under the conditions stated in § 80. Using the temperature $t_2 = 284°F$ and $w = 25.9$ lb./min. given there and applying (50), we find

$$Q_{2\text{-}3} = H_3 - H_2 = wc_p(T_3 - T_2)$$
$$= (25.9)(0.24)(540 - 744) = -1268 \text{ Btu/min.}$$

(b) What should be the diameter of the HP cylinder?

The volume V'_3, Fig. 48, corresponds to the mass of air circulating, 25.9 lb./min., or

$$V'_3 = \frac{wRT_3}{p_3} = \frac{(25.9)(53.3)(540)}{(53.75)(144)} = 96.3 \text{ cfm.}$$

The volumetric efficiency is $\eta_v = V'_3/V_{DH}$, where V_{DH} is the displacement volume of the HP cylinder (see § 79). Thus

$$V_{DH} = \frac{V'_3}{\eta_v} = \frac{96.3}{0.924} = 104.2 \text{ cfm,}$$

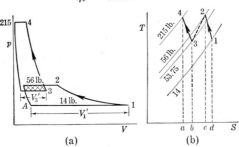

(a) (b)

Fig. 48.

where $\eta_v = 0.924$ is taken from § 80, because the clearance percentage and the pressure ratio in the HP cylinder are the same as in the LP cylinder. In terms of the dimensions of the cylinder,

$$V_{DH} = \left(\frac{\pi D_H^2}{4}\right)(L)(2n) \text{ cfm,}$$

where $n = 150$ rpm and $2n$ is the number of diagrams completed in the double-acting cylinder per minute. Since the cylinders have the same stroke, $L = 15$ in. $= {}^{15}\!/_{12}$ ft.,

$$V_{DH} = \left(\frac{\pi D_H^2}{4}\right)\left(\frac{15}{12}\right)(300) = 104.2,$$

from which $D_H = 0.595$ ft. $= 7.14$ in., or say $7\frac{1}{4}$ in.

(c) What horsepower is required to drive the HP cylinder, computed for the conventional card?

The final temperature in the HP cylinder is

$$T_4 = T_3 \left(\frac{p_4}{p_3}\right)^{(n-1)/n} = 540 \left(\frac{215}{53.75}\right)^{0.3/1.3} = 744°R = 284°F.$$

Observe that this temperature is the same as t_2, as it should be when $T_1 = T_3$ and when the pressure ratio is the same in both cylinders. The polytropic specific heat is

$$c_n = c_v \left(\frac{k-n}{1-n}\right) = 0.1715 \left(\frac{1.4 - 1.3}{1 - 1.3}\right) = -0.0572.$$

Applying equation (44) to the HP cylinder, we have

$$W = wc_p(T_3 - T_4) + wc_n(T_4 - T_3)$$
$$= (25.9)(0.24)(540 - 744) + (25.9)(-0.0572)(744 - 540) = -1570 \text{ Btu/min.} ,$$

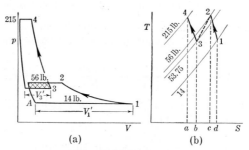

(a)   (b)

Fig. 48.   Repeated.

the minus sign indicating only that work is being done on the working substance. The corresponding horsepower is $1570/42.4 = 37$ hp. It may be noted that because the temperature range and n are the same in each cylinder, the power required for the LP cylinder is the same as that required for the HP cylinder, 37 hp. The student should make this computation for the practice. Indeed, the best plan is for the student to work for himself all details of all examples.

88. Speeds. The piston speeds in modern air compressors may be from 350 fpm for small compressors, say, with a stroke of about 6 in., to more than 700 fpm in large compressors, say, with a stroke of about 36 in. Rotative speeds of reciprocating compressors are from about 120 rpm (largest size) to 350 rpm, most values being between 200–300 rpm.

89. Gas Tables. Specific heats were assumed to be constant in the foregoing discussion. However, if accuracy is important, the effect of the variation of specific heat should be included. This can be done: (1) by using equations for c_p in which c_p is given as a function of temperature, §§ 34 and 35; (2) by using a known average value for the temperature range involved; (3) by using a chart of the properties of the substance, such as the Mollier diagram for steam found in the back of this book; or (4) by using tabulated properties of substances.   (Also, see Chapter 10.)   The Keenan and Kaye *Gas Tables* contain tabulated properties of air, certain products of combustion, nitrogen, oxygen, carbon dioxide, hydrogen, carbon monoxide, and also many other useful tables.   Since these tables are becoming a common item in an engineer's library, we shall write of them briefly.   Table VI in the Appendix is a short extract from the Keenan and Kaye air table.   The symbols h and u stand for enthalpy and internal energy, as usual, but they are pseudo absolute values computed from

$$h = \int_0^T c_p \, dT \quad \text{and} \quad u = h - \frac{pv}{J} = h - \frac{RT}{J},$$

where the integration is from absolute zero temperature to T.   Thus, the $\int c_p \, dT$ between limits of 1 and 2 is simply the difference of the enthalpy values read from the table, $h_2 - h_1$.   All of the other symbols in Table VI represent point functions, too.   The symbol ϕ, called the *entropy function*, is defined by

$$\phi = \int_0^T \frac{c_p \, dT}{T}.$$

The value of ϕ given in the air table, unlike ϕ as given in the other tables of Keenan and Kaye, is the basic value minus one.   If one value of ϕ obtained from the table is subtracted from another, the difference is the definite integral from 1 to 2 of $\int c_p \, dT/T$.   Now from $T \, ds = c_p \, dT - v \, dp/J$, equation (**k**) of § 50, we have

(**n**) $\qquad \Delta s = \int \frac{c_p \, dT}{T} - \frac{R}{J} \ln \frac{p_2}{p_1} = \phi_2 - \phi_1 - \frac{R}{J} \ln \frac{p_2}{p_1} \text{ Btu/lb-°R.}$

Thus, if the change of entropy between any two states is desired, determine it in accordance with (**n**).   (There is a table of values of the log term in Keenan and Kaye.)   For a constant pressure process only, $\Delta s = \Delta \phi$.   If the *entropy* is constant, we get from (**n**)

(**o**) $\qquad \phi_2 - \phi_1 = \frac{R}{J} \ln \frac{p_2}{p_1}, \quad \text{or} \quad \phi = \frac{R}{J} \ln p_r,$

[ENTROPY CONSTANT]

the defining relation for p_r which is called the *relative pressure*; $p_r =$ antilog $J\phi/R = e^{J\phi/R}$.   All values of p_r in the tables are ones obtained from the foregoing equation modified by a constant factor in order to have in the end a convenient range of numbers.   For an isentropic process,

(**p**) $\qquad \left(\frac{p_1}{p_2} \right)_s = \frac{p_{r1}}{p_{r2}},$

where the subscript s is a reminder that the entropy is constant for this rela-tion. The value of the **relative volume** v_r in the table is computed from

(q)
$$v_r = \frac{RT}{p_r} \text{ cu. ft./lb.,}$$

where the units of R were taken so that v_r is the specific volume in cubic feet per pound at any state in the air table when the temperature is T and when p_r is the pressure in psia. From (q), we see that

(r)
$$\left(\frac{v_1}{v_2}\right)_s = \frac{v_{r1}}{v_{r2}};$$

the constant entropy carries over from the definition of p_r.

If the values of the foregoing properties of air are desired on a mol basis, multiply by 28.970 (use 29 for slide rule work), the equivalent molecular weight of air. The properties of the other substances given in other Keenan and Kaye tables are on a mole (pound) basis ($\bar{h}$ Btu/mol, for instance). A few such enthalpy values are given in Table VII, Appendix. While, as stated, these various properties are accurate only at low pressures (ideal gases), the error involved for pressures of several hundreds of psi is negligible. Use Tables VI and VII in accordance with any of the fundamental energy equations previously presented. For ordinary compressions from atmos-pheric conditions, the results obtained from the use of the tables will be little different from those obtained by the methods already employed, constant specific heats. But as the temperature or temperature range increases, the error in using Table V values of specific heats becomes increasingly large.

90. Example. Let 1 lb. of air be compressed adiabatically and in steady flow from 14 psia and 525°R with compression ratio of 5 and a compression efficiency of $\eta_c = 75\%$. Determine the work done, the discharge temperature and pressure, and the increase in entropy.

SOLUTION. The actual work of this problem is obtained by first finding the isentropic work 1-2, Fig. 49, and then applying the efficiency. By interpolation in our Table VI, the reader should check the following values which are taken directly from Keenan and Kaye and are therefore somewhat more accurate. We have at 525°R,

$$h_1 = 125.47 \text{ Btu/lb.,} \qquad p_{r1} = 1.2560, \qquad v_{r1} = 154.84, \qquad \phi_1 = 0.59403.$$

For a compression ratio of 5 during an isentropic process, we have

$$\left(\frac{v_1}{v_2}\right)_s = 5 = \frac{v_{r1}}{v_{r2}}, \qquad \text{or} \qquad v_{r2} = \frac{154.84}{5} = 30.968.$$

Locate this value of v_{r2} in the air table and read other needed properties at state 2, which is on an isentropic line, Fig. 49:

$$T_2 = 989.5°R, \qquad h_2 = 238.37 \text{ Btu/lb.,} \qquad p_{r2} = 11.837.$$

Then from equation (29), $s = C$, p. 58,

$$W_s = h_1 - h_2 = 125.47 - 238.37 = -112.9 \text{ Btu/lb.,}$$

the ideal work done *on* the air. The actual fluid work is, § 84,

$$W' = \frac{W_s}{\eta_c} = \frac{112.9}{0.75} = 150.5 \text{ Btu/lb.}$$

Also from (29), the actual adiabatic work is $h_1 - h_{2'}$, Fig. 49.
Equating these two values of the actual work, we have

$$h_1 - h_{2'} = \frac{h_1 - h_2}{\eta_c} = \frac{-112.9}{0.75} = 125.47 - h_{2'},$$

from which $h_{2'} = 275.97$ Btu/lb. For this value of h, we interpolate to find the discharge temperature

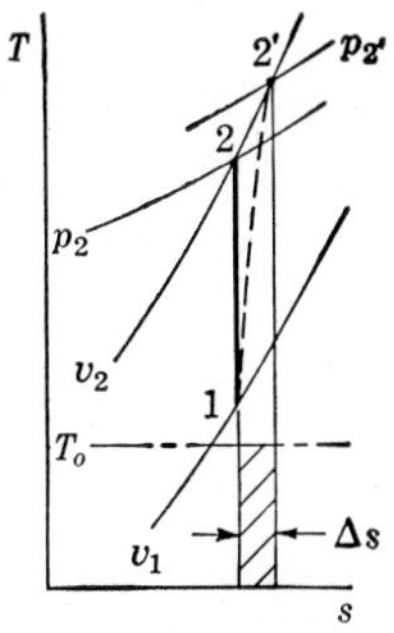

$$T_{2'} = 1139.6°\text{R} \qquad \text{and} \qquad \phi_{2'} = 0.78317.$$

Fig. 49.

Now for the given compression ratio of $v_1/v_{2'} = 5$, we have $(pv/T = C)$

$$\frac{p_1 v_1}{T_1} = \frac{p_{2'} v_{2'}}{T_{2'}}, \qquad \text{or} \qquad p_{2'} = \frac{T_{2'} v_1 p_1}{T_1 v_{2'}} = \frac{(1139.6)(5)(14)}{525} = 151.8 \text{ psia,}$$

which is the discharge pressure. Note that the relative pressure and volume at
state 2′, Fig. 49, are irrelevant because 2′ is not on the isentropic line from 1. We
can find the pressure at 2 which *is* on an isentropic line from

$$\frac{p_2}{p_1} = \frac{p_{r2}}{p_{r1}}, \qquad \text{or} \qquad p_2 = 14 \left(\frac{11.84}{1.256}\right) = 132 \text{ psia.}$$

The increase in entropy to 2′, equation (n), is

$$\Delta s = \phi_{2'} - \phi_1 - \frac{R}{J} \ln \frac{p_{2'}}{p_1}$$

$$= 0.78317 - 0.59403 - \frac{53.3}{778} \ln \frac{151.8}{14} = 0.0259 \text{ Btu/lb-°R.}$$

91. Types of Rotary Compressors. The term *compressor* is a generic
term, applying to reciprocating (Fig. 44) or rotary types for any compression
ratio. Compressors which raise the pressure only a few inches of water are
usually called *fans* (Chapter 18), their principal purpose being to move gases,
such as air through the ducts of an air-conditioning system. Compressors
that raise the pressure, say up to 35 psig, are often called *blowers,* Figs.
50–53, and they may be either reciprocating or rotary machines. Blowers
are used to furnish forced draft to blast furnaces (pressures to 35 psig), to
Bessemer converters (to 35 psig), to cupolas (to 1 psig), and to boost the
pressure of gas for other purposes. The rotary blower of Fig. 50 is a two-lobe,
positive displacement type which is used for liquids as well as gases; and,

as a blower, it is especially well adapted to low discharge pressures of the order of 2 psig. The lobes are driven at the same angular speed in opposite directions through meshing gears (not shown) mounted on each shaft. The shape of the lobes is such that they clear each other at all points of a revolution by about 0.005 in. If the flow on the discharge side is restricted or stopped, the discharge pressure will build up continuously, the maximum possible value being governed by the rate of leakage (or by a safety valve). The sliding-vane type, Fig. 51, is also common.

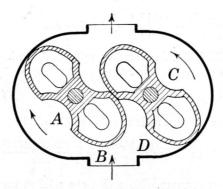

Fig. 50. Positive Displacement Blower. Suppose left-hand rotor *A* is turning clockwise. As the tip of *A* reaches the corner *B*, fluid is trapped in the left side. Continued rotation of this lobe connects this trapped fluid with the discharge side and pushes the fluid out. The right-hand rotor *C* is pushing out the fluid which was trapped when its lower tip moved past the corner *D*. The compressing or pumping cycle is performed twice in each rotation of each rotor of a two-lobe rotor. See the three-lobe rotor in Fig. 90(a), § 130.

In centrifugal compressors and blowers, the stream of fluid is first given a high velocity and high kinetic energy by the impellers; the stream then enters diffusers (§ 190) which utilize the kinetic energy to compress the gas and build up pressure. Figure 52 is a single-stage centrifugal blower; Fig. 53 is a multistage blower. See also Fig. 94, § 131.

Axial-flow compressors, Fig. 56, § 97, are frequently used with gas turbines because they can be designed with relatively high compression efficiency while handling large quantities of air.

92. Moisture in the Air. Atmospheric air is a mixture of so-called dry air and water vapor or steam. For 1 lb. of dry air at a particular temperature, less steam can exist in the mixture at high pressure than at low pressure. Hence, after the compressed air has cooled to approximately atmospheric temperature, as it usually does, some steam may be condensed to water and deposited. In order to compute the amount that would be condensed, it is necessary to know of the properties of gas-vapor mixtures, Chapter 16. To prevent moisture from being deposited in the pipe lines,

Courtesy Socony-Vacuum Oil Co., Inc., New York

Fig. 51. Rotary Compressor. The rotor is mounted eccentric to the casing. The vanes slide in the slots and are forced against the casing by centrifugal force. At the top of this picture, the vanes are extended and the volume included between the vanes and the casing is a maximum. The gas enters the compressor in this area. Observe that near the bottom, the vanes have moved inward, and, since the volume between the vanes and the casing has decreased, the gas has been compressed. Observe the hollow spaces in the casing for cooling water. This type of compressor may be driven directly connected to electric motors of standard rotative speeds.

the air should be cooled in an *aftercooler* (which operates much as an intercooler). The condensed vapor settles to the bottom and may be drained from the cooler. Moreover, if hot air is delivered to the pipes, the pipes will undergo alternate expansion and contraction as they contain alternately hot or cool air, which action may make it difficult to maintain tight pipe joints.

93. Closure. The student is urged to use the compressor as an opportunity to improve his familiarity with the law of conservation of energy.

Apply it in all problems, developing the habit of making an energy diagram and writing the energy equation for each application. There is no tool more powerful in analyzing situations involving the transformation of energy than this law.

The indicator card, the concepts of displacement, clearance, volumetric efficiency, indicated work, indicated horsepower, mean effective pressure,

Courtesy Ingersoll-Rand Co., New York

Fig. 52. Single-Stage Blower. For pressures of ¾ to 3 psig; 5 to 254 hp.

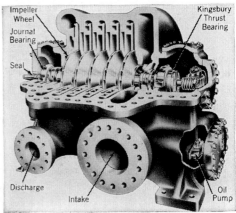

Courtesy Carrier Corp., Syracuse, N. Y.

Fig. 53. Multistage Centrifugal Blower. This machine, with proper design of impellers, is used for various gases and liquids. For gases, capacities up to 40,000 cfm; number of stages available, up to 7; speeds from 4700 rpm to 9800 rpm.

and brake horsepower are generally applicable to similar engineering problems and should be mastered at this time. These concepts will be used repeatedly in this book.

SELECTED REFERENCES

ASME *Test Code for Compressors and Exhausters*, PTC 10-1949.

Baumeister, T. Jr., *Fans*, McGraw-Hill.

Church, A. H., *Centrifugal Pumps and Blowers*, John Wiley.

Gill, T. T., *Air and Gas Compression*, John Wiley.

Stuart and Jackson, *The analysis and evaluation of compressor performance*, Mech. Eng., Vol. 76, p. 287.

Compressed Air Handbook, Compressed Air and Gas Institute.

PROBLEMS

NOTE. *Sketch the processes on pV and TS planes. Check all problems with an energy diagram showing the energy balance.*

131. Start with equation (29) for an isentropic process and show that the work of isentropic compression is given by

$$W = \frac{k p_1 V_1}{(k-1)J} \left[1 - \left(\frac{p_2}{p_1}\right)^{(k-1)/k} \right] \text{ Btu.}$$

Also show that this expression is the same as $-\int V\, dp/J$ when $pV^k = C$.

132. A compressor pumps 50 lb. per min. of air from 14.7 psia to 55 psig. During the process, the enthalpy increases 2880 Btu/min. and heat in the amount of 10 Btu/lb. of air is transferred to the cooling water. Find the work done if the kinetic energy (a) increases 1 Btu/lb. of air and (b) decreases 1 Btu/lb. *Ans.* (a) 81 hp, (b) 78.6 hp.

133. A compressor receives 110 cfm of air at 14.5 psia and 80°F, then compresses it to 100 psia with negligible change of kinetic energy. Compute the temperature at the end of compression and determine the ideal work when the process is (a) isentropic, (b) isothermal.
Ans. (a) −694 Btu/min., (b) −519 Btu/min.
-860 Btu/min　　-570

134. A polytropic compression of 5000 cfm of air occurs from 14 psia and 75°F to 30 psia with $n = 1.32$ and $\Delta K = 0$. Determine (a) the specific heat of the polytropic process and the temperature after compression, (b) the heat to the cooling water, (c) the ideal work.
Ans. (a) −0.0429 Btu/lb-°R, 184°F, (b) 1650 Btu/min., (c) −10,890 Btu/min.
1625　　$-10,760$

135. A compressor delivers 50 lb. per min. of air after compressing it from 14.7 psia and 80°F to 50 psig. If the compression is according to $pV^{1.32} = C$,
Clearance = 5%

determine (a) the heat transferred during compression, (b) the ideal work, for $\Delta K = 0$, in Btu/min. and hp, (c) the displacement based on the conventional volumetric efficiency, (d) the probable actual horsepower (ihp) for an adiabatic compression efficiency of 73%.
Ans. (a) −437 Btu/min., (b) 78.2 hp, (c) 775 cfm, (d) 110 ihp.
760

136. The conventional volumetric efficiency of a compressor is 85%. Let $n = 1.29$, $p_1 = 14$ psia, and $p_2 = 85$ psia. The volume at intake is 340 cfm. What are the percentage clearance and displacement volume?
Ans. 4.92%, 400 cfm.

137. A compressor has a displacement of 795 cfm. It is located at 6000 ft. altitude. At intake, the temperature is 90°F and the pressure is 11.2 psia; $pV^{1.35} = C$; $c = 5\%$; and the discharge pressure is 70.22 psig after a polytropic compression. (a) What mass of air is delivered? (b) Let the same compressor be located at sea level, and let the following things be the same as at 6000 ft.: the percentage pressure drop from atmosphere to the cylinder; the intake temperature; the value of $n = 1.35$; the compression ratio (V_1/V_2). Compute the mass of air delivered. (c) Let the environmental temperature in each location be 60°F and compute the capacity at both places in cfm of free air.
Ans. (a) 36.5 lb./min., (b) 45.5 lb./min., (c) 597 cfm at 6000 ft.

don't try.

138. Indicator cards taken from a 13x16-in. compressor, running at 220 rpm, have areas as follows: head end, 1.15 sq. in.; crank end, 1.1 sq. in. The length of each card is 2 in.; the diameter of the piston rod is to be neglected; the scale of the indicator spring is 80 lb.; the mechanical efficiency is 85%. What are the ihp and bhp? *Ans.* 96.5, 113.5 hp.

139. Measured at an intake of 14.6 psia and 80°F, 28,000 cfm of air are pumped adiabatically to 25 psia. At discharge, the temperature is 200°F and the velocity is 100 fps. The initial velocity is negligible. (a) What horsepower is required? (b) Determine the isentropic horsepower ($\Delta K = 0$) and the compression efficiency for the given conditions. (c) What is ΔS in part (a)? (See problem **144.**)

Ans. (a) 1400 hp, (b) 73.8%, (c) 22.9 Btu/°R-min.

140. A compressor handles 3500 cfm of air as measured at intake of 14.5 psia and 75°F. At discharge, $p_2 = 25$ psia and $t_2 = 190°F$. The initial velocity is 40 fps and the exit velocity is 120 fps. The process is adiabatic. Determine (a) the actual work, (b) the work of an isentropic ($\Delta K = 0$), (c) the compression efficiency, (d) the change of entropy in (a). (See problem **145.**)

Ans. (a) 7135, (b) 5530 Btu/min., (c) 77.6%, (d) 2.38 Btu/min-°R.

141. A 14x14-in., horizontal, double-acting air compressor with 8% clearance operates at 200 rpm. At intake, $p_1 = 14.5$ psia and $t_1 = 70°F$; at discharge, $p_2 = 101.5$ psia; $n = k$; the compression efficiency is 76%. Compute (a) the actual displacement, cfm, (b) the mass of air delivered based on the conventional volumetric efficiency, (c) the isentropic work ($\Delta K = 0$) and the actual work, (d) the actual mep. (See problem **146.**)

Ans. (a) 498 cfm, (b) 24.6 lb./min., (c) $W' = 3065$ Btu/min., (d) 33.2 psi.

142. Air enters a two-stage compressor at 80°F and 14 psia and is compressed according to $pV^{1.3} = C$. Discharge from the LP cylinder is at 42 psia and from the HP cylinder at 120 psia with a 2-psi pressure drop in the intercooler. The air leaves the intercooler at 95°F. If 20 lb./min. of air are delivered, how much heat is rejected in the intercooler? If circulating water undergoes a temperature rise of 10° in passing through the intercooler, how much water should be circulated to handle this heat? (See problem **147.**)

143. A two-stage air compressor delivers 80 lb./min. at 150 psia, after compressions following the law $pV^{1.3} = C$ in each cylinder. Intake is at 14 psia and 60°F, and the intercooler cools the air back to 60°F. Find (a) the optimum intermediate pressure, (b) the temperature at the end of compression in each cylinder, (c) the heat rejected to jacket cooling water, (d) the heat rejected in the intercooler, (e) the total ideal horsepower. (See problem **148.**)

Ans. (a) 45.8 psi, (b) 224°F, (c) 1500 Btu/min., (d) 3150 Btu/min., (e) 184 hp.

144. Solve problem **139** using the air table and compare answers.

145. Solve problem **140** using the air table and compare answers.

Ans. (a) 7141, (b) 5565 Btu/min., (c) 78.5%, (d) 2.425 Btu/min-°R.

146. Solve for the work items in **141** using the air table and compare answers.

147. Solve problem **142** using the air table and compare answers.

Ans. −674, 67.2 Btu/min.

148. Check as many answers as possible in **143** by using the air table.

149–160. These numbers may be used for other problems.

THE GAS TURBINE

94. Introduction. The first gas turbine to produce useful work was probably a windmill, wherein there is no precompression and no combustion. The characteristic features of a gas turbine power plant, as we think of the name today, include a compression process and a heat addition (or combustion) process. These features are not new, although a practical machine is a relatively recent development. Joule and Brayton* independently proposed the cycle which is the ideal prototype of the actual unit. An unsuccessful turbine unit was built as far back as 1872, and by 1906 a unit which produced net power had been built.† There were two principal obstacles to be overcome, as revealed by thermodynamic analysis. Such an analysis shows that in order for practical amounts of power to be delivered: (1) the temperature at the beginning of expansion must be high (until a few years ago, the highest permissible temperatures were about 700–800°F) and (2) the compressor must operate at a high efficiency. Metallurgical developments in recent years, for example, the use of an expensive alloy of cobalt-chromium-nickel for the turbine blades of the J47, are raising the highest permissible temperatures (1600°F and more; 2000°F if shorter life is acceptable, as for some military purposes). A better knowledge of aerodynamics has been responsible for improving the efficiency of both the centrifugal and axial-flow compressors. An axial-flow compressor is much the reverse of a turbine, but it takes a more precise knowledge of aerodynamic characteristics to design an efficient compressor.‡ Gas turbines, driven by the exhaust of internal combustion engines, have long been used for supercharging such engines (turbo-superchargers, Fig. 94, p. 155). Of further promise on the temperature problem is the use of ceramic-metal combinations.

Since we shall be thinking of a gas turbine in terms of a thermody-

---

* See footnote, p. 11. George Brayton, a contemporary of Otto, was a Boston engineer. However, his engine was conceived as a reciprocating type rather than a turbine.

† J. T. Rettaliata, *The gas turbine*, Allis-Chalmers' Electrical Review, Sept., Dec., 1941; Mar., 1942.

‡ John F. Lee, *Theory and Design of Steam and Gas Turbines*, McGraw-Hill.

namic cycle, we should at the outset become familiar with the characteristic features of a cycle.

95. The Cycle.   The essential elements of any thermodynamic cycle which involves a heat engine are: (1) a *working substance,* a medium for receiving and rejecting heat, a substance to carry energy to and from a heat engine; (2) a *source* or *reservoir of heat* or *hot body,* wherewith heat may be added to the working substance; (3) a *sink* or *receiver* or *cold body,* a reservoir to which heat may be rejected by the working substance; (4) an *engine,* wherein the working substance may do work or have work done on it.   Various other devices and accessories are essential for the completion of any particular cycle, but the foregoing elements are a part of every thermodynamic cycle wherein power is used or developed.   During every cycle operating in a steady state, the working substance goes through the same series of events or processes and returns to its initial condition.   The initial condition may be any chosen condition at any point of the cycle, for example, point 1, Fig. 54.   The condition of the substance $(p, v, T, s,$ etc.) as it passes point 1 is always the same during steady state operation.   Man, by chosen devices, may close the cycle, or he may allow nature to close the cycle for him.

An *open cycle* is one that nature closes.   As an illustration, consider the internal combustion engine.   Here, a mixture of fuel and air is drawn into the cylinder; the mixture is usually, but not necessarily, compressed, after which the fuel is ignited, combustion being supported by the oxygen of the air.   The combustion liberates a large supply of energy, a part of which is converted into work during an expansion process; the remainder is exhausted to the atmosphere.   To simplify the explanation, assume that the fuel is pure carbon, the charge being thus carbon, oxygen, and nitrogen, plus those small quantities of other gases in the atmosphere, such as argon.   The nitrogen and other atmospheric gases, except oxygen, pass through the engine unchanged in chemical composition, but they are heated to a higher temperature.   The oxygen combines with the carbon in the event of so-called complete combustion to form carbon dioxide (CO_2).   For present purposes, we may think of the exhaust then as being a mixture of hot carbon dioxide, nitrogen, and traces of other atmospheric gases.   The atmosphere (nature) cools the hot exhaust products to the original atmospheric temperature, and plant life changes the carbon dioxide back into carbon and oxygen.   For each cycle, there is supplied to the engine a new charge of fuel and air, but for each charge, nature in a sense completes the cycle.

A *closed cycle* is one closed by the inventions of man.   The H_2O in a modern steam power plant is an example of such a cycle.   Here, water is pumped into a boiler, the thermodynamic source or hot body, Fig. 54, where heat is supplied from the combustion of a fuel. As a consequence, the water is evaporated into steam, which is then conducted to a prime mover or heat engine; the prime mover transforms a part of the energy of the steam into work (between points 1 and 2, Fig. 54), after which the steam is exhausted into a condenser, which acts as the sink. The circulating water C-D through the condenser abstracts from the steam that part of the heat supplied which was not converted into work, condensing the steam into water (process 2-3, Fig. 54); thence, the water goes to a pump (or pumps) and is pumped back into the boiler.

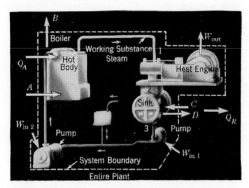

Fig. 54. Elements of a Thermodynamic Cycle. Let the circulating H_2O be the system. Then, only energy crosses the boundaries.

Thus, a *cycle* is completed by causing the working substance to pass through a *series* of processes; that is, it takes more than one process to form a cycle. This clear-cut distinction between a *process* and a *cycle* must be kept in mind.

Considering the energy quantities related to Fig. 54, we note that the energy entering is equal to the energy departing, if there is no change in the stored energy. See (4A) and (5A), § 19. Thus,

$$\text{Energy in} = \text{Energy out}$$
$$Q_A + W_{in} = Q_R + W_{out};$$

or $W_{out} - W_{in} = Q_A - Q_R$, from which

$$(51) \qquad W \;\; = \Sigma W \;\; = W_{out} - W_{in} = Q \;\; = \Sigma Q \;\; = Q_A - Q_R,$$

$$\qquad\qquad \text{[ALGEBRAIC} \quad \text{[ARITHMETIC} \qquad\qquad \text{[ALGEBRAIC} \quad \text{[ARITHMETIC}$$
$$\qquad\qquad \text{SUM]} \qquad\quad \text{DIFFERENCE]} \qquad\qquad \text{SUM]} \qquad\quad \text{DIFFERENCE]}$$

which says that the net work W done by the cycle is equal to the net heat Q for the cycle ($\Delta E = 0$). Note carefully the symbolization; with respect to a cycle, W stands for the net work of the cycle and Q for the net heat transferred. We may think of $Q = \Sigma Q$, in which case the rejected heat is a negative number and an algebraic sum is intended; or we may think of $Q = Q_A - Q_R$, in which case the rejected heat is a positive number and an arithmetic difference is intended. Each expression under this interpretation says the same thing, and the reader should be certain now that the notions are straight in his mind. The signs attached to energy quantities are arbitrary and conventional, indicating a direction of flow or a change of magnitude. Observe that if the working substance is taken as the system, the work done is the work of the fluid. The actual shaft work is somewhat less than the actual fluid work in a power-manufacturing machine because of friction related to the machine.

96. Thermal Efficiency. Thermal efficiency may well be thought of in its simplest form, *output* divided by *input*. The output of a power cycle, which is a thermodynamic cycle for the production of power, is the net work; the input is the heat added to the working substance from an external source of heat, Q_A in Fig. 54. The output of the power cycle is taken as the net work $W_{out} - W_{in}$ because some of the gross work W_{out} is used to supply the energy W_{in} to drive the pump. Therefore, the thermal efficiency of a *power cycle* is

$$(52) \qquad e = \frac{W}{Q_A} = \frac{Q_A - Q_R}{Q_A} = \frac{\Sigma Q}{Q_A}.$$

Observe that equation (52) applies only to a cycle. However, if the cycle is performed wholly within the engine, as we shall imagine for ideal internal combustion engines, then (52) gives the efficiency of the engine as well as that of the cycle.

97. Air-Standard Brayton Cycle. Before taking up the ideal cycle, consider first the practical features of operation. Air enters the compressor at condition 1, Fig. 55. After compression, it enters the combustors, some of it going around the outside of the combustion chamber proper, and the remainder furnishes oxygen for burning the fuel, which is continuously injected into the combustion chamber. Because of their temperature rise, the gases expand (Charles' law) and enter the turbine in state 3, Fig. 55. After expansion through the turbine, the exhaust to the atmosphere is in some condition 4. In an ordinary power plant arrangement, the work of the turbine W_t is great enough to drive the compressor W_c *and* deliver brake work W_B to drive, say, a generator or propellor; $W_t = W_B + W_c$. An external source of power is needed to start a gas turbine unit. Figure 56, a cutaway of a turbo-prop engine, shows in some detail the actual appearance of the simple gas turbine plant, where the excess of power produced by the turbine drives the propeller (instead of a generator). Additional driving force (thrust = rate of change of momentum) is obtained in this application in the amount of: momentum of the gases leaving the tail pipe minus the momentum of the entering air per unit time (perhaps 15–20% "jet" propulsion).

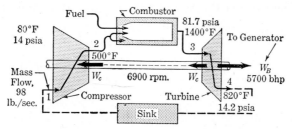

Fig. 55. Diagrammatic Layout of a Gas Turbine Unit.
The temperatures and pressures given are typical of actual values.

For the air-standard Brayton cycle, let the combustor in Fig. 55 be changed to a heat exchanger, and let the same amount of heat be added to the air at constant pressure from an external reservoir of heat. Then, let the exhausted air at 4 be led through another heat exchanger via which heat

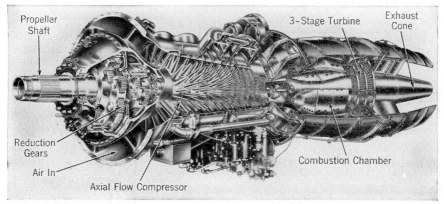

Courtesy Pratt & Whitney Aircraft, East Hartford, Conn.

Fig. 56. Turbo-prop Engine. The compressor is a 13-stage axial flow; the turbine a 3-stage; 4200 rpm. Turbo-prop engines are well adapted for airplane speeds of some 400–450 mph and for "middle" distances (up to about 1500 mi.) The axial-flow compressor presents a smaller frontal area for a particular capacity than the centrifugal type—advantageous on an airplane.

is transferred to the sink. Following the dotted path, Fig. 55, the same air, cooled to its original intake temperature, now reenters the compressor at 1 and starts the cycle anew. This is a closed cycle, spoken of as the equivalent air-standard cycle, and it is pictured on the pV and TS planes in Fig.

57.   Such closed cycles for a gas turbine are being investigated for gas turbines to be used with nuclear reactors, perhaps with hydrogen as the working substance; they have been built and operated with air and other working substances.   In the ideal cycle, the compression 1-2 and expansion
3-4 are isentropic; the heat supply 2-3 and rejection 4-1 are at constant
pressure.   The work of this cycle, with constant average c_p, is

(a) $$W = \Sigma Q = wc_p(T_3 - T_2) + wc_p(T_1 - T_4)$$
$$= wc_p(T_3 - T_2) - wc_p(T_4 - T_1).$$

The thermal efficiency is $[Q_A = H_3 - H_2 = wc_p(T_3 - T_2)]$

(b) $$e = \frac{W}{Q_A} = 1 - \frac{T_4 - T_1}{T_3 - T_2}.$$

This equation may be put into various significant forms.   First, we may use
the **pressure ratio** r_p, which is defined as the higher pressure divided by the

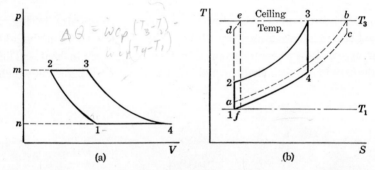

Fig. 57.   Brayton Cycle.   Also known as the Joule cycle.

lower pressure $(r_p = p_2/p_1)$, and the Tp relation for an isentropic.   With
these, we get

(c) $$\frac{T_2}{T_1} = \left(\frac{p_2}{p_1}\right)^{(k-1)/k} = r_p^{(k-1)/k}, \quad \text{and} \quad \frac{T_3}{T_4} = \left(\frac{p_3}{p_4}\right)^{(k-1)/k}$$
$$= \left(\frac{p_2}{p_1}\right)^{(k-1)/k} = r_p^{(k-1)/k},$$

whence, $T_2/T_1 = T_3/T_4$.   Rearranging, we find

$$\frac{T_4}{T_1} = \frac{T_3}{T_2} \quad \text{or} \quad \frac{T_4}{T_1} - 1 = \frac{T_3}{T_2} - 1 = \frac{T_4 - T_1}{T_1} = \frac{T_3 - T_2}{T_2};$$

(d) $$\frac{T_4 - T_1}{T_3 - T_2} = \frac{T_1}{T_2} = \frac{T_4}{T_3}.$$

Using this relation in equation (b), we get the thermal efficiency of the
Brayton cycle as

(e)
$$e = 1 - \frac{T_1}{T_2} = \frac{T_2 - T_1}{T_2} = \frac{T_3 - T_4}{T_3}.$$

Now let the compression ratio be $r = V_1/V_2$, by definition (§ 70). Then the TV relation for the isentropic is

(f)
$$\frac{T_2}{T_1} = \left(\frac{V_1}{V_2}\right)^{k-1} = r^{k-1}.$$

Using r_p from equation (c) and r from equation (f) in (e), we find

(g)
$$e = 1 - \frac{1}{r^{k-1}} = 1 - \frac{1}{r_p^{(k-1)/k}}.$$

The pressure ratio r_p is more commonly used for gas turbine units. An examination of equation (g) suggests that to improve the thermal efficiency of the gas turbine, it is necessary to increase the compression ratio, a surmise which is strictly true for the ideal cycle but which must be qualified for actual cycles, as we shall see later. One of the facts of life which the gas turbine engineer must contend with is a temperature ceiling—as previously stated. With this limitation, we would not be likely to choose the most efficient Brayton cycle, because the mep and the amount of work obtainable from a particular size of engine affects the decision. In Fig. 57(b), let the cycle under consideration be 1-d-e-f, wherein the compression ratio (1 to d) is large and the efficiency of the cycle is large. Although this diagram is not drawn to any particular scale, it is easy to see that the work done is becoming quite small. Also, if the compression ratio decreases, as to 1-a, the work of the cycle 1-a-b-c becomes quite small (and the efficiency is lower, too).

98. Intermediate Temperature for Maximum Work.

From the foregoing discussion, we see that for fixed initial and final temperatures, T_1 and T_3, there is some intermediate temperature which would result in the maximum work. This we are interested in because we may care to keep the size of engine as small as possible. From equation (d), we get

$$T_4 = \frac{T_1 T_3}{T_2}.$$

Substitute this value of T_4 into (a), differentiate W with respect to T_2, and equate the differential to zero (T_1 and T_3 are constants).

$$\frac{dW}{dT_2} = \frac{wc_p\, d(T_3 - T_2 + T_1 - T_1T_3/T_2)}{dT_2} = 0.$$

(h)
$$-1 + \frac{T_1 T_3}{T_2{}^2} = 0 \qquad \text{or} \qquad T_2 = (T_1 T_3)^{1/2},$$

the value of T_2 that results in the maximum work of the ideal cycle which is limited by the temperatures T_1 and T_3.

99. Brayton Cycle with Fluid Friction. As you know, the efficiency of an actual power cycle is the actual net work divided by the actual energy chargeable against the cycle. However, since three or more different pieces of major equipment are needed in order for this cycle to operate and since the efficiency of each piece is significant, it is customary to study the pieces separately. As steady flow machines with $\Delta K = 0$, the works for adiabatic flow are (Fig. 58):

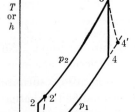

Compressor,

(i)   Ideal, $W_c = h_1 - h_2 = c_p(T_1 - T_2)$
$$= -\Delta h_s \text{ Btu/lb.}$$

(j)   Actual, $W'_c = h_1 - h_{2'} = c_p(T_1 - T_{2'})$
$$= -\Delta h'_c \text{ Btu/lb.}$$

Turbine,

(k)   Ideal, $W_t = h_3 - h_4 = c_p(T_3 - T_4)$
$$= -\Delta h_s \text{ Btu/lb.}$$

(l)   Actual, $W'_t = h_3 - h_{4'} = c_p(T_3 - T_{4'})$
$$= -\Delta h'_t \text{ Btu/lb.}$$

Fig. 58.   With Fluid Friction. The area enclosed within *irreversible* processes does *not* represent work, because the area under the curve 1-2', say, does not represent Q.

The foregoing may be considered as being obtained either from equation (10) or from an energy diagram. Compressor works are negative as given. (NOTE. If the engine is moving through the air, as on an airplane, the initial kinetic energy (relative to the plane) may be substantial . In this case, the equations given for the compressor in terms of enthalpy are all right if we use h_o for h_1, where $h_o = h_1 + K_1$ and is called the stagnation enthalpy—§ 176.)

Regarding efficiencies, we use the **adiabatic compression efficiency** η_c, § 84, for the compressor and define it as

(m) $$\eta_c = \frac{\text{Ideal work } (\Delta h_s)}{\text{Actual work } (\Delta h'_c)} = \frac{W_c}{W'_c};$$

then

$$W'_c = \frac{W_c}{\eta_c} = \frac{\Delta h_s}{\eta_c} = \frac{c_p(T_2 - T_1)}{\eta_c} \text{ Btu/lb.} \quad \text{[POSITIVE NUMBER]}$$
$$\text{[IDEAL GAS]}$$

where the subscript s designates constant entropy (1-2, Fig. 58) and where the prime mark denotes the actual change of h (1-2', Fig. 58). The negative signs are irrelevant to efficiency definitions and are ignored in equation (m). The comparable efficiency for the turbine is called the **turbine efficiency** or *engine efficiency* η_e and is defined as

(n) $$\eta_e = \frac{\text{Actual work, } \Delta h_t'}{\text{Ideal work, } \Delta h_s} = \frac{W_t'}{W_t};$$

then

$$W_t' = \eta_e W_t = \eta_e(-\Delta h_s) = \eta_e c_p(T_3 - T_4) \text{ Btu/lb.}$$
$$[\text{IDEAL GAS}]$$

where Δh_s is the isentropic change of enthalpy (3-4, Fig. 58) corresponding to the actual adiabatic expansion (3-4'; $p_4 = p_{4'}$). In this application, we shall take the actual work $W_t' = h_3 - h_{4'}$, as the work of the fluid (which is not very different from the brake work because of the small mechanical losses). Note that the actual mass of fluid flowing through the turbine is greater than that flowing through the compressor by the amount of the fuel used, Fig. 55.

100. Air Cycle Efficiency with Fluid Friction. For present purposes, let the mass flow be the same at all points of the gas turbine unit and use 1 lb. for convenience. Then the energy chargeable against the actual cycle is

$$Q_A' = h_3 - h_{2'} = c_p(T_3 - T_{2'}).$$

Since the actual net work is $W' = W_t' - W_c'$, we have

$$e' = \frac{W'}{Q_A'} = \frac{T_{3'} - T_4 - (T_{2'} - T_1)}{T_3 - T_{2'}},$$

where the variation of specific heat is ignored. Thus for some constant average specific heat,

$$e' = \frac{(T_3 - T_4)\eta_e - (T_2 - T_1)/\eta_c}{T_3 - T_{2'}}.$$

Let $T_2/T_1 = T_3/T_4 = r_p{}^{(k-1)/k}$ in this equation in order to eliminate T_2 and T_4, use the value of $T_{2'}$ obtained from equation (m), namely,

$$T_{2'} = \frac{T_2 - T_1(1 - \eta_c)}{\eta_c},$$

and rearrange to get

$$e' = \left(\frac{\eta_e T_3 - T_1 r_p{}^{(k-1)/k}/\eta_c}{T_3 - T_1 - T_1(r_p{}^{(k-1)/k} - 1)/\eta_c}\right)\left(1 - \frac{1}{r_p{}^{(k-1)/k}}\right).$$

Notice that the last parentheses enclose a term which is the efficiency of an ideal Brayton cycle with a pressure ratio of r_p. The purpose of arriving at this form is to show that the efficiency of the actual cycle depends upon the high and low temperatures as well as on the pressure ratio, and the student is advised to avoid its use in routine problems. If it is desired to know the maximum efficiency for a particular temperature range, differentiate the foregoing equation with respect to r_p and equate to zero.   There is little or nothing to be done about T_1; so let it be, say, 540°R.   Now for a particular turbine inlet temperature, say 1200°F = 1660°R, assume various pressure ratios and plot a curve.   You will find a curve such as the one labeled 1200°F

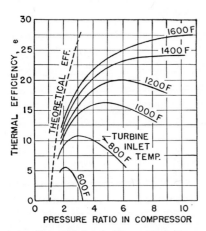

Fig. 59. *Efficiency Versus Pressure Ratio* (39).   **Each curve is for a particular value of** T_3, **as labeled, and for the simple cycle corresponding to Fig. 58. Combustor efficiency is 100%.**

in Fig. 59 which points up an important fact: *for each turbine inlet temperature, there is a certain pressure ratio which results in maximum thermal efficiency,* that is, the actual thermal efficiency does not go up indefinitely with the pressure ratio as in the case of the ideal cycle.   See the dotted curve in Fig. 59.

101. Example.   The intake of the compressor of an air-standard Brayton cycle is 40,000 cfm at 15 psia and 40°F.   The compression ratio $r = 5$ and the temperature at the turbine inlet is 1440°F.   Neglect the pressure drop between compressor and turbine, and let the exit pressure of the turbine be 15 psia.   (a) For the ideal cycle, determine the net horsepower output and the thermal efficiency.   (b) For the case of an engine efficiency $\eta_e = 85\%$ and a compression efficiency $\eta_c = 83\%$ (these are almost as high as they go), compute the net output and the thermal efficiency.   What is the percentage reduction in power? (c) What percentage of the total turbine work goes to drive the compressor in the ideal and in the actual units?

SOLUTION.   (a) Since the temperatures are relatively high, the results will be much more accurate if the air table is used than if the computations are made on the basis of constant specific heats of "cold" air.   Refer to the ideal cycle 1-2-3-4, Fig. 60 (also Fig. 58).   State 1 is located in the air table by 40 + 460 = 500°R, for which we read

$$h_1 = 119.48, \qquad p_{r1} = 1.059, \qquad v_{r1} = 174.90, \qquad \phi = 0.58233.$$

For a compression ratio of $v_1/v_2 = 5 = v_{r1}/v_{r2}$, equation (r), § 89, we have

$$v_{r2} = \frac{v_{r1}}{5} = \frac{174.90}{5} = 34.95,$$

which determines state 2 on an isentropic curve.   Interpolating for this value in the full tables, we find

$$T_2 = 944.7°R, \qquad h_2 = 227.2, \qquad p_{r2} = 9.998.$$

For a temperature of $T_3 = 1440 + 460 = 1900°R$, we have the following values from the table:

$$h_3 = 477.09, \qquad p_{r3} = 141.51, \qquad v_{r3} = 4.974.$$

Since the pressure limits on the expansion 3-4 are the same as those on the compression 1-2, $p_{r4} = p_{r3}/r_p$.

$$r_p = \frac{p_{r2}}{p_{r1}} = \frac{9.998}{1.059} = 9.44; \qquad \text{or} \qquad p_{r4} = \frac{p_{r3}}{r_p} = \frac{141.51}{9.44} = 14.99.$$

Corresponding to this value of p_{r4}, we take from the table:

$$T_4 \approx 1056°\text{R}, \qquad h_4 = 254.93, \qquad v_{r4} = 26.08.$$

Considering each device as steady flow, we get

$$W_c = -(h_2 - h_1) = -(227.2 - 119.5) = -107.7 \text{ Btu/lb.,}$$
$$W_t = h_3 - h_4 = 477.1 - 254.9 = 222.2 \text{ Btu/lb.,}$$
$$W_{\text{net}} = W = 222.2 - 107.7 = 114.5 \text{ Btu/lb.}$$

For a mass of air of

$$w = \frac{pV}{RT} = \frac{(15)(144)(40,000)}{(53.3)(500)} = 3240 \text{ lb./min.,}$$

we find the net ideal horsepower as

$$hp = \frac{(114.5)(3240)}{42.4} = 8750 \text{ hp.}$$

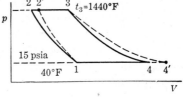

Fig. 60.

The energy chargeable against the air cycle is' Fig. 60,

$$Q_A = h_3 - h_2 = 477.1 - 227.2 = 249.9 \text{ Btu/lb.;}$$

hence,

$$e = \frac{W}{Q_A} = \frac{114.5}{249.9} = 45.8\%.$$

(b) The actual works and the corresponding net horsepower output are

$$W'_c = -\frac{107.7}{0.83} = -130 \text{ Btu/lb.,} \qquad W'_t = (0.85)(222.2) = 188.5 \text{ Btu/lb.,}$$

$$W' = 188.5 - 130 = 58.5 \text{ Btu/lb.,} \qquad hp = \frac{(58.5)(3240)}{42.4} = 4470 \text{ hp.}$$

The actual work delivered by the shaft would be of the order of 2% less than this value—allowing for the mechanical efficiency. To get the actual thermal efficiency, we need the enthalpy at state 2', Fig. 60, in order to compute $Q'_A = h_3 - h_{2'}$. From $W'_c = -130$ above, we have

$$W'_c = -130 = h_1 - h_{2'} \qquad \text{or} \qquad h_{2'} = 119.5 + 130 = 249.5 \text{ Btu/lb.,}$$

$$e' = \frac{W'}{Q'_A} = \frac{W'}{h_3 - h_{2'}} = \frac{58.5}{477.1 - 249.5} = 25.7\%.$$

$$\text{Percentage loss} = \frac{114.5 - 58.5}{114.5} = 48.9\%.$$

Even though the compression and engine efficiencies are relatively good, the loss of ideal work is large; yet this computed loss ignores losses from incomplete combustion and from the pressure drop through the combustor and other passages.

102. Heating Value of Fuels and Energy Charged Against the Gas Turbine. The heating value of a fuel is obtained by burning it completely at constant pressure (or constant volume) and then determining *the amount of heat (heating value) given up by the products of combustion on being cooled to the initial temperature,* corrected to a standard state of 1 atm and 77°F (preferably). This is not a single, simple number because of the different ways in which the test may be run and because of H_2O which is formed from fuels which contain hydrogen. Fuels used are commonly hydrocarbons such as fuel oil, kerosene, gasoline, etc., the chemical formula of which is in the form C_xH_y. When these fuels burn (react with oxygen), the hydrogen forms H_2O. If the products of combustion are "hot" (above about 125°F), this H_2O is vapor (steam); if the products have been cooled to normal atmospheric temperatures, the H_2O is condensed, or largely condensed, and the H_2O is water. During condensation it gives up the latent heat of evaporation. Thus considering this factor only, we see that there may be at least two heating values *for fuels containing hydrogen,* the **higher heating value** q_h when the H_2O formed from the fuel is condensed and the **lower heating value** q_l when the fuel is burned so that the H_2O does not condense. (See Chapter 17 for more detail.) Since tests are run sometimes at constant volume and sometimes at constant pressure, this gives two more heating values.

In the actual engine, the exhaust gases are quite hot and the steam does not come close to condensing. Since this is so, it is reasoned that it would be unfair to the engine to charge against it the higher heating value; hence, the tendency is to use the *lower heating value at constant pressure* in computing the thermal efficiency of actual gas turbine engines. (The practice in this country has been to use the higher heating value for the same purpose in computing the thermal efficiency of internal combustion engines, but there is some tendency now to use the lower. With such a confused state of affairs, courtesy demands that the kind of heating value used always be stated.)

Although the heating value is a function of the actual temperature from which it is run, it is common practice to use the "standard" heating value (unless refined calculations are significant), because these standard values are readily available in the literature. See Table XIII, Appendix. With this simplification, we let w_f be the pounds of fuel used per pound of air and q_l be the lower heating value at constant pressure and use

(o) $$Q_A = w_f q_l \text{ Btu/lb. air}$$

as the energy to be charged against the ideal or actual cycle. Ignoring the change in mass brought about by the addition of fuel and ignoring the change in the working substance from air to products, we may write

$$w_f q_l = h_3 - h_2 = \int c_p \, dT = c_p(T_3 - T_2)$$

for the ideal gas cycle, where c_p is the average specific heat for the temperature range T_2 to T_3. Thus, the thermal efficiency of the gas turbine cycle is (w_f = lb. fuel/lb. air, W = Btu/lb. air, or other consistent units)

(p)
$$e = \frac{W}{w_f q_l} \qquad \text{or} \qquad e = \frac{W'}{w_f q_l}.$$
$$[\text{IDEAL}] \qquad\qquad [\text{ACTUAL}]$$

Sometimes w_f is in pounds of fuel per hp-hr.; then $w_f q_l$ Btu/hp-hr. is called the **heat rate** and 2544 Btu/hp-hr. of work divided by $w_f q_l$ Btu/hp-hr. of energy supplied is also the thermal efficiency; $e = 2544/(w_f q_l)$. Do not overlook the different units for this w_f as compared to those for w_f in equation (p).

You are no doubt interested in actual performance data, typical values of which have been indicated here and there in this chapter. Design values as taken from the literature* are as follows:

Compression efficiency = 85%	Engine efficiency = 83%,
Engine and jet efficiency = 90%,	Nozzle efficiency = 98%,
Combustion pressure loss = 3%,	Regenerator effectiveness = 50%,
Combustion efficiency = 98%,	Regenerator pressure loss = 5%,
Ram coefficient = 85%,	Intercooler pressure loss = 3%,

Lower heating value, fuel, q_l = 18,550 Btu/lb.

103. Regenerative Heating—Ideal Cycle. Regenerative heating is widely used in various cycles, but in a power-generating cycle, it is a heating of the working substance in the colder sections of the cycle by the working substance in the hotter sections of the cycle. In particular for the gas turbine, regenerative heating is the act of using the hot exhaust gases from the turbine to preheat the air before it enters the combustor and after it has been compressed. Thus some of the energy of the exhaust which would otherwise be wasted to the atmosphere partially heats the compressed air, resulting in a saving of fuel and an increase in thermal efficiency. Note carefully that the heat involved in the regenerator *is an exchange of energy within the system;* it is not heat added to the system from an external source.

* D. D. Streid, *Gas-turbine fundamentals*, Mech. Eng., Vol. 68, p. 127.

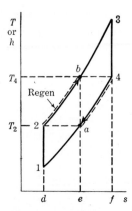

Fig. 61. Regeneration—
Ideal Cycle. With the s
axis at absolute zero,
area 4-a-e-f = 2-b-e-d,
each representing heat.

In the gas turbine application, exhaust gas at state 4, Fig. 61, and air from the compressor at state 2 are each led to a heat exchanger (regenerator) so that the hot exhaust 4 gives up heat to the air 2. See the regenerator in Fig. 62. Theoretically, if the heat exchanger were large enough and the flow were slow enough, the air from the compressor could be heated reversibly to temperature 4 at state b, Fig. 61, while the exhaust cools to temperature 2, state a. Some of the formerly discharged heat $h_4 - h_a$ is exchanged *within* the system and the heat to the sink is now $h_a - h_1$, which is less than before. Moreover, it is necessary to add only the heat equal to $h_3 - h_b$, instead of $h_3 - h_2$ as formerly. Consequently, less fuel is needed and this additional piece of equipment should materially increase the efficiency of the ideal cycle, which it does. From Fig. 61, we find the thermal efficiency as $(W = \Sigma Q, T_b = T_4,$ and $T_a = T_2)$

(q)
$$e = \frac{\Sigma Q}{Q_A} = \frac{c_p(T_3 - T_b) + c_p(T_1 - T_a)}{c_p(T_3 - T_b)} = 1 - \frac{T_2 - T_1}{T_3 - T_4}$$

$$e = 1 - \frac{T_1}{T_3}\left(\frac{T_2/T_1 - 1}{1 - T_4/T_3}\right) = 1 - \frac{T_1}{T_3} r_p^{(k-1)/k},$$

where we have used $T_2/T_1 = T_3/T_4 = r_p^{(k-1)/k}$, equation (c), § 97. With a fixed initial temperature T_1, equation (q) shows that the thermal efficiency of the regenerative cycle increases as T_3 increases and *decreases as the pressure ratio increases.* Note in contrast that without the regenerator, equation (g), the cycle efficiency *increases* as the pressure ratio increases.

104. Effectiveness of Regenerator. Study Figs. 62 and 63 until the regenerative action is clearly in mind. The state points with the prime marks indicate actual points, except that pressure drops have not been shown. There will certainly be a pressure drop of both the air and the exhaust gases in flowing through the regenerator, and it is important to keep this pressure drop small. The resistance of the regenerator to flow could easily be so great as to offset the theoretical gain of efficiency due to regeneration. As a consequence, regenerators are likely to be relatively large and costly.

The effectiveness of the regenerator is defined as

(r)
$$\eta_r = \frac{\text{Actual amount of heat transferred}}{\text{Amount that could be transferred reversibly}}.$$

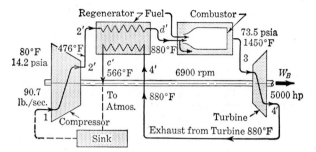

Fig. 62. *Diagrammatic Layout with Regeneration.*

Considering the actual points 2′ and 4′, Fig. 63, a reversible transfer of heat (§ 36) would result in the air being heated from 2′ to d and in the exhaust gases being cooled from 4′ to c. Actually, however, the air is heated only to some state d′ and the gases are cooled to some state c′. Thus, the effectiveness of the regenerator in terms of the states shown in Fig. 63 is

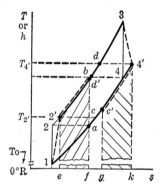

(s)
$$\eta_r = \frac{h_{d'} - h_{2'}}{h_{4'} - h_c},$$

which applies when the mass of fuel is negligible, with or without pressure drop in the heat exchanger if d′ is the actual state of the departing air (because $Q_{air} = h_{d'} - h_{2'}$ for steady flow, $\Delta K = 0$). If the analysis of the cycle is being made for the actual substances, we note that the denominator of (s) applies to the products of combustion. If the products are considered to have the same properties as air (a fair approximation in the gas turbine) and if the variation of specific heat

Fig. 63. *Imperfect Regeneration without Fluid Friction.* Area e-2′-d′-f = area k-4′-c′-g.

is to be ignored (not justifiable), use $\Delta h = c_p\Delta T$ and cancel c_p. The student should write the equations for heats added to and rejected from *external* sources (heat reservoirs) and for the work of an *air cycle* with regenerative heating.

At a particular ceiling temperature, the efficiency curve plotted against pressure ratio for a Brayton cycle with regenerator and with fluid friction rises to a peak at some pressure ratio and then decreases. Such a pressure ratio is about 3.5 for a turbine inlet temperature of 1500°F.

105. Other Variations of the Brayton Cycle. Intercooling in the compression process is used to save work, theoretically just as described in § 85. This feature together with regeneration is diagrammatically pictured in Fig. 64. The various energy quantities can be written by inspection of the

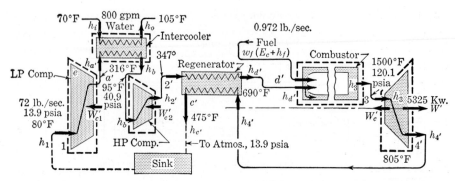

Fig. 64. *Intercooling and Regeneration.* The properties shown are typical values as rounded off from actual test data. Consider w_f as lb. fuel per lb. air. (See Fig. 65.)

individual systems in Fig. 64. For negligible changes in kinetic energy;

$$W_c = h_1 - h_{a'} + h_b - h_{2'} \text{ Btu/lb. air,}$$
$$W_t = h_3 - h_{4'} \text{ Btu/lb. products.}$$

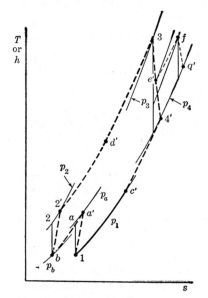

Fig. 65. *Intercooling, Regeneration, and Reheating.* The cycle 1-a'-b-2'-d'-3-4'-c'-1 shows the Ts representation of the cycle in Fig. 64. The reheating is $e'f$, so that the two turbine expansions are 3-e' and fq'.

Although the substance in the turbine is the products of combustion (not air) and the mass flow in the turbine is $1 + w_f$ lb. for each pound of air entering the compressor (w_f lb. fuel/lb. air), preliminary studies are often made on the basis of air alone and also, since the amount of fuel used in gas turbines is of the order of only 1% of the total mass flow, on the basis of $w_f = 0$. The use of this small proportion of fuel is necessary in order that the temperature rise during combustion remains within permissible limits.

The compression process may be (and is) broken into more than two stages if it should be economical and advantageous. In addition to intercooling during compression, the turbine may be divided into two turbines. In between these two turbines, we may arrange to burn more fuel. That is, the gases pass through another combustor and are reheated to approximately the original maximum temperature. The exhaust naturally leaves at a higher temperature, but some of this extra energy can be recovered via a regenerator. A second combustor, together with intercooling and regeneration, is depicted on the Ts plane in Fig. 65. In this figure, the dotted line $e'f$ represents the second combustor process and fg' represents the second turbine expansion. A common plan is to design the high pressure (HP) turbine $(3e')$ with just enough power to drive the compressor and to use the lower pressure (LP) turbine (fg') on a separate shaft to drive the generator (or do other work); but separate shafts are not necessary in order to use this idea. If the plan is used, however, the work of the HP turbine is equal to the work of compression plus whatever energy is needed to overcome friction in these two components, Fig. 65.

106. Jet Propulsion. Let us consider a turbo-jet engine, Fig. 67. If this engine can drive a plane at a speed of v_i fps in still air, the relative effect is the same as if the engine is on a stationary test block and receives air at an initial speed of v_i fps. If the entrance to the compressor is built as a *diffuser,* which is a passageway designed to convert kinetic energy into enthalpy (the reverse of a nozzle), it utilizes the kinetic energy of the entering air to compress it. This compression is called the **ram effect** (when the engine is moving through the air) and is pictured by io, Fig. 66, as an isentropic compression. If the air is moving slowly at point o $(K_o = 0)$ just as it enters the compressor, it carries energy h_o and the steady flow energy equation gives

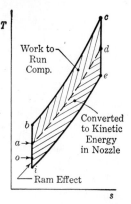

Fig. 66. Ideal Turbo-jet Cycle. The kinetic energy represented by *iade* is relative to the engine, which may be moving.

(t) $$h_o = h_i + K_i \text{ Btu/lb.},$$

where K_i is the initial kinetic energy (or, for the moving plane, the kinetic energy of the air stream corresponding to the speed of the plane, which is to say that it is the *kinetic energy relative to the plane*). The enthalpy h_o, for the stream at rest, is called the **stagnation enthalpy.** Since the diffuser is not 100% efficient in converting kinetic energy into enthalpy, the actual rise in pressure is not as large as the isentropic rise. Let o' (not shown on Fig. 66; somewhat below o) be the actual state to which the air is compressed; then the

$$\text{Ram or pressure coefficient} = \frac{p_{o'} - p_i}{p_o - p_i};$$

that is, the ratio of the actual pressure rise to that which would occur during isentropic compression to the stagnation state.

At o, compression begins in the compressor and is completed at b, Fig. 66. The process in the combustor is the same as before, and gases enter the turbine in state c, expanding to d and doing enough work $abcd$ to drive the compressor. (The areas in Fig. 66 are not to scale.) Leaving the turbine in state d, the gases expand in the nozzle according to the energy relation, Fig. 66,

$$h_d - h_e = K_e - K_d;$$ [NOZZLE]

that is, the drop in enthalpy $-\Delta h$ is converted into kinetic energy ΔK. If the gases enter the nozzle at low velocity, which is likely, we may let $K_d = 0$. Our discussion is on the assumption that the jet gases expand in the nozzle to exactly atmospheric pressure at that location. If the engine is stationary, the energy diagram is as shown in Fig. 67. No *net* work is done. The work quantities W_t and W_c are an interchange of work within the system. If the engine is in an airplane moving at a speed of v_i fps in still air, level

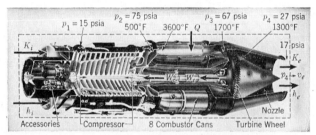

Courtesy General Electric, Schenectady, N. Y.

Fig. 67. Turbo-jet Engine. The energy diagram ignores the mass of fuel. There are 12 stages of compression, $r_k = 5.05$. Normal thrust on test is 4730 lb. at 7630 rpm with fuel consumption of 1.04 lb/hr-lb.; cruising thrust is 3700 lb. at 7000 rpm with fuel consumption of 1.03 lb./hr-lb. The temperatures and pressures given are roughly typical.

flight, an observer *on the plane* "sees" the same energy diagram. In this situation, the velocities v_i and v_e are initial and exit velocities relative to the plane, the velocities as the observer sees them. The "heat added" to the air in the combustors is the energy released by the chemical reaction of the fuel and oxygen, as this observer sees the power system, and according to our approximation is taken as $Q = w_f q_l$, where w_f is the mass of fuel (per pound of air, if the energy equation is set up on this basis; note that $1 + w_f \approx 1$ lb.):

$$h_i + K_i + w_f q_l = (1 + w_f)(K_e + h_e) \approx K_e + h_e \text{ Btu/lb. air.}$$

Since this equation does not contain a work term, we may resort to another principle to find the work.

107. Work from the Impulse-Momentum Principle. The stream moving past turbine blades does work by virtue of the continuous change of

momentum of the stream. The force exerted by an airplane or ship propeller exists by virtue of the fluid's change of momentum brought about by
the propeller. The propulsive force of jets exists for the same reason.
From your mechanics, you recall $a = dv/dt$ and $F = wa/g_o$, which latter
equation is Newton's law that the resultant force F in any direction is equal
to the mass times the acceleration in that direction. Together, these relations result in

(u) $$F \, dt = \frac{w}{g_o} \, dv,$$

which is the famous impulse $(F \, dt)$-momentum $(w \, dv/g_o)$ principle, where
w/g_o is the mass in slugs. If the mass rate of flow is constant in the air
cycle, we have the propulsive force of the jet engine as

(53) $$F = \frac{w}{g_o} \, (v_e - v_i),$$

where the time interval is taken as $\Delta t = 1$ sec. (that is, w lb./sec. is the constant mass rate of flow, v_e and v_i fps are the exit and initial velocities, respectively. The right-hand side of equation (53) is the rate of change of momentum of a stream in steady flow undergoing a velocity change of Δv. We
recall that momentum is a vector quantity* but these vectors are in the same
direction in jet engines. In applying equation (53) to a stream passing
through a moving body, an airplane, use the velocities as those *relative to
the moving body*. From the viewpoint of mechanics, F in (53) is the force
necessary to accelerate the stream from a relative velocity of v_i to a relative
velocity of v_e; but action and reaction are equal, so it is also a force on the
plane. If the plane is moving with a speed of v_p fps, the work done by F
lb. is Fv_p ft-lb./sec., or from equation (53),

(v) $$W = Fv_p = \frac{wv_p}{g_o} \, (v_e - v_i) \text{ ft-lb./sec.,}$$

where v_i is the initial relative velocity of the air with respect to the plane.
If w lb./sec. is the *actual* mass of air and if the velocities are *actual* relative
velocities, this equation gives the approximate actual propulsive work, or
rate of work, in moving the plane at a constant speed v_p (mass of fuel neglected). Or it would be the instantaneous rate of work if the plane should
be accelerating with an instantaneous speed of v_p. Orient yourself to the
fact that no work is done by F at $v_p = 0$; and that for a particular value of
the thrust F, the greater v_p, the greater the work. Thus, a jet engine producing a thrust force of 5000 lb. in the direction of motion would be develop-

* See Faires and Chambers, *Analytic Mechanics*, Macmillan.

ing horsepower as follows, for example:

$$\text{At } v_p = 550 \text{ fps, hp} = \frac{(5000)(550)}{550} = 5000 \text{ hp,}$$

$$\text{At } v_p = 1100 \text{ fps, hp} = \frac{(5000)(1100)}{550} = 10,000 \text{ hp.}$$

(550 fps $\approx$ 370 mph; 550 ft-lb./hp-sec.)

At an altitude where $p = 8$ psia, $T = 500°$R, and for $v_e = 2500$ fps and $v_p = v_i = 1100$ fps, the 5000-lb. thrust would require a flow of about 160,000 cfm; check it for yourself, using (53) and $pV = wRT$.

The thermal efficiency of turbo-jet engines is likely to be low compared to reciprocating types, but, especially for airplanes, there are some offsetting advantages, such as the smaller frontal area to produce less air resistance and less weight per horsepower developed in normal flight. Also since the efficiency of a propeller drops rapidly after some speed, say about 400-450 mph, the turbo-jet *drive* actually becomes more efficient than a reciprocating-engine-propeller drive would be at some high speed. In commercial planes, speeds of 500-600 mph with turbo-jet drives appear to be economical on long-range flight. At and above plane speeds of Mach 1, the velocity of sound in the air surrounding the plane, jet propulsion is necessary. The practical limiting speed of travel with turbo-jet engines is expected to be about Mach 1.5 to 2.

There are other means of jet propulsion than the turbo-jet; namely, ram jets and rockets. The ram jet becomes practical when the speed of body is high, well above Mach 1, say Mach 3 or about 2000 mph. At these high speeds, the ram effect produces enough compression of the entering air to develop a cycle as previously described, the ideal prototype being the Brayton cycle. Typical data for a speed through air of 2000 fps are: combustion temperature, 3600°F; jet temperature at exhaust, 2200°F; jet exhaust velocity, 4000 fps. The German V-1 buzz bomb was propelled by a ram jet engine in which the firing was intermittent, giving rise to the buzzing. The rocket is a jet propulsion device which not only carries its own fuel but also the reactant for the fuel, as liquid oxygen.

108. Closure. Inasmuch as there are books written on the subjects of gas engines and jet engines, it is easily understood that this presentation is necessarily limited in scope. Development of gas turbine engines for various purposes, for example, as an automotive drive, is being carried on actively in many laboratories, and progress has been and probably will continue to be exceptionally rapid. It is easy to understand that the various ideas of this chapter might be combined in many different ways, giving a number of modifications of the Brayton cycle. Moreover, combinations of the gas turbine engines with other apparatus, such as steam cycles, might be advisable. Since this is so, the beginner's endeavor should be to master each idea so that he can intelligently analyze any combination, or so that he might perhaps devise a useful combination.

SELECTED REFERENCES

Cohen and Rogers, *Gas Turbine Theory*, Longmans, Green.
Dusinberre, G. M., *Gas Turbine Power*, International Textbook.
Fraas, A. P., *Combustion Engines*, McGraw-Hill.
Godsey and Young, *Gas Turbines for Aircraft*, McGraw-Hill.
Jennings and Rogers, *Gas Turbine Analysis and Practice*, McGraw-Hill.
Lee, John F., *Theory and Design of Steam and Gas Turbines*, McGraw-Hill.
Sorensen, H. A., *Gas Turbines*, Ronald Press.
Vincent, E. T., *The Theory and Design of Gas Turbines and Jet Engines*, McGraw-Hill.
Zucrow, M. J., *Principles of Jet Propulsion*, John Wiley.

PROBLEMS

NOTE. *Because the air table allows for the variation of specific heat and because of the high temperatures in gas turbines, results are much more accurate if the air table is used. Where the properties of air are involved in the following solutions, the answers are for table solutions unless otherwise indicated in the statement. Since there is something to be said for the practice in using specific heats, both methods of solution are desirable from the standpoint of learning thermodynamics.*

161. A system operating as a cycle receives 1000 Btu/min. and produces a gross work of 6 hp. The pump work necessary to maintain circulation is 1945 ft-lb/min. Determine the heat rejected and the thermal efficiency of the cycle. *Ans.* 748.1 Btu/min., 25.44%.

162. A gas turbine is to be designed for air intake at 80°F and 14.7 psia. The rate of heat supply is 19,000 Btu per min. and the highest cycle temperature is to be 1100°F. For the ideal Brayton cycle with cold air as the working substance (k is constant at 1.4), determine (a) the temperature and pressure at the end of compression for the maximum work output, (b) the thermal efficiency, and (c) the horsepower developed. *Ans.* (a) 458°F, 94.1 psia, (b) 41.2%, (c) 185 hp.

163. A Brayton cycle has an adiabatic compression ratio of 4, the process beginning at 80°F and 15 psia. At the end of heating, $t_3 = 1080°F$. Considering the system as 1 lb. of cold air (k is constant at 1.4) and using specific heats, compute (a) t_2 and p_2, (b) the works of the compressor and turbine, and the net work, (c) Q_A, Q_R, ΣQ, and e. (d) Find the mep. (e) For a flow of air of 100,000 cfm at the initial state, what ideal horsepower is being developed? *Ans.* (a) 481°F, 104.2 psia, (b) $W_m = 61.3$ Btu/lb., (c) $e = 42.6\%$, (d) 17.9 psi, (e) 10,850 hp.

164. (a) If the highest permissible temperature in a gas turbine is 1540°F and if $t_1 = 70°F$, what compression ratio and pressure ratio result in the maximum ideal work (constant specific heats)? (b) For the ratios found in (a), what are the net work and thermal efficiency? (Answers by table. Note that while $p_3/p_4 = p_2/p_1$, it is *not* true that $v_3/v_4 = v_2/v_1$ when specific heats vary.) (c) If the compression ratio found above is doubled, what would be the work and thermal efficiency of the ideal air cycle (same temperature limits)? What percentage is this of the maximum work?

Ans. (a) 5.44, 10.52, (b) 120.9 Btu/lb., 47.2%, (c) $e = 58.4\%$.

165. The following data apply to a gas turbine (Fig. 58): $p_1 = 14.7$ psia and $t_1 = 80°F$; after isentropic compression, $t_2 = 458°F$; after constant pressure combustion, $t_3 = 1100°F$; the compression efficiency is 82%; the engine efficiency is 84%. Determine (a) the actual enthalpy $h_{2'}$ after compression, (b) the actual enthalpy $h_{4'}$ after expansion, (c) the net work W', (d) the actual thermal efficiency. (e) Compute the work of the corresponding ideal cycle and find the percentage of the ideal work which has been lost.

Ans. (a) 240.9 Btu/lb., (b) 252.6 Btu/lb. (c) 20.7 Btu/lb., (d) 14.34%, (e) 68.9%.

166. In a gas turbine unit, air from the compressor enters the combustor at 400°F and leaves at 1540°F. Of a fuel with $q_l = 18,600$ Btu/lb., 5% passes through unburned. The heat loss from the combustor is 800 Btu/lb. of fuel. Sketch an energy diagram showing a complete energy balance. Now ignoring the enthalpy of the liquid fuel and the effect of the mass of fuel, and treating the products as though they have the properties of air, determine the amount of fuel used per pound of air. What is the efficiency of the combustor, defined as the actual increase in enthalpy divided by the ideal increase (no losses)?

Ans. 0.0177 lb./lb. air, 90.5%.

167. The following data correspond approximately to those for a General Electric gas turbine: 4690 bhp; $q_l = 17,400$ Btu/lb.; intake at 14.5 psia and 60°F; pressure ratio, 6; turbine inlet temperature, 1400°F; compression efficiency, 83%; engine efficiency, 85%. For the air cycle with friction, find (a) the actual net work of the fluid W', $h_{2'}$, and e' (ignore the effect of the mass of fuel), (b) $h_{4'}$, $t_{4'}$, (c) the percentage of ideal net work lost by virtue of the imperfect processes in compressor and turbine. (d) Assume that the shaft (brake) work is $0.95W'$ and determine the air flow, lb./sec., (e) fuel used, lb./hr. and lb./bhp-hr. See Fig. 68.

Ans. (a) $e' = 22.2\%$, (b) 814°F, (c) 46.5%, (d) 67.4 lb./sec., (e) 0.694 lb./bhp-hr.

168. A jet-engine-driven plane is moving at a constant speed of 700 mph at an altitude of 30,000 ft. where $p_i = 4.36$ psia and $t_i = 412°R$. The engine thrust is 3200 lb.; air flow is 79 lb./sec.; ram coefficient is 80%; $r_p = 4.2$ in the compressor; turbine inlet temperature is 1500°F; engine efficiency of turbine is 75%. Find (a) the propulsive power, (b) the exhaust jet velocity relative to the plane. For the ideal cycle, compute (c) the stagnation pressure at entry to the compressor, (d) ideal compressor work, (e) ideal exhaust temperature (from turbine), (f) the ideal enthalpy drop in the jet nozzle and the ideal relative velocity at exit from the jet nozzle (expansion to atmospheric pressure from zero initial velocity).

Ans. (a) 5960 hp, (b) 2330 fps, (c) 7.74 psia, (d) 60.95 Btu/lb., (e) 1277°F, (f) 2740 fps.

169. For the gas turbine cycle in problem **164,** determine the average value of k during the process 2-3 and during 3-4 from the air table properties. (Note that the value of k during 1-2 is virtually that for cold air, 1.4.)

Ans. 1.35.

170–180. These numbers may be used for other problems.

8

INTERNAL COMBUSTION ENGINES

109. Introduction. The internal combustion engine is relatively new. The earliest attempts to build such an engine were based on the use of gun powder. Barsanti and Matteucci built a free-piston engine in 1857 which operated as follows. An explosion drove a piston vertically upward. As it started down under the action of gravity, it engaged a ratchet which was so connected as to turn a shaft. Such a clumsy machine was doomed to failure, although Otto and Langen successfully marketed a number of free-piston engines about 1867. In 1860, Lenoir proposed and built an engine without compression. This engine drew in a charge of gas and air at atmospheric pressure for half a stroke, at which point the mixture was burned. The resulting rise in pressure provided the motive force to complete this stroke, to return the piston to the end of the next stroke, to exhaust the burned gases, and to bring the piston again to the point of burning a new charge. While this engine was used for a while, its efficiency was too low for it to be an economical source of power.

Although Beau de Rochas, a Frenchman, worked out the theory and gave the conditions for high efficiency in 1862, it remained for Nicholas A. Otto (1832–1891) to build a successful engine in 1876 after he had independently invented the same cycle. This engine was called the silent Otto engine, but the word "silent" should not be taken in a literal sense. Otto was born in Holzhausen, Germany, and was a partner in a gas engine manufacturing plant at the time of his famous invention.

To circumvent Otto's patents, Sir Dugald Clerk, born in Glasgow in 1854, invented the two-stroke-cycle engine, which was first exhibited in 1881. In these early stages of the internal combustion engine, rotative speeds of the order of 200 rpm were typical. The German Gottlieb Daimler (1834–1899) was the first to conceive of small, relatively high-speed engines for greater power from a particular size, say 1000 rpm (vs. 4000 rpm and more for today's automotive engines), and he made them work by improved hot-bulb ignition. The "high-speed" engine made the automobile a practicable idea.

We have seen that the highest temperature in the gas turbine cycle, in the combustor, is sharply limited. The combustor is subjected to this temperature continuously during operation. On the other hand, since the reciprocating internal combustion engine (ICE) is subjected to the highest temperature intermittently, just after the fuel has been fired, temperature has not been much of a problem. We may use air/fuel ratios such that the amount of air is close to that which is ideally required for combustion, and let the temperature go where it may. Since the highest temperature exists for only a small portion of the cycle, the interval during the remainder of the cycle can be used for water or air cooling the cylinder in order to prevent the metal from becoming dangerously hot.

The widespread use of internal combustion engines in automobiles, on the farm, in industrial plants, on ships, in power plants, is common knowledge. Because these engines are used so much, the ideal cycles for them are particularly significant. The fuels used are natural or manufactured gas, gasoline, kerosene, oil, alcohol, and others. The most common fuels are gas, gasoline, and fuel oil.

110. The Four-Stroke Cycle. The *four-stroke cycle* is one wherein four strokes of the piston, two revolutions, are required to complete a cycle. The sequence of events, pictured in Fig. 68, is the same for any four-stroke ICE, namely:

1. A *suction stroke,* drawing fuel and air into an Otto engine, §111, or drawing air only into a Diesel engine, §126,
2. A *compression stroke,* Fig. 68(b),
3. Ignition of a fuel already in the cylinder, as by a spark plug, or the self-ignition of fuel which ideally is injected into the cylinder at the end of the compression stroke (the burning of the fuel produces energy supplied to the system),
4. An *expansion stroke* or *power stroke,* during which positive work is done, and
5. An *exhaust stroke,* during which most of the products of combustion are pushed from the cylinder; then the cycle repeats.

The end positions of a piston in any reciprocating machine are called **head-end dead center,** or in the automotive industry the **top dead center** (TDC), Fig. 68(a) and (c), and the **crank-end dead center** or **bottom dead center** (BDC), Fig. 68(b) and (d). Figure 69 reveals some of the internal construction of an automotive engine.

111. The Otto Cycle. The Otto cycle, which is the ideal prototype of most small internal combustion engines, is one wherein it is imagined that *the combustion process takes place instantaneously at top dead center to give a constant volume combustion* of the fuel (or constant volume process of heat added in the equivalent air cycle). The Otto engine may be analyzed either as a flow device or as a closed cycle.

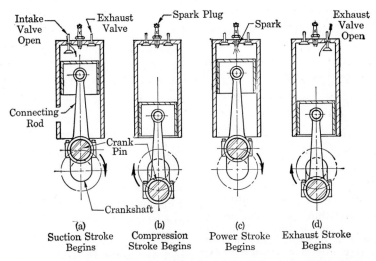

Intake Valve Open — Exhaust Valve — Spark Plug — Spark — Exhaust Valve Open

Connecting Rod

Crank Pin

Crankshaft

(a)
Suction Stroke Begins

(b)
Compression Stroke Begins

(c)
Power Stroke Begins

(d)
Exhaust Stroke Begins

Fig. 68. Four-Stroke Cycle. This diagrammatic representation shows a spark plug which ignites the fuel after compression. The same sequence of events occurs in the 4-stroke-cycle Diesel engine, except that the air is compressed to a temperature high enough to cause the fuel to burn without spark ignition.

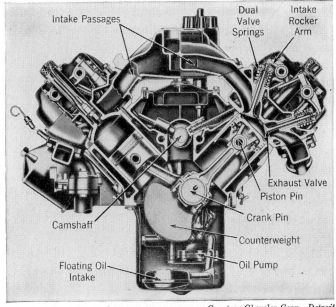

Intake Passages — Dual Valve Springs — Intake Rocker Arm

Exhaust Valve
Piston Pin

Crank Pin

Camshaft

Counterweight

Floating Oil Intake — Oil Pump

Courtesy Chrysler Corp., Detroit

Fig. 69.   Four-Stroke Automotive Engine.   A $3\frac{7}{16}$x$3\frac{1}{4}$ in. engine.

We note that ideally (no pressure drops, etc.), the suction stroke 0-1 and discharge stroke 1-0, Fig. 70, cancel one another, so to speak. The positive work under 0-1 is equal to the negative work under 1-0, and these works correspond to the ideal flow works done in getting the air into and out of an open system. Moreover, the ideal open system and the ideal closed system reject the same amount of heat, according to the first law, because in each case, if the cycles are comparable, the same heat is added and the same work is done; hence, from $Q_A - Q_R = W$, each must reject the same heat Q_R to the sink. Therefore, we see that the analysis of an ideal open air cycle is the same as that of an ideal closed air cycle. (Such analyses are called *air standard analyses*. The heat rejected at constant volume 4-1, Fig. 70, is the same as that rejected to the atmosphere *after* the gases leave the engine when the valve opens at 4 in the open cycle.)

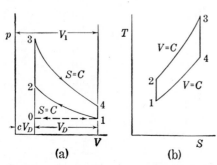

Fig. 70. Ideal Otto Cycle. The process 0–1 in (a) is a process during which fresh air is drawn in, or burned gases are discharged (1–0). It is a process of flow wherein the mass of substance varies. It is not shown on the *TS* plane, because the properties of the substance do not change from 0 to 1. Neglecting the frictional effects, as one would in the ideal case, we notice that the combination 0–1 and 1–0 has no effect whatsoever on the net work or efficiency.

Analyzing the machine as a flow device with the simplification that the working substance is air at all times (no products of combustion), we observe that the incoming energies, Fig. 71, are the chemical energy of the fuel E_c, the internal energy of the entering substance U_1 (air in the air standard), and the flow work W_{f0-1} of the fluid as it crosses the system's boundary at entrance. Outgoing energies are the internal energy U_4 (of products in the real engine, of air in the air standard), the work W, and the work W_{f1-0} in pushing the working substance from the cylinder 1-0, Fig. 70.

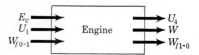

Fig. 71. Energy Diagram. All of the chemical energy E_c $(=Q_A)$ theoretically is equivalent to the transferred heat during the constant volume combustion.

$$W_{f0-1} = W_{f1-0}. \qquad \Delta KE = 0.$$

In the ideal engine, there is no loss of heat, such as actually occurs, to the water jacket of a real engine. Since as previously explained $W_{f0-1} = W_{f1-0}$ and since equivalent heat added Q_A to the ideal cycle is equal to the chemical energy of the fuel, $E_c = Q_A$, we get the energy equation in the form of energy entering equal to energy departing as

$$U_1 + Q_A = U_4 + W.$$

Solving for W, we find

(a) $$W = Q_A - (U_4 - U_1).$$

Compare this equation with equation (51), § 95, and note that it is in the form $Q_A - Q_R$, where $Q_R = U_4 - U_1$. The simplest air standard would be for constant specific heats. On this basis, $Q_A = U_3 - U_2 = wc_v(T_3 - T_2)$, the heat transferred during the constant volume heating 2-3, Fig. 70; and $Q_R = U_4 - U_1 = wc_v(T_4 - T_1)$ for an ideal gas. Substituting these values in (a), we get

(b) $$W = (U_3 - U_2) - (U_4 - U_1) = wc_v(T_3 - T_2) - wc_v(T_4 - T_1).$$
[VARIABLE SPECIFIC HEATS]   [CONSTANT SPECIFIC HEATS]

The thermal efficiency, W/Q_A, for the Otto engine is (constant c_v)

(c) $$e = \frac{W}{Q_A} = 1 - \frac{wc_v(T_4 - T_1)}{wc_v(T_3 - T_2)} = 1 - \frac{T_4 - T_1}{T_3 - T_2}.$$

Using the TV relation for an isentropic process (§ 58), we have

(d) $$\frac{T_4}{T_3} = \left(\frac{V_3}{V_4}\right)^{k-1} \quad \text{or} \quad T_4 = T_3\left(\frac{V_3}{V_4}\right)^{k-1} = T_3\left(\frac{V_2}{V_1}\right)^{k-1},$$

since $V_3 = V_2$ and $V_4 = V_1$, Fig. 70. Also

(e) $$\frac{T_1}{T_2} = \left(\frac{V_2}{V_1}\right)^{k-1} \quad \text{or} \quad T_1 = T_2\left(\frac{V_2}{V_1}\right)^{k-1}.$$

Substituting these values of T_1 and T_4 into (c), we find

(54A) $$e = 1 - \frac{\left(\frac{V_2}{V_1}\right)^{k-1}(T_3 - T_2)}{T_3 - T_2} = 1 - \left(\frac{V_2}{V_1}\right)^{k-1}.$$

Let the compression ratio V_1/V_2 be represented by r; then

(54B) $$e = 1 - \frac{1}{r^{k-1}}$$
[OTTO CYCLE]

A realistic approach to the energy flow and transformations would include an accounting of the enthalpy of the fuel, of the heating value corrected to the proper temperature instead of the chemical energy, of the dilution of the incoming fluid by the residual gases left in the clearance volume, of the products of combustion instead of air.*

* See Faires, *Thermodynamics*, Macmillan, and Hersey, Eberhardt, and Hottel, *Thermodynamic properties of the working fluid in internal combustion engines*, SAE Jour., Vol. 39, p. 409.

112. Ideal Standards of Comparison. In equation (54), we have arrived at an important characteristic of the Otto cycle, to wit, that its efficiency with constant specific heats depends only on the value of k and the compression ratio r, Fig. 72. The efficiency of the real engine is subject to many other variables, of course, including simple thermodynamic factors such as the initial temperature and the temperature at 3 (amount of heat added). Nevertheless, one of the principal aims in the development of spark ignition engines over the years has been to increase the compression ratio, whose value is now limited largely by the detonation characteristics of the fuel (§ 122). Now if we use the air standard as a basis of comparison, we may consider the air as "cold air," $k = 1.4$, and the corresponding standard is called the **cold-air standard**. Let $r = 6$ and let the actual value of the thermal efficiency be $e' = 21\%$ by test, then we might say that the actual engine is

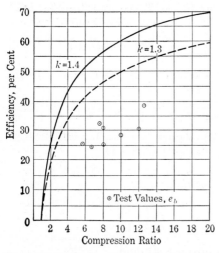

Fig. 72. Efficiency Versus Compression Ratio, Otto Cycle. The solid curve is for cold air, $k = 1.4$; dotted curve for hot air, $k = 1.3$. The test values, computed on the lower heating value and taken at random from the literature, suggest that actual efficiency tends to improve with ideal efficiency.

$$\frac{e'}{e} = \frac{0.21}{1 - 1/r^{k-1}} = \frac{0.21}{1 - 1/6^{0.4}} = 41\%$$

as efficient as the ideal engine.

The cold-air standard is unfair to the engine however, because operation is inevitably with rather hot gas most of the time. To keep the computations simple, some value of k, which is roughly the average throughout the cycle, is sometimes assumed, and the cycle is analyzed as explained above except that k is some value such as 1.3 with the corresponding [equation (26)] value of c_v (and c_p if needed, Diesel cycle). If a hot-air value of k is used, the standard is said to be a **hot-air standard**. Again, let $r = 6$ and $e' = 21\%$ by test; then as before, except that $k = 1.3$, we may say that the actual engine is

$$\frac{e'}{e} = \frac{0.21}{1 - 1/r^{k-1}} = \frac{0.21}{1 - 1/6^{0.3}} = 50.5\%$$

as efficient as the ideal. This higher ratio of the efficiencies is a better indicator (than 41%) of the possible margin of improvement as the actual engine might be made to approach the ideal, and it is a fairer indicator of how good the actual engine is.

Another alternative is to integrate $\int c_v\, dT$ with variable specific heat equations. A much less tedious approach is to use the air table, Table VI, and obtain a **variable specific-heat air standard.** Of the air standards, this one is the best.

Still another alternative is to consider the actual fuel-air mixture and the products of combustion, including the pheomenon of dissociation, if any. This method results in the most realistic standard of comparison, and certainly there could be little reason left for the real engine to complain about being compared with such a standard, which we shall call the **real mixture standard.** Such calculations as are involved would be quite tedious and time consuming were it not for available aids—charts giving properties of real mixtures allowing for dissociation and the *Gas Tables* which do not account for dissociation.

113. Clearance Volume. The *clearance volume* is the volume V_2, Fig. 70, of the combustion space when the piston is on TDC position. It is usually expressed as the **per-cent clearance** c, the percentage being of the displacement volume V_D. Thus the clearance volume is cV_D, Fig. 70, and the compression ratio is

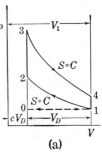

(f) $$r = \frac{V_1}{V_2} = \frac{V_D + cV_D}{cV_D} = \frac{1 + c}{c}.$$

This equation shows that for a particular engine displacement, the compression ratio may be increased by decreasing the clearance volume, and vice versa. It may be used to compute the clearance for a given compression ratio, or the compression ratio for a given clearance.

Fig. 70.   Repeated.

114. Example. An ideal Otto engine with 25% clearance operates on 1 lb. of air with an average value of $k = 1.3$. In Fig. 70, $p_1 = 14$ psia, $t_1 = 120°F$, and $t_3 = 4740°F$. (a) What is the displacement volume? (b) Find t_2, p_2, and p_3. (c) Find Q_A, Q_R, and e. (d) Find the mep of the ideal cycle and the percentage approach to perfection (commonly called engine efficiency, §§ 99 and 119), if the actual thermal efficiency is 20%.

SOLUTION. (a) First find V_1 and r.

$$V_1 = \frac{wRT_1}{p_1} = \frac{(53.3)(580)}{(14)(144)} = 15.33 \text{ cu. ft.}$$
$$r = (1 + c)/c = 1.25/0.25 = 5 = V_1/V_2.$$

From this we find

$$V_2 = V_1/r = 15.33/5 = 3.066 \text{ cu. ft.}$$
$$V_D = V_1 - V_2 = 15.33 - 3.066 = 12.26 \text{ cu. ft.}$$

(b) Use the TV relation for an isentropic process and Charles' law.

$$\frac{T_2}{T_1} = \left(\frac{V_1}{V_2}\right)^{k-1}, \quad \text{or} \quad T_2 = (580)(5^{1.3-1}) = 940°\text{R} = 480°\text{F}.$$

From $p_1V_1^k = p_2V_2^k$,

$$p_2 = p_1(V_1/V_2)^k = (14)(5^{1.3}) = 113.4 \text{ psia}.$$

From Charles' law $(T_3 = 4740 + 460 = 5200°\text{R})$,

$$p_3 = p_2(T_3/T_2) = (113.4)(5200/940) = 627 \text{ psia}.$$

(c) First, we must find c_v corresponding to the value of $k = 1.3$.

$$c_v = \frac{R}{J(k-1)} = \frac{53.3}{(778)(1.3-1)} = 0.228$$
$$Q_A = wc_v(T_3 - T_2) = (0.228)(5200 - 940) = 971 \text{ Btu/lb}.$$
$$T_4 = T_3(V_3/V_4)^{k-1} = 5200/5^{0.3} = 3210°\text{R}.$$
$$Q_R = wc_v(T_1 - T_4) = (0.228)(580 - 3210) = -600 \text{ Btu/lb}.$$
$$e = 1 - \frac{1}{r^{k-1}} = 1 - \frac{1}{5^{0.3}} = 38.3\%.$$

Noting that work is $W = eQ_A$, we find from equation (49)

$$p_m = \frac{W}{V_D} = \frac{eQ_A}{V_D} = \frac{(0.383)(971)(778)}{(12.26)(144)} = 164 \text{ psi}.$$
$$\frac{\text{Actual thermal efficiency}}{\text{Ideal thermal efficiency}} = \frac{0.24}{0.383} = 62.7\%.$$

It would be a good idea for the reader to note that during the compression process 1-2, the air is practically cold air, $k \approx 1.4$; sometime during the expansion, $k < 1.3$ if the average is 1.3, because the air in the air standard is hot. It would be revealing if the reader would solve this problem by using the air table.

115. The Indicator Card. It will be interesting to study briefly the degree in which an actual indicator card, Fig. 73, departs from the Otto cycle. After the piston has completed the exhaust stroke, the pressure in the cylinder is somewhat above atmospheric pressure, point 0. At the beginning of the suction stroke 0-m-1, there is first a small expansion to the suction pressure which is below atmospheric pressure because of the frictional resistance to flow around the valves and through the passageways. The compression 1-2 is not adiabatic because the cooling medium around the cylinder, air or water, and the previously high temperatures in the cylinder, 3 to 4, effect some transfer of heat and because there is some leakage of gases past the piston.

Ignition, by means of a spark plug or other device, usually occurs before the piston reaches the TDC position, and since it takes an appreciable time for all of the fuel to burn, combustion continues for a short time after the piston begins its power stroke. This accounts for the slope of the combustion line 2-3 and the rounded top. The actual maximum pressure and temperature at 3 are much lower than the corresponding pressure and temperature in the cold-air standard at c for several reasons: (1) the actual average specific heat is much higher than that assumed in the cold-air standard; (2) the movement of the piston increases the volume, which reduces the pressure; (3) heat is transferred during this period through the cylinder head and walls; (4) the pressure p_1 at the beginning of the compression process is below atmospheric pressure at a; (5) the leakage past the piston and through valves which are not tightly closed reduces the amount of working substance; (6) some energy is passing out as work; (7) the combustion is incomplete because of inadequate mixing of air and fuel and because of dissociation.

The expansion 3-4 is not adiabatic because of the intentional transfer of heat, a loss we must accept in order to prevent damage to the metal of the engine. The exhaust valve begins to open before the piston reaches the BDC position, for example, with the crank at some 35–45° before center in automobile engines. This early opening allows time for the pressure to drop before the piston starts on the exhaust stroke. Too *late* opening of the exhaust valve will result in a higher exhaust line 4-f-n-0, and therefore less net area enclosed within the diagram (less work done). It is observed that some of the burned gases remain in the clearance volume, so that at point 1 there is a volume V_1 of combustible mixture diluted with the amount of products at 0.

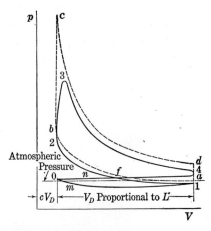

Fig. 73. *Indicator Card, Otto Engine.* **The dotted cycle is the corresponding cold-air Otto cycle. See Fig. 41.**

We notice, Fig. 73, that there is a power cycle described in a clockwise direction, f-2-3-4; and there is a loop f-n-0-m-1-f, which is described in a counterclockwise direction, representing work done *on* the substance. This reversed loop is the result of fluid friction, and it can be reduced in area by generously sizing passages and valve openings. The *net* work of the indicator card is represented by the area of the clockwise loop minus the area of the counterclockwise loop. This *net* area is automatically obtained when a planimeter, Fig. 42, is used to trace it in a continuous path. Figure 74 shows other indicator cards. See § 117.

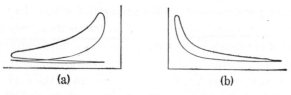

(a)   (b)

Fig. 74. Indicator Cards. These cards are drawn to different scales. Card (a) is from a 4-stroke-cycle gas (not gasoline) engine operating approximately on the Otto cycle. Card (b) is from a 3000-hp, 2-stroke-cycle, 6-cylinder Diesel engine.

116. Brake Power. The name *brake work* came about because in the early days of testing small, slow-speed engines, the power output was dissipated in the friction of a brake. Brakes are still used for this purpose over suitable ranges of power and speed. A type known as a *prony brake* is shown in Figs. 75 and 76. When the brake is clamped to the flywheel, Fig. 76, the frictional force $F(=F/2 + F/2$ at the brake shoes) tends to turn the

Fig. 75. Setup for Prony Brake. Compare this photograph with the diagrammatic arrangement of Fig. 76.

brake with the flywheel. However, the knife edge on the beam rests on scales and prevents motion of the brake. The force P, which is weighed by the scales, consists of the reaction produced by friction and a portion of the weight of the brake, called the *tare*—unless there is a counterweight to balance the brake about the center line of the flywheel. To find the tare, support the brake on an *edge* at B and weigh the tare on the scales. Thus, the net force on the scales produced by the frictional moment is $(P - \text{tare})$.

The information obtained from a prony brake test is used to compute the brake horsepower. Thus, the frictional force F acting through one revolution of the flywheel does work (force × distance) $W = F\pi D/12$ ft-lb., where D is expressed in inches (usual practice). The work for one revolution multiplied by n revolutions per minute gives the work in foot-pounds per minute. Dividing this result by 33,000 converts to horsepower; thus

$$\text{(55)} \qquad \text{hp} = \frac{F\pi Dn}{(12)(33,000)} = \frac{F(2\pi r)n}{(12)(33,000)} = \frac{Tn}{63,000},$$

where $T = FD/2$ in-lb. is the frictional torque on the flywheel. The sum of the moments of the forces on the brake about the center of the flywheel gives

$$\frac{FD}{2} = (P - \text{tare})\,L = T$$

where L in inches is the moment arm of the force P. Thus, knowing the dimension L on the brake, we may observe the value of P indicated by the

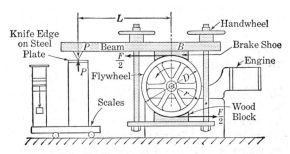

Fig. 76.   Prony Brake.

scales and the number of rpm of the engine and calculate the brake horsepower (bhp) from equation (55). Sometimes the tare is balanced by a counterweight.

Other instruments for measuring shaft work are a hydraulic brake, not illustrated, and a dynamometer, Fig. 77. Because the ordinary type of indicator, Fig. 41, has too much inertia to respond accurately at high speed, it became customary to measure the power output of automotive and other similar engines by dynamometer only. This practice brought about the common use of the **brake mean effective pressure** (bmep) p_{mB}, which is simply the pressure computed from the mep equation (48) using brake horsepower (bhp) instead of indicated horsepower (ihp) (review §§ 82 and 83);

$$\text{(g)} \qquad p_{mB} = \frac{33,000\ bhp}{LAN}.$$

While dynamometer tests are still routine industrial practice, high-speed indicators, utilizing the oscilloscope, and also optical and photographic

Fig. 77. Dynamometer Test of Automotive Engine. The leads carry pressure and temperature signals to the control room. This is an experimental 6-cylinder engine with a compression ratio of $r = 10$ and with 248-cu in. displacement. It delivers 160 bhp.

effects, have been developed so that it is now possible in high-speed engines to obtain the valuable information revealed by an indicator card.

117. Example. At 3000 rpm, a 6-cylinder, 4-stroke gasoline engine, 3¼x4 in. (always bore x stroke), develops 80 bhp. What is the bmep?

SOLUTION. To find the number of indicator cards or power strokes per minute N, we note that there are 2 rev./diagram for each cylinder, or ½ cycle per cylinder in one revolution, which is $6 \times \frac{1}{2} = 3$ cycles or diagrams per revolution for the 6-cylinder engine; therefore, $N = (3)(3000 \text{ rpm}) = 9000$ cpm. From equation (g),

$$p_{mB} = \frac{(33,000)(80)}{(4/12)(\pi 3.25^2/4)(9000)} = 106 \text{ psi.}$$

118. Thermal Efficiencies. The thermal efficiency $e = W/Q_A$ has already been defined. In general terms for a power cycle or engine,

(52A)   Thermal efficiency $= \dfrac{\text{Work output of the system}}{\text{Energy chargeable against the system}}.$

For ideal cycles and engines, the numerator and denominator are ideal values, which are defined for each ideal system studied. In this expression, (52A), the work may be other energy which is 100% available; electricity, for example. There is no single *actual* thermal efficiency, because there are several places where work and power may be measured, Fig. 78. You know about the indicated and brake power. The combined work or combined power, measured by electrical instruments on the instrument panel, say in kilowatts (kw), is the output of the generator. If we let Q'_A represent the actual energy to be charged against a system, we have three actual

Courtesy Ingersoll-Rand Co., New York

Fig. 78. Meaning of Indicated Work, Brake Work, and Combined Work; W_I, W_B, W_K,

thermal efficiencies, the indicated e_i, the brake e_b, and the combined e_k, as follows:

$$(52\text{B}) \qquad e_i = \frac{W_I}{Q_A'}, \qquad e_b = \frac{W_B}{Q_A'}, \qquad e_k = \frac{W_K}{Q_A'}.$$

The symbol Q_A' will be defined for each actual engine analyzed. You recall that we charge the heating value of the fuel against the gas turbine unit, preferably the lower, $w_f q_l$, where q_l is Btu per pound of fuel* and w_f is in units suitable for the units of the numerator of (52B). Thus, a suitable combination of units would be W Btu/lb. of air and w_f lb. fuel/lb. air. If w_f is the **specific fuel consumption** in pounds of fuel per unit of work, the term $w_f q_l$ Btu per unit of work is called the **heat rate,** which is the energy supplied to the system per unit of work. The unit of work is generally the hp.-hr. (2544 Btu) or the kw.-hr. (3412 Btu). From these values, we obtain other important equations for thermal efficiency:

$$(56) \qquad e = \frac{2544 \text{ Btu/hp.-hr.}}{w_f q_l \text{ Btu/hp.-hr.}}, \qquad \text{or} \qquad e = \frac{3412 \text{ Btu/kw.-hr.}}{w_f q_l \text{ Btu/kw.-hr.}},$$

or

$$(56\text{A}) \qquad e_i = \frac{2544}{w_{fi} q_l}, \qquad e_b = \frac{2544}{w_{fb} q_l},$$

where the specific fuel consumption is w_{fi} lb./ihp.-hr. or w_{fb} lb./bhp.-hr. If w_{fk} is in lb. per kw.-hr. output of the generator, we have

$$(56\text{B}) \qquad e_k = \frac{3412}{w_{fk} q_l}.$$

* The higher heating value has been commonly used in this country for ICE.

119. Engine Efficiencies. The engine efficiency η has been defined in connection with gas-turbine units, § 99; in general terms, let it be

$$(57) \quad \text{Engine efficiency } \eta = \frac{\text{Actual work delivered by system}}{\text{Work of the corresponding ideal system}}.$$

Applied to reciprocating internal combustion engines, this definition results in three engine efficiencies corresponding to the three actual works, W_I, W_B, and W_K. Thus for the **brake engine efficiency** η_b, the **indicated engine efficiency** η_i, and the **combined engine efficiency** η_k, we have

$$(57A) \qquad \eta_i = \frac{W_I}{W}, \qquad \eta_b = \frac{W_B}{W}, \qquad \text{and} \qquad \eta_k = \frac{W_K}{W},$$

where the ideal work W is in the same units as the numerator and is computed for the corresponding ideal system. The corresponding ideal system for an Otto engine is one which has the same compression ratio as the actual engine and the same energy supplied ($Q_A = Q'_A$). Also, for a Diesel engine, § 126, the corresponding ideal system is an ideal Diesel cycle whose r and Q_A are the same as for the actual. In each case, one must of course decide upon what standard of comparison to use, cold air, hot air, variable specific heat, or real mixture. In those cycles where the actual Q'_A and the ideal Q_A are the same, as in Otto and Diesel cycles (but not gas-turbine-unit cycles), the engine efficiencies are also ratios of the thermal efficiencies ($W = eQ_A$):

$$(\mathbf{h}) \qquad\qquad \eta_i = \frac{e_i}{e}, \qquad \eta_b = \frac{e_b}{e}, \qquad \eta_k = \frac{e_k}{e}.$$

Since $W = p_m V_D$, equation (49), p. 85, we get other ratios from equation (57) as follows

$$(\mathbf{i}) \qquad\qquad \eta_i = \frac{p_{mi}}{p_m}, \qquad \eta_b = \frac{p_{mb}}{p_m}, \qquad \eta_k = \frac{p_{mk}}{p_m},$$

where p_m is the mep of the corresponding ideal cycle and the numerators are determined from equation (48)—see equation (**g**), § 116. The reader can find other ratios which give the engine efficiency; for example, horsepowers and fuel rates.

Since the engine efficiency can often be estimated closely from previous experience with a certain kind of engine, it is a convenient design factor for use in determining the size of an actual engine to produce a specified amount of power.

120. Mechanical Efficiency. The mechanical efficiency η_m is a number which tells of the mechanical losses in a machine. For the generator, Fig.

78, it includes electrical losses also (output/input), **or**

(j) $$\eta_m = \frac{W_K}{W_B}.$$ [GENERATOR]

For a reciprocating power-producing engine of any type,

(k) $$\eta_m = \frac{W_B}{W_I}.$$ [RECIPROCATING ENGINE]

See § 84 for η_m for a compressor. The foregoing works may be expressed in any convenient work or power unit or in terms of any numbers which are proportional to the W's, but remember that engine efficiency is a dimensionless ratio. The difference (ihp) − (bhp) or $W_I - W_B$ represents the loss due to mechanical friction of the moving parts of the engine; expressed in horsepower, it is called the *friction horsepower* (fhp); $fhp = (1 - \eta_m)\,(ihp)$. Be sure to note that mechanical efficiency is not a fixed number characteristic of the machine but that it depends upon operating conditions, especially speed, power output, and lubrication.

121. Example—Size of Engine. A single-cylinder, 4-stroke gasoline engine is to operate at 400 rpm and deliver 100 bhp. Other data are: bmep = 120 psi, approximately; $\eta_m = 80\%$; specific fuel consumption, 0.55 lb./bhp-hr.; lower heating value of fuel $q_l = 19,000$ Btu/lb.; stroke/diameter ratio $L/D = 1$; $r = 6.5$; $k = 1.32$. Determine (a) the bore and stroke, (b) the expected brake thermal efficiency, (c) the indicated engine efficiency and imep.

SOLUTION. (a) Using the stroke in inches L'' instead of L ft., let $L = L''/12$ in (g) and find

$$L''A = \frac{(12)(33,000)\mathrm{bhp}}{p_{mb}N} = \frac{(12)(33,000)(100)}{(120)(200)} = 1650 \text{ cu. in.}$$

Since $A = \pi D^2/4$ and $L = D$, $L''A = D\pi D^2/4 = \pi D^3/4 = 1650$; whence $D = 12.8$ in.; use $D = 13$ in.; $L'' = 13$ in.   *Ans.*   13x13 in.

(b) Since 1 hp-hr. = 2544 Btu, equation (56), we get

$$e_b = \frac{2544}{w_f q_l} = \frac{2544}{(0.55)(19,000)} = 24.4\%.$$

(c) Since $\eta_m = W_B/W_I = e_b/e_i = p_{mb}/p_{mi}$; we find

$$e_i = \frac{24.4}{0.80} = 30.5\%.$$

$$e = 1 - \frac{1}{r^{k-1}} = 1 - \frac{1}{6.5^{0.32}} = 45.1\%.$$

$$\eta_i = \frac{e_i}{e} = \frac{30.5}{45.1} = 67.6\%.$$

$$p_{mi} = \frac{p_{mb}}{\eta_m} = \frac{120}{0.80} = 150 \text{ psi.}$$

122. Compression Ratio and Detonation, Spark Ignition. Since real engines, as well as ideal, show increased efficiencies as the compression ratio is increased, the matter of the practical limit of the compression ratio is of interest. There are two externally similar phenomena which might occur in spark ignition engines—*externally* similar in that they both cause an engine "knock." One is preignition, which is characterized by combustion starting *before* ignition by spark. Preignition happens because of a hot spot in the combustion chamber, which in turn may be due to roughened surfaces in the combustion chamber or deposits from the fuel or lubricant.

Detonation is a spontaneous burning of the fuel which is beyond the flame front *after* ignition (by spark), as explained in more detail below. As the compression ratio is increased, each of these self-ignition phenomena is more prone to happen.

When the mixture is ignited, combustion starts at the spark and spreads through the combustion chamber behind a flame front, Fig. 79. As the

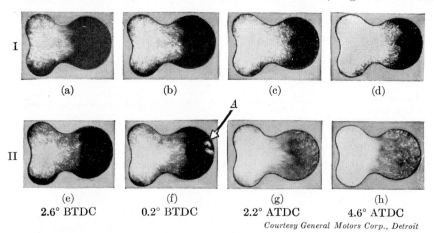

Courtesy General Motors Corp., Detroit

Fig. 79. *Combustion in the Engine Cylinder.* The top row of pictures shows the progress of combustion *without* detonation. Observe that the combustion is not yet complete in the picture (d). The times for these exposures are, for example, (a) and (e) at 2.6° before TDC position; (d) and (h) at 4.6° after TDC position. Detonation occurs in the bottom row, starting just before TDC, frame (f). At 4.6° after TDC, combustion is nearly comqlete.

temperature of the burned gases rises, the products expand and compress the yet unburned gases. If the compression ratio is too high for the particular fuel, the unburned gases are compressed so much and therefore get so hot that spontaneous combustion begins at some point remote from the spark, as at *A*, Fig. 79(f). There is a rapid and local increase in pressure at this point. Violent, vibrating pressure waves then result, the audible evidence of which is a metallic click or knock when these waves strike the wall of the combustion space. This phenomenon, called *detonation,* is accompanied by severely high pressures which will damage the engine if repeated in an aggravated form.

Compression ratio is by no means the sole determining factor affecting detonation. It is significant in that its increase results in an increase of temperature and pressure. Because the walls of an air-cooled engine run hotter than the walls of a water-cooled engine, the compression ratio of an air-cooled engine must be lower than for a water-cooled engine operating on the same grade of gasoline, in order to avoid detonation. Moreover, since detonation is a *function of the pressure* at the end of compression, a lower compression ratio is necessary in a supercharged engine. Developments in recent years which have permitted increased compression ratios without detonation include:

1. Fuels have been developed which resist spontaneous combustion, such as mixtures of benzol and gasoline, polymerized gasoline, and gasoline containing tetraethyl lead (TEL). The objective is to raise the self-ignition temperature or to increase the delay period before self-ignition occurs, thus allowing time for the flame front to travel entirely across the combustion chamber.

2. The shape of the combustion chamber above the piston has been designed to reduce detonation.

3. The rate at which heat is carried from potential hot spots is increased by the use of thinner sections on the head, by the use of materials for the head with good conductivity for heat, such as aluminum alloys, and by improving the conductance of heat from the top of the piston.

4. Local hot spots in the combustion chamber have been reduced in number by better finishing, which removes small projections which may become red-hot and cause spontaneous ignition, and by more efficient cooling of various parts in or near the combustion chamber, such as the spark plug and the valve seats.

5. At low speeds with widely opened throttle, a condition conducive to detonation, the spark is automatically retarded.

6. Injection of water and water and alcohol into the manifold and/or enrichment of the mixture (fuel/air to say 0.10) both reduce the compression temperature and the tendency to detonate. Mixture enrichment is routine practice in aircraft during take-off and when there is a large power demand for a short time.

123. Antiknock Rating of Spark Ignition Fuels.

The detonation properties of gasoline are measured by an octane number; the higher the number, the less the tendency of the gasoline to detonate. The octane of a fuel is obtained by supplying the fuel to a standard test engine and comparing its knocking property with a reference fuel of known knocking property. The reference fuel is a mixture of iso-octane, a fuel with good antiknock qualities whose octane rating is 100, and normal heptane, a fuel with poor antiknock qualities whose assigned octane rating is zero. If the fuel being tested has the same knocking characteristics as a mixture with 90% iso-octane and 10% heptane, its octane rating is 90.

The antiknock characteristics of commercial fuels have been steadily improved, until the "regular" grades of gasoline usually have octane numbers above 90 (vs. about 70 in 1942,) and "premium" grades up to (and better than) 100, at which point we run out of octane numbers. Since fuels with better detonation properties than iso-octane are available now and since the trend is evidently toward producing fuels with better and better antiknock characteristics, designation numbers for fuels with octane numbers greater than 100 are needed. One means is to arbitrarily extend the octane scale above 100 (but of course 120% octane is a figment of the imagination). A common method at this time is to let the reference fuel above 100 octane be iso-octane plus so many milliliters (ml.) of tetraethyl lead (TEL). Thus a fuel with a detonation property of 1.5 ml. TEL would have the same detonation characteristic under the specified test conditions as iso-octane plus 1.5 ml. TEL.

In the early 1920's, compression ratios as low as 3.5 were in use in automotive engines, with 4.5 being typical. Average $r = 5$ in 1930. Current passenger car engines have compression ratios from 7.5 to 10. Trucks have compression ratios somewhat lower, mostly from about 7 to 7.3. Aircraft engines have compression ratios of about 6 to 8.5. The use of a fuel with an octane rating higher than that necessary to avoid detonation in a given engine will not result in any increase in power nor, per se, in any other advantage. (Some premium fuels contain additives intended to provide other advantages.) To benefit from high antiknock fuel, the engine must be designed for it.

124. Air-Fuel Mixture in Otto Engines. There are needed approximately 15 lb. air/lb. gasoline (0.0665 lb. gasoline/lb. air—§ 278) in order to supply the amount of oxygen ideally required to burn the fuel completely. However, if no more than this amount is provided, combustion will be incomplete, and there will be unburned combustibles in the exhaust plus some unused oxygen. For complete combustion, there must be an excess of air and thorough mixing of the fuel and air. Thus, more efficient combustion occurs in general as the excess of air increases above the ideal amount. While this statement is true of spark ignition engines, it applies only to a limited increase of the air/fuel ratio (decrease of the fuel/air

ratio).   Maximum efficiency in the modern automobile engine is usually
obtained when the air/fuel ratio is somewhere between 15.3 and 16 lb.
air/lb. gasoline (fuel/air, 0.0665 to 0.0625 lb. gasoline/lb. air), Fig. 80.
The efficiency drops off rapidly as the air/fuel ratio increases above 18
(0.0555 fuel/air), and the mixture soon becomes so lean that combustion
does not occur.   In the other direction, greater power is obtained by using
more fuel than can be burned in the air available (air/fuel < 15), say
air/fuel ratios of 12 to 13.5 (fuel/air, 0.083 to 0.075).   See Fig. 80.   For

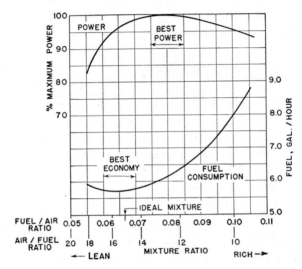

Fig. 80.   Effect of Mixture Ratio on Efficiency and Power.
These curves do not apply precisely to all gasoline
engines, but they are characteristic ones.

smooth idling, a rich mixture of the order of 11.1 lb. air/lb. gasoline (0.090
fuel/air) is required to overcome the effects of dilution with the products and
of air leakage because of the high vacuum in the manifold.   See § 125.
The modern carburetor is designed to provide approximately these ratios,
an economical mixture for ordinary operating conditions, a richer mixture
when the demand is for greater power, an especially rich mixture for idling.

125. Carburetors.   As implied in the foregoing paragraph, a carburetor
is a device whose function is to regulate the flow of fuel in accordance with
the amount of flow of air to obtained desired air/fuel ratios.   The basic
principle of the float-type carburetor is illustrated in Fig. 81, which shows
only the minimum essential elements.   The suction stroke of the engine
piston induces a flow of air into the carburetor.   As the air passes through
the venturi, Fig. 81, it moves faster at the throat or smallest section, as a

result of which the pressure at the throat drops below atmospheric pressure. Atmospheric pressure in the float chamber then pushes some gasoline through B into the stream of air.

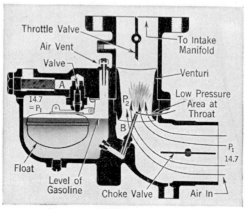

Fig. 81. Elementary Carburetor. Both the choke valve and the throttle valve are wide open. Flow of air is a maximum for a particular engine speed. Gasoline enters through passage *A*. When the level in the float chamber drops below a certain point, the tapered needle valve opens since it is operated by the float. Partly closing the throttle valve reduces the amount of mixture flowing to the engine. It is this valve which is operated by the "accelerator" pedal in an automobile. To start the engine cold, the choke valve is partially closed, an action which results in a greater proportion of fuel in the mixture (a richer mixture). The choke and throttle valves are a type called *butterfly valves*.

By considering energy quantities, we can understand better the operation of the venturi. In the carburetor, the **venturi** is the means by which the flow of gasoline is governed, but it is also a common device used to measure the flow of gases or liquids and may appear somewhat as indicated in Fig. 82.

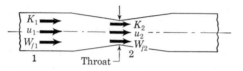

Fig. 82. Venturi.

It consists of a converging-diverging passageway, the smallest section of which is called the **throat**. In a unit of time under steady flow conditions, the same mass flows past section 2 as past section 1. Since the sectional area at 2 is less than the area at 1, the velocity of the fluid, and therefore its kinetic energy, must be greater at 2 than at 1; $K_2 > K_1$. In this instrument, friction and other thermal effects are relatively small and the actual pressure drop $p_1 - p_2$, Fig. 82, is small. Thus we may with little error make the following assumptions: $Q = 0$, $u_2 = u_1$, and $v_2 = v_1$. As a consequence, the energy relation becomes

$$W_{f1} + K_1 = W_{f2} + K_2,$$

$$\Delta K = \frac{v_2{}^2 - v_1{}^2}{2g_o} = p_1 v_1 - p_2 v_2 \approx v(p_1 - p_2).$$

Suppose state 1 is taken as the atmospheric air, outside the carburetor. Then $v_1 = 0$, $K_1 = 0$, and $p_1 = p_o$, say, is atmospheric pressure. Solving for v_2, we have*

(1) $$v_2 = [2g_o v(p_o - p_2)]^{1/2},$$

where v is taken as the specific volume of free air. The greater the flow of air through a given venturi, the faster it must move. Equation (1) shows that the faster it moves, the greater must be $p_o - p_2$. The greater the difference between atmospheric pressure and the pressure in the throat, Fig. 81, the more gasoline flows into the air stream. Thus, we see that if the jet B, Fig. 81, and the venturi are properly proportioned, there is an automatic action that results in greater fuel flow when the air flow becomes greater.

However, the ratio of fuel to air increases with an increase in air flow; the mixture becomes richer. For this reason, a good carburetor is more complicated than the one in Fig. 81. A carburetor which provides the desired mixtures, as explained in § 124, is described in Fig. 83. In addition to the features seen in Fig. 83, the automotive carburetor is designed to provide a momentarily rich mixture when the throttle is suddenly opened, and it may have a special economizer system for more economical operation under certain conditions. The most advanced designs for modern automotive engines are more complex than the model shown in Fig. 83.

Injection carburetors, which are small pumps designed to pump a metered amount of gasoline into the manifold, are in use. The idea is similar to the injectors used on Diesel engines (§ 127 and Fig. 88). However, this sytem is at present more expensive than the ordinary gasoline carburetor and has been used mostly on the airplane engine where increased economy and other advantages offset the additional expense.

* Equation (1) may also be obtained by a more complete energy analysis and a mathematical approximation.

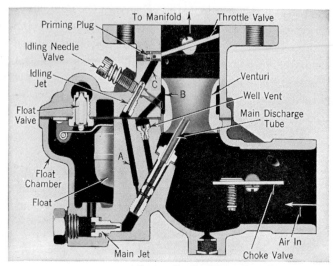

Courtesy Bendix Aviation Corp. (Zenith), Detroit

Fig. 83. Zenith Carburetor (61 Series). The float chamber (or bowl), containing gasoline, is connected to the entrance of the main jet, which meters gasoline. The outlet of the main discharge tube is at the throat of the venturi, as in the elementary carburetor. The compensation system consists of the main discharge tube and the well vent. The flow through the main jet is governed by the sizes of the well vent and the main discharge tube. The well vent controls the flow of air which bleeds into the main discharge tube from the channel *B* behind the venturi. Thus, the mixture in the main discharge tube can be made richer either by decreasing the size of the well vent or by increasing the size of the main discharge jet.

The idling system consists of the channel *A*, leading the fuel to the idling jet and idling adjusting needle. The idling needle valve controls the amount of air admitted from passage *B*. Since the throttle valve is nearly closed, there is a low vacuum on the manifold side of the throttle valve. This low vacuum causes a mixture of fuel and air to move up passage *C*, this mixture discharging into the main passage from the carburetor through the priming plug. The richness of the resulting mixture is governed by the adjustment of the idle needle valve. As the load increases above idling load (throttle valve opening wider), the pressure in the main passage at the priming plug rises, resulting in a smaller flow through the priming plug. At some load (say, at a constant speed of about 25 mph on level road), the pressure at the priming plug rises high enough that no flow of fuel occurs through the idling system, and the mixture is then governed by the venturi as previously explained.

126. Diesel Cycle. Rudolf Diesel* was primarily interested in developing an internal combustion engine to operate on coal as a fuel. The final outcome however was a four-stroke-cycle engine, § 110, in which air only is taken into the cylinder on the suction stroke, and a liquid fuel is later

* Rudolf Diesel (1858–1913), born in Paris of German parents who later moved to London because of the Franco-German War (1870), educated in Germany, obtained in

injected, the injection starting theoretically at the end of the compression stroke and continuing at such a rate that burning proceeds at constant pressure 2–3, Fig. 84. Otherwise, the cycle operates as the Otto cycle does and the air-standard (closed) cycle is 1-2-3-4, Fig. 84. The ideal open air-cycle would be the same except that 0-1 is the suction and 1-0 is the discharge. Following the same arguments as given for the Otto engine, we find the energy equation applicable to the Diesel engine to be, as before,

$$U_1 + Q_A = U_4 + W,$$

or

$$W = Q_A - (U_4 - U_1) = (H_3 - H_2) - (U_4 - U_1).$$
$$\text{[VARIABLE OR CONSTANT SPECIFIC HEAT]}$$

Since the combustion is at constant pressure, the heat added in the air-standard cycle is $Q_A = \Delta H$ or $Q_A = wc_p(T_3 - T_2)$ for constant specific heat; thus

$$W = wc_p(T_3 - T_2) - wc_v(T_4 - T_1).$$
$$\text{[CONSTANT } c_p \text{ AND } c_v]$$

Then, the thermal efficiency is

$$\textbf{(m)} \quad e = \frac{W}{Q_A} = 1 - \frac{c_v(T_4 - T_1)}{c_p(T_3 - T_2)}$$
$$= 1 - \frac{T_4 - T_1}{k(T_3 - T_2)}.$$

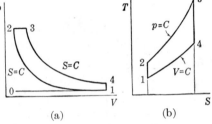

Fig. 84. Diesel Cycle. Between the same temperature limits, the constant volume curve on the *TS* plane is steeper than the constant pressure curve (§ 54). However, both curves get steeper as the temperature increases. Thus, the temperature at 3 is so high that the constant pressure curve is steeper than the constant volume curve, which is at the lower temperatures between 1 and 4.

As before, this equation may be placed in a more revealing form by eliminating the temperatures. Assuming that the working substance is an ideal gas with constant specific heats, we may express three of the temperatures in terms of the fourth; say in terms of T_1. Thus, along the isentropic 1-2, Fig. 84, $T_2/T_1 = (V_1/V_2)^{k-1}$. However, V_1/V_2 is the compression ratio r. Therefore

$$\textbf{(n)} \qquad T_2 = T_1 \left(\frac{V_1}{V_2}\right)^{k-1} = T_1 r^{k-1}.$$

Along the constant pressure line 2-3, Charles' law holds and $T_3/T_2 = V_3/V_2$.

1893 a patent on the type of engine which now bears his name. After some difficulty in financing the project, he built an engine which blew up at the first injection of fuel. Diesel narrowly escaped being killed. Four years of tedious and costly experiment elapsed before he produced a successful engine. He inexplicably disappeared in 1913 while crossing the English Channel during a storm.

Let $V_3/V_2 = r_c$, a ratio termed the fuel *cutoff ratio.* We find then

(o)
$$T_3 = T_2\left(\frac{V_3}{V_2}\right) = T_1 r^{k-1} r_c$$

by using equation (n). For the isentropic process 3-4, $T_4/T_3 = (V_3/V_4)^{k-1}$.

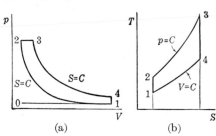

(a)   (b)

Fig. 84. Repeated.

But from 2-3, $V_3 = (T_3/T_2)V_2 = r_c V_2$. Using this value of V_3, the value of T_3 from equation (o), and using the definition of the compression ratio $(V_1/V_2 = r)$, we get

(p)
$$T_4 = T_3\left(\frac{V_3}{V_4}\right)^{k-1} = T_1 r_c^k.$$

Substituting into equation (m) the values of T_2, T_3, and T_4 just found, we have

(58)
$$e = 1 - \frac{T_1 r_c^k - T_1}{k(T_1 r^{k-1} r_c - T_1 r^{k-1})} = 1 - \frac{1}{r^{k-1}}\left[\frac{r_c^k - 1}{k(r_c - 1)}\right].$$
[DIESEL CYCLE]

Observe that this expression for the efficiency of the Diesel cycle differs from that of the Otto cycle (54) only in the bracketed factor. This factor is

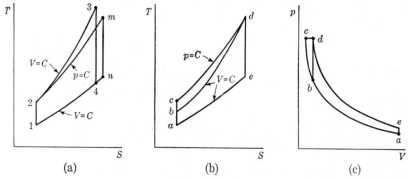

(a)   (b)   (c)

Fig. 85. Comparison of Otto and Diesel Cycles. These cycles may be compared in many different ways and these sketches, which are qualitative with respect to areas, may be of interest. In (a), they are sketched for the same compression ratio and the same heat added; that is, area under 2-3 (Otto) is equal to area under 2-m (Diesel). We see that the Diesel rejects more heat n-1 than the Otto does 4-1, a visual demonstration that the Otto is more efficient. But the compression ratio is not the same in the two cycles as they are actually used; so (b) and (c) are sketched for the same temperature and pressure d after combustion (which is not true either, except by chance). At any rate, you can see how the areas are affected.

always greater then unity because r_c is always greater than 1. Thus, for a particular compression ratio r, the Otto cycle is more efficient. See also Fig. 85. However, if the compression ratio is too high in an Otto engine, detonation occurs (§ 122).   Since the Diesel engine compresses air only, the compression ratio is much higher than in an Otto engine.   Therefore, an *actual* Diesel engine with, say, $r = 15$ is more efficient than an actual Otto engine with $r = 9$.   In passing, we may note the relation between the compression ratio r, cutoff ratio r_c, and expansion ratio $r_e = V_4/V_3 = V_1/V_3$, Fig. 84:

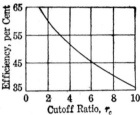

Fig. 86.   *Variation of Efficiency with Cutoff Ratio, Diesel Cycle.*   The compression ratio is maintained constant.

$$(\mathbf{q}) \qquad r = \frac{V_1}{V_2} = \left(\frac{V_3}{V_2}\right)\left(\frac{V_1}{V_3}\right) = r_c r_e.$$

Study of equation (58) shows that as r_c increases, the bracketed factor increases, and the efficiency decreases, Fig. 86.   Therefore, the lower fuel cutoff ratios are conducive to higher efficiencies, [but larger ratios result in greater power.   However, there is a limit to the amount of fuel which can be injected without excessive "smoking"; hence, the compromise ordinarily is such that cutoff seldom occurs later than 10% of the stroke, corresponding to a cutoff ratio of about 2.4, usually earlier.

As in the Otto cycle, the value of k in the cold-air standard is 1.4.   Lower values, say about 1.35, would be used in the hot-air standard.   Constant pressure combustion is not obtained in the actual Diesel engine, much of the combustion occurring at substantially constant volume.   For this reason, engines in which the high temperature of compression causes combustion are called *compression ignition engines.*

An end-view cross section of a four-stroke Diesel engine is shown in Fig. 87.   Other Diesel engines are shown in Figs. 90, 91, and 92.

127. Injection of Fuel.   For compression ignition, the compression ratio should be at least 12, but is more likely to be between 15 and 17, and sometimes as much as 22 in current models.   The compression ratio is limited in part by the fact that high peak pressures accompany high compression ratios and lead to relatively massive designs.

One of the key components of a Diesel or compression ignition engine is the fuel injector, Fig. 88.   Since the amount of oil injected per cycle is relatively small and since it must be precisely measured for satisfactory operation, the injector is a precision device.   The fuel system should filter the fuel, measure and isolate the proper amount for the next injection, inject the fuel at the right time against a pressure in the cylinder of some 500 psi, break up the fuel into a fine mist on injection so that the maximum surface is exposed to the high temperature in the cylinder, and cut off completely and cleanly.   In slow-speed engines, injection may occur very nearly at the TDC position of the piston. However, before the oil begins to burn, some of the liquid oil must be heated to its boiling point and vaporized, and some of the vapor must be heated to the temperature of combustion. This requires time, although some oils ignite more quickly than others (§ 128). Therefore, in high-speed engines, it is necessary to inject the oil very much ahead of the

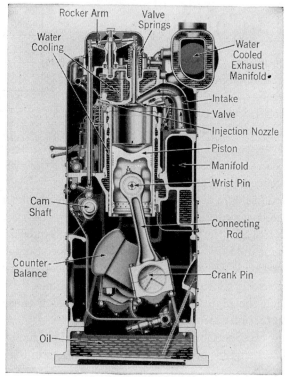

Fig. 87. Four-Stroke Diesel Engine. Study the picture for detail. A hole at the top of the drilled connecting rod serves to spray the piston head with oil for cooling. The bore and stroke are 10½x12 in., assembled with 5 to 8 cylinders; 375–600 bhp; supercharged, 570–900 bhp; supercharged with cooling of supercharged air, 600–1000 bhp; all at 720 rpm. Figure 78 is an external view of this engine.

TDC position, if it is to begin to burn at the proper time. The time of injection, when the oil is sprayed directly into the combustion space, would be some 35–45° before TDC in high-speed engines and some 7–10° before TDC in low-speed engines.

The power output of Diesel engines is controlled by varying the amount of fuel injected. The quantity of air per cycle without supercharging remains virtually constant (if the speed is constant), and at normal loads

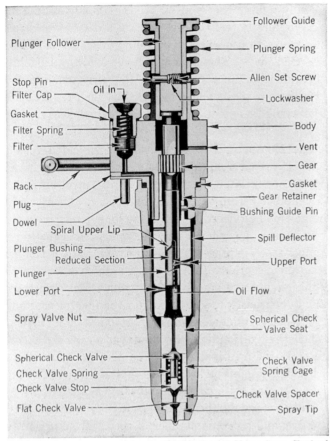

Plunger Follower
Follower Guide
Plunger Spring
Stop Pin
Filter Cap
Oil in
Allen Set Screw
Lockwasher
Gasket
Filter Spring
Filter
Body
Vent
Gear
Rack
Plug
Dowel
Gasket
Gear Retainer
Bushing Guide Pin
Spiral Upper Lip
Plunger Bushing
Reduced Section
Plunger
Lower Port
Spill Deflector
Upper Port
Oil Flow
Spray Valve Nut
Spherical Check
Valve Seat
Spherical Check Valve
Check Valve Spring
Check Valve Stop
Flat Check Valve
Check Valve
Spring Cage
Check Valve Spacer
Spray Tip

Courtesy General Motors Corp., Cleveland

Fig. 88. Fuel Injector for Diesel Engine. There is one of these
units for each cylinder. Fuel oil enters through the filter. (It
has already passed through two filters in the fuel system of
which this is part.) Oil fills the space around the plunger
bushing and beneath the plunger, shown in its upper position.
Observe the upper port and the lower port. As the plunger
moves down, oil will flow out of the lower port until it is covered
by the plunger. Moreover, the oil flows through a drilled
passage (not shown) from the bottom of the plunger to the
clearance space at the reduced section, thence flowing out of the
upper port. Thus, oil flows out of the upper port until the upper
lip on the plunger covers it. When both ports have been covered, additional movement of the plunger forces fuel into the
cylinder. Notice how the upper lip at the reduced section is cut
on a spiral and how the closing of the upper port will be delayed
if the plunger is turned to the left. This is the manner of regulating the amount of fuel injected. The position shown is
approximately that for maximum injection. When the plunger
is turned to delay the closing of the upper port, less fuel will be
injected. This action is of course automatically handled by the
governor when the load on the engine changes.

there is generally a large excess of air for the amount of fuel injected, say from 20 to 25 lb. air/lb. fuel (where 15 lb. of air is the ideal requirement). This range of fuel/air ratio will likely include the ratio for the actual maximum thermal efficiency. The maximum power which a Diesel is capable of producing is seldom obtained because for the corresponding air/fuel ratio, say about 16, there is too much smoke in the exhaust. The engine would soon foul and would be operating at low thermal efficiency.

128. Cetane Number. Diesel engines are subjected to a fuel knock but for a different reason from that of Otto engines. An ignition lag in Otto engines may allow time for the flame front to travel entirely across the combustion chamber before detonation can occur. On the other hand, if the delay in ignition in a Diesel engine is too long, a relatively large amount of fuel accumulates in the cylinder before combustion begins, and then when combustion does start, it proceeds at a very rapid rate, accompanied by an almost instantaneous pressure rise and an audible knock in the extreme cases. If ignition starts promptly, not so much fuel is in the cylinder at the beginning of combustion, and thereafter the fuel burns gradually, more or less, as it enters the cylinder. Thus, to avoid knock in Diesel engines, the aim is to reduce the ignition delay by whatever means are effective. After the engine is built, the principal means of eliminating a fuel knock is the use of a fuel with a shorter ignition lag (higher ignitability). The ignitability of a fuel oil is designated by a *cetane number.* Cetane ($C_{16}H_{32}$) has a high ignitability and a cetane number of 100; n-methylnaphthalene ($C_{11}H_{10}$) has a low ignitability and a cetane number of zero. If an actual fuel has the same ignition lag, as determined by a standard test, as a mixture of 60% cetane and 40% $C_{11}H_{10}$ by volume, the actual fuel is said to have a cetane number of 60. For high-speed engines, a cetane number greater than 50 is required; for medium speed engines, a cetane number of about 35 is sufficient; for large, slow speed engines, a cetane of 30 may be satisfactory.

129. Volumetric Efficiency. There are a number of factors which account for power loss in an internal combustion engine, among which are the obvious mechanical-friction loss and the loss which accompanies the heat rejected to the cooling medium, which is the cooling water in the automobile engine. Another factor is that combustion is not instantaneous as assumed in an ideal Otto cycle (nor at constant pressure as assumed in the Diesel cycle); nor is combustion complete—some unburned components escape in the exhaust. A significant factor is the time and work involved in pumping the working substances into and out of the cylinder, a loss which becomes relatively large at high speeds. This is a fluid friction loss. There is also a loss in multicylinder engines because the manifold is imperfect; the same mixture (air/fuel ratio) is not delivered to every cylinder. However, other factors remaining the same, the power obtained from an engine which draws in air and fuel depends upon the mass of combustible mixture drawn into the cylinders—given a mixture with the correct air/fuel ratio— and anything which reduces the mass of fuel entering the engine reduces the power output below what could have been obtained. For example:

1. In the real engine, we have found that, because of the fluid friction of flow or throttling around the valves and in the passages, the suction pressure is less than atmospheric pressure; and therefore the mass of gas ($w = pV/RT$) is less than if atmospheric pressure were maintained.

2. The internal surfaces and passages of the engine are relatively hot, so that the mixture is heated as it passes into the cylinder. In accordance with Charles' law, the increase in temperature further reduces the mass of mixture that the given displacement can contain.

3. The gases in the *clearance space* of the real engine are at a pressure *above* atmospheric at the end of the exhaust stroke and must expand during the suction stroke to the intake pressure before a new charge begins to enter, Fig. 73, p. 131.

4. The pressure of the atmosphere decreases with altitude, so that the mass of mixture drawn in at high altitudes is still further decreased below that which would be drawn in at sea level.

The mass brought into the cylinder is sometimes defined in terms of **volumetric efficiency** (§ 79), which is defined as

$$\textbf{(r)} \quad \eta_v = \frac{\text{Mass of air drawn into the engine}}{\text{Mass of air that would occupy the displacement volume at } p_a \text{ and } T_a,}$$

where p_a and T_a are the air pressure and temperature at intake, say in the test room. The value of the denominator is $w = p_a V_D/(R_a T_a)$. The numerator and denominator in (**r**) must be in the same units. Usually we use mass per engine cycle or mass per minute. The displacement volume *per engine cycle* is the volume swept out by the piston *in one stroke;* this number multiplied by the number of cycles per minute gives the displacement per minute, § 83. In a particular engine, volumetric efficiency is affected by the speed. Suppose, for example, that the valve timing has been adjusted for maximum volumetric efficiency at 2000 rpm. Then in general as the speed increases, the volumetric efficiency decreases because of the greater throttling effect (fluid friction) at higher speeds. The volumetric efficiency as defined by equation (**r**) can be made greater than unity by use of a supercharger. See § 131.

130. The Two–Stroke Cycle. Many small gasoline engines and many Diesels, large and small, operate on a two-stroke cycle. Since the exhaust stroke in the real engine is for the purpose of *scavenging* the cylinder (ridding the cylinder of the products of combustion), it is only necessary to provide

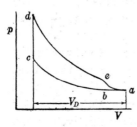

other means of scavenging in order to be able to complete the cycle in two strokes (one revolution). An idealized sort of indicator card is shown in Fig. 89. Compression has been completed at point c, Fig. 89; combustion occurrs cd, followed by an expansion. In the two-stroke cycle, exhaust begins early, at some point e, and scavenging is accomplished by blowing air (or air and fuel) into the cylinder. To allow time for scavenging or for the introduction of fuel mixtures, the valves usually

Fig. 89.   Two–Stroke Cycle.

remain open until the piston has moved from e to a to b, where compression begins.

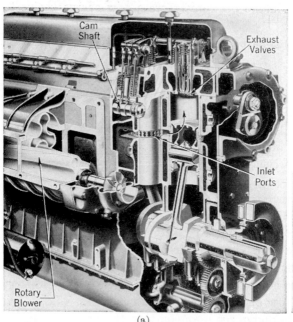

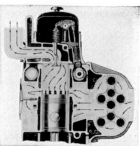

(a)   (b)

Courtesy General Motors Corp., Detroit

Fig. 90.   Two–Stroke–Cycle Diesel Engine. This engine, 4.25x5 in., is used for a wide variety of industrial purposes; driving trucks, hoists, bull dozers, tractors, pumps, boats, etc. It is put together with two to twenty-four cylinders. The blower, of the type described in Fig. 50, blows fresh air through the cylinder wall ports while the piston is at the bottom of its stroke [see (b)], sweeping out the products of combustion through the valve openings at the top. Performance data for the 6-cylinder engine are approximately: 142 hp at 1800 rpm (continuous duty) with a fuel consumption of 0.481 lb./bhp-hr. (see other performance data in Table II); $r = 17$; piston speed = 1500 fpm at 1800 rpm.

In four-stroke cycles, there is *one* power stroke for *two* revolutions; in two-stroke cycles, there is *one* power stroke for *one* revolution. However, the two-stroke-cycle engine, instead of developing 100% more power, develops only some 70% to 90% more than the four-stroke-cycle engine of the same displacement, because of (1) poorer scavenging, (2) a smaller mass of combustible mixture in a given size of cylinder, (3) a small power consumption in compressing the air which scavenges the cylinder, and (4) the loss of pressure by early exhaust.

Compressed air for scavenging is obtained from crankcase compression (as in outboard motors, lawn-mower engines) or from separate blowers. A typical two-stroke-cycle Diesel engine is shown in Fig. 90. Figure 91 shows an opposed-piston, two-stroke Diesel. A two-stroke-cycle, gas-engine-compressor unit is shown in Fig. 92. Units similar to this one are sometimes made so that they may be changed over from gas to liquid fuel, and vice versa. Internal combustion engines are made in a variety of detail.

131. Supercharging.

Supercharging, Fig. 93, is a means of pumping more air (Diesel) or air and fuel (spark ignition) into the cylinders than would otherwise be drawn in. A greater amount of air supports the combustion of more fuel and the engine delivers more torque and power, which is the purpose of the supercharger, Fig. 94. It is commonly used with aircraft engines, both to obtain more power per pound of engine and to maintain a good power output at high altitudes

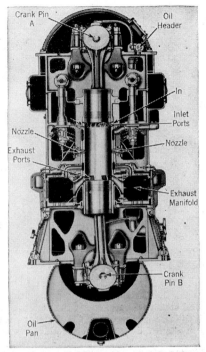

Courtesy Fairbanks, Morse and Co., Chicago

Fig. 91. Opposed-Piston Diesel Engine. As the pistons move from the central part of the cylinder and away from each other, the exhaust ports in the cylinder wall (shown exposed at the bottom) begin to open, and exhaust starts. Next, the inlet ports (at the top) are uncovered and fresh air is blown into the cylinder, scavenging it. (The opening of these ports, exhaust and inlet, occurs simultaneously, but the arrangement is such that the exhaust ports begin to open first. Notice that the lower crank *B* leads the upper crank *A* by a small amount.) As the pistons start on the compression stroke, the ports are covered by the pistons and compression begins. Near the end of the compression stroke, fuel is injected through the injection nozzle, combustion begins, and the two-stroke cycle starts over.

The two crank shafts are connected through bevel gears by a vertical shaft, parallel to the axes of the cylinders. The vertical shaft, not visible in this illustration, transmits the power of the upper crankshaft to the lower crankshaft, which delivers the power of the engine. This engine is manufactured with four to twelve cylinders. (See line (7), Table II, p. 157.)

Gear Train Drive for
Centrifugal
Scavenging
Blower

Ports

Gas Injection

Crosshead

Valve

LP Cylinder

Gas Passage

Intermediate Cylinder   HP Cylinder

Articulated
Connecting Rod

Courtesy Cooper-Bessemer Corp., Mount Vernon, O.

Fig. 92. Gas-Engine-Driven Gas Compressor. As seen, the compressor is in three stages, the various cylinders being driven from a single crankshaft. Notice the articulated construction used for the connecting rods of the V-type gas engine which operates on the two-stroke cycle; see the ports near the bottom of cylinder. The scavenging air is at about 2.5 psig; power produced is about 135 bhp per cylinder; compression ratio is 7.7 on full stroke; compression pressure is 250–265 psi; heat rate is sometimes as low as 7500 Btu/bhp-hr. This type of unit is used for pumping natural gas through pipe lines, for compressing process air for industrial needs, for various gas compressions in chemical plants and refineries, etc.; pressures up to 6000 psi.

where the density of the air is low. They are used on high-speed engines to help overcome fluid friction, and they are common on Diesel engines, both automotive and stationary. By way of comparison, observe the following actual test data for a Diesel engine: without supercharging, 475 bhp and 80 psi bmep; with supercharging to an intake pressure of about 19.5 psig, 880 bhp, and 147 psi bmep.

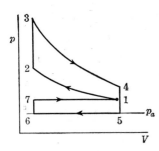

Fig. 93. Ideal Supercharged Otto Cycle. Point 1 is shown slightly displaced to make the cycle easier to follow: $V_1 = V_4$.

The idealized diagram in Fig. 93 shows the events of the cycle. The exhaust pressure at 5 is ideally atmospheric, actually somewhat above. The supercharger ideally pumps the mixture into the cylinder along 7-1; compression is 1-2. Analysis may follow the methods previously discussed.

132. Performance Data. Figure 95 shows some interesting trends in automotive engines in this country. Table II gives some typical performance data of internal combustion engines, and the curves of Fig. 96 indicate the kind of performance information obtained from a gasoline engine on a dynamometer test. Some brief remarks on these curves may help.

(*a*) *Brake horsepower.* Typically, the brake horsepower output increases to a peak, in this case at about 4100 rpm, after which the net output decreases. A value read from this curve at any particular speed is the horsepower delivered with *wide-open* throttle and with the engine warmed up. In the ordinary operation of an automobile, the throttle is seldom wide open for any length of time.

(*b*) *Friction horsepower.* The friction horsepower (fhp) is determined by driving the engine with the dynamometer and noting the consumption of power. Thus, this power *includes that necessary to pump the gases* into and out of the cylinders (fluid friction). For this reason, the frictional power goes up rapidly at high speeds.

Courtesy Elliott Co., Jeannette, Pa.

Fig. 94. Supercharger for Diesel Engine. A supercharger driven by exhaust gases (at upwards of 1200°F) which expand through the nozzles (made of stainless steel) and do work in the turbine blades (aluminum) to drive the centrifugal compressor (see §91); intended for 4-stroke-cycle engine. The compressed air enters the intake manifold, charging the engine cylinder with air at pressures greater than atmospheric, and providing upwards of 50% increase in power output. Certain engine parts must be of such design as to be able to withstand the higher pressures which accompany an increase in power.

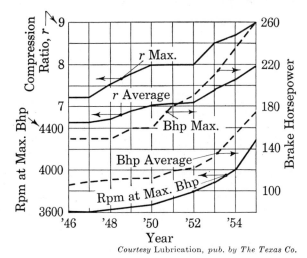

Courtesy Lubrication, *pub. by The Texas Co.*

Fig. 95. Post-War Trends in USA Automotive Engines.

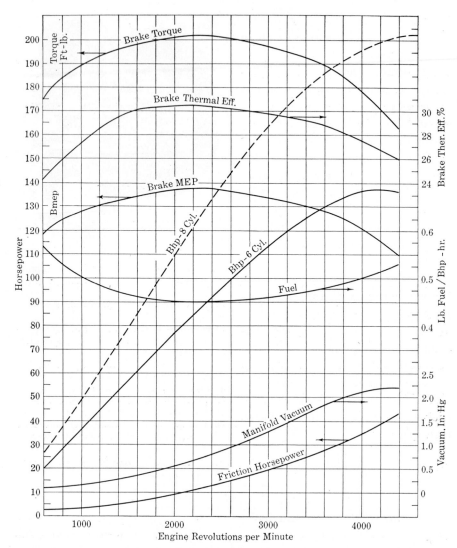

Fig. 96. Typical Performance Curves, Automobile Engine. Plotted from data by courtesy of the Ford Motor Company. The solid curves are for a 6-cylinder, **3.625x3.6-** in. engine, with a compression ratio of **8**; displacement of **223** cu. in. The test is run with *wide-open throttle.* The friction horsepower (fhp) is determined by driving the engine with the dynamometer and noting the consumption of power. In the absence of an indicator card, the indicated horsepower is taken as ihp = bhp + fhp and the mechanical efficiency is ratio bhp/ihp. An engine speed of **2000** rpm corresponds to a road speed of about **45** mph in a car with standard gear shift without overdrive. The thermal efficiency is based on the lower heating value (**18,500** Btu/lb. of fuel). The horsepower curve of the 8-cylinder engine is included for an interesting comparison.

Table II. *TYPICAL PERFORMANCE DATA OF INTERNAL COMBUSTION ENGINES*

NOTES. (a) Based on higher heating value. (b) Values at point of maximum thermal efficiency. (c) Approximate best efficiency. (d) At maximum power, except take-off. (e) Cubic feet per brake horsepower-hour at 60°F and 1 atm. (f) Data by Fairbanks, Morse & Co.; size 14x17 in. (g) Data by Fairbanks, Morse & Co.; size 8⅛x10 in.; see Fig. 91; supercharged 3 to 6 psig. (h) Data by Worthington Corp.; size 14x18 in.; supercharged 7.4 psig.

Type of engine	Comp. ratio, r	Brake th. eff., e_b (a)	Lb-fuel bhp-hr. w_f	Bmep psi, p_{mb}	Higher heat rate, Btu bhp-hr.	Remarks
(1) Gasoline	7.1	25.2%	0.5	130	10,100	Industrial V-8, (b)
(2) Gasoline	8	30%	0.42	150	8,470	Airplane (c)
(3) Gasoline	7	18.8%	0.67	189	13,530	Airplane (d)
(4) Gas	7	19.9%	127 (e)	58.9	12,800	4-Stroke, blast furnace gas (b)
(5) Gas	5.5	26.8%	9.5 (e)	68	9,500	Natural gas
(6) Diesel, 2-stroke (f)	14.45	35.6%	0.370	38 at 300 rpm	7,160	Crankcase scavenging
(7) Diesel, 2-stroke (g)	16	35.1%	0.375	85 at 720 rpm	7,256	Opposed piston
(8) Diesel, 4-stroke (h)	12.5	36.7%	0.360	160 at 450 rpm	6,950	Supercharged

(c) *Specific fuel consumption.* For this engine, Fig. 96, the fuel consumption is a minimum and the thermal efficiency is a maximum at about 2200–2400 rpm. Over a fairly wide range, the fuel consumption and the efficiency vary little, a desirable characteristic, but the curve of fuel consumption increases rapidly at high speeds, from about 3200 rpm for this engine. Thus, not only does the power necessary to drive the car at high speeds increase rapidly, about as the cube of the speed, but the efficiency of the engine falls off.

(d) *Torque.* The brake torque curve is significant for an automobile engine, because the acceleration (pickup) of the car depends upon the *available* torque, which is the maximum possible torque at a given speed minus the torque necessary to maintain the speed constant.

(*e*) **MEP.** Since the mep indicates the relative power of an engine of a given size and speed, high values are desirable. In a particular type of engine, Otto or Diesel, an increase in the mep is the result of burning more fuel per cycle, a change which may be brought about by improving the volumetric efficiency (or of course by using a supercharger).

(*f*) **Manifold vacuum.** From the manifold vacuum curve, we may check on the proper size and setting of the carburetor and the timing of the valves. Too high a vacuum (too low pressure) suggests too much resistance to flow via the intake system.

133. Closure. There are economical and advantageous uses for all kinds of prime movers. The Otto, or spark ignition, type is especially suited to low power (less than several hundred horsepower) where rotative speeds up to, say, 4000–6000 rpm are adaptable. Large Otto engines are more prone to detonation than small ones because the flame front has farther to travel in large combustion chambers, so that this is a factor in limiting the size of such engines. Diesel or compression ignition engines overlap Otto engines on size because they burn a cheaper fuel. For this reason, they are widely used on trucks and buses although they are more expensive per horsepower. Diesels are used in much larger units than Otto engines (up to several thousand horsepower, maybe 8000) and are excellent power plants for marine use, locomotives, and small electric generating stations. Internal combustion engines are appropriate for mills which operate on a seasonal basis, because of the ease of maintenance and start-up. To keep perspective, the ICE does not compete in central station power plants, in the largest of which, single compound steam turbine units of more than 100,000 hp are often found.

PROBLEMS

NOTE. *Unless otherwise stated, the answers to the following problems are for some average constant specific heats. However, where appropriate, it would be interesting and instructive to solve them also by use of the air table (the variable specific heat air standard). If the complete Keenan and Kaye Gas Tables are at hand, see the examples in the back for the method of making a real mixture analysis (exclusive of dissociation effects), if it is desired to make such an analysis. In an Otto air cycle, the computed temperature at the end of the heat addition process is likely to go beyond the top limit of the air table for normal air/fuel ratios.*

181. An Otto engine has a compression ratio of 5 and receives the working substance at 14.7 psia and 100°F. Find the ideal cycle efficiency if the working substance is (a) cold air, (b) hot air with an average value of $k = 1.3$. (c) What is the compression pressure p_2 in each case? Which of these pressures do you think is closest to the actual value? Explain.

Ans. (a) 47.5%, (b) 38.25%, (c) 139.7, 119 psia.

182. An Otto cycle operates on 0.1 lb./sec. at the beginning of compression, $p_1 = 13$ psia and $t_1 = 130°F$. At the end of the combustion process, the temperature is $5000°R$. The compression ratio is 5.5. Use an average value of $k = 1.3$. (a) Find c_v, V_1, p_2, t_2, p_3, V_3, t_4, and p_4 (Fig. 70). Compute (b) Q_A, Q_R, (c) W from TS and pV planes, (d) the thermal efficiency, (e) the corresponding horsepower.

Ans. (a) $p_3 = 607$ psia, $t_4 = 3000°R$, (c) 36.6 Btu/sec., (d) 40%, (e) 51.8 hp.

183. In an Otto cycle, state 1 at the beginning of compression is 13.8 psia, $100°F$, 1 cu. ft. After compression to 250 psia, 80 Btu/cycle are added. Using an average $k = 1.31$ for the hot-air standard, find (a) the compression and pressure ratios, (b) the percentage clearance, (c) T_3 and p_3 at the end of combustion, (d) Q_R, W, and e, (e) the displacement per cycle and the mep. (f) If this is a 6-cylinder, 4-stroke-cycle engine, turning at 300 rpm, determine the number of cycles completed per minute and the ideal horsepower.

Ans. (a) 9.09, 18.1, (b) 12.35%, (c) $6540°R$, 1470 psia, (d) $e = 49.5\%$, (e) $p_m = 240$ psi, (f) 841 hp.

184. The same as **183** except that the air table is to be used in the solution (do not use $k = 1.31$). Compare answers.

Ans. (a) 8.08, (b) $6529°R$ (obtained by extrapolation of unabridged table), 1300 psia, (d) e = 48.3%, (e) 242 psi, (f) 835 hp.

185. The mep of an ideal, cold-air Otto cycle is 160 psi. At the beginning of compression $V_1 = 1$ cu. ft. and $t_1 = 140°F$. The compression ratio is 5. Find (a) the displacement volume; (b) the work in Btu per cycle; (c) the heat added.

Ans. (a) 0.8 cu. ft., (b) 23.7, (c) 50 Btu.

186. An indicator card from a $6\frac{1}{2}$x9-in., single-cylinder, single-acting, 4-stroke-cycle gas engine is taken while the engine turns at 342 rpm. The area of the card is 1.03 sq. in.; its length is 2.93 in.; the scale of the indicator spring is 200 lb.; the mechanical efficiency is 78%. Fuel with a heating value of $q_l = 18,500$ Btu/lb. is used at the rate of 4.25 lb./hr. Determine (a) the ihp and bhp, (b) the brake heat rate and brake thermal efficiency.

Ans. (a) 9.06, 7.07 hp, (b) 11,110 Btu/bhp-hr., 22.9%.

187. A six-cylinder, $3\frac{1}{8}$x$4\frac{3}{8}$-in., 4-stroke-cycle gasoline engine is tested at 1800 rpm. The net load on the brake arm is 66 lb. at a radius of 1.75 ft. Calculate (a) the brake torque, (b) the bhp, (c) the brake mep.

Ans. (a) 1386 in-lb., (b) 39.6 hp, (c) 86.5 psi.

188. A 6-cylinder, 4-stroke-cycle, single-acting gasoline engine is required to develop 80 bhp at 3600 rpm. The probable friction horsepower, including fluid losses, is 36 fhp, and the probable brake mep is 86 psi. (a) For $L/D = 1$, what bore and stroke should be used? (b) At the stated speed, what are the probable brake torque, mechanical efficiency, and indicated mep?

Ans. (a) 3.52x3.52 in., (b) 117 ft-lb., 69%, 124.5 psi.

189. A 6-cylinder, $3\frac{5}{8}$x3.6-in. automotive engine with a compression ratio of 8 shows a fuel consumption of 0.45 lb./bhp-hr. at 3000 rpm; bhp = 113; fhp = 20 (let ihp = bhp + fhp). Let the standard for comparison be the hot-air standard with $k = 1.3$. The heating value of the fuel is $q_l = 18,500$ Btu/lb. Compute (a) the mechanical efficiency, e_b, and e_i, (b) the brake and indicated engine efficiencies, (c) the brake and indicated mep's. (d) What is the heat rate in Btu/bhp-hr. and in Btu/min.?

    Ans. (a) $e_i = 36\%$, (b) $\eta_i = 77.4\%$, (c) $p_{mb} = 134$ psi, (d) 15,700 Btu/min.

190. An ideal Diesel engine operates from $p_1 = 14$ psia, $t_1 = 140°F$, $V_1 = 1$ cu. ft. with $r = 13.5$. Make computations for a constant value of $k = 1.34$. Let the cutoff be at 6% of the stroke. Find (a) t_2, p_2, V_2, t_3, V_3, p_4, and t_4, (b) Q_A and Q_R, (c) W from pV and TS planes, (d) e and the mep. (f) For a brake engine efficiency of 60% and a fuel heating value of 18,500 Btu/lb., determine the brake fuel rate.

    Ans. (a) $t_3 = 2080°F$, $p_4 = 27.5$ psia, (c) 10.05 Btu, (d) 54.4%, (f) 0.421 lb./bhp-hr.

191. At rated load, a 2000-kw, Diesel-generator unit used 1258 lb./hr. of fuel whose heating value was 18,600 Btu/lb. The generator efficiency was 93%; the mechanical efficiency of the engine was 81%. Calculate the brake, indicated, and combined thermal efficiencies.

    Ans. 31.3%, 38.7%, 29.1%.

192. An 8-cylinder, 14¾x18-in. Diesel engine develops 1085 bhp at 267 rpm. Operating on a 2-stroke cycle, it uses 8.25 lb./min. of fuel for which $q_l = 17,400$ Btu/lb.; the average indicated mep is 81.5 psi. Determine the brake and indicated thermal efficiencies and the mechanical efficiency.

    Ans. 32.1%, 40%, 80.2%.

193. A Diesel engine has a displacement of 1 cu. ft. and $r = 15$. At the point of compression, $p_1 = 14.7$ psia and $t_1 = 140°F$; let $k = 1.34$ be a constant. The actual engine used 0.003 lb. of oil per cycle; $q_l = 17,400$. (a) Determine the clearance volume and the mass of air in the cylinder at 1. (b) Consider that the actual energy released goes to heat the air and fuel (use the properties of air for the mixture) at constant pressure and compute the temperature at 3 (after combustion). If this is the temperature in the corresponding ideal cycle at 3, what is the ideal cutoff ratio?

    Ans. (a) 0.0715 cu. ft., 0.0627 lb., (b) 4445°R, 2.95.

194. A 4-cylinder, 4-stroke-cycle, single-acting Diesel engine is to be designed to develop 1000 bhp at 300 rpm. Decisions have been made as follows: $L/D = 1.3$; $r = 13$; $r_c = 2.45$; $k = 1.35$; $p_1 = 14$ psia; probable mechanical efficiency, 80%; probable brake thermal efficiency, 30%. (a) First compute the ideal mep and then (b) determine the bore and stroke of the engine.

    Ans. (a) 105.8 psi, (b) 21.8 in. × 28.4 in.

195. A 6-cylinder, 3⅛x4⅜ in. engine is operated on methane as the fuel. At 1800 rpm, the fuel consumed is 483 cu. ft./hr. and the volume of free air inducted is 72 cfm; atmosphere is at 29.7 in. Hg and 86°F. What is the volumetric efficiency?   *Ans.* 68.7%.

196–210. These numbers may be used for other problems.

THE SECOND LAW OF THERMODYNAMICS

134. Introduction. As you have seen during the discussion of the gas cycles of the previous chapters, *a fluid undergoes a cycle when it passes through a series of processes and returns to its initial state.* The processes may be reversible ones with names, as isobaric, isentropic, etc., or they may be a series of unnamed state changes, reversible or irreversible. For a cycle to have occurred, it is only necessary that the substance return to its initial state (perhaps nature finally brings it back).

Now it is appropriate to study briefly the Carnot cycle, because no cycle operating between particular temperatures can conceivably have a higher thermal efficiency. Thus the Carnot cycle is a standard of comparison for all other ideal cycles. Moreover, from this cycle we may deduce the second law of thermodynamics, a law of great significance with respect to power-generating and power-consuming machines, and one which has extensive ramifications for all energy transformations.

135. The Carnot Cycle.* The mechanism for carrying out the Carnot cycle is described in Fig. 98. The Carnot cycle consists of two isothermal and two isentropic processes, as shown on the TS and pV planes in Figs. 97

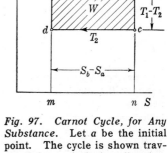

Fig. 97. *Carnot Cycle, for Any Substance.* Let *a* be the initial point. The cycle is shown traversed in a clockwise direction, which, according to our convention of signs, is a power cycle. The net work W will be a positive number. It might be noted that for the state point to return to point *a*, thus completing the cycle, it *must* move toward the left in some manner after *b* is reached. Since a movement of the state point in the leftward direction on the TS plane indicates heat rejected, we may say now that *some heat must be rejected,* that all the heat supplied cannot be converted into work.

* Nicolas Leonard Sadi Carnot (1796–1832), a quiet, unassuming Frenchman, who lived during the turbulent Napoleonic period, devised and analyzed the Carnot cycle in his *Reflections on the Motive Power of Heat* at the early age of only 23 or 24. It did not matter that the caloric theory of heat was the accepted theory in his time. Carnot's cycle is independent of the theory of heat as well as of the working substance. His life was unspectacular. He loved mottoes. One of his favorites, "Speak little of what you know, and not at all of what you do not know," reveals something of the man's nature.

and 98. Starting with point a, we find that heat is added along the isothermal process ab, that the substance expands along a reversible adiabatic (isentropic) bc, during which no heat is added or abstracted, that heat is rejected at constant temperature along cd, and that the substance is compressed isentropically along da to the starting point. The Carnot cycle on the TS plane being a rectangle, its analysis is simple. The heat supplied is the area under the curve ab on the TS plane, $mabn = T_1(S_b - S_a)$, Fig. 97. The heat rejected (as a positive number) is the area under the curve cd on the TS plane, $mdcn = T_2(S_c - S_d) = T_2(S_b - S_a)$. Therefore the net work of the cycle is

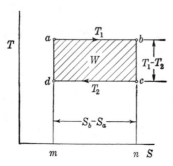

Fig. 97. *Repeated.*

$$W = Q_A - Q_R = T_1(S_b - S_a) - T_2(S_b - S_a),$$

(a) $$W = (T_1 - T_2)(S_b - S_a).$$

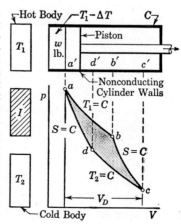

Fig. 98. *Operation of the Carnot Engine on Gas.* The pV diagram is for a noncondensing working substance. A cylinder C contains w lb. of a substance at a temperature $T_1 - \Delta T$, where ΔT approaches zero. The cylinder head, the only place where heat may enter or leave the substance, is placed in contact with the source of heat or hot body which has a constant temperature T_1. Heat flows from the hot body into the substance in the cylinder, which therefore undergoes an isothermal process ab, and the piston moves from a' to b'. Since the temperature difference ΔT is infinitesimal, the transfer of heat is reversible. The process is thus externally as well as internally reversible. Next, the cylinder is removed from the hot body and the insulator I is placed over the head of the cylinder, so that *no* heat may be transferred in or out. As a result, any further process is adiabatic. The isentropic change bc now occurs, wherein the temperature drops from $T_1 - \Delta T$ to $T_2 + \Delta T$ because of the work being done at the expense of the internal energy, and the piston moves from b' to c'. When the piston reaches the end of the stroke c', the insulator I is removed and the cylinder head is placed in contact with the receiver which remains at a constant temperature T_2. Heat then flows reversibly from the substance to the cold body, and the isothermal cd occurs while the piston moves from c' to d'. Finally, the insulator I is again placed over the head and the isentropic compression da returns the substance to its initial condition, the temperature increasing from $T_2 + \Delta T$ to $T_1 - \Delta T$, because the work of compression increases the store of internal energy. In practice, heat would flow very slowly for a small temperature difference ΔT, and therefore the movement of the piston and the *rate* of doing work would be slow. A finite temperature difference precludes reversibility. The mechanical friction of the moving parts of the machine, the internal friction due to turbulence within the substance, and the transferred heat through the cylinder walls (it is impossible to make a nonconducting substance) also preclude reversibility in any real engine.

If a cycle is composed of *internally* reversible processes,* the area *enclosed* by the path of the state point on the TS plane represents the work in Btu, because the enclosed area will always be the heat added minus the heat rejected. The thermal efficiency is

(59) $$e = \frac{Q_A - Q_R}{Q_A} = \frac{(T_1 - T_2)(S_b - S_a)}{T_1(S_b - S_a)} = \frac{T_1 - T_2}{T_1}. \qquad \frac{T_u - T_\ell}{T_u} \text{[CARNOT]}$$

Observe now that this expression for the efficiency of the Carnot cycle is independent of the working substance, inasmuch as the cycle is a rectangle on the TS plane no matter what the substance. The cycle cannot be shown on the pV plane without some knowledge of the properties of the working substance. Figure 99(a) shows the general appearance of the cycle for a gas where the equation of the isothermal is $pV = C$ and of the isentropic $pV^k = C$.

136. Example. Air, considered to be an ideal gas, is used in a Carnot cycle. At the beginning of isothermal expansion, its pressure is 100 psia, its volume is 5 cu. ft., and its temperature is 540°F. For a ratio of isothermal expansion of 2 and a low temperature of 40°F, find (a) the change of entropy during the isothermal process, (b) the heat supplied to the cycle, (c) the heat rejected, (d) the work of the cycle, (e) the efficiency.

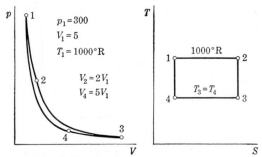

Fig. 99. The enclosed areas on each plane represent work. The unit of pV areas is footpounds; of TS areas, Btu. Since the Btu is 778 times larger than the foot-pound, it would be inconvenient to show these areas to relative size. This pV diagram is drawn approximately to scale for the data in § **136**. Notice that the enclosed area is relatively long and slender.

SOLUTION. (a) The initial temperature is 1000°R, the final temperature is 500°R, and $V_2/V_1 = V_3/V_4 = 2$, Fig. 99. The change of entropy during an isothermal process is

$$\Delta S = \frac{wR}{J} \ln \frac{V_2}{V_1} = \frac{p_1 V_1}{J T_1} \ln \frac{V_2}{V_1} = \frac{(100)(144)(5)}{(778)(1000)} \ln 2 = 0.0641 \text{ Btu/°R.}$$

* The processes of the Carnot cycle are externally reversible also. See Fig. 98.

(b) The heat supplied during 1-2 is

$$Q_A = Q_{1\text{-}2} = (S_2 - S_1)T_1 = (0.0641)(1000) = 64.1 \text{ Btu.}$$

(c) The heat rejected during 3-4 is

$$Q_R = Q_{3\text{-}4} = -(S_2 - S_1)T_3 = -(0.0641)(500) = -32.05 \text{ Btu.}$$

(d) The work is the arithmetic difference of Q_A and Q_R, or

$$W = 64.1 - 32.05 = 32.05 \text{ Btu.}$$

(e) The efficiency is W/Q_A or $(T_1 - T_2)/T_1$, or

$$e = \frac{32.05}{64.1} = 50\%, \quad \text{or} \quad e = \frac{1000 - 500}{1000} = 50\%.$$

137. The Reversed Carnot Cycle. Customarily in a *power* cycle, the state point is pictured as moving in a clockwise direction on the pV and TS planes. In a reversed cycle, the state point describing the changes of state moves conventionally in a *counterclockwise* direction. Reversed cycles are used to provide a refrigerating effect and sometimes a heating effect (Chapter 15). In a reversed cycle, the *net* work is done *on* the substance, rather than *by* the substance, Fig. 100. Inasmuch as each process of the Carnot

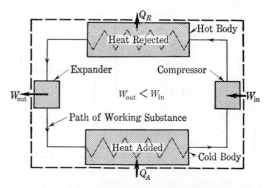

Fig. 100. Reversed Cycle—Heat Pump. This figure, with certain devices not shown, represents a reversed cycle. Note that the work is supplied *to* the system, that heat is rejected at the higher temperature, and that heat is added at the lower temperature. The *net* work is $W = W_{\text{out}} - W_{\text{in}} = \Sigma Q = Q_A - Q_R$, a negative number which indicates that work is done *on* the working substance.

cycle is reversible internally and externally, there is no reason why the cycle itself should not be performed in the opposite direction, Fig. 101. An examination of Fig. 101 shows that for a given temperature range and a given isothermal curve ad, the work must necessarily be the same as in the power cycle, the heat rejected by the reversed cycle at the higher temperature must be equal to the heat added in the power cycle, and the heat added in the reversed cycle must be the same as the heat rejected in the power cycle. A machine which operates on a reversed cycle is called a **heat pump,** because it takes heat from a relatively cold body and discharges heat to a hotter body. (In popular parlance, the name *heat pump* is applied to a machine which is used for warming space such as a residence.)

The expression *efficiency of a reversed cycle* is generally intended to mean the net work of the cycle divided by the heat transferred to the hot body, a number which is the same as that which would be obtained for the efficiency

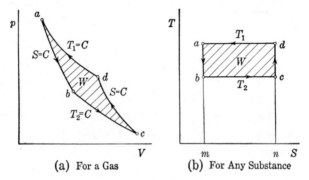

(a) For a Gas   (b) For Any Substance

Fig. 101. Reversed Carnot Cycle. An isentropic expansion *ab* lowers the temperature to a point where heat may be added to the substance reversibly along an isothermal *bc.* A compressor isentropically compresses the substance along *cd* to a temperature slightly higher than the hot body (say, $T_1 + \Delta T$), so that heat may be rejected to the hot body along *da.* The refrigeration is represented by the area *mbcn.* If the cycle is used for heating instead of refrigeration, the energy represented by the area *madn,* being the heat rejected, is the warming effect.

of the same cycle operating as a power cycle. In practice, however, a number called the **coefficient of performance** γ, abbreviated COP, is ordinarily applied to a reversed cycle to express the quality of its operation. This number for a particular reversed cycle has two values, depending upon whether the cycle is used for warming or for refrigerating. Thinking of the COP as being the *output/input*, which is logical, we have

(60) $\gamma = \dfrac{\text{Refrigeration}}{\text{Work}} = \dfrac{Q_A}{W}$ or $\gamma = \dfrac{\text{Heating effect}}{\text{Work}} = \dfrac{Q_R}{W}$

[USED FOR COOLING]   [WARMING]

or for a reversed Carnot cycle, Figs. 100 and 101,

(b) $\gamma = \dfrac{Q_A}{W} = \dfrac{T_2}{T_1 - T_2}$ or $\gamma = \dfrac{Q_R}{W} = \dfrac{T_1}{T_1 - T_2}$

[COOLING]   [CARNOT]   [WARMING]   [CARNOT]

138. Reversible Engine Most Efficient. For particular temperature limits, no engine can be more efficient than a reversible engine. The truth of this statement, known as *Carnot's principle*, is demonstrated by logical deduction. The reasoning will be clearer if numbers, instead of symbols, are used. Imagine a reversible engine R, Fig. 102(a), taking 100 Btu from the hot reservoir during any chosen time, converting 40 Btu into work, and rejecting 60 Btu to the cold reservoir. The thermal efficiency of the engine is therefore $^{40}/_{100} = 40\%$. Now we have just learned from the discussion of the Carnot cycle (§ 137) that if this engine is reversed, 40 Btu will be necessary to drive it, 60 Btu will be taken from the cold body, and 100 Btu will be discharged to the hot body. In Fig. 102(b), an irreversible engine I is driving the reversible engine. For the moment, assume that the irreversible

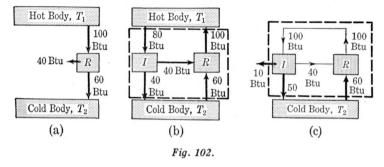

Fig. 102.

engine I is more efficient than the reversible engine R, say $e_I = 50\%$. Then, since it takes 40 Btu to drive R, engine I will need to take $Q_A = W/e = 40/0.5 = 80$ Btu from the hot body and it will discharge 40 Btu to the cold body. We now observe that we have in Fig. 102(b) an isolated system wherein the reversible engine R discharges $100 - 80 = 20$ Btu more to the hot body than the irreversible engine I takes from the hot body. Moreover, the reversible engine R takes $60 - 40 = 20$ Btu more from the cold body than the irreversible engine I discharges to the cold body. In other words, for the assumed condition that I is more efficient than R, we find that heat is being moved continuously from a cold body to a hot body without external aid. All experience indicates that net heat will not flow in any such manner of its own accord. We can cause heat to move in a system from a cold body to a hot body by supplying energy to a prime mover from a source external to the system (a steam engine or electric motor driving the compressor of a refrigerating system), but as Clausius* said (1850), "It is impossible for

---

* Rudolf Julius Emmanuel Clausius (1822–1888), born in northern Germany, a professor of physics, was a genius in mathematical investigations of natural phenomena. He elaborated and restated the work of Carnot, deducing the principle of the second law of thermodynamics. His mathematical work in optics, electricity, and electrolysis was significant. James Clerk Maxwell credits him with being the founder of the kinetic

a self-acting machine unaided by an external agency to move heat from one body to another at a higher temperature." This statement of Clausius' is a statement of the **second law of thermodynamics,** of which, more later.

Instead of simply moving heat, as in Fig. 102(b), we could direct the flow of energy from the reversible engine directly into the irreversible engine, Fig. 102(c), whose 50% efficiency would allow it to drive engine R and, at the same time, deliver 10 Btu of work to something outside of the system. Thus, this system takes energy from a single source or reservoir and delivers work. These events, Fig. 102(b) and (c), have never been known to happen; they are contrary to all of man's experience with energy. Therefore, we say that the assumption that engine I is more efficient than engine R is absurd and that it is impossible for it to be so.

Engine I could be taken as another reversible engine as easily as not, and the same sort of logic as set out above would lead to the conclusion that *one reversible engine cannot be more efficient than another when both engines operate between the same temperature limits; all reversible engines operating between the same temperature limits have the same thermal efficiency;* namely, $(T_1 - T_2)/T_1$.

139. Entropy from the Carnot Cycle. Suppose a Carnot cycle occurs in which the transferred heats are infinitesimal; that is, the change of entropy along 4-1 and 2-3, Fig. 103, is dS. For this cycle, the heat added is dQ_A, represented by the area m-4-1-n, and the heat rejected is dQ_R, represented by the area n-2-3-m. Since the cycle is a Carnot cycle, its efficiency is $(T - T_o)/T$, where the symbols are defined in Fig. 103. For any cycle,

$$e = \frac{Q_A - Q_R}{Q_A}.$$

Therefore,

$$e = \frac{T - T_o}{T} = \frac{dQ_A - dQ_R}{dQ_A} = 1 - \frac{T_o}{T} = 1 - \frac{dQ_R}{dQ_A}.$$

From this expression, we see that

(c)
$$\frac{T_o}{T} = \frac{dQ_R}{dQ_A}.$$

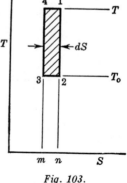

Fig. 103.

Observe that **(c)** is obtained without using in any way the conception of entropy and that to get **(c)** we did not even have to consider the cycle on a

---

TS plane.   Rearranging (c), we have

(d)
$$\frac{dQ_R}{T_o} = \frac{dQ_A}{T},$$

which forms may be compared to the definition of entropy (§ 37), $\Delta S = \int dQ/T$.   Solving for dQ_R from (d) and integrating, we get

(e)
$$Q_R = T_o \int \frac{dQ}{T},$$

where $\int dQ_R = Q_R$, where the subscript A is dropped from dQ_A, and where T_o has been taken as constant.   The temperature T_o is the temperature of the body to which heat is rejected.   In a power cycle, the cold body is the atmosphere or the water from a lake or river or other body of water.   The temperature of the cold body is a naturally available temperature, and, as such, it is lower in the winter than in the summer, lower in polar regions than in tropical regions.   At any particular time and place it has a certain value, inasmuch as the general environment does not show a significant change of temperature no matter how many heat engines are rejecting heat to it.

If equation (e) is written $Q_R = T_o \, \Delta S$, we can translate this expression into words as follows: If energy is transferred to a system during any process and causes a change of entropy of ΔS in the system, the minimum amount of heat that must be rejected to the cold reservoir if a cycle is now completed by this system is $Q_R = T_o\Delta S$.   We say *minimum* rejected heat because we know that a system of reversible (Carnot) cycles, the most efficient, will reject at least this amount.   Other less efficient cycles will reject more than this minimum.   The amount of energy represented by $T_o\Delta S$ is called the **unavailable energy** E_u, because the most efficient engine will not convert this portion of Q_A into work.

(f)
$$E_u = T_o\Delta S \text{ Btu.}$$

That is, suppose that Q_A Btu are transferred to a substance and that the entropy change of the substance during this transfer is ΔS.   Then $T_o\Delta S$ Btu are unavailable and cannot conceivably be converted into work, and $Q_A - T_o\Delta S$ is **available energy** E_a (Q_A is the only ingoing energy):

(g)
$$E_a = Q_A - T_o\Delta S.$$

A perfect engine would convert the available energy, and no more, into work, but since all actual processes are irreversible, an actual engine can convert only a portion of the available energy into work.

140. Second Law of Thermodynamics. This brings us to the *second law of thermodynamics,* one statement of which has been given on p. 167. The full consequences of Clausius' statement, that net heat will not flow of its own accord from a cold to a hot body, are not clearly evident. Lord Kelvin* expressed one significant aspect of this law when he wrote, "*It is impossible by means of inanimate material agency to derive mechanical effect from any portion of matter by cooling it below the temperature of the coldest of the surrounding objects.*" The Kelvin-Planck statement is: *It is impossible to construct an engine which while operating in a cycle produces no effects except to do work and exchange heat with a single reservoir.* See Fig. 102(c).

Many others have expressed their conception of the second law. It has been said that the first law grants that heat and mechanical work are mutually convertible, while the second law limits the amount of heat that may be converted into work. All work can be entirely converted into heat (that is, energy which is heat while it passes to the sink), but only a portion of any continuous flow of heat can be converted into work. This aspect of the second law, the most significant one for the power engineer, is embodied in the following statement: *No actual or ideal heat engine operating in cycles can convert into work all of the heat supplied to the working substance; some of the supplied heat must be discharged as heat.* Another way to express the same idea is to say that a portion of that heat transferred to a working substance is inherently unavailable. Because of this aspect, the second law is often aptly referred to as the *law of degradation of energy.*

The second law and entropy are closely related concepts. Every actual process is accompanied by a net increase in entropy; if the entropy of the system decreases, then the gain of entropy in the surroundings will be greater

* William Thomson (Lord Kelvin) (1824–1907), who was a professor of physics at Glasgow University, is credited by some as being the greatest English physicist. Certainly he possessed a rare combination of talents. His early education was received from his father, who also was a professor at Glasgow University. As a youth, he was robust and an active participant in athletics and student affairs at Cambridge. Yet he was most distinguished in his studies, and before his graduation from Cambridge at age 21, he had established an enviable reputation in scientific circles by his original contributions. An excellent mathematician, a genius at inventing and designing laboratory apparatus and models, he claimed that he could not understand his own ideas until he saw them at work in models. He contributed most to the science of thermodynamics, having established a thermometric scale of absolute temperatures which is independent of the properties of any gas, having aided in establishing the first law of thermodynamics on a firm foundation, and having stated significantly the second law. He was the inventor of some 56 instruments and machines, and in addition to all this, he was interested in the arts and was himself a musician. He was knighted for his indispensable services in laying the first successful transatlantic cable, and later was made a peer, Baron Kelvin of Larg. He vigorously denounced the "absurd, ridiculous, time-wasting, brain-destroying British system of weights and measures," favoring the metric system. He received honorary degrees from nearly every important university in Europe and was elected a member of every foreign academy of science and art. He probably received more honors for and recognition of his achievements during his lifetime than has any other scientist.

than this decrease, resulting in a net increase. Thus, entropy, like time, is unidirectional and always increasing. The greater the entropy change ΔS because of irreversibility, the greater the increase of unavailable energy ($T_o\Delta S$, § 139) and the greater the loss of available energy. Work is energy in available form, as is potential (gravitational) energy, kinetic energy, and electricity. If one of these forms is completely transformed into one of the other available-energy forms, there is no change of entropy. The second law and experience say that such complete changes can only be imagined; actual transformations are accompanied by irreversibilities and entropy increases. As implied by the second law, energy may be "graded." The energy from a reservoir at high temperature is of higher grade (larger percentage of available energy if used directly in a heat engine) than energy from a reservoir at a low temperature. Ultimately, the available energy which is evolved becomes unavailable energy; all actual work produced is eventually dissipated by friction, or the equivalent, and becomes energy in the sink. High-grade energy is constantly being degraded. The entropy of an isolated system tends to increase to a maximum, and it reaches this maximum at the dead state (when it is in equilibrium with its surroundings); on the other hand, the energy of an isolated system remains constant.

141. Closure. This chapter has two objectives; first, to acquaint the reader with a reversible cycle (the Carnot cycle is one of several reversible ones which have been conceived) and second, to look into the implications arising from a study of a reversible cycle. We may generalize these implications in a number of ways, as has already been noted in the various statements of the second law. Remember that there is a net increase of entropy wherever an irreversible process occurs, and in accordance with equation (e), the increase of entropy is a measure of the increase of unavailable energy.

Since work is energy in transition, it is in being only while it is "doing something," usually, in the end, overcoming friction. In the simplest sequence of events, this friction raises the temperatures of the systems concerned (increases the activity of their molecules); then, the systems being at a higher temperature than the surroundings lose heat until the dead state is reached.

PROBLEMS

211. A Carnot cycle operates between the temperature limits of 140°F and 500°F. If the heat supplied is 300 Btu/min., determine (a) the thermal efficiency, (b) the work and horsepower, (c) the heat rejected, (d) ΔS during the isothermal processes.

Ans. (a) 37.5%, (b) 2.66 hp, (c) 187.5 Btu/min., (d) 0.3125 Btu per °R-min.

212. A Carnot engine, whose efficiency is 40% delivers 23.6 hp when the sink temperature is 40°F. Determine the temperature of the heat reservoir and the heat supplied.

Ans. 373.3°F, 2500 Btu/min.

213. The working substance for a Carnot cycle is 10 lb. of argon. At the beginning of isothermal expansion, V_a = 10 cu. ft. and p_a = 400 psia. The isothermal ratio of expansion is 2 and the sink temperature is 100°F. Find (a) T_1 and Q_A, (b) e, W, and Q_R, (c) the volume at the end of isentropic expansion, the mep, and the overall expansion ratio. (d) Can you devise an ideal gas turbine (Brayton) cycle which will have a greater thermal efficiency than this one? Explain.

Ans. (a) Q_A = 513 Btu, (b) e = 62.5%, (c) p_m = 22.55 psi.

214. In a reversed cycle, there is a work input of 100 Btu/min., a work output of 50 Btu/min., while 150 Btu per min. are rejected. (a) What is the heat added to the system? What is the COP if the cycle is used for (b) refrigeration, (c) heating?

Ans. (b) 2, (c) 3.

215. A Carnot engine has a thermal efficiency of 25% as a power engine. It is reversed and does 900 Btu/min. of refrigeration. (a) Determine the work (hp) and COP. (b) If this system is used for heating, what is the amount of heat delivered and the COP for heating? Is more work required than in (a)? (c) What is ΔS if the heat is added to the system at 40°F? at -60°F?

Ans. (a) COP = 3, (b) COP = 4, (c) 1.4, 2.25 Btu/°R-min.

216. The COP of a Carnot cycle for refrigeration is 5.35 when the refrigeration is done at 0°F. The change of entropy during the isothermal process is 0.2 Btu/°R-min. Find (a) the amount of refrigeration, (b) the temperature at

which heat is rejected, (c) the horsepower required to drive. (d) If this reversed cycle is used for heating, what is the COP? the heating effect?

Ans. (a) 92 Btu/min., (b) 86°F, (c) 0.405 hp, (d) 109.2 Btu/min.

217. A reversed Carnot cycle, operating on 3 lb. of air, picks up heat at 20°F and discharges heat at 500°F. The lowest pressure in the cycle is 20 psia and the compression ratio during isothermal compression is 3. Find (a) ΔS during the isothermal processes, (b) Q_A, Q_R, and W, (c) the highest pressure, smallest volume, and the mep of the cycle.

Ans. (a) 0.226 Btu/°R, (b) W = 108.5 Btu, (c) 678 psia, 1.573 cu. ft., 23.3 psi.

218. An inventor claims that his engine will produce 1000 Btu of work from 1500 Btu of heat released from the fuel. Upon investigation, an engineer finds that the highest temperature in the cycle is 600°F and that the sink temperature will average about 70°F. Is the inventor's claim possible? Is the first law violated? Is the second law violated? Explain.

219. There are transferred 2000 Btu from a reservoir at 5000°F to a system which accepts this heat while remaining at a constant temperature of 300°F. The sink temperature is 80°F. What is (a) the decrease in entropy of the reservoir, (b) the increase in entropy of the system? (c) What are the available energies before and after the transfer? (d) What is the increase of unavailable energy because of the transfer? (e) What is the percentage loss of available energy? Does this violate the first law?

Ans. (a) -0.366 Btu/°R, (b) 2.63 Btu/°R, (c) E_{a1} = 1800 Btu, (d) 1222 Btu, (e) 68%.

220. During a steady flow process

through a heat exchanger ($W = 0$, $\Delta K = 0$), 1200 Btu/min. of heat are supplied to 5 lb./min. of air which is initially at 140°F. The sink temperature is 80°F and the pressure remains constant. (a) What is the available portion of the heat? Is it likely that this much work might be obtained? Explain. (b) What ideal cycle would convert all of this available energy into work? Sketch on the TS plane. What is its efficiency? (c) Under what circumstances may all of the heat be converted into work?

Ans. (a) $E_a = 564$ Btu, (b) 47%.

221. Steam at 456°F with a specific heat of $c_p = 0.6$ Btu/lb-°R is to be heated to 708°F in a heat exchanger by heat from a gas whose $c_p = 0.24$ Btu per lb-°R and whose initial temperature is 1500°F. The rate of flow of the gas is 52.5 lb./sec. and of the steam, 25 lb./sec. Each substance remains at constant pressure (nearly). Compute (a) the final temperature of the gas, (b) the change of entropy of the steam and of the gas, (c) the net ΔS, (d) the net loss of available energy for the system when $T_o = 530$°R.

Ans. (a) 1220°F, (b) 3.63, −2.09 Btu/°R-sec., (d) 816 Btu/sec.

222. From 80°F and 6 cu. ft., 10 lb. of air receive energy continuously until the state is defined by 150°F and 10 cu. ft. (*a*) For a sink temperature of 40°F, how much of the energy received by the system is unavailable if it enters as heat? as paddle work? (*b*) Comment on the change of entropy of the surroundings in each case.

Ans. 278.5 Btu.

223. If a system does 70 Btu of work while 40 Btu of heat are being transferred to it, does it follow that the first or second law is being violated? Discuss what happens to the system in this circumstance.

224–230. These numbers may be used for other problems.

$$\mathscr{E}\ \boldsymbol{10}$$

LIQUIDS AND VAPORS

142. Introduction. Up to this point, we have considered substances which were entirely gaseous or entirely liquid. However, one of the most common situations in practice concerns a mixture of a liquid and its vapor, called a two-phase system, such as the water and steam in a boiler. Frequently, either the liquid is being evaporated or the vapor is being condensed. Also, it often happens that a mixture of a vapor with some liquid suspended in it enters a process or emerges from one. In any event, we must be able to determine the properties of liquid-vapor (two-phase) mixtures and of vapors, which, as a rule, do not act in accordance with the ideal gas laws.

An ideal gas is distinguished from an actual gas by having molecules which exert no force upon one another and which occupy no space. The molecules of diatomic and monatomic gases are so small in mass and volume that at ordinary pressures these gases perform closely according to ideal gas laws. Nevertheless, they begin to deviate from ideal gas laws at high pressure, and most other substances are composed of molecules so large and so heavy that their vapors are likely to act as ideal gases only at rather low pressures (well below atmospheric pressure), where their molecules are spaced far apart. Equations of state (§ 44) for these imperfect gases are relatively complex. Indeed, the mathematics is sufficiently involved to make it worth while to develop tables which give the most useful properties of common substances; for example, of ammonia, carbon dioxide, sulfur dioxide, several of the Freons, and water-steam. See the tables in the Appendix. For illustrative purposes, steam will be used most often, but the methods outlined apply to any substance whose properties are available in tabular form.

All energy equations in general terms and symbols (K, h, u, pv, Q, W), Chapters 2, 3, and 5, apply to any substance in the given circumstance. Thus, the principal objective is to learn how to determine properties and changes of properties using vapor tables instead of ideal gas laws.

143. Vaporizing a Liquid at Constant Pressure. To understand the states in which a liquid, a vapor, and a mixture of a liquid and vapor may exist, consider the phenomenon of a liquid being heated while the pressure remains constant.   Let there be 1 lb. of water in a cylinder, Fig. 104(a), and let the weight w be such that the pressure on the water is 100 psia. Suppose further that the temperature of the water is 32°F.   Now let heat be added to the water.   The temperature increases, and during most of the time the volume of the liquid increases.   The increase in volume causes the piston and weight to move up; thus, work is done in moving the piston against this pressure.   This work, however, is only a very small portion of the heat added to the liquid during the rise in temperature; that is, the temperature change of liquids substantially is a measure of the change of internal energy.

The temperature of the liquid is soon such that it begins to boil.   The temperature at which a liquid boils depends upon the pressure on it.   *For each pressure, there is a precise temperature that marks the boiling point of a*

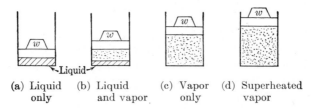

(a) Liquid   (b) Liquid   (c) Vapor   (d) Superheated
   only   and vapor   only   vapor

Fig. 104.   Heating at Constant Pressure.

particular liquid.   This temperature is called the **saturation temperature,** and when a liquid is at this temperature, it is called a **saturated liquid.** *The saturation temperature is a function of the pressure.*   As you know, water boils at 212°F when the pressure is atmospheric (14.696 psia).   At 100 psia, water boils at 327.81°F.   At 100 psia, ammonia boils at 56.05°F.   (These data are taken from vapor tables, § 144.)   Another characteristic of the boiling process is that the temperature of the liquid and vapor remains constant at the saturation temperature as long as there is any liquid present.*   Thus, while the water in the cylinder of Fig. 104(a) and (b) is evaporating, the temperature remains at 327.81°F.

In Fig. 104(b), part of the water has evaporated.   The cylinder has in it a mixture of steam and water.   A mixture of a vapor and its liquid is called a **wet mixture** or **two-phase mixture.**   The state of a wet mixture at a given pressure is expressed by its quality or percentage moisture.   The **quality** x of a mixture is the percentage by weight which is vapor.   Thus, if the quality is $x = 75\%$, then in 1 lb. of mixture, 0.75 lb. is vapor and 0.25 lb. is liquid.

---

* This statement assumes a condition of internal equilibrium and is substantially true, but of course actually, small differences of temperature in the various parts of the mixture are bound to exist.

The *percentage moisture* is the per cent by weight of the mixture which is liquid, so that 25% moisture means that in 1 lb., 0.25 lb. is liquid and 0.75 lb. is vapor.

If the transfer of heat to the mixture continues, all of the liquid will eventually be evaporated, Fig. 104(c). At the point when the last drop of liquid is evaporated, the temperature of the vapor is the saturation temperature. Vapor that is at the saturation temperature and 100% quality is known as **saturated vapor** (sometimes *dry and saturated vapor*, the *dry* indicating that there are no liquid particles suspended in the vapor). The mixture in Fig. 104(b) is one of saturated liquid and saturated vapor and is therefore also called a **saturated mixture.**

Finally, if further heat is added to the vapor, its temperature will rise, its volume will increase, Fig. 104(d), and the vapor is said to be **superheated.** **Superheated vapor** is vapor at any temperature above saturation temperature. If thermal equilibrium exists within the superheated vapor, there can be no liquid in it. To define the state of a superheated vapor, we usually state the pressure and the temperature. Often we speak of the **degrees of superheat,** which is the difference between the actual temperature of the superheated vapor and the saturation temperature for the existing pressure. For example, suppose the steam is at a pressure of 100 psia and a temperature of 500°F. Since the saturation temperature of steam at this pressure is 327.81°F (see above), the degrees of superheat are $500 - 327.81 = 172.19°$.

144. Vapor Tables. The computations of the properties of vapors are based upon the data of extensive and carefully conducted experiments. Different sets of vapor tables may give slightly different values for the properties of a saturated vapor or liquid at a particular pressure. Such differences arise largely because of variations in experimental data from which the values in the tables are computed. However, so many data have now been accumulated for steam that we can say confidently for most values that the true property lies between certain limits which are quite close together. Both the values quoted in the Appendix, Tables VIII, IX, and X, from Keenan and Keyes, *Thermodynamic Properties of Steam,*[*] and those quoted in *Problems on Thermodynamics* (by Faires, Brewer, and Simmang), from *Steam Tables*, published by the Combustion Engineering, Inc., fall within the tolerances agreed upon by an international group of scientists.

The nature of these tables is best explained by quoting briefly from the contents. The first two columns of Tables VIII and IX are corresponding saturation values of p and t. Beginning with the third column:

* Published by John Wiley and Sons, Inc., New York.

f = fluid
g = gas

v_f is the volume of 1 lb. of saturated liquid, the *specific* volume of the water at the stated pressure or temperature;

v_{fg} is the *change* of volume undergone when 1 lb. of water evaporates to 1 lb. of steam;

v_g is the *specific* volume of the steam;

h_f is the enthalpy of 1 lb. of water, the specific enthalpy;

h_{fg} is the *change* of enthalpy during the vaporization of 1 lb. of liquid;

h_g is the specific enthalpy of (1 lb.) saturated steam;

s_f is the entropy of 1 lb. of saturated liquid;

s_{fg} is the *change* of entropy during the evaporation of 1 lb. of liquid;

s_g is the specific entropy of saturated vapor;

u_f and u_g are the specific internal energies of saturated liquid and saturated vapor, respectively (in Table IX only).

In connection with these tables, note that the volume of the liquid v_f increases as the pressure and temperature increase. However, the change of volume is practically independent of the change in pressure, unless the change in pressure is very large. This statement is made on the assumption that the liquid is nearly incompressible, a satisfactory assumption for the average practical problem. It follows that the noted increase in volume is due to the increase in temperature; so

When the specific volume of the liquid is desired the volume corresponding to the actual temperature should be found

no matter what the pressure may be.* The tables show that the volume of the saturated vapor v_g *is equal to* the volume of the saturated liquid v_f *plus* the change in volume during vaporization v_{fg}; that is,

(a) $$v_g = v_f + v_{fg}.$$

By definition, the enthalpy h_f of saturated liquid at 32°F is zero, Table VIII. Since the enthalpy of any substance is defined by $h = u + pv/J$, the internal energy u_f for saturated water at 32°F is

(b) $$u_f = h - \frac{pv}{J} = 0 - \frac{(144)(0.08854)(0.01602)}{778} = -0.00026 \text{ Btu/lb.}$$

The negative sign indicates merely that the measurement is below our chosen datum.

We see from Table VIII that if the pressure is 0.08854 psia, water will boil at 32°F. To bring about this evaporation, we must add heat to the water, the amount needed for saturated water being $h_{fg} = 1075.8$ Btu/lb., Table VIII, when the pressure is maintained constant. The transferred heat for a constant pressure process is equal to the change of enthalpy.

---

* At very high pressures, the assumption of incompressibility of water is in error, and some liquids are more compressible than water. See Table III and § 149.

The heat transferred to 1 lb. of saturated liquid to evaporate it is often called the *latent heat of evaporation,* or simply the *latent heat.* We observe from Tables VIII and IX that the latent heat of steam h_{fg} decreases as the saturation pressure and temperature increase. Notice, too, that

(c) $$h_g = h_f + h_{fg}.$$

As in the case of enthalpy, the datum of entropy is saturated water at 32°F, where $s_f = 0$. Observe that $s_g = s_f + s_{fg}$.

145. The *pv* and *Ts* Planes. Since we shall now be dealing with mixtures of liquids and vapors, it will be convenient to draw on the *pv* and *Ts* planes lines that mark the boundaries of regions representing the various phases. From the values in the tables, we may plot points through which may be drawn curves which are called the *saturated liquid line* and the *saturated vapor line* or *dry vapor line.* See Fig. 105 for the method. We

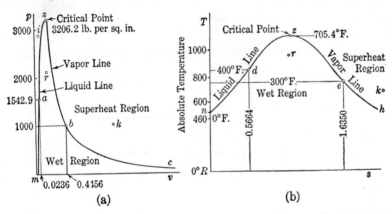

Fig. 105. Liquid and Vapor Lines on pv and Ts Planes. The curves are obtained as follows. Plot the pressures against v_f (as taken from vapor tables) to find the saturated liquid line in (a). For example, let the pressure be 1542.9 lb./sq. in. abs.; the corresponding $v_f = 0.0236$ cu. ft. (Table VIII). Lay off these values in (a) and locate point *a*. Other points are plotted in a similar manner. A smooth curve through these points will give the *liquid line*. Points on the *vapor line* in (a) are found by plotting pressure against v_g as taken from the tables. Point *b* in (a) is for $p = 1000$ lb./sq. in. abs. and $v_g = 0.4456$ cu. ft. (from Table IX). The curves on the *Ts* plane are found by plotting $T°R$ against s_f (for the liquid line) and $T°R$ against s_g (for the vapor line). See points *d* and *e* in (b) and compare the coordinates of these points with values in Table VIII. The volume scale in (a) has been distorted because the volume of the liquid is so very small as compared to the volume of the vapor at low pressures.

commonly use the terms *liquid line* and *vapor line* for short, and they are so labeled in Fig. 105, but the word *saturated* is always understood. The liquid line meets the vapor line on both *pv* and *Ts* planes at a point called the *critical point,* § 150.

Whenever a point such as r, which represents the state of a substance, lies *within* the curves mzc, Fig. 105(a), and nzh, Fig. 105(b), the substance is a *wet* or *two-phase* mixture, part liquid and part vapor.

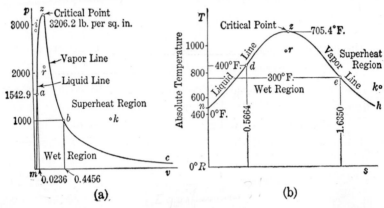

Fig. 105. Repeated.

If the state point is on the liquid line, for example, a or d, Fig. 105, the substance is a saturated liquid. If the state point is on the vapor line, for example, b or e, the substance is a saturated vapor.

Whenever the substance is a superheated vapor, its state point will lie to the right of the vapor line; for example, point k.

Observe how the saturated vapor line on the pv plane flattens out at low pressures, indicating that the volume increases at an increasing rate at low pressures. Refer to steam tables for quantitative data. In the solution of problems concerning vapors, the Ts plane is particularly helpful. The student should acquire the habit of sketching one or both of these planes for each problem, showing in each case the liquid and vapor lines, drawn, of course, freehand.

146. Internal Energy. Ordinarily, vapor tables do not give internal energies, yet they are needed now and then. Values of internal energy are computed from $u = h - pv/J$. For a saturated *liquid*, the internal energy is approximately equal to the enthalpy, unless the temperature is quite high; $u_f \approx h_f$.

The internal energy of saturated *vapor* is

(d) $$u_g = h_g - pv_g/J \text{ Btu/lb.},$$

where h_g and v_g are found in the tables according to the pressure p (or the corresponding temperature). For example, at 100 psia, the internal energy of saturated vapor is

$$u_g = 1187.2 - \frac{(100)(144)(4.432)}{778} = 1105.2 \text{ Btu/lb.}$$

147. Properties of a Wet Mixture. Consider any liquid under some pressure p psia and at 32°F. If p is greater than the saturation pressure corresponding to 32°F, the liquid is not saturated and is called a *compressed liquid*. If the datum of enthalpy be taken as zero for a saturated liquid, then this compressed liquid does not have zero enthalpy, since $h = u + pv/J$. However, the pv/J term is small unless the pressure is quite large and, for the purpose of a visual aid in remembering the properties, we may consider it as negligible. In this event, the enthalpy of the liquid at t, Fig. 106, is nearly zero, and if it is heated at constant pressure to the boiling point (saturation temperature) at m, the area under the constant pressure curve tm on the Ts plane represents heat $Q = \Delta h$ for $p = C$. That is, the area under tm represents closely the enthalpy of the liquid at m. The s coordinate of m is the entropy of the liquid exactly. Now if part of the liquid is evaporated, the increase in any property is a part of the change that that property undergoes during complete vaporization. Take any property for illustration, say s. The entropy of a two-phase system represented by point 1, Fig. 106, is the entropy s_f of the liquid plus the fraction x of the liquid evaporated (x = quality) times the entropy s_{fg} of evaporation, or

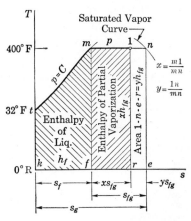

Fig. 106. Properties of Wet Mixture.

$$\textbf{(e)} \qquad\qquad s_1 = s_f + xs_{fg}.$$

In terms of the percentage moisture $y = 1 - x$, start at point n. The entropy at 1 is equal to the entropy s_g of saturated vapor at n minus the fraction y of the liquid which has *not* evaporated times the entropy of evaporation, or

$$\textbf{(f)} \qquad\qquad s_1 = s_g - ys_{fg}.$$

All properties of a two-phase system can be obtained by similar reasoning. For 1 lb.,

(g) $\qquad h = h_g - yh_{fg}, \qquad\qquad h = h_f + xh_{fg},$
(h) $\qquad v = v_g - yv_{fg}, \qquad\qquad v = v_f + xv_{fg}.$
$\qquad\qquad$ [HIGH QUALITY] $\qquad\qquad\qquad$ [LOW QUALITY]

The expressions with y give more accurate slide-rule answers when the quality is high (above 75%); the expressions with x give more accurate answers when the quality is low (below 25%). There is little difference in the intermediate range. If the internal energy of a wet mixture is needed, compute h and v from (**g**) and (**h**), and then $u = h - pv/J$ Btu/lb.

It takes two coordinates to locate a point in a plane. Since the pressure and temperature in the wet region both locate the same line, it is necessary to give still another property in order to define the state point. The entropy or the volume will serve, but it is common practice to define the state of the two-phase system by giving either the pressure or temperature and the quality or moisture content.

148. Properties of Superheated Steam. Modern vapor tables usually give the necessary properties of superheated vapors. In Table X, Appendix, for steam, we find the values of v, h, and s, the values of h and s being measured above saturated water at 32°F. In order to define the state of a substance in the superheat region, it is necessary to specify two properties. Any two may be used, but the most common practice is to give the pressure and temperature.

At low pressures, when the state of a superheated vapor falls outside of the limits of the superheat table, the vapor may be treated as an ideal gas.

Examples. (a) What is the internal energy (above 32°F) of steam at 100 psia and 600°F? From Table X, we find $h = 1329.1$ and $v = 6.218$. Therefore

$$u = h - pv/J = 1329.1 - \frac{(100)(144)(6.218)}{778} = 1214 \text{ Btu/lb.}$$

(b) What is the entropy of steam at 297 psia and 512°F? This problem illustrates the method of making a double interpolation. By comparing the temperature given with the saturation temperature corresponding to 297 psia, we note that the steam is superheated. From more complete tables than Table X, we have taken the following values of entropy:

At 500° F:		At 520° F:	
For $p = 295$,	$s = 1.5725$	For $p = 295$,	$s = 1.5847$
For $p = 300$,	$s = 1.5701$	For $p = 300$,	$s = 1.5824$
Difference	$= 0.0024$	Difference	$= 0.0023$
$(\tfrac{2}{5})(0.0024)$	$= 0.00096$	$(\tfrac{2}{5})(0.0026)$	$= 0.0009$
For $p = 297$,	$s = 1.5715$	For $p = 297$,	$s = 1.5838$

At $p = 297$ psi:

For $t = 500°$,	$s = 1.5715$
For $t = 520°$,	$s = 1.5838$
Difference	$= 0.0123$
$(1\tfrac{2}{20})(0.0123)$	$= 0.0074$
For $t = 512°$,	$s = 1.5789$ Ans.

149. Compressed Liquid. *If the pressure on a liquid is greater than the saturation pressure corresponding to its temperature, the liquid is said to be* *compressed liquid* or *subcooled liquid*. To obtain compressed liquid, one could allow saturated liquid at d, Fig. 107, to cool at constant pressure to some temperature T_b. In cooling, it would follow a path somewhat above but close to the saturated liquid line ad on the Ts plane, a path whose location is grossly exaggerated in Fig. 107(b) in order to separate significant points enough to identify them. A compressed liquid may also be obtained by starting with a saturated liquid at a, Fig. 107, and increasing the pressure on it (say, by passing it through a pump). This increase in pressure may come about through various processes ab, ac, aB, etc.

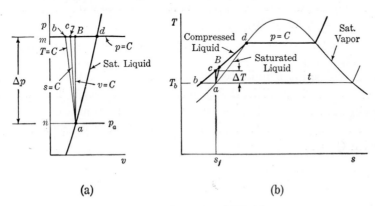

(a)   (b)

Fig. 107.   Compressed Liquid.

There is little information in general about the properties of liquids in the subcooled region. For water, Keenan and Keyes steam tables include certain changes in properties as shown by Table III, abstracted by permission. With the complete table available and with the temperature of the liquid *after* it has been compressed or subcooled, the properties v, h, and s of subcooled liquid at some point b, Fig. 107, are obtained from

$$(v - v_f)10^5 = \text{value from table}, \qquad (h - h_f) = \text{value from table},$$
$$(s - s_f)10^3 = \text{value from table},$$

where v_f, h_f, and s_f are values for saturated liquid at a with the customary units. For example, the entropy of compressed liquid b at 2000 psia and 500°F, Table III, is

$$s_b = s_f - (5.58)(10^{-3}) = 0.68871 - 0.00558 = 0.68313 \text{ Btu/lb-°R}.$$

On the same page with the table of compressed water properties in Keenan and Keyes is a chart from which one may obtain the change of enthalpy of water which has been compressed isentropically ac, Fig. 107. Whenever accuracy is desired, the properties of compressed water should be used.

However, at low temperature and pressure, water acts very much as an incompressible fluid, in which case the points b, c, and B become quite close together. These three points are defined by an isothermal compression ab, an isentropic compression ac, and a constant volume compression aB. As these points approach each other at low pressures, their properties approach equality. One cannot say exactly where a line should be drawn, but for pedagogical purposes, let us say that for pressures and temperatures of steam below 400 psia and 400°F, use properties of saturated liquid; do not correct for the compressed liquid effect.

If a liquid is pumped reversibly in steady flow to a higher pressure, the work is ($\Delta K = 0$, $\Delta P = 0$)

(i)
$$W = -(\Delta h)_s,$$
[EQUATION (29A)]

where the subscript s indicates constant entropy. This change can be evaluated accurately with the properties of subcooled liquid. In the absence of known properties, we can obtain a good estimate of (i) for liquids which are nearly incompressible by the relation from equation (16A), § 30, with $Q = 0$:

(j)
$$\Delta h = \frac{1}{J} \int v \, dp = \frac{v \Delta p}{J}.$$
[$v = C$]

Table III. COMPRESSED WATER

Taken with permission from Table 4 of Keenan and Keyes, *Thermodynamic Properties of Steam*, published by John Wiley & Sons, Inc.

Temperature, °F =		32°	100°	200°	300°	400°	500°	600°
Saturated liquid	$p =$	0.08854	0.9492	11.526	67.013	247.31	680.8	1542.9
	$v_f =$	0.016022	0.016132	0.016634	0.017449	0.018639	0.020432	0.023629
	$h_f =$	0	67.97	167.99	269.59	374.97	487.82	617.0
	$s_f =$	0	0.12948	0.29382	0.43694	0.56638	0.68871	0.8131
Abs. press. (Sat. temp.)								
200 (381.79)	$(v - v_f)10^5$	−1.1	−1.1	−1.1	−1.1			
	$(h - h_f)$	+0.61	+0.54	+0.41	+0.23			
	$(s - s_f)10^3$	+0.03	−0.05	−0.21	−0.21			
1000 (544.61)	$(v - v_f)10^5$	−5.7	−5.1	−5.4	−6.9	−8.7	−6.4	
	$(h - h_f)$	+2.99	+2.70	+2.21	+1.75	+0.84	−0.14	
	$(s - s_f)10^3$	+0.15	−0.53	−1.20	−1.64	−2.00	−1.41	
2000 (635.82)	$(v - v_f)10^5$	−11.0	−9.9	−10.8	−13.8	−19.5	−27.8	−32.6
	$(h - h_f)$	+5.97	+5.31	+4.51	+3.64	+2.03	−0.38	−2.5
	$(s - s_f)10^3$	+0.22	−1.18	−2.39	−3.42	−4.57	−5.58	−4.3
3000 (695.36)	$(v - v_f)10^5$	−16.3	−14.7	−16.0	−20.7	−30.0	−47.1	−87.9
	$(h - h_f)$	+9.00	+7.88	+6.76	+5.49	+3.33	−0.41	−6.9
	$(s - s_f)10^3$	+0.28	−1.79	−3.56	−5.12	−7.03	−9.42	−12.4

Observe that $v\Delta p$ is the rectangular area $naBm$, Fig. 107(a); $v = v_a = v_f$ and $\Delta h = h_B - h_a = h_B - h_f$, where the subscript f indicates properties of saturated liquid. Thus, from (j), we have

$$(\mathbf{k}) \qquad\qquad h_B = h_f + \frac{v_f\Delta p}{J} = h_f + \frac{v_f(p' - p_s)}{J},$$

in which h_f and v_f are taken for saturated liquid at the temperature of the liquid *before* compression; p' is the actual pressure and p_s is the saturation pressure. The point B, at a temperature slightly higher than that at a, is not very far from c, the state after isentropic compression, and the approximation of equation (**k**) will usually be better than no allowance for the subcooling effect.

150. Critical Point. The liquid and vapor lines for many, but not all vapors, for example, ammonia, sulfur dioxide, and carbon dioxide, will look much like those in Fig. 105 for steam. In each case, there is a point z where the liquid and vaporous phases merge and become identical in every respect. Observe that the saturated liquid line *ends* at this point. Therefore, if a vapor is at a temperature greater than the temperature at the critical point, it is impossible to liquefy it, no matter how much pressure may be applied. The temperature at the critical point is called the **critical temperature.** The *saturation* pressure corresponding to this temperature is called the **critical pressure.** The critical temperatures of a few common substances are as follows.

Steam,	705.4°F	Oxygen,	−181.8°F
Ammonia,	270.3°F	Hydrogen,	−399.8°F
Carbon dioxide,	87.8°F	Nitrogen,	−232.8°F
Sulfur dioxide,	315 °F	Helium,	−450.2°F

151. Other Vapors. Properties of many other vapors are available in tables and charts, a few samples of which are found in the Appendix. Before using unfamiliar tables, study them carefully. There are different arrangements, different nomenclature, and different symbols. They are not all based on the same datum state, which does not matter if one does not become confused with signs. For example, the properties of **refrigerants** are generally measured from a state of saturated liquid at −40°F, as in Table XI for ammonia, extracted from *Tables of Thermodynamic Properties of Ammonia*, Bulletin No. 142, U. S. Bureau of Standards.* Refrigeration temperatures go below −40°F in some industrial processes, in which case the enthalpy and entropy of saturated liquid are negative. The negative

---

* Bulletin No. 142 may be obtained from the Superintendent of Documents, Government Printing Office, Washington, D. C. In view of its reasonable price, students are urged to obtain a copy.

signs mean only that measurement is below the datum. Carry the sign into the basic equations and stick to the rules of algebra.

The saturated liquid and vapor lines for several substances are shown in Fig. 108, as plotted for 1 lb. Notice the variability of the latent heat of

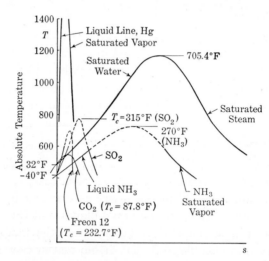

Fig. 108.   Various Fluids on Ts Plane.

evaporation, proportional to the distance between the liquid and vapor lines at a particular temperature. Sulfur dioxide, carbon dioxide, ammonia, and Freon 12 are refrigerants (H_2O is also used as a refrigerant). Mercury (Hg) is used to generate power in turbines in so-called binary vapor cycles.

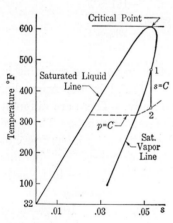

Fig. 109. *Saturation Curve for Acetic Acid.*

Not all saturated vapor curves slope downward toward the right. Some show a double curvature, for example, benzene; and several such curves slope downward toward the left as, for example, the saturated vapor curve of acetic acid, Fig. 109. If a substance with this characteristic undergoes an isentropic expansion, it becomes dryer or more highly superheated, whereas other substances discussed here become wetter or lose superheat.

152. Closure. The purpose of this chapter is to acquaint the reader with the characteristic phenomena of liquids and vapors and the use of the vapor tables. Study available vapor tables carefully. If you should happen to have two different tables for the same substance, differences in a particular property should not alarm you. However, do not mix values from different tables in a particular problem.

In studying the examples concerning vapors later in this text, you are urged to work out each example independently, looking up all values needed from the vapor tables. Those energy equations in Chapter 5 which are in terms of general symbols (h, u, Q, W, K) are true for processes of vapors. But be careful not to use ideal gas equations.

PROBLEMS

Note. *Unless otherwise stated, the answers given to the problems are based on* Steam Tables, *published by Combustion Engineering, Inc. If other tables are used, some differences in answers are to be expected. Combustion Engineering may be willing to furnish their tables for loan to students. A copy of their tables is found in* Problems on Thermodynamics *by Faires, Brewer, and Simmang. In some of the problems, also in later chapters, the data are chosen for a convenient fit with these tables. Where appropriate, show energy diagrams and locate the state points on pv and/or Ts planes.*

231. (a) What are the temperature, volume, enthalpy, entropy, and internal energy of 3 lb. of saturated steam at 350 psia? (b) The same as (a) except that the steam is at 350 psia and 520°F. (c) The same as (a) except that the steam is wet with 10% moisture.
Ans. (c) 431.7°F, 3.5847 cu. ft., 3374.7 Btu, 4.2242 Btu/°R, 3143 Btu.

232. (a) A 10-cu. ft. drum contains saturated steam at 85.3 psig. What are the temperature and mass of steam in the drum? Determine the enthalpy, entropy, and internal energy. (b) The same as (a) except that the drum contains 3 lb. of steam (not saturated). (c) The same as (a) except that the mass is 1.241 lb. of steam.
Ans. (c) 900°F, 4434 Btu, 5.6442 Btu/°R, 4249 Btu.

233. For practice in interpolation, find the enthalpy, volume, entropy, and internal energy of 1 lb. of steam at 462 psia and 625°F.
Ans. 1316.2, 1.3034, 1.5777, 1204.6.

234. (a) Ammonia at 15 psia has an entropy of 1.5 Btu/lb-°R. What are

its specific enthalpy and volume? (b) Ammonia at 15 psia has enthalpy of 130.6 Btu/lb. What are the specific volume and entropy? (c) Ammonia at 110 psia has an enthalpy of 650 Btu/lb. Determine its temperature and degrees of superheat, its specific volume, and specific entropy.
Ans. (a) 653.1, 21.96, (b) 3.553, 0.3038, (c) 94.7°F, 2.943 cu. ft./lb., 1.268 Btu/lb-°R.

235. (a) Compressed liquid water is at 3000 psia and 200°F. For 1 lb., what are its enthalpy, entropy, and volume? (b) Saturated water at 200°F is pumped to 3000 psia. Find the approximate increase of enthalpy (pump work), using $\int v\,dp$. Show these state points on a large scale Ts plane.
Ans. (a) $h = 174.75$, (b) 9.2 Btu/lb.

236. (a) Water at 3000 psia and 300°F is heated at constant pressure in a steam generator to steam at 800°F. How much heat is added per pound? (b) Saturated water at 300°F is pumped to 3000 psia and then heated to steam at 3000 psia and 800°F. How much heat is added? See equation (k), § 149. (c) The same as (b) except that $p =$ 85.3 psig. (d) Is it advisable in either (b) or (c) to account for the enthalpy increase during compression of the liquid?

Ans. (From Keenan and Keyes) (a) 992.1, (b) 993, (c) 1159.2 Btu/lb.

237. Two boilers discharge equal amounts of steam into the same main. The steam from one is at 200 psia and 550°F, from the other at 200 psia and 8% moisture. (a) What is the equilibrium condition after mixing? Sketch an energy diagram for this event. (b) What is the change of entropy of the higher-temperature steam? of the lower-temperature steam? (c) Is the overall change an increase or decrease?

Ans. (a) 200 psia, 404.3°F, (b) −0.0882, +0.0974, (c) +0.0092 Btu per lb-°R.

238. (a) Freon 12 at 43.15 psia and 10% quality has what temperature, volume, enthalpy, and entropy (for 1 lb.)? (b) What is the internal energy of Freon 12 at 115 psia and 120°F?

Ans. (a) $h = 21.6$ Btu/lb., (b) 83.22 Btu/lb.

239. An internally reversible isobaric process occurs from water at 200°F and 160 psia to 600°F. (a) For 1 lb., determine Δh, Δs, Δv, and Δu. (b) If the process is nonflow, what are the values of $\int p\,dV$, W, and Q? See §54. (c) For a steady flow process through a steam generator with $\Delta K = 0$, what are the $\int V\,dp$ and Q? *See P 183, Top.*

Ans. (a) $\Delta u = 1042.7$, (b) $W =$ 113.4, (c) $Q = 1156.1$ Btu/lb.

240. (a) A 14.02-cu. ft. tank contains 5 lb. of steam at 190 psia. Determine h_1 and u_1. (b) After some cooling of the tank, its pressure drops to 80 psia, state 2. For $v_1 = v_2$, compute x_2, h_2, and u_2. (c) Considering the nonflow energy equation, determine the heat rejected.

Ans. (a) $u_1 = 1161.3$ Btu/lb., (b) $h_2 = 741$ Btu/lb., (c) −2309 Btu.

241. If 6 lb./sec. of steam pass through an isentropic process from 200 psia and 450°F to 5 psia, find (a) y_2 (by equating $s_1 = s_2 = s_{g2} - y_2 s_{fg2}$), ΔH, ΔU, and ΔS. See §§ 57, 58. (b) If the process is nonflow, what are Q and W and $\int p\,dV/J$? (c) If the process is steady flow with $W = 0$, what is ΔK? (d) If the process is steady flow with $\Delta K = 200$ Btu/sec., what is W? (e) If the process is an irreversible adiabatic with the entropy increasing to $s_{2'} = 1.8437$ Btu/lb-°R., what is the steady flow work ($\Delta K = 200$ Btu/sec.)?

Ans. (a) $y_2 = 15.85\%$, $u_2 = 915$, (b) $W = 1370$ Btu/sec., (c) 1581 Btu per sec., (d) 1955 hp, (e) 432.4 Btu per sec. (d) 1393.6 Btu (e) 454 Btu

242. Ammonia in a refrigerating machine is compressed isentropically from 20 psia to 200 psia and 200°F. See §§ 57, 58. For 1 lb., find (a) y_1 (by equating $s_2 = s_1 = s_{g1} - y_1 s_{fg1}$), Δh, Δu, Q, and Δs. (b) For a nonflow compression, what is the work? (c) What is the work during a steady flow if $\Delta K = 0$?

Ans. (a) $y_1 = 5.83\%$, (b) 107.4, (c) 131.9 Btu/lb.

243–250. These numbers may be used for other problems.

$\mathscr{B}$ **11**

HEAT EXCHANGERS

153. Introduction. A system which is designed to bring about a flow of energy in the form of heat from one substance to another is called a *heat exchanger*, Fig. 110. Many heat exchangers are so widely used that they

Inside of Oil Tank

Steam

Oil

Oil Out

Fig. 110. Heat Exchanger, Extended Surface. Used to heat viscous oils in order to reduce the pumping work. Tubes which have attached circumferential or longitudinal fins are said to have *extended surface*. The longitudinal fins in this exchanger offer the least resistance to flow. Oil enters from the oil tank through the open left end. Steam circulates through the tubes.

have well-known names, such as boiler, condenser, feed-water heater, air preheater, economizer, evaporator, radiator (on automobile and elsewhere), and the intercooler with which you are already familiar, § 86. The construction and function of the various exchangers are widely diverse but they have certain thermodynamic theory in common. This chapter will include enough descriptive matter on the various heat exchangers to make possible an understanding of their operation and function.

154. The Heat Exchanger Process. Typically, a heat exchanger is an open system, assumed to be in steady flow, involving two substances, one rejecting heat and the other receiving the heat which is being rejected. The substances exchanging heat may be physically mixed, as in cooling water by placing ice in it, or the substances may be in separate passages. Heat flows, as always, because of a temperature difference between the substances. In a thermodynamic analysis, we may take either substance as the system or consider both together.

A counterflow exchanger (fluids flow through in opposite directions) is represented diagrammatically in Fig. 111. It is nearly always true that the changes of kinetic energies are negligible; $K_1 \approx K_2$ and $K_a \approx K_b$. No shaft work W is done and as usual $\Delta P \approx 0$. Considering the hot substance as the system with respect to the steady flow energy equation (10B), we have $Q_h = \Delta H = H_2 - H_1 = w_h(h_2 - h_1)$, which is a negative number because

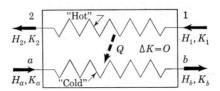

Fig. 111.   Heat Exchanger.

the "hot" fluid cools; $t_2 < t_1$. Considering the "cold" substance as the system, we have $Q_c = \Delta H = H_b - H_a = w_c(h_b - h_a)$, which is a positive number indicating heat added. Since the loss of heat of the hot fluid is the gain of the cold one, the foregoing Q's have the same magnitude. In general then, the amount of heat transferred can be computed by considering either fluid in steady flow in accordance with equation (50) of § 86:

(50) $Q = \Delta H = w\Delta h$ Btu   or $Q = \Delta h$ Btu/lb.,
                   [REVERSIBLE OR IRREVERSIBLE FLOW]

where for an ideal gas $\Delta H = wc_p\Delta T$, § 47, in which c_p is the average specific heat for the temperature interval ΔT.

If we consider the whole exchanger as the system, the heat Q is an internal exchange and does not appear in the energy balance. We may arrive at the resulting equation by $\Sigma Q = 0$ or by equating entering energy to departing energy in Fig. 111 ($H_1 + H_a = H_2 + H_b$). Either way gives the same result. By ΣQ, we have

$$w_c(h_b - h_a) + w_h(h_2 - h_1) = 0$$

or

(a) $w_c(h_b - h_a) = w_h(h_1 - h_2)$ Btu,

where w_c is the mass of "cold" fluid flowing and w_h is the mass of "hot" fluid, usually in lb./hr., lb./min., or lb./sec.

155. Example. A steam turbine discharges to the condenser 77,000 lb./hr. of steam at 120°F and $y = 11.1\%$ moisture. The condenser water enters at $t_a = 70°F$, leaves at $t_b = 85°F$, and condenses the steam to a saturated liquid at 120°F. How much water is needed, lb. water/lb. steam and lb./hr.?

SOLUTION. Let the subscripts 1 and 2 apply to the steam, Fig. 111. From the steam tables at 120°F, we find

$$h_f = 87.92, \qquad h_{fg} = 1025.8, \qquad h_g = 1113.7 \text{ Btu/lb.}$$

Then $h_2 = h_f = 87.92$ Btu/lb., and for $y = 11.1\%$,

$$h_1 = h_g - yh_{fg} = (1113.7) - (0.111)(1025.8) = 999.8 \text{ Btu/lb.}$$

The enthalpies of the condenser water may be found in the tables, but for this range of temperatures, a specific heat $c = 1$ Btu/lb-°F is reasonably accurate. Using $c = 1$ and letting $w_h = 1$ lb. of steam in equation (**a**), we get

$$w_c(1)(85 - 70) = 1(999.8 - 87.9),$$

from which $w_c = 60.8$ lb. water/lb. steam or $w_c = (60.8)(77,000) = 4,680,000$ lb. per hr.

156. The Steam Power Plant. To be able to fit the various pieces of equipment to be described later into their proper places, we should first become familiar with the steam power plant as a whole. The basic elements of a simple plant, shown in Fig. 112, are the **steam generator** or **boiler,** the

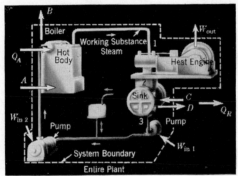

Courtesy Power, *New York City*

Fig. 112. Steam Power Plant. The source of the heat added to the steam is in the entering fuel and air stream at A in the form of chemical energy. Operation: water is evaporated into steam in the boiler; steam flows to the prime mover (engine) and some of its energy is converted into work W_{out} leaving the system; exhaust steam enters the condenser and is condensed to water by circulating cooling water, in and out at C and D, where heat is rejected from the cycle; the two pumps pump the water back into the boiler and it repeats the cycle. The energy required by the pumps is (W_{in1} and W_{in2}). The *net* work of the cycle is $W = W_{out} - W_{in}$.

prime mover (steam engine or turbine), the **condenser,** the **condensate pumps** (or **vacuum pumps**) which pump the condensate to atmospheric pressure, the **surge tank** or equalizing reservoir, and the **feedwater pumps** (or **boiler feed pumps**) which pump the water from atmospheric pressure into the boiler.

A modern central station power plant is shown in Fig. 113. Considering the entire plant as the system, we note first the flow of the fuel (on a coal *conveyor,* dumped into the coal *bunker*) which carries with it energy in an amount taken equal to the heating value of the fuel. This is the principal energy input. In this plant, the coal is pulverized and blown into the *furnace* where it is burned. For burning, there is a flow of air into the system, first through *forced-draft fans,* then via an *air preheater* (§ 166) to the furnace. The air preheater is a heat exchanger which allows a transfer of energy from the hot *flue gases* (products of combustion) to the air entering

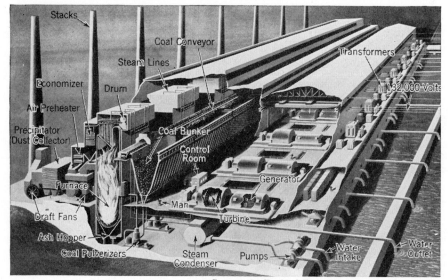

Courtesy the Cleveland Electric Illuminating Co., Cleveland

Fig. 113. Central Station Power Plant. An artist's conception of how the Company's Eastlake power plant will look when its capacity reaches the eventual 1,000,000 kw.

the furnace. Returning to the flow of air-coal, we know that heat is transferred from the products of combustion to the water and steam, and then the flue gases (products) pass through an economizer (§ 165), thence through the air preheater and to the stack. Some of the ash leaves the system via the ash hopper, but much of it, possibly 50%, moves along with the flue gases, and as it comes out of the stack, it is called *fly ash.* Since fly ash settling about the countryside is often a serious nuisance, large plants especially must take steps to remove it from the gases; hence, the *precipitator,* Fig. 113, or some other type of dust collector. The fan nearest the stack is an *induced-draft fan,* which helps along the flow of gases.

Another circuit of matter is the condenser water, which enters at the *water intake* and is pumped through the condenser, picking up heat from the condensing steam. Condenser water is discharged where it says *water outlet*, Fig. 113. Large quantities of condensing water are needed and are taken from a river, stream, or lake, if such a source is available. If the cooling water is taken from a lake, the discharge into the lake is so located that the warmer water from the condenser must circulate for some time in order to cool before it again reaches the intake. When the supply of cooling water is limited or expensive, the discharge is to a cooling tower (§ 264) or a spray pond for atmospheric cooling.

The working substance H_2O remains entirely within the system, except for unavoidable leakage, which is cared for by **make-up water,** added as needed. There will be feedwater heaters (§ 167), not indicated in Fig. 113, and all of the feedwater passes through the **economizer,** which is a heat exchanger using energy from the hot flue gases to heat the feedwater. The name *feedwater heater* is customarily applied only to a heat exchanger which utilizes condensing steam to heat the feedwater. After evaporation in the boiler, the steam passes through the superheater (Figs. 114 and 120), thence to the turbine, thence to the condenser. The work crossing the boundary of the system is the electricity through the 132,000-volt lines.

157. Steam Generators. The terms *steam generator* or *steam-generating unit* or *boiler unit* mean the boiler-furnace plus some or all of various accessories such as fuel burning equipment, superheater, reheater coils, economizer, and air heater, Fig. 114. The term *boiler* applies strictly to that part of the unit in which water (or other liquid, in general) is vaporized. In the beginning, a steam generator consisted solely of a boiler, a name which has come to be applied to all types of steam generators. Of the many types of boilers available, we shall mention only a few—after a short discussion of performance.

158. Output of Steam Generators. The thermodynamic theory and resulting equations for output and performance of boilers are the same for all types, except that the performance computations may sometimes account for the power used to drive auxiliaries, such as draft fans, pulverizer, or chain grate. The output of a boiler is often expressed as simply the number of pounds of steam delivered per hour. However, since steam at different boiler pressures and temperatures contains different amounts of energy, the number of pounds of steam does not constitute an absolute unit. It is evident that an absolute unit of capacity must measure the amount of heat transferred to the steam. The ASME recommends a unit of 1000 Btu/hr, called a kilo Btu (kB) per hour; or a unit of 1,000,000 Btu/hr, called a mega Btu (mB) per hour.

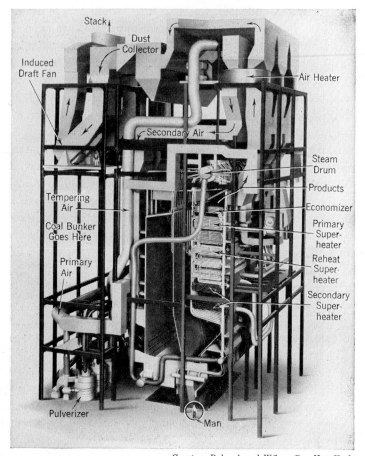

Induced
Draft Fan

Stack

Dust
Collector

Air Heater

Secondary Air

Steam
Drum

Products

Economizer

Tempering
Air

Coal Bunker
Goes Here

Primary
Super-
heater

Primary
Air

Reheat
Super-
heater

Secondary
Super-
heater

Pulverizer

Man

Courtesy Babcock and Wilcox Co., New York

Fig. 114. *Large Open-Pass Steam Generator.* An open-pass boiler
is one in which the gas flows in two or more directions through open
areas whose bounding walls are heating surface; adapted to large
central station sizes from **300,000 to 1,750,000 lb./hr.** of steam
(and more) at up to **2650 psi and 1100°F.** Furnace walls are usually
touching tubes in which steam is generated largely by radiant heat
(little or no convective boiler surface in this type, but as seen, superheaters, etc. are in the convective stream). Designed for the highest
efficiencies with products sometimes leaving at as low a temperature
as **250–300°F.**

We know, Fig. 115, that the heat transferred to the steam is $Q = h_2 - h_1$
Btu/lb., equation (50), § 154, where h_2 is the enthalpy of the steam as it
leaves the unit and h_1 is the enthalpy of the incoming feedwater. If $w_{bo.}$
lb./hr. stands for the steam delivered by the boiler, the total transferred
heat in one hour is $w_{bo.}(h_2 - h_1)$ Btu/hr., which may be used to express
precisely the output of the boiler. To reduce the size of the number to be

handled, we had better express it in kilo Btu,

(b) $\qquad$ Boiler ouput $= \dfrac{w_{bo.}(h_2 - h_1)}{1000}$ kB/hr.,

or in mega Btu,

(c) $\qquad$ Boiler output $= \dfrac{w_{bo.}(h_2 - h_1)}{1,000,000}$ mB/hr.

If the mass of steam $w_{bo.}$ is the maximum amount that the boiler can produce, these equations give the maximum capacity. The mass $w_{bo.}$ of water that the boiler actually evaporates may be any amount less than this maximum. If the pressure is high, the properties of compressed liquid, § 149, should be used for the water entering the boiler at 1.

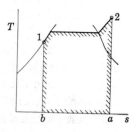

A unit of boiler output or boiler capacity that has been commonly used for years is the *boiler horsepower*. Although, at one time 1 bo. hp produced roughly 1 hp in the prime mover, today, because of the greater efficiency of modern prime movers and the widely different states of steam from a steam generator, there is no relation between a boiler horsepower and the horsepower of an engine. Since this is true, the name boiler horsepower is misleading; it causes much confusion in the mind of the novice, and its use is discouraged. Specifically, 1 bo. hp is the evaporation of 34.5 lb. of water per hour from and at 212°F. By *from and at* is meant from saturated water at 212°F into saturated steam at 212°F. For a saturation temperature of 212°F, the pressure obviously must be 14.696 psia (see steam tables). Now the amount of heat required to evaporate 1 lb. of water from and at 212°F is h_{fg} = 970.3 But, p. 409; hence, the amount of heat for 34.5 lb. of water is (34.5)(970.3) = 33,475.3 Btu. Consequently,

Fig. 115. Point 1 represents the condition of the feedwater entering a steam generator. Point 2 represents the condition as it leaves the superheater. The area 1–2–a–b represents approximately the heat added.

$\qquad$ 1 bo. hp = 33,475.3 Btu/hr.

or closely 33,480 Btu/hr. of transferred heat. We see then that the output or capacity of a boiler may be expressed as

(d) $\qquad$ Boiler horsepower (bo. hp) $= \dfrac{w_{bo.}(h_2 - h_1)}{33,480}$,

where $w_{bo.}$, h_2, and h_1 are as previously defined. Although the unit *boiler horsepower* is frowned upon, the use of it is so widespread that it is essential for the engineer to know its meaning.

159. Heating Surface and Rated Boiler Horsepower. The heating surface of a boiler is defined as that surface on one side of which is the fluid receiving heat while on the other side is the gas or refractory being cooled; it is measured on the surface of higher temperature. Formerly, there were required roughly about 10 sq. ft. of heating surface to produce 1 bo. hp; that is, to transfer 33,475.3 Btu/hr. From this, the practice arose of rating boilers according to the number of square feet of heating surface, counting 10 sq. ft./bo. hp. Thus, a boiler with 1000 sq. ft. of heating surface would be rated at 100 bo.hp. Modern large boilers, however, operate efficiently at outputs much greater than 1 bo. hp to 10 sq. ft. Intermittent operation at 500% to 600% of rated capacity is not uncommon (1 bo. hp per about 2 sq. ft.), and continuous operation at 300% of rated capacity frequently occurs. Two boilers might be rated the same, but one might be operated at an output much larger than the possible output of the other on account of a particular arrangement and distribution of heating surface.

At one time, the area of the grate surface was taken as the measure of the capacity of a boiler; but with the advent of forced and induced draft, such figures became meaningless.

160. Efficiency of a Steam Generator. The overall efficiency of a boiler at any operating condition is the percentage of the *higher* heating value of the fuel which is transferred after combustion to the working substance (steam and water). The efficiency is in accordance with the usual concept, *output/input*, the output being the heat transferred to the H_2O, the input being considered as the higher heating value of the fuel. Let w_f lb./hr. be the fuel fired, let q_h Btu/lb. be the higher heating value of the fuel; then the input to the furnace is $w_f q_h$ Btu/hr. The heat, as before, is $w_{bo.}(h_2 - h_1)$ Btu/hr. Therefore

(e) $$\text{Overall boiler efficiency} = \frac{w_{bo.}(h_2 - h_1)}{w_f q_h},$$

where $w_{bo.}$ lb./hr. is steam delivered, h_2 is the specific enthalpy of the delivered steam, and h_1 is the enthalpy of the entering water. As given, equation (e) includes the effect not only of the furnace, the boiler, and the grate, but also of heat transfer accessories, such as superheater, water walls, economizer, air preheater.* Heating values of some common fuels are given in Table XIII, Appendix.

---

* However, no account is made in equation (e) of the energy used to drive certain boiler auxiliaries, such as the forced-draft and induced-draft fans, the pulverizer, a chain grate. To find what we might term the *net* overall boiler efficiency, we should subtract from the numerator of (e) an amount $w_{aux.}(h_2 - h_1)$, where $w_{aux.}$ is the mass of boiler steam used to drive these auxiliaries. If the auxiliaries are electrically driven, an amount of energy equivalent to this expression should be subtracted. Note that in equation (e), the numerator is intended to be simply the amount of heat transferred from

161. Performance of Steam Generators. In considering the performance of a boiler, we find interesting and pertinent such statistics as the time rate of combustion (in pounds of fuel burned per hour-square foot of grate area, or in pounds per hour-cubic foot of furnace volume), the

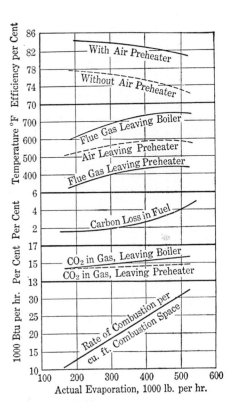

Fig. 116. *Typical Performance Curves for Steam Generator.* After Fig. 7 in *Some operating data for large steam generating units,* by Kreisinger and Purcell, ASME Transactions, FSP, Vol. 50.

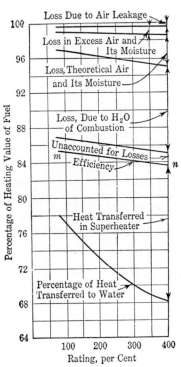

Fig. 117. *Energy Balance for Steam Generator.* These curves show what becomes of the heating value of the fuel at various rates of operation, where a rated boiler horsepower is taken as 10 sq. ft. of heating surface. Oil was used as the fuel. After Fig. 9 in *Comparative performance of a large boiler using oil and natural-gas fuels,* by F. G. Philo, ASME Transactions, FSP, Vol. 54.

pounds of steam generated per pound of fuel, the hourly rate of heat transfer per square foot of heating surface, the temperature of the stack gases (which measures the heat loss via the stack), the percentage of CO_2 in the flue gases (which is an indicator of the excess air supplied for combustion). See

gases to water or steam. Hence, if there should be a resuperheater (Fig. 114) which utilizes heat from furnace gases, the increase in the enthalpy of the steam which passes through the reheater should be added to the numerator of equation (e).

§ 162. After installation, an efficiency test is made on the steam generator. The amount of CO_2 in the flue gas at the point of maximum efficiency is noted. If thereafter the amount of air is regulated so that this optimum amount of CO_2 is present in the flue gas, it is expected that the maximum efficiency is being obtained. Other interesting items of performance data are the unburned combustible in the ash (which measures the loss at the grate) as well as items which have already been mentioned, such as overall

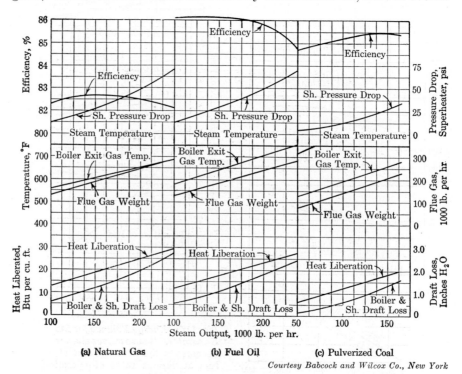

(a) Natural Gas   (b) Fuel Oil   (c) Pulverized Coal

Courtesy Babcock and Wilcox Co., New York

Fig. 118. Performance with Various Fuels. Observe that the efficiency when gas is the fuel is less than for the other two cases. This difference is accounted for largely by the high hydrogen content of gas as compared to the other fuels and the consequent greater loss due to the uncondensed water vapor (item 2, § 162).

efficiency, boiler horsepower, and the condition of the steam leaving the boiler. These and other items may be plotted in the form of curves in order to picture graphically a boiler's performance.

Figure 116 shows some typical performance curves. Figure 117 shows graphically an energy balance for a boiler at different operating loads. An energy balance (or heat balance) is an accounting of the energy supplied to a device, a statement of how the supplied energy is expended when, in the case of a steam generator, the supplied energy is the higher heating value of the coal. The curves of Fig. 118 show an interesting comparison of the operating characteristics of a particular steam generator fired with different fuels.

162. Water Tube Steam Generators. A water tube boiler, as the name says, is one in which water circulates inside of the tubes and gases on the outside, as contrasted with a fire tube boiler (§ 163) in which flue gases (products) circulate inside and water surrounds the tubes. The small boiler shown in Fig. 119 shows clearly several details worth noting. The feedwater

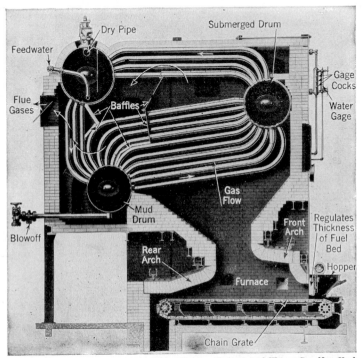

Courtesy Babcock and Wilcox Co., New York

Fig. 119. Low-Head, Water Tube Boiler, Three Drums. Gage cocks are placed at three levels. From time to time, they are opened successively to check the water level indicated by the gage glass.

is delivered close to the bottom of the steam drum. All boilers have something in the way of a **dry pipe** (see also Fig. 121), which, in its simplest form, is a short length of pipe perforated with small holes. It is located in the top of the steam space in the steam drum and is connected to the steam outlet of the boiler. As water boils, small droplets fly into the steam space and some remain suspended. Thus, the steam above the water may be relatively wet, particularly if boiling is violent. The steam in passing through the perforations of the dry pipe tends to be separated from the water, so that the steam which reaches the main is nearly 100% quality. The glass **water gage** indicates the water level at a glance and the *gage cocks* are used to check the gage glass indication. The *blowoff* valve, located at or near the lowest level of water, is opened from time to time so that sediment in the bottom of the vessel will be flushed out. *Baffles* in some form are found in most water tube furnaces, and their function is to direct the flow of the hot gases across the heating surfaces so as to convect heat advantageously to these surfaces. Every time the gases change direction, they are said to have made a pass (and they are starting another pass if they have not left the furnace).

Fig. 120. *Stirling Boiler.* Capacity: 200,000 lb./hr. at design pressure of 450 psia and temperature of 550°F.

The boiler of Fig. 119 is a three-drum, three-pass boiler, designed especially for installations where the amount of head room is limited and where moderate quantities of steam are needed. The front drum is submerged; that is, it is entirely below the water level. The fuel should be anthracite coal, because the design of the furnace and the arrangement of the arches (small passageway between arches) are especially made for coal in which there is little volatile matter. Note the chain grate stoker (§ 287).

A bent tube boiler, known as a Stirling four-drum boiler, is shown in Fig. 120. Stirling boilers may be designed to burn any kind of fuel, coal on various types of grates, oil, or gas, but this illustration shows a pulverized coal unit. The four-drum boiler has a relatively large water capacity and is therefore appropriate for situations in which the load fluctuates rapidly.

The furnace gases pass upward, Fig. 120, across the tubes to the front drum and across the superheater coils, if any, down between the baffles, up again on the last pass, finally over the top of the rear baffle to the preheater. This boiler is a three-pass boiler. Any number of passes can be obtained by a suitable arrangement of the baffles. Although the rate of heat transfer increases with the velocity of flow of the gases, it would not be economical to increase the number of passes indefinitely (in order to increase the speed of travel), because the smaller space for flow would result in a greater frictional loss and therefore in greater power consumed by the draft fans. In each design, an attempt is made to balance off various related factors and to secure proportions which will result in the maximum efficiency.

The walls of the furnace of Fig. 120 are water cooled. Water pipes or tubes, connected to the main steam-generating system, run vertically on the furnace walls. These tubes add to the heat-absorbing surface of the boiler, and they also keep the refractory lining of the furnace from becoming too hot, which in turn makes it possible to step up the rate of combustion and consequently the output of the boiler without excessive damage to this lining. Furnace walls protected by water tubes are called *water walls.*

The feedwater enters the rear drum, Fig. 120, and circulates down the rear bank of tubes to the mud drum. In general, the coldest water in the tubes is surrounded by the coldest gases, and the hottest water in the tubes is surrounded by the hottest gases (just over the furnace). The steam naturally collects at the top of the three upper drums. Observe that the upper drums are connected by steam passages. Steam which is practically saturated is taken from the rear drum and led to the superheater coils. Stirling-type boilers are made in a wide range of sizes and forms. They may be designed to deliver up to 1,000,000 lb./hr. of steam and for pressures as high as 750 psi.

In the larger modern boilers, Fig. 114, where the rate of steam separation is high, the matter of preventing water from leaving with the steam becomes more complicated. One solution is shown in Fig. 121. The steam-water mixture rising from the tubes is guided by the deflector to cyclone separators, where it is admitted tangentially, causing it to whirl at such a speed that the centrifugal force (equivalent to several g's) causes the water to go to the sides of the cyclone and thence downward and out. The steam, being lighter, moves upward in the center, passing to corrugated scrubbers. The corrugations provide a large surface which intercepts water particles as the steam flows sinuously between the closely fitted plates.

There are innumerable types of boilers which space requirements forbid mentioning. Improvements which have been made in the operating efficiency of large central stations have been notable since World War II. Central station plants are now commonly designed for operating pressures greater than 2000 psi. A plant with initial steam at 4500 psi and 1150°F has recently been put into operation. Another with 5000 psi and 1200°F steam is on the way.

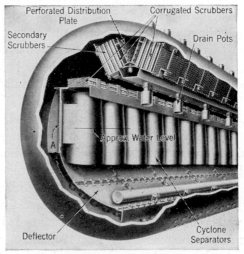

Courtesy Babcock and Wilcox Co., New York

Fig. 121. Cyclone Separators and Scrubbers.

163. Fire Tube Boilers. Like water tube boilers, fire tube boilers are made in a variety of styles, but only in the smaller capacities (seldom over 12,000 lb./hr. of steam), and are often portable. A two-pass boiler is shown in Fig. 122. Fire tube boilers wherein the gases pass toward the rear *along the underside of the shell* (not through tubes) and return to the front through fire tubes are called **horizontal-return-tubular boilers.**

164. Superheaters. As you have probably observed, superheaters are heat exchangers usually placed in the furnace of the boiler (Figs. 114 and 120), and the steam is led from the steam drum through the superheater coils, thence to the steam main. (Sometimes superheating and resuperheating are done in separately fired furnaces, a plan which facilitates good control of the steam temperature on delivery.) When the steam is heated by the flow of hot products of combustion across the tubes, the heater is said to be a **convection superheater.** Another arrangement is to place some or all of the superheater tubes against a wall or partition, in which event a large part of the heat used to superheat the steam is radiant heat, even though the gases flow past, but not across, the tubes. Such a superheater is called a *radiant superheater*. With increased load, the convection superheater results in greater superheating, while the radiant superheater produces less superheating, and vice versa. With the optimum proportion of superheating surfaces, part in convection tubes and part in radiant tubes, the fluctuation of the outgoing steam temperature is reduced to a minimum.

If a steam generator is to be operated under a steady load at all times, the right amount of superheater surface may be provided so that the steam

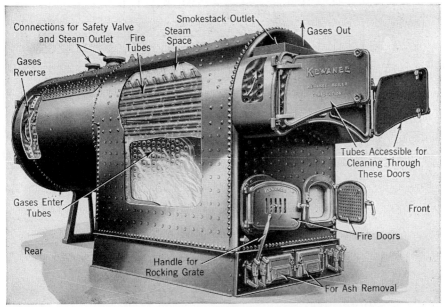

Connections for Safety Valve and Steam Outlet
Gases Reverse
Fire Tubes
Smokestack Outlet
Steam Space
Gases Out
Tubes Accessible for Cleaning Through These Doors
Gases Enter Tubes
Front
Fire Doors
Rear
Handle for Rocking Grate
For Ash Removal

Courtesy Kewanee Boiler Corp., Kewanee, Ill.

Fig. 122. Two-Pass, Fire-Tube Boiler. This boiler, an updraft type, has a steel fire box and the tube diameter is **3** in. It is made for gage pressures of **100** to **150** lb./sq. in. and in sizes from **25** to **304** bo.hp, corresponding to heat transfer rates of about **835** to **10,300** kB/hr. The upper group of tubes may be cleaned through the doors at the top front. These boilers may be hand fired or stoker fired.

is delivered at the desired temperature (for example, it reaches the turbine at the temperature for which the turbine has been designed). If the load fluctuates significantly, something special must be provided to maintain the outgoing steam temperature within reasonable limits. There are several ways of providing temperature regulation. Figure 123 shows the results of the use of both radiant and convection heaters.

165. Economizers. An economizer is a heat exchanger which heats the feedwater (inside tubes) with hot flue gases flowing across the tubes. Notice the location of the economizer in Figs. 114 and 120. Figure 124 shows some-

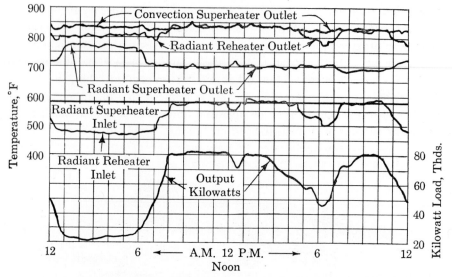

Fig. 123. This illustration shows the delivery temperature of superheated steam when radiant and convection superheaters are used and when the output of the power plant varies.

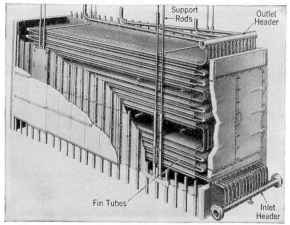

Fig. 124. Fin Tube Economizer. Look for the longitudinal fins on the tubes, added to increase the heat transfer surface. Extended surface in some heat exchangers is also provided by circular fins (Fig. 125).

thing of the construction of one with extended-surface heating elements. The heat taken from the flue gas represents a saving of energy that might be dissipated to the atmosphere, and therefore results in an increase of the overall efficiency of the steam generator. When the water reaches the economizer, it has passed through the last feedwater pump and is somewhat above boiler pressure. For this reason, its temperature can be raised almost to the saturation temperature in the boiler, much above 212°F corresponding to the boiling point at atmospheric pressure.

The tubes may be continuous, as in Fig. 124, in which case the water must be good enough so that internal cleaning of tubes is unnecessary—

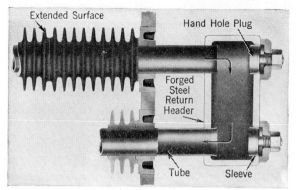

Courtesy Foster Wheeler Corp., New York

Fig. 125. *Extended-Surface Tube and Return Header.* Observe the hand-hole plugs. These plugs are tapered and will pass through the hole in the return header. They are inserted from the outside, the sleeve is placed in the hole, and the plug is wedged into the sleeve by tightening up on the nut. The heating surface of extended-surface tubes is some 6 to 9 times that of a plain tube.

except as they may be cleaned with chemicals. If the feedwater is not so good, the ends of the tubes must be connected by *headers* which can be removed for internal cleaning, Fig. 125. All heat transfer surfaces lose effectiveness rapidly as foreign matter is deposited on them. Since the flue gas is always dirty, soot blowers are installed in the economizer to clean the outside of the tubes intermittently.

166. Air Preheaters. An air preheater, also called an air heater, heats the air needed for combustion by heat from the flue gas, which is beneficial because the combustion air is inevitably heated in any case. Experience shows that not only is the efficiency improved, but there may be an increase in capacity, and combustion occurs with a more stable flame. On the other hand, the ducts and passageways handling heated air must be larger because of the increase of volume with temperature, provided that the velocity of flow and pressure drop are to remain the same. Each additional piece of equipment requires a certain amount of maintenance, no matter how simple it is. A tubular air preheater is shown in Fig. 126. The air is usually outside the tubes, the flue gas inside. Observe the **baffles** which force the air to crisscross the tubes several times. There is a lower limit, usually about 300°F, below which it is inadvisable to cool the flue gas. This limit applies when there may be sulfur trioxide in the flue gas (whenever there is sulfur in the fuel), because sulfur trioxide in the presence of water vapor may form sulfuric acid, whose presence raises the dew point of the mixture over what it would be with water vapor alone. The efficiency of the boiler unit is increased about 2% for each 100°F rise of temperature of the combustion air.

Gas into Tubes

AIR.

Baffles

GAS

Exit

Air Around Tubes

Courtesy Combustion Engineering Co., New York

Fig. 126. Tubular Air Preheater. The tubes are 2½ in. OD. Typical data are: boiler capacity, 40,000 lb./hr. of steam; air temperature *in,* 100°F; air temperature *out,* 515°F; flue gas temperature *in,* 650°F; flue gas temperature *out,* 350°F.

The most widely used of the regenerative air heaters is the Ljungstrom, Fig. 127. In their simplest form, the elements through which the gases flow are made up of a series of corrugated sheets with plates on each side. The corrugations form the passageways for the gases. Modern elements are somewhat modified from this elementary construction. A cleaning device for removing deposits is available. As seen in Fig. 127, hot flue gas enters from below on the left, passing up through the elements, and heat passes from the gas to raise the temperature of the metal elements. Since the rotor turns slowly and continuously, from 2 rpm to 4 rpm, the elements heated by the flue gas on the left are rotated onto the right side. Atmospheric air entering top right picks up heat from the heated elements. Thus, there is a continuous supply of heated elements entering the air-flow zone and a continuous supply of cooled elements moving into the gas-flow zone. Observe that heat is transferred from gas to air by first storing energy in the metal elements, then taking away the energy so stored. See the air heater in Fig. 114.

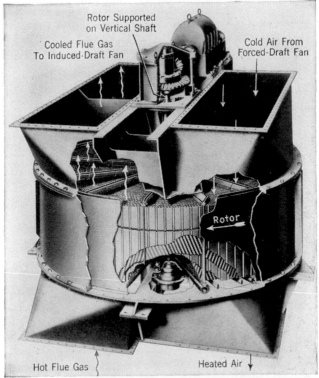

Courtesy Air Preheater Corp., New York

Fig. 127. Ljungstrom Regenerative Air Preheater. Typical operating conditions: boiler rate, 550,000 lb./hr. of steam; air temperature *in,* 80°F; air temperature *out,* 602°F; gas temperature *in,* 720°F; gas temperature *out,* 346°F. The data for this illustration and Fig. 126 are not comparable because they are for different conditions.

167. Feedwater Heaters. A *feedwater heater* uses steam to heat the boiler feedwater, and it should not be confused with an economizer which heats the water with flue gas. There are two types of heaters—an *open feedwater heater,* Fig. 128, wherein the heating steam and heated water mix, and a *closed feedwater heater,* wherein the two are kept separate, as in a surface condenser (see Fig. 129). The closed heater is a typical heat exchanger, with tubes or coils of pipe, with the water inside the tubes. The steam used for heating the feedwater may come from auxiliary engines which exhaust at atmospheric pressure, especially in small power plants. In central station and other large plants, the steam for heating the feedwater is extracted at various pressures from the turbine, usually at several different points so that the water is heated "gradually." This is the system of heating feedwater in a regenerative cycle, § 217 and Fig. 153.

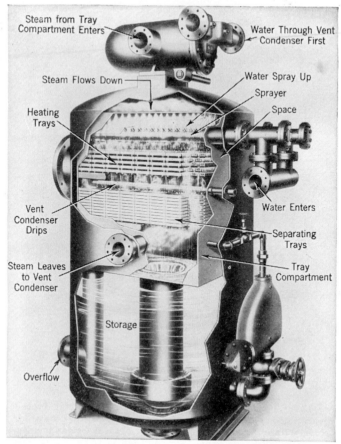

Steam from Tray Compartment Enters

Water Through Vent Condenser First

Steam Flows Down

Water Spray Up

Sprayer

Heating Trays

Space

Vent Condenser Drips

Water Enters

Separating Trays

Steam Leaves to Vent Condenser

Tray Compartment

Storage

Overflow

Courtesy Cochrane Corp., Philadelphia

Fig. 128. Open Feedwater Heater. The water enters first the vent condenser and is used to condense the steam discharged from the tray compartment. This steam is a small part of the total steam supplied, most of it being used to heat the water. The vent condenser also receives the gases given up by the water. If the pressure in the heater is equal to or greater than atmospheric, the gases escape directly to the atmosphere. If the heater pressure is below atmospheric, an ejector or gas pump is necessary. The water from the vent condenser is sprayed upward and meets steam coming down. Most of the heating and steam condensation occurs here. By the time the water leaves the heating trays, it is practically at saturation temperature. Separation of the gases from the water is prolonged through the separating trays. The vent condenser drips are led to the separating trays for gas removal. As noted, such heaters serve the purpose of deaerating raw water because hot water can "hold" less air than cold water; the gases are deleterious (§309).

168. Condensers. If an air engine should allow the air to expand to pressures lower than atmospheric pressure, there would result no net gain in power output, because the engine could not rid itself of the expanded air unless it were picked up by a pump and pumped back to atmospheric pressure. As a matter of fact, there would be a net loss (second law) due to the inevitable frictional losses of all real processes and machines. The situation is different in the case of steam engines and turbines. If the steam is allowed to expand to pressures below atmospheric pressure, it may be condensed to water, and the water is pumped to atmospheric pressure with the expenditure of relatively little work. The cold water used to condense the steam (circulating water) must usually be pumped through the condenser, but this work too is small as compared to the gain in expanding the steam in the engine to low pressures. The net gain in power output in expanding to subatmospheric pressures is large, and this gain is the primary reason for using condensers.

There are two basic types of condensers, the surface condenser and the jet condenser. Within each classification, there are many variations in details, but fundamental principles remain the same. The steam and condensing water being separated by a surface do not mix in the *surface condenser,* Fig. 129. Water circulates inside the condenser tubes, steam passes around the tubes. Preventing mixing of the water and steam is advantageous when the cooling water is too impure to be used directly as boiler feedwater. The condenser or cooling water picks up and carries away the heat released by the condensing steam, keeping the condenser relatively cool. If the condenser is maintained at a temperature of 100°F, the pressure in the condenser will be very nearly 0.95 psia (see steam tables).

The condensate is pumped through the feedwater heaters to the boiler. Air invariably finds its way into the condenser and it, too, must be pumped out, because the presence of air in the condenser increases the condenser pressure (according to Dalton's law of partial pressures) and the back pressure on the turbine. Moreover, air reduces the rate of transfer of heat and therefore the capacity of the condenser. The removal of the air, which is costly, may be by *wet pumps* or by separate air pumps. A wet pump is one which pumps both condensate and air. It is not capable of maintaining the lowest pressures. A separate air pump may be a piston pump or, more commonly, an ejector, Fig. 143, p. 235.

The velocity of flow of the water through the tubes will be some 6 to 7.5 fps. The amount of steam condensed per square foot of tube surface should fall between 4 and 18 lb./hr. Circulating water required should fall between 0.5 and 1.8 gpm. for each square foot of tube surface for a two-pass condenser. Tube diameters vary from $\frac{5}{8}$ to $1\frac{1}{4}$ in.

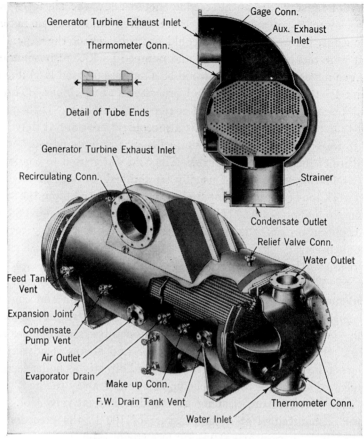

Generator Turbine Exhaust Inlet

Thermometer Conn.

Gage Conn.

Aux. Exhaust Inlet

Detail of Tube Ends

Generator Turbine Exhaust Inlet

Recirculating Conn.

Strainer

Condensate Outlet

Relief Valve Conn.

Water Outlet

Feed Tank Vent

Expansion Joint

Condensate Pump Vent

Air Outlet

Evaporator Drain

Make up Conn.

F.W. Drain Tank Vent

Thermometer Conn.

Water Inlet

Courtesy Foster Wheeler Corp., New York

Fig. 129. Surface Condenser. The insert in the upper right-hand corner is a sectional view through the exhaust *inlet.* It is a two-pass condenser, water entering the right bottom connection and leaving the right top connection. The perforated sheets to which the tubes are attached are called *tube sheets.* There is one at each end of the condenser. The condenser water enters the lower half of the condenser tubes, flows leftward in this illustration, and returns rightward in the top half of the tubes.

In a *jet condenser,* the incoming steam mixes with a jet of water. We have chosen a barometric jet condenser, Fig. 130, to illustrate this type. The cooling water enters at the point labeled "injection water" to a water weir and overflows onto the umbrella baffle, from which it flows, striking a deflector ring. The deflector ring causes the water to fall in an inverted cone shape. The exhaust steam enters at the steam inlet, surrounds and mixes with the cone of water, and condenses. Air and other noncondensable gases entering with the steam or water are removed at the top by a piston pump or

ejector. The gases in the steam chamber pass up through the cooler water.
As these gases are cooled, some of the moisture in them condenses out and
falls to the bottom. This process of cooling the gases to remove some of the
moisture (just as water condenses from the air on cold window-panes) is
advantageous because there results less mass of material for the suction
pump to handle. The drain pipe extends into a seal tank, and atmospheric

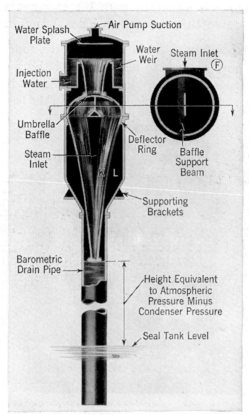

Courtesy Pennsylvania Pump and Compressor Co.,
Easton, Pa.

Fig. 130. Byer Barometric Condenser.

pressure causes the water to rise in the drain pipe a distance equivalent to
atmospheric pressure (about 34 ft. of water) *minus* the pressure in the condenser. As the injection water and the condensate fall to the level of the
water in the drain pipe, an equivalent amount of water flows from the bottom of the pipe to the seal tank, because atmospheric pressure could not support an increased length of column of water. It is this use of the barometric
pressure which gives this type its name.

The water may be removed from the bottom of the jet type of condenser by pumps, instead of via the barometric drain.   If pumps are used, the long length of drain pipe, an essential part of the barometric condenser, is unnecessary.   Such condensers are called *low-level jet condensers* and may be installed directly below the turbine, or steam engine, as is the surface condenser.   Barometric condensers, due to the vertical space needed, are commonly erected outside the power plant building.   A *surface condenser* permits higher vacuums; moreover, since the condensate and condenser water are kept separated, the condensate remains clean for use as feedwater.

169. Steam Evaporators.   A relatively expensive, sometimes necessary, way of obtaining pure water is to distill it.   For this purpose, the usual method is to use evaporators, where steam is the source of heat for evaporating water, Fig. 131.   Steam is inside the coils, and the coils are submerged

Courtesy Foster Wheeler Corp., New York

Fig. 131. Submerged Evaporator. In this illustration are visible the heating coils, the baffle, and vapor separator (at the top).   There are 600 sq. ft. of heating surface in a 72-in. shell.   The steam for evaporation is at 81.5 psia and the vapor produced from the raw water is at 28.5 psia.

in the water to be evaporated.   The condensate from the coils (or tube bundle) may be used in another heat exchanger to preheat the raw water fed to the evaporator.   Since distilled water may carry entrained gases, it may be necessary to deaerate it to eliminate the corrosive oxygen.

To reduce the cost of distilled water, multiple-effect evaporators are used.   To illustrate the principle, we shall use a simple numerical illustra-

tion.   Suppose the raw water to be evaporated is at 80°F and that the live
steam available for the purpose is dry and saturated at 340°F.   The 80°F
water is to be heated and evaporated into saturated steam at 140°F.   (The
condensate of this 140°F steam is the distilled water.)   Basing the calculation on 1 lb. of 340°F steam, we have, according to the law of conservation of
energy,

$$\left.\begin{array}{l}\text{Heat given up by 1 lb.}\\ \text{340°F steam condensing}\\ \text{to saturated liquid}\end{array}\right\} = \left\{\begin{array}{l}\text{Heat received by 80°F raw water}\\ \text{in evaporating to 140°F}\\ \text{saturated steam}\end{array}\right.$$

$$-\Delta H_s = \Delta H_w$$
$$1(1190.1 - 311.13) = w(1122 - 48.02),$$
$$w = 0.817 \text{ lb.}$$

evaporated per pound of 340°F steam.   Check the properties of steam in
Table VIII; $\Delta H = w\Delta h$.   Now suppose this process is made to have a
double effect, the first effect evaporating the raw water to saturated steam
at 240°F; then this steam being used in the second effect to evaporate the
raw water to saturated steam at 140°F.   Thus,

$$\left.\begin{array}{l}\text{Heat given up by 1 lb.}\\ \text{340°F steam condensing}\\ \text{to saturated liquid}\end{array}\right\} = \left\{\begin{array}{l}\text{Heat received by 80°F raw water in}\\ \text{in evaporating to 240°F}\\ \text{saturated steam}\end{array}\right.$$

$$-\Delta H_s = \Delta H_w$$
$$1(1190.1 - 311.13) = w_1(1160.5 - 48.02),$$
$$w_1 = 0.79 \text{ lb.}$$

evaporated per pound of 340°F steam in first effect.   The second effect uses
the evaporated H_2O of the first effect and therefore receives 0.79 lb. of
saturated steam at 240°F.

$$\left.\begin{array}{l}\text{Heat given up by 0.79 lb.}\\ \text{240°F steam condensing}\\ \text{to saturated liquid}\end{array}\right\} = \left\{\begin{array}{l}\text{Heat received by 80°F raw water}\\ \text{in evaporating to 140°F}\\ \text{saturated steam}\end{array}\right.$$

$$-\Delta H_s = \Delta H_w$$
$$0.79(1160.5 - 208.34) = w_2(1122 - 48.02),$$
$$w_2 = 0.7 \text{ lb.}$$

evaporated in second effect per pound of 340°F steam used in first effect.
We see that the amount of distilled water obtained in two effects (0.79 + 0.7
= 1.49) is slightly less than twice as much as that obtained from one effect
(0.817) for the same consumption of 340°F steam.

The output of the foregoing evaporators could be increased by more cooling of the hotter fluid (below 340°F saturated liquid, for example). More evaporators could be added (and are used), stepping up the amount of distilled water obtained from each pound of "live" steam used, but the returns are diminishing since the extra investment and upkeep are increasing. The number of effects used is therefore defined by economic considerations and the problem is often tied in with the energy balance of the plant. It should be observed that the addition of an evaporator of the same heating surface as the first evaporator, in the manner assumed in the foregoing example, does not increase the time rate of the production of distilled water, as the rate of flow of heat is only half as fast, because the temperature difference in each evaporator is half of what it was in one evaporator. Thus, each evaporator in the two-effect arrangement produces approximately half as much distilled water in a unit of time as the single-effect arrangement produces.

170. Desuperheaters. In many plants with relatively high-temperature boilers, there is need for low-temperature steam, which can be obtained from a desuperheater. Lower pressure is an outcome of the throttling process, which lowers the temperature of superheated steam only a small amount. Similar heat exchangers are also used to maintain a constant temperature of the main steam supply under varying load conditions. The desuperheating technique is one way of providing this regulation. In operation, desuperheating is a mixing of water and superheated steam. The heat required to evaporate the water is taken from the steam being desuperheated. Figure 132 shows one way in which desuperheating is accomplished.

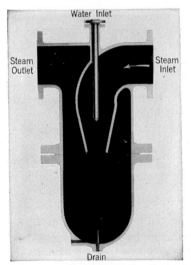

Water Inlet

Steam Outlet

Steam Inlet

Drain

Courtesy The Swartwout Co., Cleveland

Fig. 132. Desuperheater. A temperature control is used to regulate the flow of water.

171. Converting Mass into Energy. A nuclear reactor is not called a heat exchanger, but it is an instrument wherein the problem exists of getting atomic energy into storage in a circulating substance, so that this energy can be used elsewhere for a useful effect. In a general way, a heat exchanger may perform a similar function of getting energy stored into a substance for for later use, and moreover, true heat exchangers are currently necessary adjuncts to reactors used for power production. In any event, most engineers are interested in how atomic energy may be converted into work. Hence this brief discussion.

We have previously mentioned that according to Einstein's equation $E = mc^2$, the amount of energy equivalent to a mass of 1 lb. is 39×10^{12} Btu, a misleading number because at this time, we do not know how to convert more than about 0.1% of a *fissionable* mass into energy, much less any other mass. Einstein's equation is more truthfully written $E = \Delta mc^2$, where E is the energy equivalent of the mass which disappears. If the process of using this energy from mass is via thermal processes or heat engines, the second law introduces certain additional limitations. Moreover, there is perhaps some law not yet formulated concerning the "availability" of mass for conversion into energy.

We should start our study with a review of some definitions. An *atom* is the smallest unit of a particular chemical element. An *element* is a basic kind of matter (such as oxygen, uranium, etc., of which 102 have been found in nature or artificially created). The current picture of the atom, which is substantiated by imposing experimental evidence, is that it has a nucleus about which *electrons* (negatively charged particles) move, much as planets move about a sun. The electrons have a relatively small mass, so that practically all of the mass of an atom is in its nucleus. The nucleus is composed of **protons,** which are positively charged particles, and **neutrons,** which are neutral particles, both of virtually the same mass. A normal atom of a particular element has a certain number of negatively charged electrons, which is the **atomic number** Z, moving about a nucleus in which there is the same number of protons (positively charged); so the atom is neutral. The atomic number identifies the element. The isotopes of a particular element have the same number of electrons and protons (the same atomic number), but they differ in mass because they have different numbers of neutrons. The total number of protons and neutrons in the nucleus is called the **mass number** A, which is the integer nearest the atomic weight. Thus, the atomic weight of the most common isotope of uranium is 238.07, and its mass number A is therefore 238, which is the total number of protons and neutrons in its nucleus. Uranium 235, the kind which fissions, has 235 protons and neutrons in its nucleus, but the same number of protons (and electrons) as U238. To identify a particular atom, the following symbolization is used:

(f) $_ZX^A$ $\begin{cases} X = \text{chemical symbol of substance,} \\ A = \text{mass number (of atom),} \\ Z = \text{atomic number.} \end{cases}$

You recall that the "atomic weight" of oxygen is arbitrarily taken as 16 by the chemist. However, oxygen has three isotopes; hence the value of 16 is the average value for oxygen as it is normally found. Since the physicist must distinguish between the isotopes, he has assigned the mass of 16 to the lightest and most abundant (about 99.8%) isotope ($_8O^{16}$), which results in "atomic weights" of the other two isotopes of oxygen as 17.0045 ($_8O^{17}$) and 18.0049 ($_8O^{18}$), and an average atomic weight somewhat greater than 16 (16.0044). Thus the scale of relative atomic weights as used by the nuclear physicist is slightly different from the established chemical scale. A few values of atomic numbers Z and mass numbers A are:

	Z	A		Z	A
Americium (Am)	95	243	Barium (Ba)	56	137
Boron (B)	5	10	Carbon (C)	6	12
Cesium (Cs)	55	133	Hydrogen (H)	1	1
Krypton (Kr)	36	84	Lithium (Li)	3	7
Nitrogen (N)	7	14	Oxygen (O)	8	16
Plutonium (Pu)	94	239	Rubidium (Rb)	37	85
Sodium (Na)	11	23	Uranium (U)	92	238

By way of illustration, we see from this tabulation and equation (**f**) that the nuclear designation of uranium 238 is $_{92}U^{238}$; uranium 235 would be $_{92}U^{235}$.

We obtain energy from a chemical reaction (combustion) accompanied by a change to a new molecular structure. The mass equivalent of the energy released (heat of combustion) is so small as to go undetected. Nuclear energy is obtained (or consumed) when there are changes in the structure of the atom's nucleus. In particular, we obtain energy by virtue of the splitting of an atom of a certain substance into two atoms which are two different substances, called *fission fragments*. (Energy is also obtainable from certain of the light atoms by a fusion, rather than a fission, process, as in the "hydrogen bomb." If and when the fusion process becomes controllable, it may turn out to be a better means of obtaining work from atomic energy.)

There are only three atoms whose nuclei we are now able to split with a resulting advantageous output of energy: *uranium 235*, the rare isotope occurring in nature; *uranium 233*, which is an isotope formed when neutrons are captured by thorium 232; and *plutonium 239*, which is formed when an atom of uranium 238 captures a neutron. When one of these atoms splits, it changes into two atoms of different elements; and in order to deliver energy, the stored energy (or mass) of the *fission fragments* must be less than the stored energy (or mass) of the original atom. Now we are using the words *mass* and *energy* in the same sense. In other words, the mass which "disappears" on fission reappears as energy, in accordance with Einstein's equation.

The unit of energy used in nuclear physics is the electron-volt (ev) which is the energy acquired by an electron (its charge is 1.6×10^{-19} coulombs) in "falling" through a potential difference of 1 volt. Since this unit is small, a million electron-volts (mev) is often used; 1 ev $= 1.6 \times 10^{-12}$ ergs; 1 mev $\approx 1.2 \times 10^{-13}$ ft-lb.

The excess of stored energy of the original atom above the stored energy of the fission fragments at rest is mostly (about 83%) in the form of kinetic energy of the fragments which are moving at enormous speeds immediately after fission. The total energy release per fission is about 200 mev. The breakdown is given by Murray[*] as: fission fragments, 166 mev; electrons (called *beta particles*, a convenient name to distinguish high-speed electrons) and neutrinos, 18 mev; gamma rays, 10 mev; neutrons, 5 mev. The high kinetic energy of the fragments (the *two* atoms) is dissipated as they repeatedly bump nearby atoms and molecules, which are thereby speeded up (temperature increases). Because of the higher temperature, heat is transferred toward lower-temperature regions, which may ultimately be water to be evaporated into steam for use in a steam turbine. A representative reaction is

$$\textbf{(g)} \qquad {}_{92}U^{235} + {}_{0}n^{1} \rightarrow {}_{56}Ba^{144} + {}_{36}Kr^{90} + 2{}_{0}n^{1},$$

where n represents a neutron (zero charge, mass number 1). The fission is caused by the neutron ${}_{0}n^{1}$ on the left of the equation, but we notice two neutrons on the right. The average number of neutrons after fission is about 2.5, the actual number possible varying from zero to 7. These 2.5 neutrons are available to penetrate another U235 nucleus and will do so provided that they are not captured by structural or protecting materials or contaminants and provided that they do not escape. Compare the fragments ${}_{56}Ba^{144}$ and ${}_{36}Kr^{90}$ with the tabulation of atomic and mass numbers above and notice that these atoms are unstable, being "too heavy" for their atomic number. Therefore, they begin immediately to change toward a more stable form, the complete evolution taking anywhere from hours to years, being different for different elements. For example, the ${}_{36}Kr^{90}$ eventually becomes a stable isotope of zirconium, ${}_{40}Zr^{90}$, half of the original atoms having been converted in 65 hr. (half-life). During the evolution to a stable element, called **radioactive decay,** there are emitted gamma rays and beta particles, both of which are dangerous emanations. Exact masses of each element and particle must be used to determine the "mass" of the released energy. The data needed for this calculation are not given here.

We should emphasize that the fragments ${}_{56}Ba^{144}$ and ${}_{36}Kr^{90}$ are only two of the many pairs of elements which may be the outcome of fission. The

[*] R. L. Murray, *Nuclear Engineering*, Prentice-Hall.

sum of the Z's on the right side of the equation should be the same as the Z of the fissioned nucleus; in equation (**g**), $56 + 36 = 92$. Also, the mass numbers should balance; in equation (**g**), $235 + 1 = 144 + 90 + 2 = 236$. The most likely number of neutrons n is 2 or 3. If n is equal to 2 or 3, the sum of the mass numbers *of the fission fragments* would be either 234 or 233. Moreover, elements with atomic numbers below about 72 or above about 165 are very rarely formed, the most likely ratio of the atomic numbers of the fragments being approximately $\frac{3}{2}$.

A schematic picture of how a chain reaction can occur is shown in Fig. 133. If the first neutron n_1 fissions the nucleus N_1, there results the two

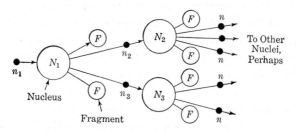

Fig. 133.   Chain Reaction, Explosive.

high-energy fragments F and, say, the two neutrons n_2 and n_3. Possibly each of these neutrons fissions other nuclei N_2 and N_3, which in this illustration produces five more neutrons. Then each of these five neutrons are available, though not so likely, to fission five more nuclei. At any rate, there is a possible multiplication effect. If on average more than one of the released neutrons fissions a nucleus, something will eventually "burn" up, or there will be an explosion when the multiplication rate is fast enough. For a steady chain reaction, the neutrons from one split nucleus sooner or later split one other nucleus, which is the condition to be maintained in a reactor for a power plant in a steady state. If less than an average of one released neutron per fission splits another nucleus, the reaction rate decreases. To have a sustaining reaction, there is also the matter of a *critical mass,* which we shall not go into except to say that if the mass is too small, so many of the emitted neutrons will escape before they find a nucleus to split that the average of future fissions becomes less than one fission per fission.

172. The Reactor. The present plan of obtaining power from atomic energy is to have a reactor in which the chain reaction proceeds, to provide means of using the released energy for heating a working substance, and then to use the working substance in a heat engine. There are a number of different reactors, including the pressurized water type, the boiling water type, the fast breeder, and the homogeneous type, but space does not permit complete descriptions here. The basic components of power reactors include:

1. **Core.** A core of fissionable material in an amount greater than or equal to the critical mass is necessary.

2. **Control rods.** Control rods are made of a material with a high affinity for neutrons. When these rods are fully inserted, they absorb a large proportion of the neutrons from fissioning, and the rate of fissioning is reduced to a low value. When the rods are entirely withdrawn, the rate of fissioning accelerates. The control rods can be automatically moved in and out to maintain the fissioning at the desired rate. Materials used include cadmium, boron, hafnium. Not all reactors require a control rod. An exception is the aqueous homogeneous reactor which is highly stable because of its negative temperature coefficient of reactivity. Its reactivity decreases as the temperature rises, providing an automatic correction.

3. **Coolant.** A coolant is used to pick up and carry away the energy released by the reaction.

4. **Moderator.** There may or may not be a *moderator*, which is any substance used for the purpose of slowing the neutrons to thermal energies. By *thermal energy* is meant energies of the order of those possessed by gaseous molecules (0.025 mev), in contrast with the relatively very high energy (speed) which a neutron possesses on emission (2 mev). These very high-speed neutrons are not so likely to cause fission as the slow neutrons; thus, to use as many neutrons as possible for fission, we arrange to have them traverse a moderator, carbon or water, for example, where they gradually lose energy, reaching a range of kinetic energy called *thermal energy*. A reactor which contains a moderator is called a thermal reactor; one which does not is called a *fast reactor*, because it depends upon the high-speed neutrons to cause fission.

5. **Shielding.** Shielding is used to protect life against the lethal radiation of gamma rays and beta particles (electrons). There are of course many other items involved, such as pumps, instruments, etc., which are not concerned with this discussion.

In the homogeneous reactor of Fig. 134, the reacting material, (fuel), is a solution of uranyl sulphate (UO_2SO_4) in heavy water or liquid metal, enriched with uranium 235. The fission of the U235, in critical mass in the reactor core, provides the energy which is transferred to generate steam in the heat exchanger as the fuel is pumped through. The steam rises to the steam drum, thence to a prime mover. If superheated steam is needed in the prime mover, and it is quite advantageous (§ 217), the superheating could be done in a furnace fired by the usual (fossil) fuels.

This type of reactor, Fig. 134, has several advantages. Some regulation is obtained by controlling the concentration of U235 in the solution, but the significant regulation occurs automatically because of the large negative temperature coefficient of reactivity. No control rod is necessary. The fuel can be continuously purified by chemical processing which removes the fission and corrosion products. A possibility, not shown in Fig. 134, is that it may be advantageous to surround the core of such a system by a *blanket* of *fertile material*, say a thorium compound. Under neutron bombardment, thorium 232 changes to U233, a process called *breeding* because

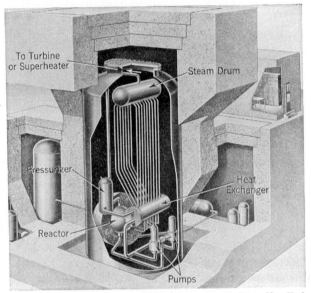

Courtesy Foster Wheeler Corp., New York

Fig. 134. Homogeneous Reactor.

the U233 is fissionable and is later used as the primary fuel. In this type, heat is also generated in the blanket material.

The amount of electricity generated from nuclear reactors is expected to increase rapidly over the next several years. One prediction is that by 1980 about half of the newly installed electric power will be nuclear steam generators. In the same year, electrical power obtained from nuclear reactors will be only about 20% of the total electrical power generated. In the meantime conventional steam-generating plants will about double in capacity every ten years; hence, the conventional plant is not to be outmoded soon.

173. Closure. You have probably observed that the heat exchangers of this chapter are used largely or exclusively in steam power plants. There are of course many other heat exchangers. Often the most difficult thermo-dynamic problem in the design of a heat exchanger is the determination of the heat transfer rate through the walls separating the fluids. The details of the mechanism of the flow of heat across such boundaries are studied in books on *heat transfer** and are beyond the scope of this work.

SELECTED REFERENCES

Babcock and Wilcox Co., *Steam.*
Combustion Engineering-Superheater, Inc., *Combustion Engineering.*
Glasstone and Edlund, *The Elements of Nuclear Reaction Theory*, Van Nostrand.
Murray, R. L., *Nuclear Engineering*, Prentice-Hall.
Ridenour, L. N., *et al.*, *Modern Physics for the Engineer*, McGraw-Hill.

PROBLEMS

251. The intercooler of an air compressor receives 80 lb./min. of air at 237°F and cools it to 90°F. The cooling water at 70°F passes first through the jackets of the cylinders picking up 1500 Btu/min. What mass and volume (gpm) of water should be pumped if its final temperature is to be 80°F?

Ans. 432.5 lb./min., 51.9 gpm.

252. A steam generator evaporates 118,250 lb./hr. of water from a feedwater temperature of 170°F and it burns 14,100 lb./hr. coal whose higher heating value is 12,800 Btu/lb. coal as fired. The steam leaves the steam generator at 280 psia and 600°F. Compute (a) the output in kB/hr. and in boiler horsepower, (b) the overall efficiency.

Ans. (a) 139,300 and 4160, (b) 77.2%.

253. A boiler with 2992 sq. ft. of heating surface evaporated 23,100 lb. per hr. of water from a feedwater temperature of 140°F into saturated steam at 156.3 psig. The barometric pressure was 27.9 in. Hg. The coal consumed was 2580 lb./hr.; higher heating value of 13,400 Btu/lb. as fired. Calculate (a) the output in kilo Btu/hr. and in boiler horsepower, (b) the overall efficiency. (c) For a rated capacity of 10 sq. ft. of heating surface per boiler horsepower, what percentage of the rated capacity was being developed?

Ans. (a) **750** bo. hp, (b) **72.5%**, (c) 251%.

254. The higher heating value of a natural gas is 1000 Btu/cu. ft., measured at standard conditions. A steam generator using this gas has an efficiency of 80% while delivering 200,000 lb./hr. of steam at 450 psia and 700°F and receiving feedwater at 300°F. (a) How much gas, measured at standard conditions, is consumed per hour? (c) If the gas costs 20 cents per 1000 standard cu. ft., what is the fuel cost for 1000 lb. of steam?

Ans. (a) 272,000 cu. ft./hr., (b) 27.2¢.

255. Saturated steam at 285 psia enters a convection superheater and leaves at 280 psia and 600°F. Hot gases (with $c_p = 0.241$ Btu/lb-°R) depart from the superheater at 1150°F at the rate of 1.6 lb. gas/lb. steam. What is the entering gas temperature?

Ans. 1443°F.

* A chapter on this subject is included in the author's *Thermodynamics*, Macmillan.

256. Steam enters a superheater with an enthalpy of 1190 Btu/lb. and departs at 900 psia and 900°F. There are 1.5 lb. flue gas/lb. steam. If the combustion gases start across the superheater at 2300°F, determine their average temperature drop and final temperature for $c_p = 0.28$ Btu/lb-°R? *Ans.* 1678°F.

257. (a) Flue gases enter the breeching at a temperature of 500°F and are discharged to the atmosphere whose temperature is 80°F without further recovery of energy. The heating value of the coal used is 13,000 Btu/lb., the mass of the dry flue gases ($c_p = 0.24$ Btu/lb-°R) is 13 lb./lb. fuel. What percentage of the heating value of the fuel is carried away by the dry gases? (b) The same as (a) except that an economizer and an air heater are used with the result that the dry gases enter the breeching at 350°F.
Ans. (a) 10.1%, (b) 6.48%.

258. From an economizer, 330,000 lb./hr. of flue gases ($c_p = 0.243$) enter an air preheater at 509°F and leave at 289°F. How much air is being heated if it enters at 90°F, leaves at 332°F? *Ans.* 304,000 lb./hr.

259. For the purpose of heating feedwater, 0.15 lb. of steam (per lb. of throttle flow) are extracted from a turbine at 295 psia and 420°F. This steam goes to an open heater (steam and water in direct contact) and mixes with 0.85 lb. of water (per lb. of throttle steam) entering at 230°F (§ 217). At what temperature does the water (including condensed steam) leave the heater? Solve this problem two ways: by an energy balance of heat given up by steam equal to heat added to water and by an energy balance as a steady flow device.
Ans. 377°F.

260. A turbine discharge 100,000 lb./hr. of steam to a surface condenser where the pressure is maintained at 1 psia. The condensate leaves the condenser and enters the first stage open feedwater heater at 100°F. For this heater, there are extracted (§ 217) 10,000 lb./hr. of steam at 15 psia and 2% moisture. If no losses occur, at what temperature does the water leave this heater. *Ans.* 197°F.

261. From an 85,000-kw turbo-generator, 770,000 lb./hr. of steam with an enthalpy of 1000 Btu/lb. enter a condenser in which the temperature is 92°F. This H_2O leaves the condenser as saturated water. The cooling water is expected to undergo a 14°F temperature rise from an entering temperature of 70°F. How much cooling water is needed, lb./hr. and gpm?
Ans. 103,600 gpm.

262. A 20,000-kw turbo-generator discharges to a surface condenser 134,000 lb./hr. of steam at 110°F and 95% quality. This steam is condensed to saturated water. The circulating water enters the condenser at 85°F in the amount of 1 gpm for each square foot of tube surface, and 1 sq. ft. of surface will condense 8 lb./hr. of steam. Determine the area of surface needed and the temperature of the exit circulating water. *Ans.* 16,750 sq. ft., 100.7°F.

263. An evaporator is used to supply 4000 lb./hr. of pure make-up water for a power plant. Saturated steam at 15 psia supplies heat for evaporating the water which enters at 168°F and leaves as saturated steam at this temperature. What mass of steam is required? *Ans.* 4120 lb./hr.

264. Distilled water is obtained in a three-effect evaporator. The raw water to be evaporated is from 90°F and saturated steam at 360°F is used in the high-temperature effect. In the final effect, the raw water is to be evaporated to saturated steam at 120°F. In each effect, the temperature difference between the condensing steam and the evaporating water is to be taken as ⅓ of the temperature range of 360 to 120°F. Assume that no losses occur and that condensation is to saturated liquid in each effect. (a) Determine the amount of distilled water, lb./lb. of 360°F steam. (b) How much water would be obtained in a single effect, between 360 and 120°F, lb./lb. of 360°F steam?   *Ans.*   (a) 1.957, (b) 0.817.

265. A steam generator delivers steam at 350 psia and 700°F. However, 1000 lb./hr. of saturated steam at 350 psia are needed and are obtained from a desuperheater which is supplied with water at 80°F. If equilibrium is achieved and no losses occur, how much water is used?   *Ans.*   123 lb./hr.

266. Two boilers are delivering steam into the same main at 180 psia.   The output of one is 3000 lb./hr. with 5% moisture, and of the other, 2000 lb./hr. at 480°F.   For internal thermal equilibrium, what is the state of the mixture?
              Ans.   100% quality.

267. What is the mass number and atomic number of each of the following substances?   Answer by statement and by symbolization.   (a) Americium, (b) nitrogen, (c) lithium, (d) plutonium, (e) sodium.

268. (a) What is meant by a fission fragment?   (b) What are beta particles?

269. Name and describe the function of the essential elements of any reactor.

270–280. These numbers may be used for other problems.

NOZZLES AND FLUID FLOW

174. Introduction. From a steam generator in a power plant, the steam proceeds to the prime mover, which in large plants will be a turbine. On entering the turbine, the steam first passes through nozzles which are devices for converting some of the fluid's initial energy into kinetic energy. The issuing jet of high-velocity steam (gas for gas turbine) passes across turbine blades which have been designed to change the momentum of the stream. The consequence of the change of momentum is a force (Newton) which does work turning the turbine shaft. This chapter covers the flow of expansible fluids, not only through nozzles, but also through some other devices used to measure and control flow. Since the approach is from the point of view of the energy relations, the reader should be informed that the general subject of *fluid mechanics* says much more about the phenomena of flow.

Inasmuch as we shall be dealing with both gases and vapors, this chapter provides an excellent opportunity to clarify in your mind the differences in handling these substances.

175. Flow Through Nozzles. A nozzle is a device (open system) used for the purpose of guiding the expansion of a substance to a state in which the kinetic energy of the substance is relatively large. There are two types, *convergent-divergent nozzles,* Fig. 135, and *convergent nozzles,* Fig. 136. They may have any cross-sectional shape to suit the application; see Figs. 171 and 174. Sometimes the section is circular. The elements of the internal surface of the divergent section, Fig. 135, are generally straight, for convenience in manufacture. The smallest cross-sectional area of a convergent-divergent nozzle is called the *throat,* Fig. 135. The customary manner of proportioning a convergent-divergent nozzle is to determine the throat area, as explained later, to provide a well-rounded entrance, to choose a nozzle length L, Fig. 135, such that the flare of the sides of the divergent section is within good limits in accordance with experience. With respect to the flare, too large an angle θ, Fig. 135, above about 12–15°, results in excessive turbulence and consequent irreversibility. The nozzle will be excessively long if θ is too small, say less than about 6°.

A convergent nozzle with a short section of parallel elements, Fig. 136(b), tends to discharge a better-formed jet than that in Fig. 136(a). Convergent nozzles as used in turbines are commonly foil nozzles; that is, they are formed by stationary blades which are small foils (similar to air foils on a plane).

For any nozzle, the shaft work is zero, $W = 0$. The length of time that a particular mass of substance is within the nozzle is a small fraction of a second; therefore, for practical purposes the flow is adiabatic. The only pertinent energies are therefore the internal energy and flow work (enthalpy)

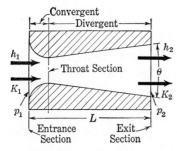

Fig. 135. *Convergent-Divergent Nozzle.* The pressure drop per unit of length is not constant. (See § 181.)

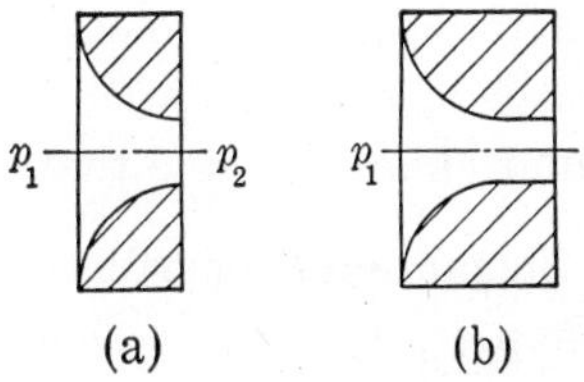

Fig. 136. *Convergent Nozzles.*

and the kinetic energy K, as shown in the energy diagram of the system in Fig. 135. Letting $K = v^2/(2g_oJ)$, we have for steady flow, $dK = -dh$, or

(a)
$$\frac{v_1^2}{2g_oJ} + h_1 = \frac{v_2^2}{2g_oJ} + h_2 \text{ Btu/lb.,}$$
$$[\text{ANY FLUID, } Q = 0, W = 0]$$

applicable to ideal or actual expansions when state 2 is the ideal or actual state at the exit section. The initial velocity v_1 is usually difficult to determine and sometimes it is negligible $(K_1 \approx 0)$; in which case,

(b)
$$v_2 = [2g_oJ(h_1 - h_2)]^{1/2} = 223.8(h_1 - h_2)^{1/2},$$
$$[\text{GAS OR VAPOR, } v_1 \text{ NEGLIGIBLE}]$$

applicable to any expansible fluid, where $2g_oJ \approx 50,000$ and $(2g_oJ)^{1/2} \approx 223.8$. These constants are convenient ones to memorize for current use. As necessary, we use the conservation of mass equation (6), § 20, $A_1v_1/v_1 = A_2v_2/v_2$, from which

(c)
$$v_1 = \left(\frac{A_2v_1}{A_1v_2}\right)v_2 \text{ fps,}$$

in which A sq. ft. is the cross-sectional area and v cu. ft. is the specific volume. Substituting the value of v_1 from (c) into (a) and solving for v_2, we get

(61)
$$v_2 = \left[\frac{2g_oJ(h_1 - h_2)}{1 - [A_2v_1/(A_1v_2)]^2} \right]^{1/2} \text{fps,}$$

[GAS OR VAPOR, IDEAL OR ACTUAL FLOW]

where the states 1 and 2 are at any two sections 1 and 2, wherever taken. Comparing equations (61) and (b), we see that the factor

(d) $\quad I = \left[\dfrac{1}{1 - \left(\dfrac{A_2v_1}{A_1v_2}\right)^2} \right]^{1/2} = \left[\dfrac{1}{1 - \left[\dfrac{A_2}{A_1}\left(\dfrac{p_2}{p_1}\right)^{1/k}\right]^2} \right]^{1/2} = \left[\dfrac{1}{1 - \left(\dfrac{A_2\rho_2}{A_1\rho_1}\right)^2} \right]^{1/2}$

cares for the effect of initial velocity and it may be kept in mind as a correction factor applicable to equations obtained later; ρ lb./cu. ft. ($= 1/v$) is the density; $v_1/v_2 = (p_2/p_1)^{1/k}$ for an ideal gas in an isentropic expansion. For circular channels, note that $A_2/A_1 = (D_2/D_1)^2$.

176. Stagnation Properties. Stagnation properties, which will be useful in this chapter, *are those thermodynamic properties which a moving stream of fluid would have if it were brought to rest by an isentropic compression.* If a moving stream with a kinetic energy K Btu/lb. and enthalpy h Btu/lb. is brought to rest isentropically, the resulting kinetic energy is zero and the enthalpy is h_o. At the entrance to the nozzle, Fig. 135, $h_o = h_1 + K_1$. Thus, we see that h_o includes the effect of initial velocity. Refer to § 106 which deals with stagnation enthalpy relative to a body moving in a fluid at rest.

If the substance is a flowing vapor for which vapor tables are available and if the state where the enthalpy and kinetic energy are h and K is defined (say, pressure and temperature in the superheated region), the properties in the stagnation state are easily found from

$$h_o = h + K \qquad \text{or} \qquad h_o - h = K \qquad \text{and} \qquad s_o = s,$$

which locate the state in the tables. If the substance is an ideal gas, the property relations of an isentropic process apply; repeated for convenience from § 58,

$$p_o v_o^k = pv^k, \qquad \frac{T}{T_o} = \left(\frac{p}{p_o}\right)^{(k-1)/k} = \left(\frac{v_o}{v}\right)^{k-1}.$$

The ideal gas equation of state applies, $p_o v_o = RT_o$, where T_o is the stagnation temperature; p, v, and T in the foregoing equations are values at any other state on the isentropic line. Since $\Delta h = c_p \Delta T$ for an ideal gas, we have

(e) $\qquad\qquad c_p(T_o - T) = K \qquad \text{or} \qquad T_o = T + \dfrac{v^2}{2g_oJc_p}.$

In terms of stagnation enthalpy, the energy equation for a steady flow nozzle is obtained from (a) as

(62) $$h_o = h_2 + K_2, \quad \text{or} \quad v_2 = 223.8(h_o - h_2)^{1/2}$$
$$[\text{GAS OR VAPOR}, \ s = C \text{ or } s \neq C, Q = 0]$$

where $h_o = h_1 + v_1^2/(2g_oJ)$. Equation (62) is the same as (61) when the initial velocity is significant and it is the same as (b) when v_1 is negligible.

177. Mass of Flow Through Nozzle. The mass rate of flow is computed from equation (6),

(6) $$w = \frac{Av}{v} \text{ lb./sec.,}$$

where v fps, obtained from (62), and v cu. ft./lb. are values at a section whose area is A. This equation may be applied at any section of the nozzle, but it is most often applied to the throat and exit sections. The method of finding the volume $v = v_2$ at any section depends upon whether the substance is an ideal gas or a vapor. For an ideal gas in an isentropic expansion,

(f) $$v_2 = v_o \left(\frac{p_o}{p_2}\right)^{1/k} = \left(\frac{RT_o}{p_o}\right)\left(\frac{p_o}{p_2}\right)^{1/k},$$

where p_1 and v_1 may be used in place of p_o and v_o, because $p_o v_o^k = p_1 v_1^k = p_2 v_2^k$.

178. Example—Air Nozzle. At the rate of 5 lb./sec., air at 200 psia and 60°F enters a nozzle with negligible velocity and expands isentropically to 15 psia. Determine the final velocity, specific volume, and the area of the exit section.

SOLUTION. The final temperature is

$$T_2 = T_1 \left(\frac{p_2}{p_1}\right)^{(k-1)/k} = (520)\left(\frac{15}{200}\right)^{0.4/1.4} = 248°R.$$

Using $\Delta h = c_p \Delta T$, we have from (62),

$$v_2 = 223.8 \sqrt{(0.24)(520 - 248)} = 1810 \text{ fps.}$$

The specific volumes are

$$v_1 = \frac{RT_1}{p_1} = \frac{(53.3)(520)}{(200)(144)} = 0.962 \text{ cu. ft./lb.,}$$

$$v_2 = v_1 \left(\frac{p_1}{p_2}\right)^{1/k} = (0.962)\left(\frac{200}{15}\right)^{1/1.4} = 6.1 \text{ cu. ft./lb.}$$

From (4) and for $w = 5$ lb./sec., we get the area of the exit section as

$$A_2 = \frac{wv_2}{v_2} = \frac{(5)(6.1)}{1810} = 0.01685 \text{ sq. ft., or 2.425 sq. in.}$$

179. Equilibrium Flow of a Vapor. When a vapor starts its expansion in a nozzle from the superheat region, as at 1, Fig. 137, and follows an isentropic path 1-*a*-2, it should start condensing at *a* where the process line crosses the saturated vapor line, and it should become progressively wetter as the expansion proceeds to 2. If this should be true (which it is not—

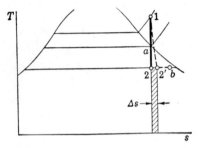

§ 185), the vapor-liquid mixtures would at all times be an equilibrium mixture and the expansion would be an equilibrium expansion. Hence, for internal *equilibrium conditions,*

$$s_1 = s_2 = (s_g - y_2 s_{fg})_2,$$
$$h_2 = (h_g - y_2 h_{fg})_2$$

and
$$v_2 = (v_g - y_2 v_{fg})_2,$$

Fig. 137. Equilibrium Expansion.

where s_1 may be s_o if stagnation properties are known. These equations, together with (6) and (62), give the solution to problems in which equilibrium conditions are assumed.

180. Example—Steam Nozzle, Equilibrium Flow. Steam enters a nozzle with negligible velocity at 160 psia and 400°F, flowing at the rate of 10 lb./sec. If it expands isentropically to 10 psia, what should be the area of the exit section (process 1-2, Fig. 137)?

SOLUTION. From the steam tables, we find

$h_1 = 1217.6$	$s_{g2} = 1.7876$	$h_{fg2} = 982.1$
$s_1 = 1.5908$	$s_{fg2} = 1.5041$	$v_{g2} = 38.42$
$v_1 = 3.008$	$h_{g2} = 1143.3$	$v_{fg2} = 38.4$

$$s_1 = s_2 = 1.5908 = 1.7876 - 1.5041 y_2, \quad y_2 = 13.05\%.$$
$$h_2 = 1143.3 - (0.1305)(982.1) = 1015.1 \text{ Btu/lb.}$$
$$v_2 = 38.42 - (0.1305)(38.4) = 33.4 \text{ cu. ft./lb.}$$
$$v_2 = 223.8(h_1 - h_2)^{1/2} = 223.8(1217.6 - 1015.1)^{1/2} = 3180 \text{ fps.}$$
$$A_2 = \frac{wv_2}{v_2} = \frac{(10)(33.4)(144)}{3180} = 15.1 \text{ sq. in.}$$

181. Variation of Velocity, Specific Volume, and Area of Section of a Nozzle. It will be revealing to investigate the manner in which the velocity, specific volume, and sectional area vary as the pressure drops through a nozzle, an investigation which may be made for either a gas or a vapor. The method of procedure for a gas is as shown in detail in § 178, those calculations being repeated for several different p_2's. The answers are tabulated below Fig. 138 in which the values are plotted.

The most notable feature, true for vapor as well as gas nozzles, is that the area decreases to a minimum, already named the *throat*, and then increases; that is, the nozzle *must* be converging-diverging if the expansion goes far

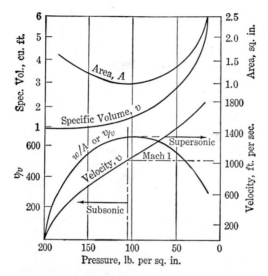

Fig. 138. *Specific Volume, Area, and* $\mho/v$ *Plotted Against Pressure.* Vapors and other gases flowing through nozzles have attributes quite similar to these curves plotted for air. Observe that the velocity may be very large, the maximum in this case being 1810 fps = 1259 mph. It is apparent that the nozzle for this expansion must have a convergent portion followed by a divergent portion. This illustration is plotted for a uniform pressure drop (abscissa). However, the pressure drop in the nozzle is not constant per unit length of nozzle. There is no reason for it to be.

p_2 Psia	v_2 Cu. ft./lb.	$\mho_2$ Fps	A_2 Sq. in.	$\mho_2/v_2 = w/A_2{}^*$
200	0.962			
175	1.059	483	1.578	456
150	1.18	700	1.212	593
125	1.346	887	1.091	659
106	*1.515*	*1020*	*1.070*	*673*
100	1.58	1060	1.072	671
50	2.59	1431	1.302	553
25	4.24	1675	1.821	395
15	6.1	1810	2.425	297

* A_2 in sq. ft.

enough. Since w is the same for all sections, the A/w curve would look like the A curve, Fig. 138; then since $A/w = v/\upsilon$, the $w/A = \upsilon/v$ curve naturally moves to a maximum and then down. The reason that these curves move as they do is that in the early part of the expansion, the velocity increases at a greater rate than the specific volume, but later the specific volume increases at the more rapid rate. Study the curves.

Note that it is *necessary* for the area to increase after the throat section if the expansion (volume increase) is to continue. In the above tabulation, the minimum area is 1.07 sq. in. at $p_2 = 106$ psia. If this nozzle, cut off at the throat section, should discharge into a passage of 1.07-sq. in. area, Fig. 139, there would be no further expansion, and in the absence of friction and heat, the air would continue to move in this passage at a pressure of 106 psia and $\upsilon = 1020$ fps for an indefinite distance. If the pressure p_2 at the end of the pipe B, Fig. 139, is less than 106 psia, there is a sudden uncontrolled expansion as the air leaves the pipe, resulting in a chaotic condition, the degree of chaos increasing as the pressure drop increases. If the pressure p_2 were 100 psia, that is, any pressure a little lower than 106, much of the acquired kinetic energy could be converted into work in turbine blades. On the other hand, if the pressure were 15 psia, the confusion in the stream would be so great that much of the acquired kinetic energy would be lost in internal friction before it could do work on turbine blades. When the expansion in the nozzle does not guide the stream with continuously decreasing pressure to the pressure of the surroundings at the exit section, **underexpansion** is said to have occurred. If the expansion is guided, as suggested by the dotted lines at B, Fig. 139, not only is the kinetic energy acquired at C conserved, but additional kinetic energy is generated during the further expansion, all of which is available for work on turbine blades.

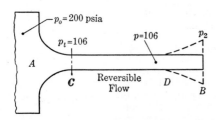

Fig. 139. The properties of the fluid do not change from, say, C to D.

Now suppose that the pressure p_2 is greater than 106 psia, say 175 psia. Then in the absence of friction, this pressure would build up in the pipe line theoretically to the section C; that is, p_t would be 175 psia. If this should be true, the velocity acquired at C would be 483 fps (instead of 1020 fps) as shown in the tabulation under Fig. 138, but to obtain the same flow w, the area at C would have to be increased to 1.578 sq. in. If the passageway is flared as shown dotted DB, Fig. 139, and if $p_2 > p_c = 106$ psia, say 175 psia, the pressure in the passage CD will fall below 175 and then rise. If the length CD were zero, the pressure at the throat would fall below the exit pressure, likely falling to about the critical pressure. When the pressure falls below the exit pressure within the nozzle, *overexpansion* is said to have occurred.

The final state defines the area A_2 of the final section, which is computed from $w = A_2 v_2 / v_2$. If, in the tabulation of Fig. 138, the final pressure is 25 psia, the area of the exit section should be 1.821 sq. in., as seen in the tabulation; if the final pressure is 50 psia, the exit area should be 1.302 sq. in. In both cases, the discharged mass would be the same.

182. Critical Pressure in a Nozzle. The pressure at the throat of the nozzle discussed above is the critical pressure, and it will be true in a convergent-divergent nozzle that the throat pressure is the critical pressure whenever the overall expansion is to a pressure lower than the critical pressure. Therefore, if there is a direct way to compute the critical pressure, it will not be necessary to plot curves in order to find the throat area. A relatively simple mathematical procedure* shows that for a gas

$$(63) \qquad p_c = p_o \left(\frac{2}{k+1} \right)^{k/(k-1)}$$

where p_c is the critical pressure which exists at the throat of a convergent-divergent nozzle. The significance of the critical pressure lies in the phenomena:

1. For a particular nozzle, the mass flow is *less* than the maximum attainable if the final pressure is *greater than* p_c;

2. The mass flow is the maximum for final pressures equal to and *less than* p_c and is the same for all final pressures less than p_c.

Observing that the curves for A and v/v, Fig. 138, do not change abruptly at the critical pressure, we correctly conclude that the throat area is not sensitive to the true value of the critical pressure; that is, k in equation (63) may vary somewhat from its true value without significant effect on the nozzle design. For this reason, equation (63), which strictly applies to an isentropic expansion, is commonly used for computing critical pressures. The actual expansion is practically adiabatic and, because a correctly designed and well-made nozzle is highly efficient, the expansion is only slightly irreversible. For ideal gases with $k = 1.4$ (which means diatomic gases at temperatures not too far from atmospheric), the critical pressure is ($p_c = p_t$, throat pressure)

$$(g) \qquad p_t = p_o \left(\frac{2}{k+1} \right)^{k/(k-1)} = p_o \left(\frac{2}{2.4} \right)^{1.4/0.4} \approx 0.53 \, p_o.$$

* See V. M. Faires, *Thermodynamics*, Macmillan, and other works on thermodynamics.

The critical pressure of air for an initial stagnation pressure of 200 psia is $(0.53)(200) = 106$ psia (see Fig. 138). For $k = 1$, the critical pressure ratio is 0.606; for $k = 1.67$, $p_t/p_o = 0.487$. Note the relatively small variation. Other values in common use are:

Superheated steam, $k = 1.3$, $p_t = 0.545p_o$;
Supersaturated steam, $k = 1.3$, $p_t = 0.545p_o$;
Wet steam, $k = 1.13$, $p_t = 0.58p_o$.

183. Throat Velocity. The velocity at the throat of a nozzle is the same as the velocity of sound in the fluid when the fluid is in the thermodynamic state defined by the throat properties. In the tabulation of Fig. 138, the sonic velocity of the air at the throat is 1020 fps. Thus, the throat velocity may be computed not only from (62) but from the equation from physics for the sonic velocity in any gas, $v_s = (g_okpv)^{1/2}$, where the symbols have their usual meanings and units. In some situations, it is convenient to express velocities in terms of Mach numbers **M** which is the ratio of the actual velocity of the substance (or of a body in the substance) divided by the velocity of sound in the substance; that is,

$$(\text{h}) \qquad\qquad \mathbf{M} = \frac{v}{v_s} = \frac{v}{(g_okpv)^{1/2}}.$$

Mach numbers greater than unity are **supersonic velocities:** Mach numbers less than unity are **subsonic velocities.** We note that in a convergent nozzle, the velocity of the substance is always subsonic (or sonic at the maximum); in a convergent-divergent nozzle, the velocity is $\mathbf{M} < 1$ up to the throat, Mach 1 at the throat, and $\mathbf{M} > 1$ in the divergent part, Fig. 138.

184. Example—Throat Size. What should be the throat area for the steam flow defined in the example of § 180; that is, $p_1 = 160$ psia, $t_1 = 400°F$, $p_2 = 10$ psia, 10 lb./sec., isentropic process.

SOLUTION. The throat pressure for superheated steam, from § 182, is $p_t = (0.545)(160) = 87$ psia (nearly). Taking values from the full Keenan and Keyes steam tables for 87 psia, we find

$$s_1 = s_t = 1.5908 = 1.6139 - 1.153y_t, \qquad \text{or} \qquad y_t = 1.99\%.$$
$$h_t = 1184.6 - (0.0199)(896.5) = 1166.8 \text{ Btu/lb.}$$
$$v_t = 223.8(1217.6 - 1166.8)^{1/2} = 1592 \text{ fps.}$$
$$v_t = 5.055 - (0.0199)(5.037) = 4.95 \text{ cu. ft./lb.}$$
$$A_t = \frac{wv_t}{v_t} = \frac{(10)(4.95)(144)}{1592} = 4.47 \text{ sq. in.,}$$

which is the necessary throat area to pass 10 lb./sec. of steam in an ideal expansion.

185. Supersaturated Flow. As previously mentioned, the time that it takes for a particular molecule of substance to pass through a nozzle is short (of the order of 0.001 sec.).   Therefore it should not be too surprising that condensation does not start at a, Fig. 140, where the expansion line 1-a-c crosses the saturated vapor line.   Instead, the steam remains all vapor until some point c is reached when condensation suddenly occurs.   Such steam as that between a and c is called **supersaturated steam,** and the state of this

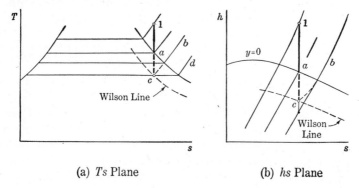

(a) Ts Plane   (b) hs Plane

Fig. 140.   Ideal Supersaturated Flow.

steam is spoken of as a *metastable state,* meaning that it would take more than a very small action to cause the steam to achieve internal equilibrium states along ac—say an action as big as a spray of fine water drops into the stream ahead of point a (not that this result is desired).   The actual pressure at the supersaturated state c is p_b, Fig. 140; but the saturation pressure corresponding to the temperature t_c is p_d, Fig. 140(a), which is the pressure which would have existed at c if an equilibrium expansion had occurred to t_c.   The ratio of these pressures p_b/p_d is called the *degree of supersaturation* or *supersaturation ratio.* The expansion of supersaturated steam is handled in accordance with the energy equations ($\Delta K = -\int v\, dp$) for $pv^k = C$, where $k \approx 1.3$. |

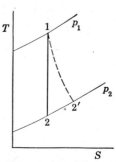

Fig. 141.   Gas Expansion. If $\upsilon_1 = 0$, state 1 is the same as the stagnation state.

186. Losses in Nozzles.   The *nozzle efficiency* e_n is defined as the actual kinetic energy at discharge divided by the ideal kinetic energy, each measured to the same final pressure and each for 1 lb.   Let $2'$ be the actual final state, Figs. 137 and 141: then

(i) $e_n = \dfrac{K_{2'}}{K_2} = \dfrac{h_o - h_{2'}}{(h_o - h_2)_s} = \dfrac{\upsilon_{2'}^2/(2g_oJ)}{(h_1 - h_2)_s + K_1}$,

where the subscript s is a reminder of constant entropy; $K_1 = \upsilon_1^2/(2g_oJ)$. In a convergent-divergent nozzle, K_1 is nearly always relatively negligible and can be omitted; this is also true when there is a substantial expansion in a convergent nozzle.   If the nozzle "fits" the expansion, the efficiencies are high, ranging from some 92% for long convergent-divergent nozzles to 98–99% for convergent nozzles.   The efficiency of convergent-divergent nozzles *up to the throat* is similarly some 98–99% for well-made ones.

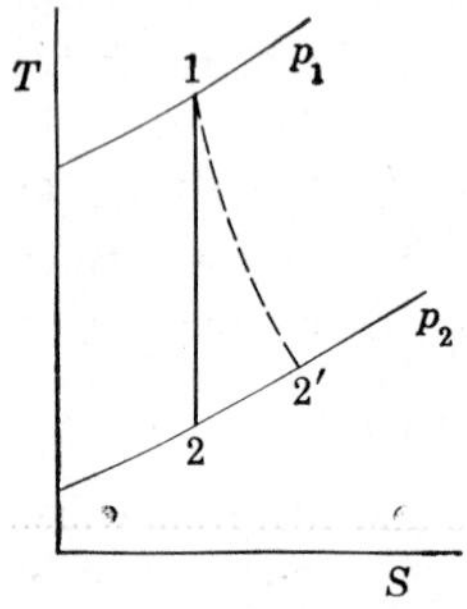

The **nozzle coefficient** η_n is the ratio of the actual velocity divided by the ideal velocity

(j) $$\eta_n = \frac{v_{2'}}{v_2} = \frac{[2g_oJ(h_o - h_{2'})]^{1/2}}{[2g_oJ(h_o - h_2)_s]^{1/2}} = \sqrt{e_n}.$$

Engineers experienced in this phase of design know from past experience about what nozzle efficiency or nozzle coefficient to expect under certain circumstances, and this knowledge can be used for the purpose of computing $h_{2'}$ from equation (i) or (j).   Notice that the actual velocity is now given by

Fig. 141. Repeated.

(k) $$v_{2'} = [e_n(2g_oJ)(h_o - h_2)]^{1/2} = \eta_n[2g_oJ(h_o - h_2)]^{1/2} \text{ fps.}$$

Similarly, any of the other equations giving v_2 may be multiplied by $\eta_n = \sqrt{e_n}$ to get $v_{2'}$.

The shaded area in Fig. 137 represents the *lost work* due to the irreversibilities in the nozzle.   Since kinetic energy is 100% available energy, it can all be converted into work in an ideal engine; thus lost kinetic energy is the same as **lost work**, which may be defined as the actual work subtracted from the corresponding ideal work.   For adiabatic processes, lost work

$$= h_1 - h_2 - (h_1 - h_{2'}) = h_{2'} - h_2$$

in either Fig. 137 or 141.

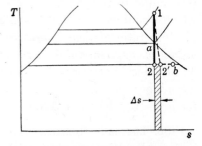

Fig. 137. Repeated.

187. Coefficient of Discharge.   The ideal rate of flow is related to the actual rate of flow through a nozzle (or other flow device, such as an orifice) by a **coefficient of discharge** η_d, defined as

(l) $$\eta_d = \frac{\text{Actual mass of flow per unit time}}{\text{Ideal mass of flow per unit time}}.$$

The value of this coefficient can be determined by test on a particular device.

Also, it can be estimated, sometimes with considerable accuracy, from past data on similar devices.

188. Actual Volume After Expansion. To be consistent in applying the continuity of mass law, one should use the actual flow $w' = A_{2'}v_{2'}/v_{2'}$, where all values are actual simultaneous values at some section 2. However, the actual specific volume $v_{2'}$ at a throat section is so little different from the ideal v_2 that in preliminary calculations, they are often taken as the same. In your problem work, you may let $v_{2'} \approx v_2$ at the throat if the efficiency is high (but account for the change in velocity).

189. Example. Let the data be the same as that in §§ 180 and 184, from which we have $p_1 = 160$ psia, $t_1 = 400°F$, $p_2 = 10$ psia at exit, $w = 10$ lb./sec. ideal flow, equilibrium expansion of steam, $p_t = 87$ psia, $h_t = 1166.8$ Btu/lb., $A_t = 4.47$ sq. in., $v_t = 4.95$ cu. ft., and $v_t = 1592$ fps. (a) If the nozzle efficiency up to the throat is 98%, compute the mass flow based on equilibrium expansion and the coefficient of discharge. (b) If the overall nozzle efficiency is 93%, what are the actual exit enthalpy and the lost work?

SOLUTION. (a) See Fig. 137. For an efficiency of 98%, we can compute the enthalpy $h_{t'}$ at the throat from

$$h_1 - h_{t'} = e_n(h_1 - h_t)$$
$$1217.6 - h_{t'} = 0.98(1217.6 - 1166.8);$$

or $h_{t'} = 1167.8$ Btu/lb. The corresponding percentage moisture is found from

$$h_{t'} = (h_{gt} - h_{fgt}y_{t'}) = 1167.8 = 1184.6 - 896.5y_{t'},$$

or $y_{t'} = 1.88\%$. Then $v_{t'} \approx xv_g = (1 - 0.0188)(5.055) = 4.96$ cu. ft./lb., which as previously suggested is little different from the ideal volume (4.95). Also $v_{t'} = \sqrt{e_n}\, v_t = (\sqrt{0.98})(1592) = 1578$ fps. It follows that the actual flow as computed is

$$w' = \frac{A_t v_{t'}}{v_{t'}} = \frac{(4.47)(1578)}{(144)(4.96)} = 9.87 \text{ lb./sec.}$$

Then $\eta_d = w'/w = 9.87/10 = 0.987$ (§ 187). (NOTE. The true actual flow will be somewhat greater because supersaturated steam is denser than the corresponding equilibrium steam, and the steam is sure to be supersaturated at the throat of this nozzle.)

(b) With a nozzle efficiency of 93%, we have

$$h_1 - h_{2'} = e_n(h_1 - h_2)$$
$$1217.6 - h_{2'} = 0.93(1217.6 - 1015.1),$$

from which $h_{2'} = 1029.3$ Btu/lb. The work lost because of losses in the nozzle is $h_{2'} - h_2 = 1029.3 - 1015.1 = 14.2$ Btu/lb. and is represented by the area under 2-2', Fig. 137. The value of $h_2 = 1015.1$ is taken from § 180.

190. Diffuser. A diffuser, Fig. 142, receives a fluid at a (relatively) high velocity and discharges it at a higher pressure and lower velocity—the reverse of the nozzle process. That is, some of the initial kinetic energy, which is 100% available, is used as the work of compression. The same

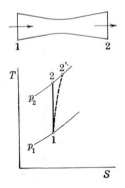

Fig. 142. Diffuser.

conditions, $Q = 0$ and $W = 0$, are applied to diffusers to get the same energy relation, equation (a),

$$\frac{v_1{}^2}{2g_oJ} + h_1 = \frac{v_2{}^2}{2g_oJ} + h_2 \text{ Btu/lb.,}$$

except that often the final velocity v_2 (and K_2) is negligible. Let the critical pressure ratio be p_t/p_o, defined by equation (63); then by way of comparison:

Nozzle	Diffuser
If $\dfrac{p_2}{p_1} < \dfrac{p_t}{p_1}$,	If $\dfrac{p_2}{p_1} > \dfrac{p_t}{p_1}\left(\dfrac{p_1}{p_2} < \dfrac{p_1}{p_t}\right)$,
$v_2 >$ sonic velocity,	$v_1 >$ sonic velocity,
converging-diverging nozzle.	converging-diverging diffuser.
If $\dfrac{p_2}{p_1} > \dfrac{p_t}{p_1}$,	If $\dfrac{p_2}{p_1} < \dfrac{p_t}{p_1}$,
$v_2 <$ sonic velocity,	$v_1 <$ sonic velocity,
converging nozzle.	diverging diffuser.

In each instance, p_1 is the initial pressure and p_2 is the final pressure. It is convenient to use a diffuser efficiency e_d,

(m) $$e_d = \frac{(h_2 - h_1)_s}{h_{2'} - h_1},$$

in which, strictly, states 2 and 2' are stagnation states, ideal and actual.

191. Ejector. The diffuser is also an integral part of the *injector* or *ejector*. These two terms, **injector** and **ejector,** are applied to essentially the same instrument—an instrument used to pump fluids from a lower to a higher pressure. The operation of an injector or ejector is as follows. Steam enters the usual type of divergent nozzle at A, Fig. 143. At B, the exit of the nozzle, the pressure is low and the velocity high. The low pressure in the region B causes the gas or liquid to be sucked into the device

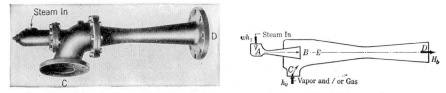

Fig. 143. Ejector. AB is a steam nozzle; *ED* is the diffuser. Substance being pumped enters at *C*. The injector, used as a feedwater pump, is similar to this device, and it pumps the water to a higher pressure at *D* than exists at *A*.

through C, and the momentum of the fast-moving jet of steam carries the substance into the diffuser ED, where the velocity decreases and the pressure increases until the exit section D is reached. Ejectors are commonly used

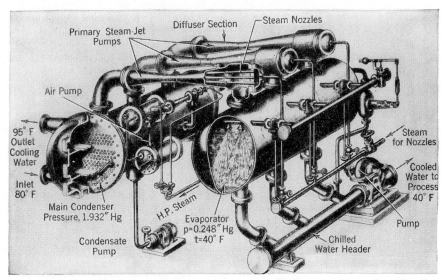

Courtesy Foster Wheeler Corp., New York

Fig. 144. Vacuum Refrigerating System. Since the pressure in the evaporator is maintained at 0.248 in. Hg by the ejectors, the temperature is the saturation temperature (= 40°F) corresponding to this pressure. Warmer water entering the evaporator is cooled by the evaporation of some of it until equilibrium is obtained. The steam from the steam nozzles and the steam being pumped from the evaporator is condensed in the main condenser. The resulting *water* is inexpensively pumped to atmospheric pressure.

to rid evacuated spaces (steam condensers, for example) of noncondensable gases, such as air, and also as pumps, called jet pumps, in vacuum refrigerating systems, Fig. 144. A single-stage ejector can maintain a vacuum of some 26 in. Hg; a two-stage, up to about 29.3 in. Hg; a three-stage, up to 29.9 in. Hg; and a four-stage, absolute pressures of the order of 1 mm. Hg. Since the thermal efficiency of the ejector is low, rotary or reciprocating pumps are generally preferred except when large volumes of gases or vapors are to be handled.

192. Equations for the Approximate Ideal Velocity, Small Expansion. When the pressure drop is small, as happens in flow-metering devices (see below), the accurate evaluation of (62) becomes difficult. If the fluid is a gas and we use $h_o - h_2 = c_p(T_o - T_2)$, one of the temperatures must be computed and the difference of temperatures, being small, is subjected to large error. In short, it is more accurate to make assumptions which are approximate and get an equation in a different form. Start with the energy equation in the form

$$u_2 + P_2 + K_2 + p_2 v_2 + Q = u_o + P_o + p_o v_o + W \text{ ft-lb./lb.,}$$

where the subscript o refers to the stagnation state, arrived at as the limit while the velocity approaches zero; that is, $K_o = 0$. Also let $W = 0$ because it is irrelevant; let $\Delta P = 0$ for horizontal flow; $\Delta u = 0$, which is only approximately true; and $Q = 0$ for a small temperature differential or a well-insulated line. Moreover, assume $v_2 \approx v_o = v$; that is, an incompressible type of flow (this assumption is closely true for small Δp). Then, for $K_2 = v_2^2/(2g_o)$,

(n) $$\frac{v_2^2}{2g_o} + p_2 v_2 = p_o v_o \quad \text{or} \quad \frac{v_2^2}{2g_o} = v_o(p_o - p_2).$$

Usually in cases where this approximate equation is appropriate, the effect of the initial velocity must be included by using the stagnation properties as shown, or by using the initial velocity correction factor I, equation (d), in accordance with the following equation. Let the o subscripts be replaced by 1 and use $v_1 = RT_1/p_1$.

(o) $$v_2 = I \left[2g_o v_1(p_1 - p_2)\right]^{1/2}$$

$$= I \left[2g_o RT_1 \left(\frac{p_1 - p_2}{p_1}\right)\right]^{1/2} = \left[2g_o RT_o \left(\frac{p_o - p_2}{p_o}\right)\right]^{1/2}$$

Since v is practically constant in the applications of this equation, a simplified value of I may be used:

(p) $$I = \left[\frac{1}{1 - (A_2/A_1)^2}\right]^{1/2} = \left[\frac{1}{1 - (D_2/D_1)^4}\right]^{1/2}.$$

Pressures are often stated in terms of the height z of a column of fluid, as in manometers. Imagine any column of fluid whose cross-sectional area is A sq. in., whose height is z in., and whose specific weight is γ lb./cu. in. The weight of this total volume Az is $Az\gamma$ lb.; the pressure on a section A at the bottom of the column z is $Az\gamma/A = z\gamma$ psi. The specific weight can be computed from the density, $\gamma = \rho g/g_o$, when the local acceleration of gravity g is different from the standard g_o; $\gamma = \rho$ when $g = g_o$. From the foregoing, we see that the pressure represented by a column of any fluid is

(q) $p = z\gamma =$ (Height of column, in.) (Specific weight, lb./cu. in.) psi.

For mercury at 60°F, $\rho = 0.491$ lb./cu. in.; for water at 60°F, $\rho = 0.0361$ lb./cu. in. If the fluid is water and if the temperature of the water is known, the density of water is accurately obtained from the steam tables as $\rho = 1/v_f$.

193. Pitot Tube. If a tube is bent and pointed into a stream of gas (or vapor), as shown at M, Fig. 145, the gas is brought to rest at the end of the tube by a compression that is very nearly isentropic. Thus, the pressure at the point of the tube is higher than that of the moving stream, and if the tube is open at this point and connected to a gage, the gage registers this impact pressure, which is the stagnation pressure p_o, called the *total pressure* or *impact pressure* in this context. On the other hand, an opening parallel to the stream line, such as that at N, is subjected to the so-called static pressure p_2, which is that pressure unaffected by the velocity

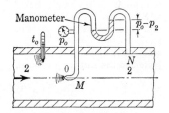

Fig. 145. The fluid in contact with the end of the impact tube at 0 is at rest.

of the substance. If a substance should expand isentropically from pressure p_o to p_2, it would acquire an ideal velocity in accordance with equation (62); it follows that if a substance should be compressed isentropically from p_2 to p_o to a state of rest, it would *lose* velocity as expressed by equation (62). Thus, these pressures p_o and p_2, together with the temperature t_o (which is the temperature *after* isentropic compression, since the thermometer, too, is in the stream line), may be used to calculate the velocity of flow in the pipe. However, since the pressure difference $p_o - p_2$ is usually small, equation (o) in § 192 will be more convenient to use. To find the quantity of flow in a pipe, it is necessary to make *a traverse* of the pipe in a standard specified way in order to find the mean velocity. This mean velocity v substituted in $w = Av/v$ will give the mass of gas flowing in the pipe. The value of v in the continuity equation should correspond to the subscripts 2 and is such that $v = v_2 = v_o(p_o/p_2)^{1/k}$, where $v_o = RT_o/p_o$. However, there is often so little change in the pressure that v_o is nearly equal to v_2, § 192.   See books on laboratory procedure for the method of making the traverse, which gives readings of the total pressure at selected points across a section of the pipe.

A pitot tube, Fig. 146, is a convenient instrument which consists of two concentric tubes.   The inner tube has an opening which faces the stream

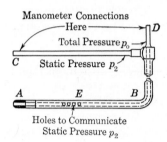

Manometer Connections

—Here—

Total Pressure p_o

C Static Pressure p_2

A E B

Holes to Communicate
Static Pressure p_2

Fig. 146.   Pitot Tube.   The length AB is inside the pipe and the parts C and D are outside for the connections as indicated.   The small holes at E are parallel to the stream and are subjected to the static pressure only.   The inside tube, open at A, is subjected to the impact pressure.

line and which is therefore subjected to the total pressure p_o.   The outer tube has openings parallel to the stream line which are subjected to the static pressure p_2.   These openings are connected through a manometer so that the pressure difference $p_o - p_2$ can be read directly. The pressure difference $p_o - p_2$ is often termed the **velocity pressure** or the **velocity head** when the pressure is expressed in inches of a column of fluid.

194. The Venturi Meter.   The pitot tube is one of several devices used for the purpose of determining the mass rate of flow in a pipe line. Of the others, we shall mention briefly the venturi, the flow nozzle, and the orifice.   Each of these devices is of fundamental importance and is used to measure the flow of liquids and gases.

The venturi meter consists of two sections, a nozzle section 1-2, Fig. 147, in which the velocity increases and the pressure drops in accordance with the explanation of nozzles; and a second section 2-3, called the diffuser section, § 190.   The fluid in steady flow must necessarily flow faster through the small section at 2, provided the law of con-servation of mass holds, so that the other properties change accordingly.   A manom-eter, connected to the main section as at 1 and to the minimum or throat section (where minimum pressure exists) at 2, Fig. 147, gives the pressure drop $p_1 - p_2$. Knowing this pressure drop, the initial static pressure p_1 obtained from a pressure

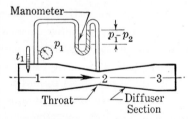

Manometer

p_1

$\overline{p_1} - p_2$

t_1

—1—   →   2   —3—

Throat   Diffuser
Section

Fig. 147.   Venturi Meter.

gage, the initial temperature t_1, and the initial velocity correction factor I, we may calculate the ideal velocity at the throat from equation (o).   Now the ideal mass rate of flow is determined and then the actual flow w' is computed:

$$w = \frac{A_2 v_2}{v_2} \quad \text{and} \quad w' = \eta_d w \text{ lb./sec.,}$$

where η_d is the coefficient of discharge. When the pressure drop $p_1 - p_2$ is small, the entire process 1-2-3 is nearly reversible and the discharge coefficients are high, say 97–98%.

195. Example. A 3x1½-in. venturi, whose $\eta_d = 0.98$, is used to measure the flow of air in a 3-in. *ID* pipe. The barometer is 30.05 in. Hg; room temperature is 96°F (556°R). The temperature of the air flowing in the pipe is 114°F (574°R) and its pressure is $p_1 = 3.9$ in. H_2O gage. The pressure drop in the venturi is $\Delta p = 11.4$ in. H_2O. (a) How much free (room) air is flowing, measured in cfm? (b) Estimate the velocity pressure and the stagnation pressure ahead of the venturi.

SOLUTION. (a) See Fig. 147. The atmospheric pressure $p_a = 30.05$ in. Hg. or $(30.05)(0.491) = 14.74$ psia or $14.74/0.0361 = 408$ in. H_2O. (See the conversion factors in Table XIV in the Appendix.) Also $p_1 = (3.9)(0.0361) = 0.1408$ psig, or $14.74 + 0.14 = 14.88$ psia; $\Delta p = (11.4)(0.0361) = 0.411$ psia.

$$v_2 \approx v_1 = \frac{RT_1}{p_1} = \frac{(53.3)(114 + 460)}{(14.88)(144)} = 14.27 \text{ cu. ft./lb.}$$

Using equation (o), and the simplified correction factor for initial velocity, we have

$$v_2 = \left[\frac{2g_oRT_1}{1 - (D_2/D_1)^4} \left(\frac{p_1 - p_2}{p_1} \right) \right]^{1/2}$$
$$= \left[\frac{(2)(32.2)(53.3)(574)(0.411)}{(1 - (1.5/3)^4)(14.88)} \right]^{1/2} = 241 \text{ fps.}$$

Notice that the pressure units cancel.

$$w' = \eta_d w = \frac{\eta_d A_2 v_2}{v_2} = \frac{(0.98)(\pi 1.5^2)(241)}{(4)(144)(14.27)} = 0.203 \text{ lb./sec.}$$

The volume V_a of free air is

$$V_a = \frac{wRT_a}{P_a} = \frac{(0.203)(60)(53.3)(556)}{(14.74)(144)} = 170 \text{ cfm.}$$

(b) To obtain an estimate of the velocity pressure, one may use equation (n). For a flow of 0.203 lb./sec., the average upstream velocity is

$$v_1 = \frac{w'v_1}{A_1} = \frac{(0.203)(14.27)(144)}{\pi \, 9/4} = 59 \text{ fps.}$$

Then the average velocity pressure from (n) is

$$(n) \qquad \Delta p = p_o - p_1 = \frac{v_1^2}{2g_o v_o} = \frac{59^2}{(64.4)(14.27)(144)(0.0361)} = 0.729 \text{ in. } H_2O,$$

and the total (or stagnation or impact) pressure is

$$p_o = p_1 + \Delta p = 14.89 + (0.729)(0.0361) \approx 14.92 \text{ psia.}$$

(NOTE. A machine calculator and/or logarithms should be used on these problems. Some slide rule answers may have a large percentage error.)

196. Flow Nozzle.   A flow nozzle is simply a converging nozzle installed in a line with taps for obtaining pressure and temperature readings, Fig. 148.   If the diameter of the nozzle at 2 is $D_2 > 0.22 D_1$, and it ordinarily is, the correction for initial velocity should be used with p_1 and t_1.   Since the expansion is guided by the nozzle, the coefficients of discharge η_d are fairly high, 96–99%.   There is an advantage in making the nozzle in accordance with ASME power test codes, because of the availability of reliable test data to match.

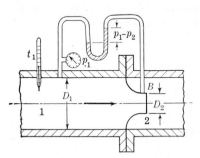

Fig. 148.   Flow Nozzle.

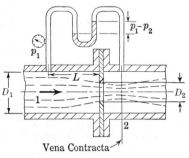

Vena Contracta

Fig. 149.   Orifice Plate. The distance L should be at least one pipe diameter.

197. Orifice.   Since an orifice is usually a hole in a thin plate, Figs. 149 and 150, it is sometimes called a ***thin-plate orifice.***   After the stream leaves the orifice, it continues to contract in cross-sectional area until a minimum area is reached at a section called the ***vena contracta,*** Fig. 149.   At some

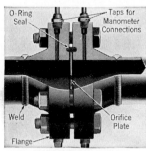

Courtesy Tube Turns, Louisville, Ky.

Fig. 150.   Orifice Flanges. There are several approved locations for taps for manometer connections.

downstream section, the stream again fills the pipe at a pressure slightly lower than that ahead of the orifice.

There is a pressure drop across the orifice, with the minimum pressure at the vena contracta.   The downstream tap is not necessarily located as drawn in Fig. 149 at the vena contracta, whose location is variable but roughly a function of the pipe diameter and diameter ratio.   Another approved position in the flange is shown in Fig. 150.   The method of computing the flow from the measured data is the same as before.   The coefficients of discharge vary over a wider range for orifices than for the other devices.   Typical values are 0.592 to 0.616 for a square-edge orifice across which the pressure drop is not over 5 in. of water; although actual values may be much different from these.

198. Closure. Many books are devoted solely to the flow of fluids, so that our aim here is only to touch upon topics which are of immediate interest. One of the most common errors made by students is in the units of A and p, which should be square feet and pounds per square foot, respectively, unless conversion constants are used or unless the pressures are in a ratio, such as (p_2/p_1).

Maybe the reader has wondered about "the velocity" of a stream flowing in a channel, inasmuch as there are different velocities at different points of a cross section. Thus, we have been obviously thinking of the velocity as a mean or average value, otherwise computations of w from $w = Av/v$ are meaningless.

PROBLEMS

NOTE: *If the initial velocity is unstated, it is assumed negligible.*

281. An ideal nozzle passes 7200 lb./hr. of methane (CH_4), which expands from 100 psia and 90°F to 80 psia. Find the temperature, velocity, and area at the exit section. Is this nozzle convergent-divergent or convergent only?
Ans. 860 fps, 1.455 sq. in.

282. A nozzle is to pass 1 lb./sec. of helium, which is at 10 psig and 80°F, to a discharge pressure of 14.7 psia. For an isentropic expansion to the exit section, determine the exit temperature, velocity, and area. Is this nozzle convergent only?
Ans. −20°F, 4.61 sq. in.

283. Air expands isentropically in a nozzle from 120 psia and 80°F to 15 psia at the rate of 10 lb./sec. Determine the throat area needed. If each nozzle is to have an area of 1 sq. in., how many nozzles should be provided?
Ans. 3.63 sq. in., 4 nozzles.

284. An ideal nozzle expands 2 lb. per sec. of air from 100 psia and 90°F to 15 psia. (a) For the throat section, determine the temperature, velocity, and area. (b) If the nozzle efficiency is 90%, what are the actual exit velocity and area? What is the nozzle coefficient?

Ans. (a) 0.868 sq. in., (b) 1.63 sq. in., 94.8%.

285. The flow through a nozzle is 60 lb./min. of air, which enters at 10 psig and 80°F and departs at atmospheric pressure. (a) For an isentropic expansion, determine the temperature, velocity, and area at the exit section. Is this nozzle convergent only? (b) For a nozzle coefficient of 0.95, compute the nozzle efficiency, the actual exit temperature, volume, and area.
Ans. (a) 1.808 sq. in., (b) 90.2%. 1.933 sq. in.

286. An ideal nozzle allows 1.6 lb. per sec. of methane (CH_4) to expand from 100 psia and 80°F to 15 psia. Determine (a) the pressure, temperature, velocity, and area at the throat, (b) the same for the exit section. (c) For a nozzle efficiency of 90%, what is the actual exit velocity?
Ans. (a) $A_t = 0.965$ sq. in., (b) $A_2 = 1.58$ sq. in., (c) 2145 fps.

287. A substance flows at the rate of 2 lb./sec. through a nozzle from 140 psia and 500°F to 80 psia. The expansion is isentropic. If the initial velocity is zero (state 1 is the stagnation state), find the temperature and area at the exit section when the substance is (a) steam (in equilibrium), (b) air. (c) The same as (b) except that the initial velocity is 200 fps. Show an energy diagram.

Ans. (a) 380°F, 1.068 sq. in., (b) 821.5°F, 0.871 sq. in. (air tables). (c) 0.833 sq. in.

288. The flow through a nozzle is 240 lb./min. of steam initially at 500 psia and 620°F. Discharge pressure is 300 psia. (a) For an isentropic expansion, determine the area of the exit section. (b) If the nozzle efficiency is 97%, compute the actual exit velocity and the nozzle coefficient. Is this nozzle convergent-divergent?

Ans. (a) 0.624 sq. in., (b) 1607 fps, 0.985.

289. A nozzle receives 1 lb./sec. of steam at 165 psia and 460°F and discharges it at p_c. Let the critical pressure be 0.546 p_1. The actual temperature at the throat is 350°F. (a) Using a steam table solution, determine the efficiency up to the throat. (Do not interpolate for entropy differences as small as 0.0003.) (b) Find the actual volume of steam and the area at the throat.

Ans. (a) 89.4%, (b) 0.474 sq. in.

290. Steam enters a nozzle at 1050 psia and 650°F and expands to 450 psia. The actual exit temperature is 460°F; the flow is 2 lb./sec. Determine (a) the actual exit velocity and nozzle area, (b) the nozzle efficiency.

Ans. (a) 1960 fps, 0.153 sq. in., (b) 96.4%.

291. A nozzle flow is 2 lb./sec. of steam initially at 145 psia and 360°F. Discharge is at 15 psia and the nozzle efficiency is 97% up to the throat. For supersaturated flow, compute the actual velocity and throat area.

Ans. 1510 fps, 0.96 sq. in.

292. Steam flowing at the rate of 2400 lb./hr. enters a nozzle at 180 psia and 126.92°F superheat and expands to 114°F in equilibrium. Let $p_c = 0.556 p_1$. Find (a) the velocities at the throat and exit sections and (b) the areas of the throat and exit sections of an ideal nozzle. If the nozzle efficiency between the entrance and throat is 96% and between entrance and exit is 92%, find (c) the areas of these sections. (d) What is the Mach number at exit? Let $k = 1.13$.

Ans. (a) 1140 mph, 2800 mph, (b) 0.276, 4.61 sq. in., (c) 0.283, 4.95 sq. in., (d) 3.2.

293. An airplane powered by a jet engine is moving with an air speed of 3500 fps (about 2385 mph) where the atmospheric pressure is $p_a = 7$ psia and $t_a = 40°F$. (a) If the compression is isentropic, what is its stagnation temperature (constant specific heat)? (b) If the air is brought to rest (relative to the plane) at the exit from the diffuser, what is its (stagnation) pressure? (c) Should the diffuser be converging-diverging or diverging?

Ans. (a) 1060°F, (b) 343 psia.

294. Helium enters a diffuser at 20 in. Hg vacuum and 40°F with a speed of 4200 fps. For an isentropic process to 14.7 psia, what are the final temperature and velocity? *Ans.* 316°F, 625 fps.

295. Steam at 25 psia and 250°F enters a diffuser and is compressed to 200 psia. (a) If the process is isentropic and the final speed negligible, what must be the entering speed? What is the final temperature? (b) If the efficiency of the process is 80%, what are the initial speed and the final temperature (same pressure limits)?

Ans. (a) 3215 fps, 700°F, (b) 3590 fps, 800°F.

296. If steam enters a diffuser with an enthalpy of 905.5 Btu/lb., an entropy of 1.5891 Btu/lb-°R, and a velocity of 4000 fps and undergoes an isentropic process to a state of negligible velocity, what is the final state (p and t)?   *Ans.* 185 psia, 420°F.

297. A pitot tube traverse of a 10-in. *ID* duct indicates a mean velocity head of 0.37 in. H_2O. The impact temperature and pressure are 100°F and 7.75 in. H_2O gage, respectively. The barometer reads 29.85 in. Hg and the room temperature is 95°F. Determine the mean velocity and the cfm of free (room) air flowing. What mass of air is flowing? What are the stagnation pressure and static pressure in psia?

Ans. 41.3 fps, 1365 cfm, 1.62 lb. per sec.

298. To measure the air used by an internal combustion engine, a 3x1⅛-in. venturi with a coefficient of discharge of 0.97 is placed in the intake line. At the entrance of this venturi, the pressure is atmospheric, barometer 29.45 in. Hg, and $t = 80°F$ (room or free air conditions). The pressure drop to the throat is 10.25 in. H_2O. (a) Compute the amount of free air flowing. (b) Compute the temperature at the throat from energy relations (show energy diagram).

Ans. (a) 85.8 cfm, (b) 76°F.

299. A 1.5-in. flow nozzle is used to measure the flow of air in a 3-in. *ID* pipe. The initial temperature is 110°F;

the static pressure ahead of the nozzle is 22 in. H_2O gage; the static pressure drop in the nozzle is 13 in. H_2O; barometer is 29.98 in. Hg; room temperature is 96°F; coefficient of discharge is 0.96. Determine (a) the absolute static pressure in the pipe and in the nozzle, (b) the nozzle velocity, (c) the actual flow in cfm of free air. (Compute v_2 in nozzle for isentropic flow.) (d) Compute the impact pressure in the pipe. Make an energy diagram, using $u + pv/J$ instead of h and letting u be constant. (Compare results with (o), § 192.)

Ans. (a) 15.49, 15.02 psia, (b) 250 fps, (c) 177 cfm, (d) 15.52 psia.

300. A 2-in., thin-plate orifice is used in a 6-in. *ID* pipe to measure the flow of methane. Upstream from the orifice, the static pressure is 31 psig and the temperature is 80°F. The coefficient of discharge is 0.61; the pressure drop across the orifice is 60 in. H_2O. Determine (a) the theoretical velocity at the downstream side of the orifice, (b) the mass and cfm flowing. (c) Compute the average velocity head upstream from the orifice. Make an energy diagram, using $u + pv/J$ instead of h and letting u be constant. (Compare results with (o), § 192.)

Ans. (a) 398 fps, (b) 317 cfm, (c) 0.275 in. H_2O.

301–310. These numbers may be used for other problems.

✒ *13*

STEAM TURBINES

199. Introduction. The steam turbine is a relatively new instrument for producing work, the first successful ones having appeared in the early 1890's. It is inherently a high-speed machine, as compared to reciprocating machines; turbo-electric units generally operate at 1800 rpm or 3600 rpm in this country; some gas turbines (Chapter 7) run at much higher speeds. Since power is proportional to speed for a particular driving force, large power can be obtained from a reasonable volume of machine when the machine is a turbine. Unit capacities of 100,000 kw to 450,000 kw and more are practical in steam turbines but out of the question for any kind of reciprocating engine. (Large reciprocating engines may have to turn as slowly as 100 rpm.) Small turbines are, however, also very common, especially where their high rotative speed is advantageous, as in driving high-speed rotary pumps. Moreover, large and small turbines with gear reductions are being used for slower speed requirements, with capacities up to the requirements for the largest marine drives.

200. Reaction and Impulse. The first known turbine is Hero's toy (175 B.C.?), Fig. 151. A fire under a vessel evaporated water which passed upward within the vertical supports and into the sphere. The steam issued from nozzles, top and bottom of the sphere in Fig. 151, and the change of momentum due to its speeding up produced a reaction which caused the sphere to turn. Since the pressure was low, no useful power was obtained. Observe that the drop in pressure occurs *in the moving part* (the nozzles on the sphere) and when expansion occurs in the moving blades of a turbine stage, it is called a *reaction stage*. The Hero plan of exhausting to atmosphere as in Fig. 151 could be used for the generation of power in stationary plants, but it would be comparatively inefficient. Note in passing, however, that the principle of a jet passing directly into the atmosphere is the method used in jet engines in aircraft.

The second steam turbine noted in history is Branca's impulse wheel (1629 A.D.), frontispiece, where a fire, built under the gentleman shown, generated steam which rushed out of the stationary nozzle (in his mouth) and impinged on the wheel, causing it to rotate. Some crude gearing is shown above the turbine wheel, but there is no authenticated record that useful work was obtained from this device. Notice that the pressure drop

Courtesy Johnson Publishing Co., Cleveland

Fig. 151.　Hero's Reaction Turbine.

occurs *in the stationary part;* when substantially all of the pressure drop occurs within the stationary part of a stage in a turbine, that is, in the nozzles, Fig. 152, the stage is said to be an ***impulse stage*** (practically no pressure drop in moving impulse blades).

Carl Gustav Patrik De Laval (1845–1913), born in Sweden, trained at the University of Uppsala in engineering, had a passion for inventing. One of his best inventions is the centrifugal cream separator. While he was working on this machine, he realized that he would need a high-speed prime mover to drive it. So his single-wheel *impulse* turbine was a by-product of his needs for the separator project. However, his work was so thorough that his turbine is a major contribution to our mechanical civilization. See Fig. 152. With no precedent for guidance, only a genius could have been so successful. Two of

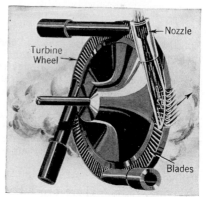

Courtesy De Laval Steam Turbine Co., Trenton, N. J.

Fig. 152.　Impulse Turbine Wheel and Nozzles. The elements attached to the rotor through which the steam passes are called blades or buckets.

the principal features were a nozzle designed on correct principles and a flexible shaft that permitted a rotative speed (30,000 rpm) above the critical speed, not to mention the design of the turbine blades and other details.

The work of Sir Charles Algernon Parsons (1854–1931) on the reaction turbine was carried on during the same period that De Laval was developing his turbine, but neither knew of the other's work until public announcements were made. Parsons was motivated in large measure by the desire to devise a more suitable prime mover for marine use. The first turbine ship, *Turbinia*, was launched in 1895. This turbine, directly connected to the

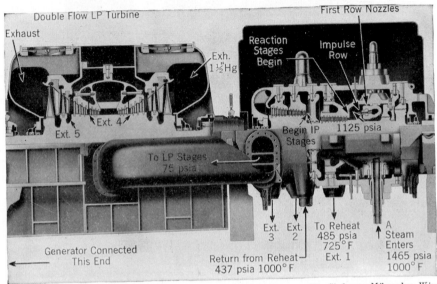

Courtesy Allis-Chalmers, Milwaukee, Wisc.

Fig. 153. *Large Steam Turbine, Tandem Compound.* A 100,000-kw unit. There are five entry pipes, one of which is shown at *A*, individually controlled by the governor, each leading to a nozzle chest or bank of nozzles. As the load increases, the governor opens additional entry pipes for a greater flow of steam. The first stage is a single impulse; others are reaction stages. By IP is meant intermediate pressure; LP means low pressure; Ext. stands for extraction; Exh. stands for exhaust. The one reheat occurs just before the IP section, at which section steam is also extracted for feedwater heating. All five extraction points are designated, but only the locations for stages 4 and 5. The LP unit is double flow. The final blades are 23 in. long. Notice the pressures and temperatures at the various sections.

propeller, had two sets of blades, one for the forward drive, and one for reversing. Since there are advantages in using impulse blading in high pressure stages and reaction blading in low pressure stages, the typical large turbine, Fig. 153, is a combination.

201. The Rankine Engine. The turbine is a complete expansion engine, meaning that the working substance expands within the turbine essentially to exhaust pressure. The ideal prototype of this engine is the Rankine*

* William John M. Rankine (1820–1872), a professor at Glasgow University, was a contemporary of those giants of thermodynamics, Joule, Maxwell, Kelvin, Clausius. It was during the lifetime of and largely due to the efforts of these five men that the laws

engine in which there is no frictional loss, no change of kinetic energy; the expansion is isentropic, Fig. 154. Thus in the energy equation (10), $W = -\Delta h - \Delta K + Q$, let $Q = 0$, $\Delta K = 0$, let $W = W_t$, the turbine (engine) work, and find, Figs. 154 and 155,

(a) $W_t = -\Delta h = h_1 - h_2$ Btu/lb.,   [RANKINE ENGINE]

which of course is the same as (29), the work of any other steady flow engine meeting the same conditions ($\Delta K = 0$, $Q = 0$).

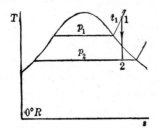

Fig. 154. Isentropic Process.

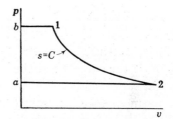

Fig. 155. Work of Rankine Engine. Observe that this area is that of an indicator card for a complete expansion reciprocating engine without clearance.

The pv plane, Fig. 155, can be taken as a representation of a complete expansion reciprocating engine, with b-1 representing the flowing in of steam (area under b-1 is the flow work across the boundary of the system as the steam enters), with 1-2 being the isentropic expansion, and with 2-a representing the flowing out of the steam (area under it is the outgoing flow work). The enclosed area 1-2-a-b represents the work of a Rankine engine in ft-lb. units. Observe that the general shape of the diagram is similar to that of the compressor without clearance, Fig. 31, p. 73.

202. Efficiency and MEP of the Rankine Engine. In setting up the expression for the efficiency of steam engines and turbines, we must decide concerning the quantity of energy E_c that should be charged against the engine. Custom requires that the engine be *credited* with the enthalpy of saturated liquid at the exhaust pressure, h_{f2}. It is argued that the water from the condensation of the steam may be returned to the boiler without

and the science of thermodynamics were formulated and interpreted. Rankine had no small part in these developments. He was a man of versatile genius and a prolific contributor to the engineering and scientific literature of his day. Among his published writings are included an important textook on mechanics, a civil engineer's manual, and works on water supply, the steam engine, shipbuilding, and many other subjects of a technical nature, not to mention *Songs and Fables*—for he was also a composer of music and a vocalist of good talent. Rankine's modification of Gordon's column formula is in wide use today.

further loss of enthalpy. Moreover, the steam prime mover is not designed to obtain work from liquids, and it would therfore be unfair to charge the enthalpy of the liquid against the engine. This practice of crediting the engine with the enthalpy of saturated liquid at the exhaust condition is followed whether the engine exhausts to a condenser, whence the condensate *is* returned to the boiler, or whether the engine exhausts to the atmosphere with the consequent actual loss of the enthalpy of the liquid. Therefore, the thermal efficiency of the Rankine engine is

$$(64) \quad e = \frac{\text{Work (output)}}{\text{Energy chargeable to engine (input)}} = \frac{W_t}{E_c} = \frac{h_1 - h_2}{h_1 - h_{f2}},$$

where h_1 is the enthalpy of the *throttle* steam (steam at entrance to the engine), h_2 is the enthalpy of the steam leaving the engine, and h_{f2} is the enthalpy of saturated liquid at the exhaust pressure.

The mean effective pressure (mep) of the Rankine engine is, equation (49), the work in foot-pounds divided by the displacement in cubic feet; that is,

$$(b) \qquad\qquad p_m = \frac{W}{V_D} = \frac{J(h_1 - h_2)}{v_2} \text{ psf},$$

where v_2 is taken as the effective displacement *per pound of steam* of the complete expansion Rankine engine. If this expansion occurs against the piston of a reciprocating engine, it has the usual physical meaning (see § 83). Applied to a turbine, it is a significant number sometimes used for comparison purposes.

203. Example. A Rankine turbine receives steam at 600 psia and 550°F and exhausts at 110°F. Determine the ideal work per pound, the thermal efficiency, and the mep.

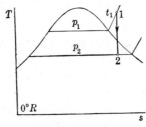

Fig. 154. Repeated.

SOLUTION. The expansion is represented by 1-2, Fig. 154. From Table X, Appendix, for the initial conditions, we find $v_1 = 0.8753$, $h_1 = 1255.5$, and $s_1 = 1.4990$. The properties of the steam at the exhaust are taken from Table VIII:

$t_2 = 110°F$	$h_{f2} = 77.94$	$s_{f2} = 0.1471$	$v_{f2} = 0.01617$
$p_2 = 1.2748$	$h_{fg2} = 1031.6$	$s_{fg2} = 1.8106$	$v_{fg2} = 265.3$
	$h_{g2} = 1109.5$	$s_{g2} = 1.9577$	$v_{g2} = 265.4$

First, find the quality x_2 at the end of the isentropic expansion ($s_1 = s_2$);

$$1.4990 = 0.1471 + 1.8106x_2, \quad \text{or} \quad 1.4990 = 1.9577 - 1.8106y_2$$
$$x_2 = 74.7\%. \qquad\qquad\qquad y_2 = 25.3$$

The enthalpy at 2, Fig. 154, is

$$h_2 = h_{f2} + x_2 h_{fg2} = 77.94 + (0.747)(1031.6) = 849 \text{ Btu/lb.}$$

The ideal or Rankine work is

$$W_t = h_1 - h_2 = 1255.5 - 849 = 406.5 \text{ Btu/lb.}$$

The ideal thermal efficiency, from (64), is

$$e = \frac{W_t}{h_1 - h_{f2}} = \frac{406.5}{1255.5 - 77.94} = 34.5\%.$$

To get the mep, we next compute the specific volume at 2.

$$v_2 = v_{f2} + x_2 v_{fg2} = 0.01617 + (0.747)(265.3) = 198 \text{ cu. ft./lb.}$$

The ideal mep is

$$p_m = \frac{W_t}{V_D} = \frac{(778)(406.5)}{(198)(144)} = 11.1 \text{ psi.}$$

204. Steam Rate. The water rate or *steam rate,* an indicator of the performance of steam prime movers, is the number of pounds of steam to be supplied to an engine in order to do a unit of work. The unit of work is usually either the hp-hr. or the kw-hr.; therefore, steam rate is expressed as pounds per hp-hr. or pounds per kw-hr. Let the work W be in Btu per lb. and note that there are 2544 Btu/hp-hr. Then, the steam rate w is

(65A)
$$w = \frac{2544}{W} = \frac{\text{Btu/hp-hr.}}{\text{Btu/lb. steam}} = \frac{\text{lb. steam}}{\text{hp-hr.}},$$

(65B)
$$w = \frac{3412}{W} = \frac{\text{Btu/kw-hr.}}{\text{Btu/lb. steam}} = \frac{\text{lb. steam}}{\text{kw-hr.}}.$$

As we have learned, the work output of an engine may be measured at any one of three points (see Fig. 78, p. 135). It follows that for the actual engine, there may be stated three steam rates, one each based upon the indicated work W_I, brake work W_B, or combined work W_K. If actual steam rates are known, we may find from them actual work quantities. Thus, let w_i = indicated steam rate in lb. per ihp-hr., w_b = brake steam rate in lb. per bhp-hr., and w_k = combined steam rate in lb. per kw-hr. output of the generator. Then, from (65), we have

(c)
$$W_I = \frac{2544}{w_i} \text{ Btu/lb.}, \qquad W_B = \frac{2544}{w_b} \text{ Btu/lb.},$$

(d)
$$\text{Combined work, } W_K = \frac{3412}{w_k} \text{ Btu/lb.}$$

It should be remarked that the relative performances of two or more prime movers cannot be determined from the steam rates alone. An engine or turbine operating through a large pressure range may have a relatively small steam rate, while the engine operating through a small pressure range may have a relative large steam rate; yet the latter engine may more nearly approach perfection, the approach being measured by the engine efficiency. Moreover, the Btu consumed by the latter engine to produce a unit of work may be less than the Btu consumption of the engine operating on the large pressure range. Thus, while the steam rate is a convenient number, easily found on test, we must use the thermal and engine efficiencies for reliable indices of absolute and comparative performances.

205. Efficiencies in Terms of Steam Rates. In each pound of steam, there is an amount of energy chargeable to the engine of $h_1 - h_{f2}$ Btu, § 202. If w lb. are supplied to the engine, the corresponding energy is $w(h_1 - h_{f2})$ Btu; and if w is the steam rate, lb. per hp-hr., then $w(h_1 - h_{f2})$ is the Btu per hp-hr. chargeable to the engine and is called the **heat rate.**

(e)   Heat rate, Rankine engine $= w(h_1 - h_{f2})$ Btu/hp-hr.

We know that the work output in Btu per hp-hr. is 2544. The thermal efficiency of the *engine* is therefore

(f) $$e = \frac{\text{(Btu of work)}/\text{(hp-hr.)}}{\text{(Btu of net input)}/\text{(hp-hr.)}} = \frac{2544}{w(h_1 - h_{f2})},$$

where h_1 is the enthalpy of the throttle steam and h_{f2} is the enthalpy of saturated liquid at the exhaust pressure.

Now *the ideal engine corresponding to any actual engine* is one wherein

1. The pressure and quality (or superheat) at the beginning of isentropic expansion in the ideal engine (point 1, Fig. 154) are the same as the pressure and quality (or superheat) at the throttle of the real engine;

2. The pressure at the end of isentropic expansion in the ideal engine is the same as the exhaust pressure of the real engine.

It follows that h_1 and h_{f2} in equation (f) are the same for both actual and ideal engines. Therefore, equation (f) will yield the ideal thermal efficiency, the indicated thermal efficiency e_i, or the brake thermal efficiency e_b, depending upon whether the steam rate is respectively the ideal w, the indicated w_i, or the brake w_b. That is,

(g) $$e_i = \frac{2544}{w_i(h_1 - h_{f2})}, \qquad e_b = \frac{2544}{w_b(h_1 - h_{f2})}.$$

If the combined steam rate is w_k lb./kw-hr., then the **combined thermal** *efficiency* is

(h)
$$e_k = \frac{3412}{w_k(h_1 - h_{f2})},$$

where $w_k(h_1 - h_{f2})$ is called the **combined heat rate.**

The **engine efficiency** η not only is used to measure the approach of the actual engine to the ideal but is useful in estimating the performance of a newly designed engine where old data on the efficiencies of similar engines are available.   We recall the definition of engine efficiency, § 119, as

(i)
$$\eta = \frac{\text{Actual work}}{\text{Ideal work}} = \frac{W'}{W_t}.$$

Thus, the indicated, brake, and combined engine efficiencies are:

(j)
$$\eta_i = \frac{W_I}{W_t}, \qquad \eta_b = \frac{W_B}{W_t}, \qquad \eta_k = \frac{W_K}{W_t}.$$

In each expression W_t is the value for the proper ideal engine.

The **mechanical efficiency** is the ratio of the brake work to the indicated work; or

(k)
$$\eta_m = W_B/W_I = \text{bhp/ihp, etc.}$$

206. Actual Expansion in a Turbine.   The actual expansion in a turbine is of course irreversible and only approximately adiabatic.   Because the turbine is well insulated in practice, the radiated heat is small, of the order of 1% of the entering enthalpy $(0.01h_1)$ to 0.1% of the work in large turbines, and the actual expansion is often taken as adiabatic.   Assuming then an adiabatic expansion, the actual work W' done by the fluid in its flow through the turbine, as obtained from the energy equation, is

(1) $W' = h_1 - h_{2'}$ Btu/lb.,

where, as in § 201, $\Delta K = 0$ and $Q = 0$, and where $h_{2'}$ is the specific enthalpy of the actual exhaust whose condition is represented by the actual state point 2′, Fig. 156. The expansion 1-2′ in Fig. 156 is shown dotted because the path is an irreversible path, and showing it dotted reminds us that the area

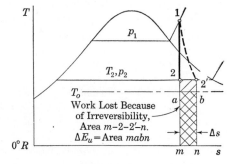

Fig. 156.   *Reversible and Irreversible Expansions.*

"under" it does not represent transferred heat, as do areas under internally reversible curves on the Ts plane.   If the state point 2′ could be determined easily by test, equation (1) could be used to compute the actual work W' of the working substance.   However, point 2′ is generally well in the wet region so that pressure and temperature readings give the same line 2-2′ and they do not therefore locate a point.   If point 2′ were in the superheated region, the pressure and temperature would locate it precisely.

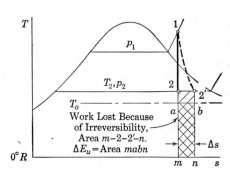

Fig. 156.   Repeated.

Equation (1) may be used to estimate the actual enthalpy of the exhaust $h_{2'}$, since the work of the fluid can be approximately determined from test.   In the case of a turbine, this work of the fluid is nearly equal to the brake work W_B since the friction of the bearings is a rather small percentage of the amount of energy involved.   Thus, letting $W' = W_B$, we get

(m) $$h_{2'} = h_1 - W' = h_1 - W_B \text{ Btu/lb.}$$
[APPROXIMATE, TURBINE]

Test data commonly include the steam rate; hence one may find W_B from equation (c).   The actual enthalpy of the exhaust is useful in the design of the condenser, if the steam is to be condensed.

The work lost because of the irreversible expansion is equal to the ideal work $h_1 - h_2$ minus the actual work $h_1 - h_{2'}$.   Thus,

(n)   Lost work $= W_t - W' = h_1 - h_2 - (h_1 - h_{2'}) = h_{2'} - h_2$ Btu/lb.

The area m-2-2′-n, Fig. 156, is a graphical representation of this lost work. The area under the naturally available sink temperature, $T_o \Delta s$, § 139, is the increase in unavailable energy, represented by the double cross-hatched area in Fig. 156.

207. Example.   A turbine operates under the end conditions defined in the example of § 203: $p_1 = 600$, $t_1 = 550°F$, $t_2 = 110°F$.   The combined engine efficiency is $\eta_k = 65\%$ and the efficiency of the generator is 92%.   (a) Determine the combined thermal efficiency, the combined work, the brake work, the combined and brake steam rates.   (b) Estimate the actual quality of the exhaust, the lost work for a combined output of 50,000 kw, and the increase of unavailable energy for a sink temperature of 90°F.

SOLUTION.   (a) The combined thermal efficiency is

$$e_k = \eta_k e = (0.65)(0.345) = 22.4\%,$$

where $e = 34.5\%$ is taken from § 203.   The combined work is

$$W_K = e_k(h_1 - h_{f2}) = (0.224)(1255.5 - 77.94) = 264 \text{ Btu/lb.}$$

The efficiency of the generator is (output)/(input) $= W_K/W_B$; hence, the brake work is

$$W_B = \frac{W_K}{\text{Eff. of generator}} = \frac{264}{0.92} = 287 \text{ Btu/lb.}$$

The combined steam rate is

$$w_k = \frac{3412}{W_K} = \frac{3412}{264} = 12.92 \text{ lb./kw-hr.}$$

The brake steam rate is

$$w_b = \frac{2544}{W_B} = \frac{2544}{287} = 8.86 \text{ lb./bhp-hr.}$$

(b) From equation (m), we find the approximate enthalpy of the exhaust to be

$$h_{2'} = h_1 - W_B = 1255.5 - 287 = 968.5 \text{ Btu/lb.}$$

This value of $h_{2'}$ is equal to $h_{f2} + x_{2'}h_{fg2}$, or

$$968.5 = 77.94 + (x_{2'})(1031.6),$$

from which $x_{2'} = 86.3\%$, the approximate quality of the actual exhaust.

The lost work (in the turbine) is $W_t - W_B$, or $h_{2'} - h_2 = 968.5 - 849 = 119.5$ Btu/lb. For 50,000-kw combined output, the steam flow is

$50,000w_k = (50,000 \text{ kw})(12.92$
    $\text{lb./kw-hr.}) = 646,000 \text{ lb./hr.,}$

and the lost work is $(119.5)(646,000) =$ 77,200,000 Btu/hr. or 77,200,000/3412 $= 22,600$ kw.

The entropy at 2 is $s_2 = 1.499$ Btu/lb-°R from § 203. The entropy at 2' is

$s_{2'} = 0.1471 + (0.863)(1.8106)$
    $= 1.708 \text{ Btu/lb-°R,}$

whence the increase of unavailable energy is $(T_o = 80 + 460 = 540°R)$

$\Delta E_u = T_o\Delta s = 540(1.708 -$
    $1.499) = 112.9 \text{ Btu/lb.}$

208. Charts of Properties. Using any two point functions of substances, such as temperature and entropy, we may construct a diagram

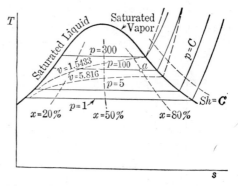

Fig. 157. Temperature-Entropy Diagram for Steam. The point a, for example, represents steam at a pressure of 100 lb. per sq. in. abs. and a quality of 80%. These two coordinates could be used to locate a, and then the volume could be determined from the constant volume lines; in this case, between $v = 1.5433$ and $v = 5.816$. (There are not enough constant volume lines on this figure for accurate interpolation.)

containing a series of lines, each representing a constant pressure, another series where each line represents a particular volume, another series for constant quality, etc. On the Ts plane, Fig. 157, have been plotted several constant-pressure, constant-volume, and constant-quality (also superheat) lines.

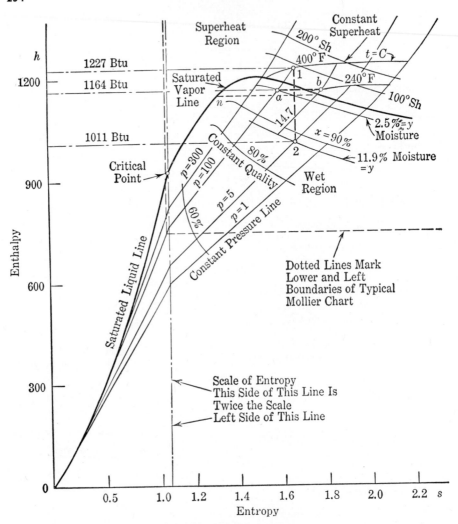

Fig. 158. *Enthalpy-Entropy (Mollier) Diagram for Steam.* **Example 1.** Steam in the main is at $p_a = 100$ psia. The sample in the calorimeter is at 14.7 psia and 240°F. What is the moisture content y_a of the steam in the main?

Solution. From the conditions in the calorimeter, locate point b at the intersection of the curves $p_b = 14.7$ psia and $t_b = 240$°F. Since the throttling process into the calorimeter is a constant enthalpy process, $h_a = h_b$, move along a horizontal line until the pressure line $p_1 = 100$ is reached, and locate point a. Read the answer $y_a = 2.5\%$. If the initial pressure is too high, $p_1 > p_n \approx 1800$ psia, expansion does not reach superheat at 14.7 psia and a throttling calorimeter could not be used.

Example 2. Steam enters a turbine at a pressure of 100 psia and 400°F, point 1, and then expands isentropically to a pressure of 5 psia. What work is done if $\Delta K = 0$?

Solution. Using the properties of the entering steam, locate point 1 at the intersection of the curves $p_1 = 100$ psia and $t_1 = 400$°F. Now follow a constant entropy (vertical) line until the 5-psia line is reached, and locate point 2. Move to the left ordinate from point 1 and read $h_1 = 1227$ Btu per lb.; move to the left ordinate from point 2 and read $h_2 = 1011$ Btu/lb. Then equation (a), § 201, gives $W = 1227 - 1011 = 216$ Btu/lb. Also, we read the moisture at 2; $y_2 = 11.9\%$.

Thus, a point may be located by any two of these coordinates, after which all other properties pictured may be read from the diagram. The degree of accuracy of the reading will depend upon the spacing of the lines and the size of the diagram. Such a chart as this to scale is found in Keenan and Keyes' steam tables.

More convenient than the Ts diagram for the solution of certain problems in practice is the Mollier diagram, a chart on which enthalpy is the ordinate and entropy the abscissa. On this chart, Fig. 158, are plotted a series of constant pressure lines a series of constant-quality and superheat lines, and a series of constant temperature lines. The constant temperature lines of course coincide with the constant pressure lines in the wet region (below the saturated vapor line), but bend toward the right away from the constant pressure lines in the superheat region. The Mollier chart in your steam tables shows a section similar to that marked off by the dotted lines of Fig. 158.

The Mollier chart is most useful in connection with isentropic processes and steady flow processes. On these diagrams, the constant quality lines are labeled according to their per cent of moisture y ($=1 - x$). The constant pressure lines in Fig. 158 are straight in the wet region, the break shown being the result of a change of scale for entropy. See the examples in the caption to Fig. 158 for the method of using the chart. The horizontal lines for constant enthalpy and the vertical lines for constant entropy, which appear on commercial charts, are omitted here for the purpose of clearness.

Example 2 in the caption to Fig. 158 explains how the chart may be used to obtain the work for the Rankine engine. The chart is a great time saver when many computations are to be made. For the meaning of example 1 of Fig. 158, see § 209.

209. Throttling Process. The throttling process is an irreversible steady flow adiabatic ($Q = 0$) in which no work is done. This process occurs as a fluid flows from a high pressure region to a low pressure region. If a valve on a tank of compressed air is opened, the compressed air flows into the atmosphere. At the valve, there is a speeding up of the movement of the gas and therefore a change of kinetic energy. However, this energy is dissipated as the air from the tank diffuses into the atmosphere, so that the overall effect is one of little or no change of kinetic energy. For these conditions, we can find an expression from the energy equation to define the process. That is, if $\Delta K = 0$, $W = 0$, and $Q = 0$ in the energy equation $Q = \Delta h + \Delta K + W$, we have the additional condition for the throttling process as $\Delta h = 0$, or

(66)
$$h_1 = h_2.$$

This process is used in power plant practice to determine the quality of wet steam in an instrument known as a calorimeter (§ 211). Suppose it is desired to know the quality of steam, represented by point 1, Fig. 159, just as it enters a turbine from the steam main. If a sample of this high pressure steam is throttled to a lower pressure, then, within limitations, it will become superheated, state 2. In the superheated condition, we have convenient instruments with which to measure its pressure and its temperature, thus locating state 2 precisely. With pressure and temperature known, the enthalpy h_2 may be obtained from the superheat tables. With this value of h_2, we use equation (66) in the form

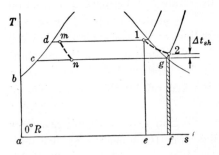

$$(o) \quad h_2 = h_{f1} + x_1 h_{fg1} = h_{g1} - y_1 h_{fg1},$$

and solve for x_1 or y_1 after looking up h_{f1} or h_{g1} and h_{fg1} for the known mainline pressure p_1.

However, ordinary calorimeter readings will usually require a two-way interpolation in the superheat tables to determine h_2, inasmuch as the actual pressure p_2 and temperature t_2 may not be listed in the tables. A practical alternative to this interpolation is to find the enthalpy of saturated vapor at the calorimeter pressure, h_g in Fig. 159, and add to this the enthalpy of superheat as computed with the specific heat c_p of superheated steam at constant pressure. Thus,

Fig. 159. Throttling Process. (Area a–b–d–1–e) = (area a–b–c–2–f), because these areas represent respectively h_1 and h_2 and $h_1 = h_2$. If the quality is high, as at point 1, the vapor may become superheated as at 2. If the initial quality is low, as at m, the vapor will still be wet after throttling but of a higher quality, as at n.

$$(p) \qquad h_2 = h_g + c_p(t_2 - t_g) = h_g + c_p \Delta t_{sh} = h_g + 0.48 \Delta t_{sh},$$

where Δt_{sh} = the degrees of superheat in the calorimeter (state 2, Fig. 159) and where $c_p = 0.48$ Btu/lb-°R is the approximate average specific heat of the steam for the conditions usually found in the calorimeter. Observe that

Δt_{sh} = (Actual temperature at 2) − (Saturation temperature corresponding to p_2).

In the event that the Mollier chart gives a sufficiently accurate solution, the method of solving a throttling calorimeter problem in this manner is explained in example 1 of Fig. 158.

210. Example. The pressure in the steam main is 130 psia. The temperature and pressure readings in the calorimeter are $t_2 = 228°$F and $p_2 = 14.123$ psia. What is the quality of the steam in the main?

SOLUTION. The saturation temperature corresponding to a pressure of 14.123 is 210°F (Table VIII), and h_g at this pressure is 1149.7. Therefore, from equation (p),

$$h_2 = 1149.7 + 0.48(228 - 210) = 1158.3 \text{ Btu/lb.}$$

From Table IX, we find $h_{g1} = 1191.7$ and $h_{fg1} = 872.9$. Then from (o),

$$h_1 = h_2 = 1158.3 = 1191.7 - 872.9y_1,$$

from which $y_1 = 3.83\%$ and $x_1 = 96.2\%$. The quality in such situations as this is usually high and it is more accurate to solve first for y, the percentage moisture.

211. Calorimeters. In finding the quality of the steam, as explained in § 209, we allow a sample of steam to flow into an instrument known as the *throttling calorimeter,* Fig. 160, thence to the atmosphere. Before temperature readings are taken at the calorimeter, the steam should flow long enough for steady state conditions to obtain; that is, long enough for all parts to be heated to a temperature which remains constant. To maintain adiabatic conditions, the instrument should be well insulated. Moreover, to obtain reliable results, the steam should have at least 10° of superheat in the calorimeter. If the steam is initially very wet, it may not become superheated in the calorimeter, in which case the calorimeter readings are meaningless, the temperature and pressure being those at saturation. This condition is illustrated by process mn, Fig. 159. The minimum quality that can be reliably measured by the throttling calorimeter depends upon the initial pressure p_1 (the final pressure p_2 being nearly atmospheric) and varies from about 97% for $p_1 = 50$ psig to 94% for $p_1 = 600$ psig.

If the steam is too wet to be measured by a throttling calorimeter, a separating calorimeter, Fig. 161, or a combination separating and throttling calorimeter may be used. In the separating calorimeter, the moisture is separated from the steam. The amount of collected water is determined. The corresponding mass of dry steam is calculated from flow equations applied to a flow nozzle (see Chapter 12) or read from a gage, or the steam leaving the nozzle may be condensed and weighed. The quality is then computed from the formula

(q) $$x = \frac{\text{(Mass of dry steam)}}{\text{(Mass of water)} + \text{(Mass of dry steam)}}.$$

Obviously, incomplete separation of water and steam and inaccuracies in the devices and methods used to find the mass of flow of dry steam will result in an incorrect evaluation of the quality.

212. Rankine Engine As a Standard of Comparsion. The Rankine engine is the standard of comparison for turbines which expand all of the steam from the throttle condition to the exhaust pressure; that is, for the same initial condition and exhaust pressure, no actual turbine can produce as much work per pound of steam, nor can an actual turbine have as high a thermal efficiency, as a Rankine (ideal) turbine. Thus, by comparing the

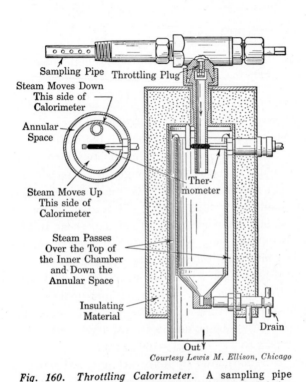

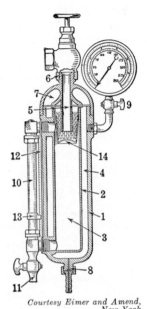

Courtesy Lewis M. Ellison, Chicago

Fig. 160. Throttling Calorimeter. A sampling pipe extends into the steam main, with perforated holes facing upstream. The sampling pipe should be as far as possible downstream from elbows and valves in order for the sample to be representative, and preferably in a vertical steam line. The steam flows through the nozzle into the inner chamber. A thermometer gives the temperature. The pressure is virtually atmospheric. Flowing down one side of the inner chamber, up the other, the steam turns downward into the annular space and leaves the instrument at the bottom. The hot steam surrounding the inner chamber (a patented feature) is an effective aid in insulating against loss by radiation.

Courtesy Eimer and Amend, New York

Fig. 161. Separating Calorimeter. The wet steam, entering at the top through the valve, undergoes a sudden reversal of direction of motion when it strikes the baffle plate 14. This causes the water, which has a greater inertia, to separate from the mixture. The water collects in the inner chamber and can be measured by the gage glass 10. The steam moves upward from the inner chamber 3 and downward in the annular space 4.

actual performance with that of the corresponding Rankine engine, we can better judge how good, how near to perfection, the actual engine is. We see then that the Rankine engine is used just as the ideal Otto and Diesel engines are, as an aid to judgment and a basis of analysis. The ratio expressing the comparative efficiency is the engine efficiency η.

213. Rankine Cycle. The ideal cycle for simple steam plants is called a Rankine cycle and, of course, it is a cycle in which there are no losses. The devices necessary to carry out a Rankine cycle are pictured in Fig. 112, p. 189, and the thermodynamic processes are shown in Fig. 162 on the pv and Ts planes. The expansion through the prime mover, which may be a reciprocating engine or a turbine, designated 1-2 on Fig. 162, is followed by condensation at constant pressure, 2-3. The water leaves the condenser in condition 3 and is pumped to the steam generator. In a hypothetical plant, this water-pumping operation may take place in a single pump, but in the actual case, a minimum of two pumps would be used, a *condensate pump* and a *feedwater pump,* as shown in Fig. 112.

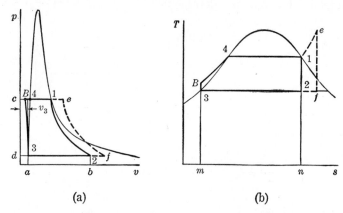

(a)   (b)

Fig. 162.   *Rankine Cycle.* The volumes of the liquid in (a) and the temperature rise 3B in (b) are greatly exaggerated.

We see from this description of the operation of the system which is the working substance that work crosses the boundary inward as well as outward. This is characteristic of all steam power plants; pump work W_p done on the system is essential for operation. The engine (Rankine engine in this case) produces the outgoing or gross work. The *net* work W produced by the system is the turbine work W_t minus the pump work W_p; $W = W_t - W_p$. In Fig. 162, the ideal pumping process is represented by 3-B. Water enters the boiler in state B and is heated B-4-1 (or B-4-1-e, if superheated). Boiling (evaporation) begins at state 4. Superheating, if any, begins at 1. Steam at 1 (or e) is transported to the turbine where it expands 1-2 (or ef); whence the steam passes to a condenser and is condensed 2-3 (or f-3).

214. Pump Work   To get a simple expression for the pump work, we make two assumptions: one, that the process is isentropic (usual for ideal machines) and two, that the liquid is incompressible. The assumption of an isentropic process is usually offset by an efficiency number to get the actual work. The incompressibility assumption becomes seriously in error at high pressures, which are now above the critical pressure in some new plants, and high temperatures. Thus, anyone concerned with such high pressures should not use the approximation which we get below. The energy equation in the form of equation (14), p. 30,

$$ (14) \qquad\qquad -\int v\,dp = \Delta K + \Delta P + W, $$

applies to the reversible process. Now if $\Delta K = 0$ (which will usually be approximately true) and if $\Delta P = 0$ (which will not necessarily be true for a liquid pumped through a considerable height), we get $W = -\int v\,dp$. Then

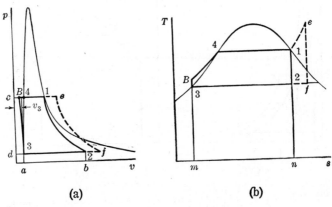

Fig. 162.   Repeated.

if the fluid is incompressible, $v = v_{f2}\ (=v_3$, Fig. 162) is constant and we have, as a positive number,

$$ (\mathbf{r}) \quad W_p = -v_{f2}\int_{p_1}^{p_2} dp = -v_{f2}(p_2 - p_1) = v_{f2}(p_1 - p_2) \text{ ft-lb./lb.}, $$

the total ideal pump work ($p_3 = p_2$ and $p_B = p_1$); v_{f2} is the volume of saturated liquid at the condenser temperature. This work is represented by the rectangular area of width d-3, Fig. 162(a). See also § 149.

For ordinary low- and medium-pressure power plants, the energy to drive the pumps is relatively small. For example, let the boiler pressure be 100 psia and the condenser temperature be 150°F; then

$$ W_p = \frac{v_{f2}}{J}(p_1 - p_2) = \frac{(0.01634)(100 - 3.718)(144)}{778} = 0.29 \text{ Btu/lb.} $$

On the other hand, at a discharge pressure of 10,000 psia, a 5% improvement in the pump efficiency may bring about 0.5% improvement in the cycle efficiency (a sizeable amount in a large plant).*

215. Efficiency of the Rankine Cycle. In any power cycle, § 95, the net heat transferred (ΣQ or $Q_A - Q_R$) is equal to the net work, and the thermal efficiency, § 96, is the *net* work divided by the heat added. In the Rankine cycle, Fig. 162, the water enters the boiler in state B, where (positive W_p)

$$h_B = h_3 + W_p = h_{f2} + W_p$$

and W_p is the ideal pump work. It leaves the boiler in state 1, where the enthalpy is h_1. For $\Delta K = 0$, the heat added, § 154, is

(s) $$Q_A = \Delta h = h_1 - h_B = h_1 - h_{f2} - W_p \text{ Btu/lb.},$$

and the heat rejected in the condenser is

(t) $$Q_R = h_2 - h_3 = h_2 - h_{f2} \text{ Btu/lb.},$$

as a positive number. Thus, the net work is

(u) $$W = W_t - W_p = Q_A - Q_R = h_1 - h_2 - W_p,$$

and the thermal efficiency is

(v) $$e = \frac{W}{Q_A} = \frac{h_1 - h_2 - W_p}{h_1 - h_{f2} - W_p}.$$

By comparing this equation with that for the efficiency of the Rankine engine, equation (64), we see that the efficiencies are virtually the same when the pump work is negligible, as it is when the boiler pressure is low. It is also true for steam cycles in general that if the pump work is subtracted from the gross work ($W_t - W_p$) and subtracted from the energy chargeable against the engine ($E_c - W_p$), the ratio ($W_t - W_p$)/($E_c - W_p$) gives the cycle thermal efficiency. It is not possible to draw a precise line, below which pump work is ignored and above which it is included in cycle analysis, because the line depends upon the desired accuracy; but for academic purposes, we may decide to include the pump work when the boiler pressure is at or above 400 psia and omit it when below 400 psia.

216. Factors Which Affect Efficiency. Although there are limitations to this statement, we have found by experience that when certain changes bring about an increase in the efficiency of the ideal cycle, analogous changes in the actual cycle generally increase the actual thermal efficiency. This is one reason for the importance of the ideal cycles. For the Rankine cycle, a study of equation (v) will show that the following changes increase the Rankine efficiency.

---

* J. E. Downs, *Margins for improvement of the steam cycle*, ASME paper No. 55-SA-76.

1. *If the condenser temperature is lowered,* Fig. 163, the heat rejected will be less, the work will be greater, and therefore the efficiency will be increased. Nature, however, precisely defines the limit of improvement that may be obtained by this means. In order to condense the steam, some cooling medium, at a temperature lower than that of the steam in the condenser, must be available for carrying away the rejected heat. Since we know from the second law of thermodynamics that there will be no net gain if artificial cooling is resorted to, we must be satisfied with a condenser temperature somewhat (often less than 10°) above that of condensing water from rivers, lakes, etc. The best condensers are now so well designed that we may confidently expect no significant thermal improvement in this phase of the cycle. See Figs. 164(b) and 165.

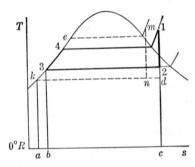

Fig. 163. *Effect of Operating Pressures on the Efficiency of the Rankine Cycle.* A lowering of the final pressure from 2 to d increases the Rankine work by the amount of the area 2–d–k–3, reduces the heat rejected from 2–3–b–c to dkac. For the increased boiler pressure at m, it is assumed that the maximum temperature remains the same, $t_m = t_1$. Subcooling effect (pump work) is ignored.

2. *If the boiler pressure is raised,* the evaporation line is raised, say, from 4-1 to em, Fig. 163, and the work area mnke is greater than 1-d-k-4. True, more heat is transferred to the working substance at the higher pressure, but a greater *proportion* of the heat supplied is converted into work. Accordingly, we find that the efficiency of actual plants using higher pressures is greater than that of plants using lower pressures, which accounts in part for the modern trend toward high pressures. The high pressures now being planned, 4500 psia and upwards, introduce complicated design problems, and operating experience is required to eliminate the "bugs."

3. Although it is not evident from a *Ts* diagram or from equation (v), *the use of superheated steam,* for example, cycle e-f-3-4-e, Fig. 162(b), improves the thermal efficiency as compared to a cycle with the same pressure limits and with saturated steam at the beginning of expansion. In fact, the improvement in the actual thermal efficiency [see Figs. 164(e) and 165] is usually greater than the corresponding ideal improvement. Small particles of water in steam moving at high speed past the blades of the turbine, besides having an eroding effect on the blades, reduce the efficiency of the transformation of energy. Observe from Fig. 163 that the higher the pressure for a given initial temperature, the wetter the steam at the exhaust, point n versus point d. Consequently, at higher steam pressures, superheat

becomes more desirable in order to reduce the degree of wetness in the low pressure stages of the turbine. Superheated steam improves the efficiency of the actual reciprocating steam engine because it reduces the loss from

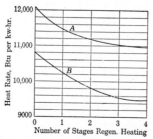

(a) Variation of Heat Rate with No. Stages. Rated 20,000 kw; exhaust 1.5 in. Hg; Curve A: $p_1 = 400$ psig, $t_1 = 750°$F. Curve B: $p_1 = 1250$ psig, $t_1 = 950°$F.

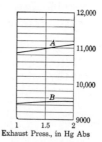

(b) Variation, Ht. Rate with Exh. Pres. Rated 20,000 kw; 4 stages regen. ht. Curve A: $p_1 = 400$ psig, $t_1 = 750°$F. Curve B: $p_1 = 1250$ psig, $t_1 = 950°$F.

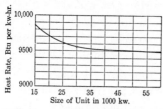

(c) Variation of Heat Rate with Size. $p_1 = 850$ psig, $t_1 = 900°$F, $p_{ex} = 1.5$ in. Hg, 4 stages regenerative heating.

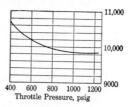

(d) Variation of Heat Rate with Throttle Pressure. Rated 20,000 kw, $t_1 = 825°$F $p_{ex} = 1.5$ in. Hg, 4 stages regen. heating.

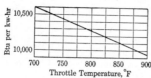

(e) Variation of Ht. Rate with Throttle Temp. Rated 20,000 kw, $p_1 = 600$ psig, $p_{ex} = 1.5$ in. Hg, 4 stages heating.

Fig. 164. Variation of Heat Rates. These curves represent typical actual combined heat rates for the conditions specified. They are drawn from data in a publication of the Westinghouse Electric Corporation. Observe that the thermal efficiency varies indirectly as the heat rate [$e_k = 3412/$(heat rate)] in Btu per kilowatt-hour. As the heat rate decreases, thermal efficiency increases, and vice versa.

initial condensation (§ 232). For these reasons, modern central-station power plants invariably use superheated steam.

The curves of Fig. 164 show something of the nature of the variation of heat rates (and efficiencies) for the conditions as specified above. In Fig. 164(c) and (d), notice how the curves level off, indicating that not much improvement in efficiencies can be expected of larger units or from higher throttle pressures, other conditions remaining the same. However, other conditions do not remain the same. If the initial pressure is increased, the size of unit which shows the most favorable heat rate also increases, and also the most favorable heat rate for this higher-pressure larger unit is better than the best heat rate of a lower-pressure unit.* The variations of steam rates with variations of load and other conditions are shown in Fig. 165. The way the lessons learned from thermodynamic studies have been put into practice is illustrated in Fig. 166.

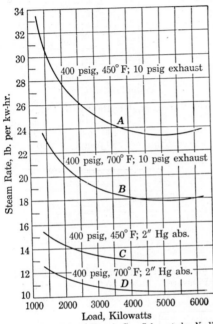

Courtesy General Electric Co., Schenectady, N. Y.

Fig. 165. *Variations of Steam Rates.* These curves are for units rated at 5000 kw. Compare curve A with curve B, and curve C with curve D, to see how the steam rate is improved by using superheated steam. Compare A with C, and B with D, for an evaluation of the improvement that comes from using a condenser. Exhaust at 10 psig (= 24.7 psia at sea level) is at a relatively high pressure unless steam in this condition is needed for industrial processes.

217. Reheat and Regeneration. If steam should be expanded from a very high pressure through an efficient turbine, it would be relatively wet in the lower-pressure stages, the water particles resulting in low efficiency and eroding of blades; § 216, paragraph (3). Roughly, each per cent of moisture reduces the efficiency of the turbine stage by 1%. In order to maintain a lower moisture content, *resuperheating* or *reheating* is practiced. By this is meant that after the steam has had some expansion in the turbine, it is returned to a steam generator, Fig. 114, p. 192, or to a separately fired furnace or other heat exchanger, and superheated again. Reheating is generally practiced when the initial steam pressure is 1250 psi or higher and the throttle temperature is about 750°F.

If the initial temperature at this pressure is 900–950°F, there is some question as to whether reheating is justified. When the pressure is greater than about 1800 psia, reheating is probably advantageous for any throttle temperature now used (1050–1100°F), and above-critical-pressure plants may use two or more reheats.

* Anyone interested in pursuing this matter further should see the references given in the caption to Fig. 166 and C. C. Franck, *Superpressure steam turbines*, a paper presented to the Southeastern Electric Exchange, Sept., 1955.

Modern power plants also practice **regenerative feedwater heating.**
When feedwater at the temperature in the condenser is introduced into the
boiler, which is at a high temperature, the process of heating the cold water
is irreversible (because heat flows only from the hot to the cold), and the
greater the temperature difference, the "greater" the irreversibility. By
this is meant that if heat flows because of a small temperature difference,

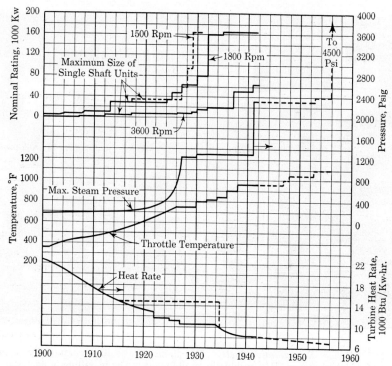

Fig. 166. *Trends in Turbine Designs.* **The curves up to 1942 were taken
from R. K. Fischer,** *Modern turbines—types and designs,* **Iron and Steel
Engineer, July, 1943. The dotted extensions on pressure and temperature
[are taken from J. E. Downs,** *Margins for improvement of the steam cycle,*
**ASME paper No. 55-SA-76. Data for extension of the turbine-size and heat-
rate curves are not readily available. The extension of the heat-rate curve
is approximate.**

there is a greater conservation of *available energy* than if it flows because of a
large temperature difference. The manner in which feedwater is heated
with small temperature differences is as follows. Small percentages of the
steam flow are **extracted** (or **bled**) at various points during the expansion in
the turbine. See Figs. 153 and 167. That steam bled at the lowest pressure
has a temperature closest to the exhaust; hence, the condensate is first heated
by this steam, then by the steam bled at the next highest pressure, and so on.
In each feedwater heater, the temperature difference is only a fraction of the

total difference, and as the number of heaters approaches infinity, the entire process of heating the feedwater approaches reversibility. The actual number of heaters used is purely a problem of economics. Each new heater added brings about a smaller percentage of improvement in efficiency than the previously added heater. So it is a matter of diminishing returns. See Fig. 164(a) for heat rate versus the number of stages.

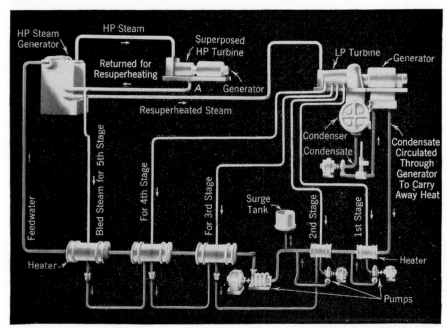

Courtesy, Power, *New York City*

Fig. 167. *Reheat-Regenerative Cycle.* This picture shows diagrammatically the installation of a high-pressure (HP) turbine in an old plant. The installing of an HP turbine under these circumstances has been widely practiced in recent years in order to modernize and improve the efficiency of older plants, and it is spoken of as "topping" a plant. An HP steam generator, say, for about 1250 psi, is installed for the HP turbine. Expansion in the HP turbine may be to, say, 400 psi. After this expansion, the steam is returned to the furnace where it is *resuperheated,* before being introduced into the LP turbine. This plant has five stages of regenerative feedwater heating, with four bleeding points on the LP turbine. Some of the exhaust from the HP turbine is used to heat the feedwater in the fifth stage. See the Dec., 1938 issue of *Power* for a number of interesting arrangements of power machinery and hookups.

The processes of an ideal reheat-regenerative engine, with three stages of regenerative heating, are pictured in Fig. 168. Because the mass of working substance varies with each extraction, it is advisable to note the mass involved in each process on the diagram as shown. The engine can be taken as a series of Rankine engines, 1-2, 3-4, 4-5, and 5-6, in which case it is easy to write the work equation as

(w) $W_t = h_1 - h_2 + (1 - m_1)(h_3 - h_4) + (1 - m_1 - m_2)(h_4 - h_5)$
$+ (1 - m_1 - m_2 - m_3)(h_5 - h_6)$ Btu/lb.

of throttle steam.   Note that for 1 lb. at the throttle, m_1, m_2, and m_3 are fractions of 1 lb.   The energy E_c *is* the enthalpy of the entering steam h_1

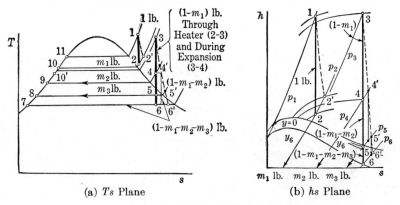

(a) *Ts* Plane (b) *hs* Plane

Fig. 168.   *Diagrams for Reheat-Regenerative Engine.*

credited with the enthalpy of the water as it leaves the last heater h_{f10} *plus* the heat added in the reheater; to wit,

(x)	$E_c = h_1 - h_{10} + (1 - m_1)(h_3 - h_2)$ Btu/lb.

of throttle steam.   The thermal efficiency then is

(y)	$$e = \frac{W_t \text{ [from (w)]}}{E_c \text{ [from (x)]}}.$$

The efficiency of the corresponding ideal cycle is obtained by subtracting the total ideal pump work from the numerator and denominator of (y); see equation (v).   There is another important difference between the engine and the cycle.   For the engine, state 1 is the state at the throttle; for the cycle, state 1 is that as the steam leaves the superheater.

Steam is also extracted for industrial processes and for heating.   If large amounts of steam at low pressure are needed for process or heating purposes, considerable power may be generated for a very low cost.   The cost of producing a pound of steam at low pressure is not much different from the cost of producing it at high pressure.   So if high pressure steam is generated and allowed to expand in a turbine to the pressure required for other purposes, the cost of the power obtained is nearly the cost which would be associated with the turbine alone.   Other books should be consulted for more detail on regenerative cycles and extraction processes.

218. Classification of Turbines.   Large turbines are designated in such a way as to describe the arrangement of the major components; for example, the turbine of Fig. 153 is called a tandem compound, as distinguished from a cross compound, Fig. 169. However, there are so many various arrangements that there is not space here to cover them all.

The fundamental transformations of energy occurring in a turbine are first the conversion of some of the energy in the entering steam into kinetic energy in the nozzles, then the conversion of a portion of this kinetic energy, via the action of the jet on a row of moving **blades** or **buckets**, into shaft work. To understand the mechanism of the conversion of kinetic energy into shaft work, the reader should recall certain principles of analytic mechanics. For example, impulse is equal to the *change* of momentum, and impulse is the product of a force times the time during which the force acts. If the force acts continuously, we may use the impulse for any convenient length of time, say 1 sec. The principle of impulse and momentum then may be expressed in the form

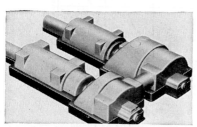

Courtesy General Electric Corp., Schenectady, N. Y.

Fig. 169. Cross Compound Steam Turbine. The plan shown here is built in sizes from **125,000–250,000 kw**, with throttle steam at **1450–2400 psig** and **1000–1050°F**, reheat (§ 217) to **1000–1050°F**. The HP unit runs at 3600 rpm; the LP unit at 1800 rpm. The advantage of the lower speed of the LP unit is that a larger exhaust annulus (longer blades) may be used giving more room for steam flow.

$$(\mathbf{z}) \quad F_x t = \frac{w}{g_o} v_{x2} - \frac{w}{g_o} v_{x1} = \frac{w}{g_o} (v_{x2} - v_{x1}),$$

where w/g_o is the *mass* in slugs. The linear momentum is the product of the mass and the velocity of the body (all points in the body are assumed to be moving with the same velocity at any instant). The force F_x (a vector quantity) acting in a particular direction (x direction) during some time t produces the change of momentum in the x direction in which the force is acting. This direction is not necessarily in the direction of the absolute velocity. The subscript x in the velocity symbols, v_{x1} and v_{x2}, indicates that the vectors for these velocities are parallel to the vector for F_x, and that, for example, v_{x1} may be the x component of some absolute velocity v_1.

We have already spoken of impulse and reaction types of turbines. The impulse type may be further classified as single stage, velocity compounded, and pressure compounded. The following paragraphs will further explain the meaning of these terms.

219. Single-Stage Impulse Turbine. The De Laval turbine has a single rotor or disk to which are attached the turbine blades, Fig. 152. The steam is fed in through several convergent-divergent nozzles. As a rule the nozzles of impulse turbines do not extend completely around the periphery; there-

fore at a particular time, not all of the blades are acted on by steam.   In
the diagrammatic representation of Fig. 170, we see that the pressure drops
to the exhaust pressure of the blades *before* the steam enters the blades.   No
pressure drop occurs during the passage through the blades.   On the other
hand, the velocity is a maximum at entrance to the blades, and, as the steam
passes through, kinetic energy is converted to shaft work and the velocity
decreases, the final velocity being some value v_2.

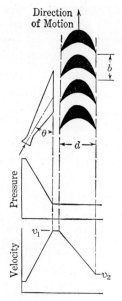

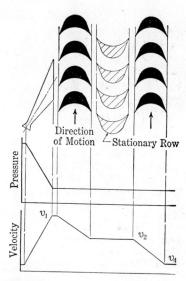

Fig. 170. *Impulse Stage.* J. F. Lee (*Steam and Gas Turbines*) gives the following proportions as good practice: $0.5 < b/d < 0.6$.   See Fig. 152, p. 245.

Fig. 171. *Curtis Stage.* Since the steam is moving slower through the second row of moving blades, a greater area of passageway must be provided in the second row—by making the blades thinner or by making them longer, or both.

220. Velocity-Compounded Stage.   For maximum efficiency, the periph-
eral speed of the buckets should be about half the initial speed of the
steam.   Thus, if we should use the steam from the nozzle of § 180, a blade
speed of some 1500 fps would be necessary.   This speed is unusually high,
where the more common speeds are 500 or 600 to some 1000 fps.   At very
high speeds of the steam it is difficult or impossible to convert efficiently the
kinetic energy of the jet into shaft work in one row of blades.   Moreover,
the necessary speed of the rotor can become so large that no material safely
resists the centrifugal force.   One solution to this dilemma was invented by
C. G. Curtis, who proposed using two rows of moving blades to absorb the

kinetic energy from one set of nozzles, Figs. 171 and 172. Between these two moving rows is a row of stationary blades to guide the steam properly into the second set of moving blades. Such a stage is also called a *Curtis stage*. Figure 171 shows that ideally the entire pressure drop occurs in the nozzle, that the velocity decreases during passage through the first moving row, remains constant in the stationary row, and decreases to the exit value v_4 as it passes through the second moving row.

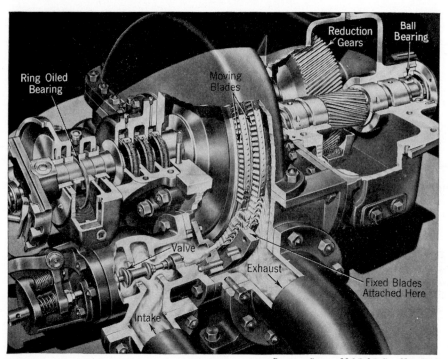

Courtesy Socony Mobil Oil Co., New York

Fig. 172. Geared Turbine, Velocity Compounded. Notice the two rows of moving blades on each side of the fixed blades. The moving blades are mounted on a single wheel. Nozzles occupy only a part of the circumference of the wheel, so that steam is not actively passing across all the blades in the wheel.

The effect of velocity staging may be obtained with a single row of buckets by especially contrived means. In one such turbine, the blading is the conventional type, but, as the steam leaves the wheel the first time through, it enters a reversing chamber which directs it back into the blades. Emerging for the second time from this row of blades, the steam may again be reversed and directed through the blades, and so on, thus providing three or more velocity stages. Structural limitations, the speed of the steam as it leaves the nozzle, and losses due to turbulence determine the practicable number of reversals. Velocity staging is obtained in another type of wheel, as shown in Fig. 173.   Here the steam enters radially and follows a helix-like path.   As the steam leaves the first bucket, it enters a reversing chamber placed over the wheel, which turns it back.   This reversing continues until the steam may have entered the wheel buckets three or four times. There may be several nozzles spaced around the periphery, four in Fig. 173, with a set of reversing chambers for each nozzle.   Turbines in which the steam enters a single wheel two or more times are called *reentry turbines*. There are in use many unique features of construction; but inasmuch as this work must be limited largely to principles, the interested reader should search for further details in more specialized books.

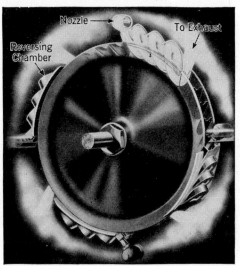

Courtesy The Terry Steam Turbine Co., Hartford, Conn.
Fig. 173.   Reentry Turbine.

221. Pressure-Compounded Turbine.   The losses attendant upon the high velocities following large expansions may be reduced by breaking up the total expansion from throttle to exhaust into a series of small expansions. There is provided a set of nozzles for each small expansion and a row of blades for each set of nozzles.   Such a turbine made up of a number of pressure stages is often called a *Rateau turbine*, after its originator.   Figure 174 illustrates the idea with two pressure stages, although usually there are several more stages than two.   Suppose there are N stages.   Then the total enthalpy drop Δh during an isentropic expansion from throttle to exhaust is divided by N to find the enthalpy drop per stage of the ideal turbine, equal to $\Delta h/N$.   This plan results in the same ideal work being done in each stage, but the pressure drop per stage will vary.   As shown in Fig. 174 the velocity, and therefore the kinetic energy, is the same at the entrance of each row of blades. Since the pressure in region A, Fig. 174, is greater than that in region B, it is necessary to separate the pressure stages by a diaphragm. This diaphragm, which carries the nozzles, is attached to the casing and extends inward to the shaft. Since there must be clearance between the diaphragm and the moving shaft, there are at this point some losses due to leakage from stage to stage.

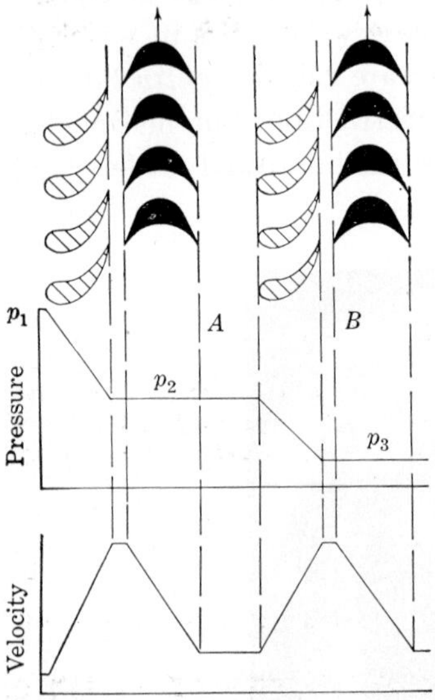

222. Reaction Turbine. In reaction turbines, the fixed blades are nozzles, shaped to allow a relatively small expansion of the steam, Fig. 175; but also the moving blades are shaped to provide a further expansion (§ 200). Let a *reaction stage* be composed of one row of stationary blades and one row of moving blades. In Fig. 175 is indicated diagrammatically the pressure drops in both stationary and moving blades and the variation of the velocity. The steam speeds up in the nozzles and loses velocity in the blades as kinetic energy is converted into work.

Fig. 174. Pressure Staging (Rateau). The pressure drops per stage are usually so small that the nozzle passages are converging only. Nozzles formed by stationary blades as shown are called *foil nozzles.*

In reaction turbines, the steam is admitted all around the periphery, a practice called *full admission;* otherwise, there would be an excessive leakage from the blading filled with steam into lower pressure regions.

The passage area through succeeding rows of blades must increase as the pressure drops in order to accommodate the increasing volume of steam. Also, to help in caring for the large volume, the diameter of the drum to which the blades are attached is increased in the low pressure sections, because an annular area of a particular height increases as the mean diameter increases. Notice in Fig. 153, p. 246, how the drum diameters of the reaction sections are increased in three steps. (Keep a marker at Fig. 153 for easy reference during this discussion.) The rapid increase in specific volume of steam at very low pressure creates a design problem in large turbines in the matter of providing sufficient area for the passage of steam through the low pressure elements and through the exhaust passages. A great help in this respect is to make the low pressure section double flow, as in Fig. 153 (or triple or quadruple flow), where a row of blades must handle only half as much steam as in a single flow turbine of the same size.

Another advantage of the double flow idea is in connection with the axial

thrust. Because of the pressure drop across the blades, the rotor is subjected to an axial thrust whose mag-
nitude is a function of the sum of
these pressure drops. By using double flow, we avoid "dummy" or balancing pistons which are used to maintain the axial forces approximately
in equilibrium in single-flow reaction
turbines.

223. Combination Turbine. Since
the basic patents on the foregoing
arrangements have expired and since
both impulse and reaction stages have
certain advantages, it is common for
manufacturers to use combinations of
these principles in medium and large
turbines. The turbine of Fig. 153

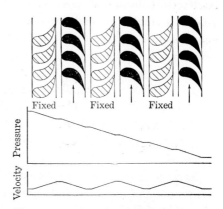

Fig. 175. *Reaction Stages.* The teardrop form of reaction blades, as shown,
is now standard practice except in the
lowest pressure stages.

has a single impulse stage first, followed by reaction blading to the exhaust.
The first stage of many large turbines is a Curtis stage. The subsequent

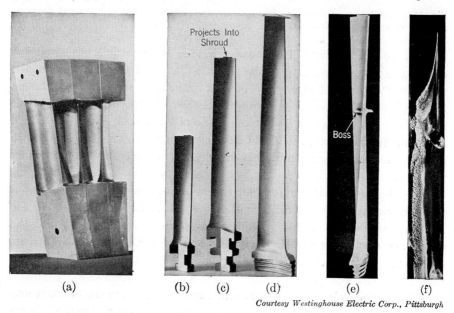

(a) (b) (c) (d) (e) (f)

Courtesy Westinghouse Electric Corp., Pittsburgh

Fig. 176. *Turbine Blades.* The group (a) shows some impulse blades; (b), (c), and (d)
are reaction blades with different constructions at the bottom for assembly onto the
rotor; (e) shows a long reaction blade with boss (the bosses on a row of blades are in
contact on assembly and are welded together to make long blades more rigid); (f) shows
the effect of erosion on a blade. The tips of reaction blades are tied together with a
shroud. A modern practice is to weld the shroud to the tips.

stages in general may be either reaction or Rateau stages. Reaction stages have certain disadvantages in the high pressure region. Because the specific volume is small, the blades would be very small, so that the necessary clearance between the tip of the blades and the casing would be a relatively large *percentage* of the blade height, the consequence of which would be an excessive percentage of steam spilling over the blade tips without doing any work. Since the pressure in impulse blading is virtually constant, the tip clearance is not too significant. The best means of regulating the steam flow to the turbine is via the opening and closing of nozzles at the initial stage, which is another reason that the impulse stage is favored at the beginning of expansion.

Several blade forms are shown in Fig. 176; and Fig. 177 shows how the cross section of reaction blading has evolved as a result of our better knowledge of air foils.

1900–1915   1915–1930   1930–194–   Present Development
Courtesy Westinghouse Electric Corp., Pittsburgh

Fig. 177. *Evolution of Reaction Blade Sections.* **Observe that the present development is toward the teardrop shape.**

224. Losses in Steam Turbines. There is an inevitable but small loss due to the residual velocity of the steam as it leaves the last stage of the machine. A blade efficiency of 100% is impossible even in a frictionless turbine because of the obliquity of the nozzle; that is, because the nozzle must slope at some angle θ with the plane of the wheel, Fig. 170. For a nozzle angle of $\theta = 20°$, the ideal efficiency is about 88%. The loss due to radiation from the casing and other metal parts of the turbine is practically negligible.

The loss due to leakage from one region to another within the turbine is of the order of 1% or 2% of the enthalpy supplied to the turbine. In the Rateau impulse turbine, this leakage occurs between the shaft and the stationary diaphragms which carry the nozzles and separate the various pressure regions. In the reaction turbine, the leakage is about the blade tips.

Another minor loss is that due to mechanical friction in the bearings and at various other points where there is relative motion, such as in the governing mechanism and in the oil pumps. This loss is only a fraction of 1% of of the energy supplied, and in percentage form, it declines as the size of the turbine increases.

By far the greatest single loss is due to turbulence, which occurs at several points.   First, there is the frictional loss in the nozzles and blades.   Further fluid friction occurs due to the steam and gases adjacent to the surface of the rotating disks carrying the blades.   Moreover, centrifugal action causes some of the steam to flow radially to the casing, to be dragged along the surface of the casing by the moving blades.   Since full admission is not generally used in impulse wheels, there is a fanning or churning of the vapor in the inactive blades of the wheel.

225. Closure.   The interested reader can find many good books on steam turbines and steam power plants to fill out the brief remarks of this chapter. Because of the great and rapidly growing demand for power, this is an important study and splendid engineering work is being quite actively carried on in designing, literally, bigger and better power plants.   To get higher efficiencies, we use higher pressures and temperatures.   But if the very high pressures are to be used to best advantage, the turbines must be larger.   At the extreme pressures, the volume of the steam is small and the unit must be large in order to get a practical volume of steam through the first high pressure stage.   If detailed computations are made for each throttle pressure, it will be found that the efficiency at first increases as the size increases, reaches a maximum, and then decreases as the size continues to increase. For example, if the throttle pressure is 5000 psi, the size of unit for maximum thermal efficiency is about 500,000 kw.

SELECTED REFERENCES

Barnard, Ellenwood, and Hirshfeld, *Heat-Power Engineering*, Vols. II, III, John Wiley.
Church, E. F., Jr., *Steam Turbines*, McGraw-Hill.
Faires, V. M., *Thermodynamics*, Macmillan.
Gafford, G. A., *Steam Power Stations*, McGraw-Hill.
Goudie, W. J., *Steam Turbines*, Longmans, Green.
Lee, J. F., *Steam and Gas Turbines*, McGraw-Hill.
Morse, F. T., *Power Plant Engineering and Design*, Van Nostrand.
Newman, Lyons, and Wales, *Modern Turbines*, John Wiley.
Salisbury, J. K., *Steam Turbines and Their Cycles*, McGraw-Hill.
Skrotyki and Vopat, *Steam and Gas Turbines*, McGraw-Hill.
Stodola-Lowenstein, *Steam and Gas Turbines*, McGraw-Hill.
Zerban and Nye, *Steam Power Plants*, International Textbook.

PROBLEMS

NOTE.   *Be sure to use Ts-plane diagrams and energy diagrams freely.   Solve problems by a steam table solution unless otherwise specified, but always check as many answers as possible by the Mollier chart (at rear of book).*

311. A Rankine engine expands steam from 540 psia and 750°F to a condensing temperature of 90°F. Determine (a) the work, (b) the thermal efficiency, (c) the steam rate, (d) the mep of the ideal engine.

Ans. (a) 492.1 Btu/lb., (b) 37.16%, (c) 5.17 lb./hp-hr., (d) 7.11 psi.

312. (a) A Rankine engine receives saturated steam at 110 psia and exhausts it at 15 psia. For 1 lb., calculate the work and thermal efficiency. (b) Suppose the exhaust from the foregoing engine is passed without loss through a steam separator which removes all the liquid. Suppose now that the remaining saturated steam at 15 psia enters another Rankine engine and expands to 1 psia. How much work is done for 1 lb. of original steam and what is the overall thermal efficiency? (c) Does it appear that the work to be obtained by carrying the expansion of steam below atmospheric pressure is significant? Is a low pressure of 1 psia feasible?

Ans. (a) 145.6 Btu/lb., 14.47%, (b) 151.1 Btu/lb., 29.5%.

313. A turbo-generator unit consumes 250,000 lb./hr. of steam while delivering 30,000 kw. The steam expands from 800 psia and 900°F to 1 psia. The efficiency of the electric generator is 93%. (a) For the ideal engine, determine the thermal efficiency, steam rate, and mep. (b) For the actual engine, compute the combined steam rate, combined work, combined thermal efficiency, and the combined and brake engine efficiencies. (c) Estimate the enthalpy of the actual exhaust.

Ans. (a) 38.9%, 6.34 lb./kw-hr., 10.7 psi, (b) $W_K = 410$ Btu/lb., $\eta_k = 76.2\%$, (c) 1013.9 Btu/lb.

314. Steam with an enthalpy of 1507.2 Btu/lb. enters a turbine whose brake steam rate is 6.1 lb./bhp-hr. The condenser pressure is 5.3 in. Hg abs.

The radiation from the turbine is 18 Btu/lb. of steam flowing and $\Delta K = 5$ Btu/lb. (a) What are the approximate enthalpy and quality of the exhaust? Sketch an energy diagram. (b) What is the stagnation enthalpy of the exhaust if the initial kinetic energy is negligible? (c) For a total steam flow of 610,000 lb./hr., what horsepower is being delivered?

Ans. (a) 94.9%, (b) 1072.5 Btu/lb., (c) 100,000 bhp.

315. A 5000-kw turbo-generator receives saturated steam at 210 psia and exhausts it at 5 psia as process steam (i.e., steam used in some industrial process). At full load, the combined steam rate is 17 lb./kw-hr., and the efficiency of the generator is 93%. For the Rankine engine, find (a) W, (b) e, (c) w. For the actual engine, find (d) W_K, W_B, and w_b, (e) e_k and e_b, (f) η_k and η_b. (g) What is the brake heat rate? Determine (h) the approximate quality of the actual exhaust, (i) the total steam consumption at rated load, (j) the lost work (with respect to W_B) in Btu/min., (k) the loss of available energy for $t_o = 74°F$.

Ans. (b) 24%, (d) $w_b = 11.8$ lb. per bhp-hr., (f) $\eta_b = 84.4\%$, (g) 12,600 Btu/bhp-hr., (h) 85.3%, (j) 56,800 Btu per min., (k) 32.6 Btu/lb.

316. Steam enters the blades of a turbine with an enthalpy of 1300 Btu per lb. and an absolute speed of 1600 fps. It leaves the blades with an enthalpy of 1304 Btu/lb. and an absolute speed of 420 fps. What work is done by the steam on the blades? Sketch an energy diagram.

Ans. 43.66 Btu/lb.

317. At an output of 20,000 kw, a turbine has a combined steam rate of 7.75 lb./kw-hr. Water enters the steam generator at 380°F and steam leaves at 900 psia and 900°F. During a test, the efficiency of the steam generator was found to be 85%. The coal with a heating value of 14,000 Btu/lb. costs $5.00 per ton. The electrical generator efficiency is 95%. Assume no losses between the steam generator and turbine and neglect the effect of the pump work. Determine (a) the kB/hr. and boiler horsepower, (b) the bhp of the turbine, (c) the boiler horsepower required per bhp, (d) the coal needed, lb./kw-hr., (e) the fuel cost, in cents per kw-hr. (f) If the combined engine efficiency of the turbine is 75%, what is the work of the corresponding ideal (Rankine) engine?

Ans. (a) 5070 bo. hp, (b) 28,200 bhp, (c) 0.18, (d) 0.715, (e) 0.179 ¢/kw-hr.

318. A Rankine engine expands steam at the rate of 10 lb./sec. from 175 psia and 4.231 cu. ft./lb.to 20 psia. Find (a) y_2 or t_2, (b) the work and thermal efficiency. During actual expansion, the increase in entropy is $\Delta s = 0.0847$ Btu/lb-°R. Determine (c) the actual work, (d) the lost work, (e) the increase of unavilable energy for a sink temperature of 70°F. Designate areas on the Ts plane representing (d) and (e).

Ans. (b) $e = 23.5\%$, (c) 2310 hp, (d) 705 Btu/sec., (e) 449 Btu/sec.

319. The pressure in a steam main is 160 psia. A sample of this steam is led into a calorimeter where the state is defined by 15 psia and 250°F. What is the quality of the steam sampled? Solve (a) by using the superheat tables, (b) by using the saturated steam tables and the specific heat of steam, and (c) by using the Mollier chart, making a sketch to show your solution.

Ans. 97%.

320. A throttling calorimeter receives a sample of steam from a steam main at 162 psig. In the calorimeter,

the state is defined by 16.5 psia and 245°F. How much moisture is in the sampled steam? Solve by chart only, showing a sketch of your solution.

Ans. 3.5%.

321. A separating calorimeter is used to determine the quality of steam. During a 10-min. test, the mass of water collected was 0.065 lb. and the mass of steam passing through the discharge orifice of the calorimeter was 6.12 lb. What was the quality and percentage moisture? *Ans.* $x = 98.95\%$.

322. Steam leaves a boiler at 570 psia and 500°F. As it flows to the turbine, its pressure changes adiabatically to 470 psia, due to friction and a throttling valve (overall, a throttling process). The condenser temperature is 104°F. (a) What is the temperature of the steam on entering the turbine blades? What is the work done in a Rankine engine (b) if the expansion starts at the boiler condition? (c) if it starts at the turbine condition. (d) What is the lost work between the boiler and engine, and what is the loss of available energy for a 104°F sink?

Ans. (b) 398.1, (c) 832.3 Btu/lb., (d) $T_o\Delta s = 10.2$ Btu/lb.

323. Steam leaves a boiler at 240 psia and 480°F. It reaches the throttle of the turbine at 220 psia and is then throttled to 200 psia before it enters the nozzles. Exhaust is at 2 in. Hg abs. Make an energy diagram of the pipe between the boiler and turbine for $Q = 0$. Using the Mollier diagram only, find (a) the loss of Rankine work between boiler and turbine, (b) the loss through the throttling valve.

Ans. (a) 6, (b) 4 Btu/lb.

324. In a Rankine cycle, saturated steam is generated at 450 psia and condensed at 106°F. For 1 lb., find (a) Q_A, (b) Q_R, (c) net W, (d) e. (e) What is the ideal pump work and the gross work of the engine for the same end states?

Ans. (a) 1129.7, (b) 755, (c) 374.7, (d) 33.2%, (e) 376.

325. A reheat turbine operates as follows. It receives steam at 1650 psia and 780°F (state 1) and expands it (Rankine engine) to 430 psia (state 2). The steam now returns to the furnace where it is resuperheated, whence it returns to the turbine (another Rankine engine) and arrives there at 410 psia and 600°F (state 3). The steam now expands to the condenser temperature of 96°F (state 4). Sketch these events on the Ts plane. (a) Find the work done by the first Rankine engine, that done by the second engine, and the total. (b) Find the reheat turbine's thermal efficiency (E_c is as defined in § 202 where h_{f2} is the liquid enthalpy at exhaust temperature, except that the heat added during resuperheating must be included). (c) Let the cycle work be the gross work found above less the pump work, and find the cycle efficiency.

Ans. (a) 134.3, 428.5, 562.8 Btu per lb., (b) 40.8%, (c) 40.6%.

326. Steam enters an ideal reheat turbine (see problem **325** for details of events) at 1400 psia and 900°F. After doing total ideal work of 654 Btu/lb., it exhausts at 1 psia and a quality of 87%. What is the ideal thermal efficiency? Draw an energy diagram.

Ans. 42.1%.

327. An ideal turbine, in a regenerative cycle, receives steam at 520 psia and 900°F (state 1), expands it to 32.53 psia (state 2), at which point m lb./lb. of entering steam is extracted for feedwater heating. The remainder of the steam $(1 - m)$ lb. continues expansion to 1.175 in. Hg abs. (state 3), whence it enters a condenser and is condensed to a saturated liquid (state 4).

This condensed $(1 - m)$ lb. enters the feedwater heater and mixes with the m lb. of steam that was extracted at state 2; the condensation of the m lb. of steam heats the $(1 - m)$ lb. of water to state 5. From state 5, the H_2O reenters the boiler and starts a new cycle. (a) Make an energy diagram of the feedwater heater, write the equation for an energy balance, and solve for the value of m if the condensate is heated to the saturation temperature for the pressure at the bleeding point (state 2). (b) What is the total ideal work (two Rankine engines)? (c) What are the thermal efficiency, the heat rate, and the steam rate? (d) What is the approximate ideal pump work?

Ans. (a) 0.154 lb./lb., (b) 507.6 Btu/lb. throttle steam, (c) 40.8%, 8360 Btu/kw-hr., 6.73 lb./kw-hr., (d) 1.545 Btu/lb.

328. An ideal reheat-regenerative turbine receives steam at 1650 psia and 780°F and expands it to 430 psia, whence it all leaves the turbine and passes through a reheater, returning to the turbine at 410 psia and 600°F. Expansion now continues to 135 psia where $m = 0.227$ lb. steam/lb. throttle steam is extracted for feedwater heating; the balance of the throttle flow expands to a condenser temperature of 96°F. Sketch the processes on a Ts plane. Do not interpolate for entropy differences as small as 0.0001 Btu/lb-°R. Determine (a) the work of the engine, (b) its steam rate and thermal efficiency, (c) the heat picked up by the condenser circulating water (per pound of throttle steam). (d) What is the approximate ideal pump work?

Ans. (a) 489.7 Btu/lb., (b) 6.97 lb. per kw-hr., 43.7%, (c) 628 Btu, (d) 4.92 Btu/lb. throttle steam.

329–340. These numbers may be used for other problems.

14

RECIPROCATING STEAM ENGINES

226. Historical Sketch. The first steam engine to accomplish a useful purpose was Thomas Savery's (1650–1715) pumping engine. Prior to Savery's invention, steam engines had been discussed philosophically by several people, many of whom had contributed useful ideas, but no one had constructed an engine. In Savery's engine, steam acted directly upon the surface of the water, the pressure of the steam forcing the water from the pumping chamber through a pipe line in which there was a crude check valve to prevent a reversal of flow. After the pumping chamber had been cleared of water, the steam supply was cut off (by hand). Next cold water flowing over the chamber condensed the steam. A partial vacuum was thereby created which caused a new chamber full of water to be sucked in. Steam was then admitted again, the water was forced from the chamber into the delivery line, and the cycle of events was repeated. Because of the direct contact of steam and cold water, the loss from condensation of steam was very large. Although the safety valve was a contemporary invention, Savery did not use one. As a result, explosions were not infrequent. The pressures used were for the most part between 50 and 100 psig, and the coal consumption was perhaps 110 lb./hp-hr.

Denis Papin (1647–1712), a contemporary of Savery, Boyle, Huygens, Leibnitz, and other important scientists, is credited with the invention of the safety valve. Having heard of Savery's engine from a friend, he outlined plans for an engine with a piston to separate steam and water. It is thought, however, that the Papin engine was never built. Another contemporary of Savery, Thomas Newcomen (1663–1729), did design and build a steam engine with a piston. It is possible that Newcomen's engine was built as early as Savery's but Savery controlled the basic patent. Both Savery and Newcomen were inspired by the desire to provide a mechanical means for pumping water from the coal mines, but Newcomen conceived the idea of also driving machinery with his engine. However, it remained for Watt to see this dream realized. In the Newcomen engine, steam was admitted to a cylinder where it pushed the piston to the top of the stroke against little resistance. Next the steam in the cylinder was condensed by a jet of cold water.   Now with a vacuum in the cylinder, the atmospheric pressure out-side forced the piston to make a working stroke.   Because of this distinctive feature, the engine was called an "atmospheric engine."   The pressure of the steam was very little above atmospheric pressure.   The steam piston was connected to one side of a beam which rocked about an intermediate point.   The piston for the pump cylinder was connected to the other side of the beam.   With the pumping cylinder and steam cylinder separate, the intensity of pressure on the water was not dependent on the intensity of pressure on the steam piston alone.   The relative areas of the pistons affected the pressure on the water being pumped.   The operation of the valves which controlled the admission of steam and water to the power cylinder was at first manual.   It finally dawned on one small boy, hired to operate the valves and lazier than the others, that the oscillation of the beam and the operation of the valves occurred in a regular pattern.   He thereupon rigged up strings between beam and valves in such a manner that the movement of the beam controlled the valves, the first instance of automatic valve action.   Or so the story goes.   The Newcomen engine used about 30 lb. of coal per hp-hr.

The Newcomen engine was a commercial success.   About 60 years later, James Watt* developed the features of the modern steam engine: the separate condenser (in order that the cylinder be kept hot to reduce the loss through condensation), the double-acting engine, the expansion of the steam (to get work from its internal energy), the flyball throttling governor, the conversion of reciprocating motion into rotary motion.   In addition he had to invent Watt's straight-line mechanism to keep the end of the piston rod

---

* James Watt (1736–1819), born of Scottish, middle-class parents, was a delicate, timid child who had little desire to play as children play.   Because of an evident manual dexterity, he was trained to be an instrument maker.   As such, he was called upon to repair a model of a Newcomen engine.   While working on this engine, he decided that it could be improved, with the result that before his life was over he had conceived of most of the basic features of the modern steam engine.   Watt's education was largely self-directed, but it was a good education.   Also, he had a tenacity of purpose that is rare in the ordinary run of men but so often is found in those who accomplish great things.   Fortunately, he had intelligence, too.   Before the first model of his engine was built, he carried on extended researches on the properties of steam, about which prac-tically nothing was known at the time.   After two unsuccessful models and with his money gone, Watt was about to give up when he persuaded Dr. Roebuck to finance his experiments.   Again two more unsuccessful engines were built, and now Dr. Roebuck was in financial difficulties of his own.   After about five years, Roebuck sold his interest to a manufacturer, Mathew Boulton, who was able to furnish further financial aid. Shortly thereafter, with better workmanship, a successful engine was manufactured, and a commercial success was assured.   After installing one of his engines, Watt wrote to Boulton as follows: "The velocity, violence, magnitude, and horrible noise of the engine give unusual satisfaction to all beholders . . . .   I have once or twice trimmed the engine to end its strokes gently and make less noise; but Mr. _____ cannot sleep unless it seems quite furious . . . and by the by, the noise seems to convey great ideas of its power to the ignorant, who seem to be no more taken with modest merit in an engine than in a man."

in a straight path.   This mechanism was necessary because the machine tools of the day could not make an accurate plane surface to act as a guide. He introduced the float valve as a regulator of the water supply to the boiler and devised the engine indicator.   The action of the steam cylinder was similar to that of modern engines, but the engine was a beam engine like Newcomen's.   Watt's engine of 1782 used only 8 lb. of coal per hp-hr.

The next major improvement was the Corliss (1817–1888) valves and valve gear, which provided quick closing of the intake valves, thereby reducing the throttling and friction of flow during the closing periods. The Corliss engine of that day used about 4 lb. coal/hp-hr.   The most recent development is the Stumpf unaflow engine, described later in this chapter, which was designed to reduce again the loss from condensation of steam.   For comparison, we note that central station (turbine) plants are being built to use about 0.53 lb. coal/hp-hr. (0.71 lb./kw-hr.)   Projected are plant heat rates of about 8500 Btu/kw-hr., corresponding to a thermal efficiency of 45.5%.

227. The Indicator Card.   Most steam engines run slowly enough so that the indicator card obtained with a conventional indicator, Fig. 41, gives an accurate measure of the work done in the cylinder (indicated work), provided the passageways to the indicator are large enough in diameter and short enough in length so that fluid friction is negligible.   The events of the steam engine are pictured in the indicator card of Fig. 178.   The intake ceases at A, the *point of cutoff.*   Expansion occurs from A to B.   At B, the *point of release,* the exhaust valve opens, and the amount of steam discharged from the cylinder from B to C is the amount admitted w_a when the load is steady.   Point C is the *point of compression,* where the exhaust valve closes, and the

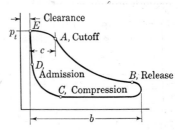

Fig. 178.   Indicator Card.

trapped or cushion steam is compressed with all valves closed to D, the *point of admission.*   The intake valve opens at D just before the piston has reached the end of the stroke and the pressure jumps to throttle pressure p_t.

The area of the indicator card, found by a planimeter, Fig. 42, *divided by* the length of the card b, Fig. 178, is the average height of the card.   The average height of the card *times* the scale of the spring in the indicator is the average net pressure (the mep) on the piston, p_m.   The rate at which work is being done when the card is taken, or the indicated horsepower, is (see § 83)

(a)
$$ihp = \frac{p_m LAN}{33,000},$$

which is equation (48); L ft. is the stroke of the engine, A sq. in. is the area of the piston, p_m psi is the mep, and N is the number of indicator cards or engine power "cycles" that would be made per minute. *Per cylinder end, N is the number of revolutions per minute.* If the indicator cards from the head and crank ends have the same area, the total indicated horsepower of the engine is obtained by letting $N = 2n$, where n is the rpm. However, although the work quantities as a rule differ very little, the work of the head end is not equal to the work of the crank end. Not only may the valves on the two ends of the cylinder be differently adjusted, but an allowance should be made for the area of the piston rod; that is, A in equation (a) above should be the area of the piston *minus* the area of the piston rod when it is applied to the crank end. Therefore, the horsepower output should be computed separately from cards taken from each end of the cylinder.

A term frequently used in relation to steam engines is *percentage cutoff,* which is defined as (expressed as a percentage number)

$$\frac{\begin{bmatrix} \text{The distance piston moves from} \\ \text{dead center to point of cutoff} \end{bmatrix}}{\text{Length of stroke}} = \frac{\text{Distance } c, \text{ Fig. 178}}{\text{Distance } b, \text{ Fig. 178}}.$$

228. Ideal Incomplete Expansion Engine. From the description of an actual indicator card, we see that the reciprocating steam engine is an incomplete expansion engine, inasmuch as the pressure at the point of release B is above the exhaust pressure. Since this is true, a complete expansion (Rankine) engine is not considered as the fairest standard of comparison for the incomplete expansion engine, although sometimes it is so used. The ideal engine will be taken as one without clearance, so that the idealized diagram on the pv plane is as shown in Fig. 179. On the Ts plane, Fig. 180, the expansion 1-2 is isentropic. At 2, the exhaust valve opens and some of the steam in the cylinder has a free and irreversible expansion to the exhaust pressure, indicated by 2-e, where e represents the condition of the exhaust steam. That part of the steam in the cylinder which does not have the free expansion is pushed from the cylinder by the piston, an action represented by line 3-a, Fig. 179.

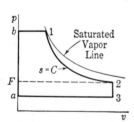

Fig. 179. *Diagram for Incomplete Expansion Engine.* This diagram may be thought of as a conventional indicator card for an engine without clearance. Only 1-2 is a thermodynamic process.

This ideal engine will be considered, as before, to be perfectly insulated, so that $Q = 0$, and the expansion 1-2 is taken as isentropic. Again, too, we shall consider the change of kinetic energy to be negligible ($K_1 = K_2$), as indeed it generally is. Thus, we see that we shall be dealing only with internal energy, flow work, and shaft work. The steam (1 lb.) enters the cylinder along b-1, Fig. 179, and in doing so does work (the same as the flow work as the steam crosses the system's boundary) of p_1v_1/J Btu/lb. At 1, the point of cutoff, the steam contains internal energy of u_1 Btu/lb. So the energy entering the system (cylinder) is $u_1 + p_1v_1/J$.

At 2, where the working substance starts to leave the engine, it contains internal energy u_2 Btu/lb., which is out-going energy. The work of pushing out the steam along 3-a is p_3v_3/J Btu/lb., inasmuch as the pressure has dropped to p_3 when the piston starts pushing the sub-stance out. Since $v_3 = v_2$, this work can be written as p_3v_2/J. Thus, the energy equation applied to this engine yields

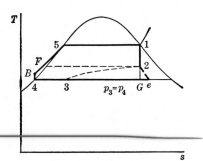

$$u_1 + \frac{p_1v_1}{J} = u_2 + \frac{p_3v_2}{J} + W,$$

(b) $$W = h_1 - u_2 - \frac{p_3v_2}{J} \text{ Btu/lb.,}$$

Fig. 180. Incomplete Expansion Cycle. Actually, points B and 4 are so close together that, plotted to a scale as small as this, the separation is not visible.

where h_1 has been substituted for $u_1 + p_1v_1/J$. This equation can be placed in a form which is easier to use by adding and subtracting p_2v_2/J from the right side; thus

$$W = h_1 - u_2 - \frac{p_2v_2}{J} + \frac{p_2v_2}{J} - \frac{p_3v_2}{J},$$

(67) $$W = h_1 - h_2 + \frac{v_2}{J}(p_2 - p_3) \text{ Btu/lb.,}$$

the work of the incomplete expansion engine. In finding the thermal efficiency of this ideal engine, we credit the engine with the enthalpy of the liquid at the exhaust pressure (§ 202) and get

(c) $$e = \frac{h_1 - h_2 + v_2(p_2 - p_3)/J}{h_1 - h_{f3}},$$

where h_{f3} is the enthalpy of saturated liquid corresponding to the pressure along 3-a, Fig. 179. The steam rate of the ideal engine is

(d) $$w = \frac{2544}{W} = \frac{2544}{h_1 - h_2 + v_2(p_2 - p_3)/J} \text{ lb./hp-hr.,}$$

in accordance with § 204. Since we may consider the steam engine as a steady flow machine, its work could be written from the energy equation as $W = h_1 - h_e$, where h_e is the enthalpy of the exhaust steam. However, there is usually no way to determine h_e except by analysis as given above. A comparison of $W = h_1 - h_e$ with equation (67) shows that

(e) $h_e = h_1 - W = h_2 - v_2(p_2 - p_3)/J$ Btu/lb.,

a relation that may be useful in computing the enthalpy of the ideal exhaust.

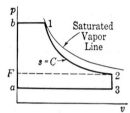

Fig. 179. Repeated.

The *mean effective pressure* of the ideal incomplete expansion engine is $p_m = W/V_D$, or

(f) $$p_m = \frac{J(h_1 - h_2) + v_2(p_2 - p_3)}{v_2} \text{ psf,}$$

where both work and displacement are values per pound of steam. The volume v_2, Fig. 179, is the maximum required in the cylinder when 1 lb. of steam is admitted.

To determine the operating conditions of an ideal engine corresponding to some real engine, let p_1 (ideal engine) be equal to the throttle pressure of the real engine, let the quality (or superheat) at 1 in the ideal engine be equal to the quality (or superheat) at the throttle of the real engine, let p_2 (ideal engine) be equal to the release pressure of the real engine, and let p_3 (ideal engine) be equal to the exhaust pressure of the real engine. Of course, the ideal expansion 1-2 is isentropic.

229. Actual Work and Efficiencies. As in the case of the Rankine engine, the actual work is determined from test. If actual steam rates are known, we have the relations from § 204,

(g) $$W_I = \frac{2544}{w_i} \text{ Btu/lb.,} \qquad W_B = \frac{2544}{w_b} \text{Btu/lb.,}$$

where the symbols have the meanings previously defined. And from §§ 119 and 205, the engine efficiencies are

(h) $$\eta_i = \frac{e_i}{e} = \frac{W_I}{W} = \frac{w}{w_i}, \qquad \eta_b = \frac{e_b}{e} = \frac{W_B}{W} = \frac{w}{w_b},$$
                 [INDICATED]   [BRAKE]

where W, e, and w are as found for the ideal engine. Typical values of the *indicated engine efficiency* for 100-hp simple engines are: single-valve engine, 56%; Corliss engine, 65%; unaflow engine, 73%. These values tend to increase as the size of the engine increases; for example, a 1000-hp unaflow engine may be expected to have an indicated engine efficiency of about 83%. (These types of engines are described below.)

The heat rates, as before, are expressed in Btu per hp-hr. or Btu per kw-hr., and are given by

(i)   Heat rate $= w(h_1 - h_{f3})$,

where the subscripts refer to Fig. 179. When the steam rate w is in lb. per ihp-hr., the heat rate is in Btu per ihp-hr.; when the steam rate is in lb. per bhp-hr., the heat rate is in Btu per bhp-hr., etc.

Applying the energy equation to an actual engine, letting $\Delta K = 0$ and $Q = 0$ (which presumes good insulation), we get $h_1 = h_{e'} + W'$ Btu/lb., where $h_{e'}$ is the enthalpy of the actual exhaust and W' is the actual work in Btu per lb. of the fluid. In a reciprocating engine W' is about equal to the indicated work, so that the actual enthalpy may be estimated from

(j) $h_{e'} = h_1 - W_I$ Btu/lb.   [RECIPROCATING ENGINE]

Point e' is to the right of e, Fig. 180, on the exhaust pressure line, at greater entropy than s_e because of the irreversibilities of the actual processes.

230. Single-Valve Engines. Figure 181 shows a typical small steam engine. It has a D-slide valve H, so-called because a sectional view is

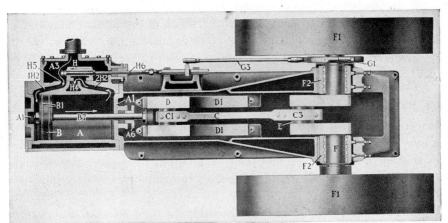

Courtesy Socony Mobil Oil Co., New York

Fig. 181. Center-Crank Steam Engine. The names of certain parts are as follows: *F*1, flywheels; *F*, journal; *F*2, bearing; *C*, connecting rod; *D*, crosshead; *D*1, crosshead guides; *B*7, piston rod; *B*1, piston rings; *B*, piston; *G*1, eccentric for operating the valve.

shaped something like a D turned through 90°. The valve H reciprocates, being driven by an *eccentric* $G1$ on the crankshaft through the *eccentric rod* $G3$ and the *valve stem* $H6$. The valve is so located that steam is entering the head end of the cylinder from the *steam chest* $A3$, while on the crank end steam is leaving the cylinder via the *exhaust port* $H4$. After the piston has moved to the right some 20–25% of its stroke, the valve H has closed the intake port on the head end, but the exhaust port on the crank end will not be completely closed until the point of compression (see Fig. 178) is reached. Just before the piston reaches the crank-end, dead-center position, the position of the valve is such that the crank end is connected to the steam chest $A3$ and the head end is connected to the exhaust passage $H4$.

231. Losses in the Steam Engine. As we well know, we must resign ourselves to certain losses in any actual engine. However, many of the losses common to the average engine can be reduced or eliminated. For this reason, it is well to analyze these losses in order to place ourselves in a position to determine the economic advisability of trying to reduce any of them.

1. The **mechanical friction** of the moving parts of the machine is a minor loss which, in modern, well-built engines, is practically a minimum. This loss, measured by the mechanical efficiency, is kept low by a proper design of bearings and of the lubrication system, a judicious selection of lubricants, and the occasional use of ball or roller bearings.

2. In the better class of engines, the **heat loss of conduction and radiation** is of a lower order than that from friction of the moving parts. It is kept at a minimum by **lagging** (that is, by insulating the cylinder).

3. **Steam leaking** about valves and past the piston represents a loss that can be reduced by better fitting of parts and by better maintenance.

4. The loss due to **incomplete expansion** of the steam is compensated wholly or in part by reduced friction; that is, it would be necessary to have a longer stroke (with additional friction of motion) or a larger diameter (with a heavier piston and larger frictional force) in order to provide for complete expansion. Also the mep and the power output for a given size of engine (or per dollar expended) would be less for a complete-expansion reciprocating engine.

5. There is a relatively large loss due to **fluid friction or throttling.**

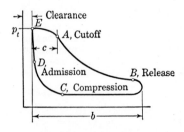

Fig. 178.   Repeated.

Observe that the admission line in Fig. 178 slopes downward from E to A. The drop in pressure is due to the friction of flow through steam passages. Further throttling occurs because of the slow movement of the valves in opening and closing. Notice in Fig. 178 the rounding of the curve at A and at B as compared to the sharp changes at points 1 and 2 of the ideal engine, Fig. 179. When the valve begins to open or is just about to close, the space for the steam to pass through is quite small. As a result there is a large degree

of throttling.   Simple slide valves are bad offenders in that the opening
and closing movements are relatively slow and the period of restricted
flow is of relatively long duration.   George Corliss, an American, devised
valves and a valve gear to reduce this loss.   We observe from Fig. 182 that
there are four valves in the Corliss engine, an exhaust valve at each end of
the cylinder ($1H1$ and $2H1$) and an intake valve at each end ($1H$ and $2H$).
These valves are operated by a **wrist plate** $H10$, which in turn is caused to
oscillate by an *eccentric* on the crankshaft to which the *eccentric rod* $H11$ is

Courtesy Socony Mobil Oil Co., New York

Fig. 182. Cylinder for Corliss Engine, A special feature of the operation of the inlet
valves is that they are very quickly closed by the *dash pots* $H13$.   When the inlet valve
$1H$ opens, the crank arm $H9$, keyed to the valve stem $H7$, moves upward and, through
the dash-pot rod $H12$, pulls the *dash-pot piston* $H13$ up from the bottom of the dash-pot
cylinder $H14$.   Below the dash-pot piston there is now a vacuum.   Thus, when the
valve is released, the atmospheric pressure on top of the piston quickly pushes the
piston down and closes the port.   The valve is opened by the wrist plate through valve
rod $H6$, bell crank $H16$, and the arm $H9$.   The bell crank $H16$ is free to move on the
valve stem $H7$ and has on its other arm a latch $H5$.   This latch, as it moves upward,
engages the latch plate $H17$ attached to the arm $H9$ which, as you recall, is keyed to the
valve stem $H7$.   Now the valve closes when the latch is disengaged.   The latch is
shaped as an inverted V, and when the side of the V opposite the hook strikes a cam $H18$
on the arm $H15$, the latch is released.   The position of the arm $H15$, and therefore of
the cam, is controlled by the governor through the governor rod $H4$.   Thus, the governor
controls the output of the engine by varying the point of cutoff, a more economical
system of governing than by throttling the flow.

connected. The exhaust valves are connected to the wrist plate by the valve rod $H6b$ and the crank arm $H9b$. The oscillation of the wrist plate thus positively opens and closes the oscillating exhaust valves. Figure 183 shows the exhaust line $H4$ and the shape of the section of the valves.

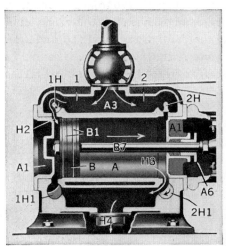

Fig. 183. Action of Valves in Corliss Engine. As shown, exhaust valve $2H1$ is open and $1H1$ is closed; inlet valve $1H$ is open and $2H$ is closed.

The quick closing of the inlet valves, as explained in Fig. 182, is the means by which fluid friction (throttling) is reduced in this engine. Note that throttling is a more serious matter at the higher intake pressure than at the exhaust or release pressure; hence, the quick-closing mechanism for the intake valve and the slower-closing, directly-connected drive for the exhaust valves.

Quick action and decreased throttling are obtained also with poppet valves, Fig. 185. Also, poppet valves are suited for high pressures and temperatures, which of course permit high thermal efficiencies.

6. The largest loss in the ordinary steam engine is that due to *initial condensation,* a condensation of hot steam in contact with the relatively cold surfaces in the cylinder.

232. Initial Condensation. From the inception of the steam engine, the low proportion of Rankine work produced by the real engine has been due in large measure to initial condensation. The thermal action is simply explained by use of the Ts diagram. If the engine receives saturated steam, the temperature range of the steam in the cylinder is from t_1 to t_2, Fig. 184. After the engine has warmed up, the walls of the cylinder will attain some mean temperature t_m between the limits t_1 and t_2. Of course this mean will not be one single steady temperature, because the walls will alternately be heated and cooled as the adjacent steam is hot or cold; but for purposes of explanation, we shall assume it to be steady, and, in any case, it varies through a relatively small range. Thus, hot steam at temperature t_1 enters a cylinder which is at a temperature of t_m. Heat begins immediately to flow from the steam to the cylinder walls. Let this transfer of heat be *internally* reversible. The loss of available energy occurs because of the *external* irreversible transfer of heat, as we shall see. While the steam is flowing into the cylinder at substantially constant pressure, condensation 1-A, Fig. 184, occurs. The amount of steam so condensed is sometimes as much as 50% of the feed. At A, the intake valve closes and the steam starts expanding. But not until the temperature of the steam falls to t_m does heat cease to flow from the steam to the cylinder. Thus there is further rejection of heat along AB. Now assume that the radiation from the cylinder is zero, that the heat lost by the steam is stored in the material of the cylinder. This stored energy can be returned to the steam as the expansion proceeds and as the temperature of the steam falls below t_m. If the engine is operating in a steady state, just as much heat must be returned to the steam below t_m as left the steam above t_m. Since the line BC representing this addition of heat to the steam is lower than 1-A-B, and since the area under 1-A-B (the outgoing heat) must be equal to the area under BC, evidently the curve BC must be longer than 1-A-B, and point C must fall some distance to the right of the isentropic 1-2.

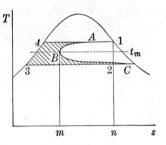

Now, accounting for condensation but assuming all other processes to be ideal, we have a thermodynamic cycle 1-A-B-C-3-4, Fig. 184. The enclosed shaded area is the work of the cycle. We see now that, *even though all the heat given up by steam is restored to it, the energy available for doing work may be substantially reduced*, roughly, by the amount of the area 1-2-B-A-1. The reevaporation of the water on the cylinder walls during the exhaust stroke requires a considerable

Fig. 184. Condensation and Reevaporation.

amount of heat; and this heat for reevaporation coming from the walls results in a lower mean temperature t_m and therefore a more rapid rate of condensation when the hot steam enters the cylinder.

233. Means of Reducing Condensation. Watt, recognizing the need for reducing condensation in the Newcomen engine, aimed to reduce this loss by proper design of his own engine. He achieved such a large percentage of improvement that it was many years before engineers began again to think of reducing this loss in simple engines by means other than insulation. Steam cylinders and heads are sometimes jacketed with "live" steam, in order to maintain the temperature of the walls at approximately throttle temperature. The condensation is then limited practically to condensation of the *jacket steam.* The net saving in condensation is due largely to the absence of reevaporation and to the lower surface conductance of the dry inside walls. In determining the thermal efficiency of a jacketed engine, charge the loss of enthalpy of the jacket steam against the engine.

The use of superheated steam reduces the loss due to initial condensation. If there is very much water on the walls at the exhaust pressure, a large amount of heat is necessary to evaporate this water. This evaporation cools the walls and lowers the mean temperature, just as evaporation of moisture from the human body is cooling. Hence, any step which reduces the moisture on the walls, as the use of superheated steam, improves the performance by raising the mean temperature through reduced reevaporation.

A basic improvement in engine construction, designed to reduce condensation, was made (1908) by Johannes Stumpf, a professor in Charlottenburg, Germany. The engine is called the *unaflow* (sometimes *uniflow*) engine, Fig. 185, to distinguish it from the usual counterflow engine. In

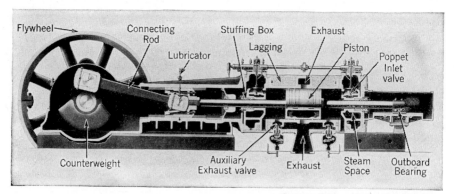

Courtesy Skinner Engine Co., Erie, Pa.

Fig. 185. Unaflow Steam Engine. The horizontal unaflow engine is available in sizes from 75–1200 hp. The cylinder heads are steam jacketed. Multicylinder, vertical unaflow engines are made in sizes from 300–2400 rated horsepower for land service, and up to 7000 hp for marine service. Reciprocating steam-engine power plants are especially suited to small power requirements, as in laundries, hotels, office buildings, refrigerating plants, hospitals, factories—particularly when steam is needed for other purposes such as for heating or industrial processes. Initial steam pressure varies from some 125–200 lb./sq. in., occasionally higher.

the engines previously discussed, the steam is admitted and exhausted at the same end of the cylinder. During the exhaust period, the relatively cold exhaust steam is flowing back over surfaces which hot steam will touch immediately thereafter. The movement of the cold steam increases the rate of heat removal from the walls. While the idea of eliminating this flow of cold steam was not new, Stumpf produced the successful engine embodying it.

In the unaflow engine, Fig. 185, the exhaust ports are located at the midpoint of the cylinder and are opened and closed by the piston itself. For this reason, the piston is quite long. The advantages of this engine are fully realized only when it operates condensing. With the piston at or near the dead-center position, the inlet poppet valve opens for admission. After cutoff and when the piston has moved about 0.9 of its stroke, it begins to uncover the exhaust ports (point B, Fig. 186), and the steam leaves the cylinder at the end of the stroke opposite the point of admission. It is apparent that the point of compression occurs when the piston covers the exhaust ports on its return stroke (point C, Fig. 186), and that therefore the compression period lasts about 90% of the stroke, instead of, say, 10% as in the counterflow engine. With so much compression and with the usual small and advantageous clearance characteristic of unaflow engines, it is necessary for the pressure at the beginning of compression to correspond to

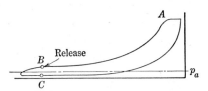

Fig. 186. *Indicator Card for Unaflow Engine.* The indicated work per power cycle of the unaflow engine is less than that of a counterflow engine of the same size, because of the early point of compression. It follows that, for a given output, the displacement of the unaflow engine is greater than that of the counterflow engine.

some vacuum. If compression should start in this type of engine at atmospheric pressure, it may happen that the pressure at the end of the compression stroke is above the throttle pressure.

Observe that the cylinder at the exhaust end of the stroke never comes into contact with hot steam. The admission end of the cylinder is kept hot by steam jackets. Thus at no time is there any considerable irreversible transfer of heat. Hot steam is in contact with hot surfaces; cold steam is in contact with cold surfaces. For these various reasons the economy of the unaflow engine is distinctly better than that of a counterflow engine of the same size (see Fig. 193). Moreover, the efficiency at one-quarter load is nearly as high as at full load; that is, the steam rate is less variable than in a counterflow between one-quarter and full loads. This characteristic makes the engine particularly suited for widely varying loads.

234. Compound Engines. The loss through condensation is reduced also by the use of multiple expansion engines. To take advantage of the internal energy of steam expanding through a large pressure range, we must provide a large expansion ratio. The simple unaflow engine, because of the features which we have just discussed, is very effective in this respect. On the other hand, the simple counterflow engine with an expansion ratio greater than about 5 is seldom economical, inasmuch as a greater ratio results in excessive condensation. If, for example, a ratio of expansion of 16 were desired, we could let the steam expand to four times its initial volume in one cylinder, then lead it to another cylinder and allow it to undergo another fourfold expansion. Such an engine is called a compound engine. The condensation in compound engines (and in multicylinder engines in

general) is reduced mainly because of the lower temperature *range* per
cylinder. The maximum difference between steam and cylinder temperatures ($t_1 - t_{mH}$) in a compound engine is roughly half that in a simple

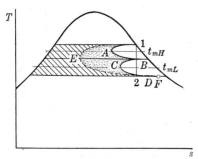

engine operating between the same temperature limits as the compound engine.
For this reason, the rate of transfer of
heat will be roughly half that of the corresponding simple engine. Comparative
losses might be as pictured in Fig. 187;
curves 1-*A*-*B* and *BCD* are for the high-
and low-pressure cylinders, respectively,
and the dotted curve 1-*E*-*F* is for a sim-

*Fig. 187. Condensation—Simple
Versus Compound Engine.* The
cross-hatched area represents the
work from a simple engine allowing
for initial condensation along 1-*E*-*F*.
The dotted area represents the reduction of this initial condensation due to
compounding.

ple engine with the same total ratio of
expansion.

Steam engines have often been made
triple expansion, of which there are many
in use in marine service. Quadruple
expansion engines are also used.

235. Governors. Steam engines are usually designed as constant speed
engines. The speed is not really constant, since it changes when the load

changes. Even for a constant load, the
speed fluctuates a small amount about an
average speed during a revolution, because
the working substance does not do its work
at a uniform rate. To maintain the speed
approximately constant, a governor is used.
When the load on an engine decreases, the
engine speeds up and, if no governor were
used, it would "run away." If a heavier
load comes on the engine it slows down,
and it would stall unless more steam were
admitted to do the additional work being
demanded of the engine. The governor
must also be designed not to overrun a
stable position; that is, to cause the engine
to "hunt." A governor which moves too
far with increasing speed will cause the
engine to slow down too much; then, the
governor will move too far in the other
direction, causing the engine to speed up

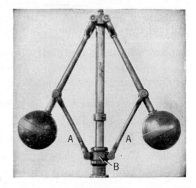

Fig. 188. Flyball Governor. If
the steam engine speeds up, the
flyballs move outward and upward
because of an increase in centrifugal force. Through links *A*, the
sleeve *B* is moved upward. This
sleeve is connected to a valve,
which is partially closed by the
outward movement of the balls,
thus reducing the amount of steam
admitted to the cylinder by
throttling.

too much, and so on. Such a fluctuation of engine speed is called *hunting.*

Steam engine governors regulate the speed either by *throttling* the steam or by changing the point of *cutoff*. In throttling governing, the engine has a fixed point of cutoff, and a valve at the inlet to the engine is adjusted by the governor. Decreasing load results in a partial closing of the valve, so that the intake pressure of the steam in the cylinder is decreased, and vice versa for increasing load. The process across the valve is a throttling process (§ 209), steam flowing from line pressure to some lower pressure in accordance with the load on the engine, whence the method of governing

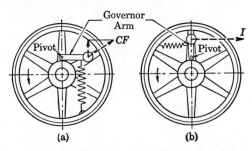

Fig. 189. *Action of Flywheel Governors.* This illustration shows diagrammatically the principle of the action of centrifugal and inertia governors as used on flywheels. If the speed increases in a counterclockwise direction, the centrifugal force in (a) increases and the governor arm rotates upward (when in the position as shown), stretching the spring. This arm is suitably connected, so that its movement varies the point of cutoff, decreasing the percentage cutoff when the load gets lighter, increasing it when the load gets heavier. In (b), when an increase in speed occurs, the weighted arm lags (inertia effect only), moving clockwise relative to the flywheel, and in this motion, it decreases the percentage cutoff through a suitable link work.

gets its name. A disadvantage of this method is that the throttling process is destructive of available energy.

In cutoff governing, the point of cutoff is made earlier or later according to whether the load becomes smaller or greater. If the cutoff is too early, the loss from initial condensation may be large; nevertheless, cutoff governing is generally more efficient than throttling governing.

Governors operate by virtue of the centrifugal force or the inertia (or both) of a body attached to a rotating member. A typical flyball governor for a Corliss is shown in Fig. 188. Figure 189 demonstrates the principles of using centrifugal force and inertia in a flywheel application. Notice in Fig. 189(b) that the relative movement of the weighted arm depends upon the suddenness of the speed change (i.e., upon the acceleration). Hence,

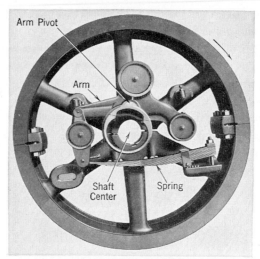

Courtesy Skinner Engine Co., Erie, Pa.

Fig. 190. Flywheel Governor. The center of gravity of the arm and its attached weights is located so that the centrifugal force tends to produce the same effect on the arm as its inertia. Only the top part of the pivot pin for the arm is visible.

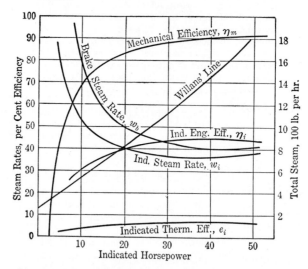

Fig. 191. Performance Curves for Steam Engine. The curve showing the total steam consumption is called a *Willans line,* after P. W. Willans, an Englishman, who first observed that the curve of *total steam* against *output* is very nearly a straight line. These curves are typical for a simple, slide-valve engine operating non-condensing. Four-valve engines, unaflow, and compound engines operate more economically.

the inertia effect is most useful for quick changes in load and may be practically useless if the change is very gradual. For this reason, so-called inertia governors, Fig. 190, utilize centrifugal force, which varies as the square of the speed, and can be counted on to exert a certain force at a certain speed, as well as the inertia force, which depends upon the amount of the acceleration. In the history of steam engines and turbines, many designs of governors, differing in details, have used these principles.

Flyballs are commonly used in governing internal combustion engines and turbines. In the Otto type of engine, the action of the flyballs affects the throttle valve, opening it wider when the load increases. In Diesel engines, the amount of injected fuel is regulated by the flyballs.

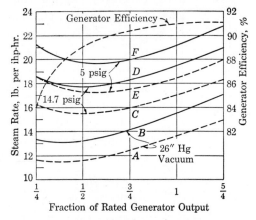

Fig. 192. *Steam Rates for Various Operating Conditions.* These curves are drawn from data furnished by the Skinner Engine Company for a unaflow engine supplied with steam at 175 psig. The rated size is 300-kw output of the direct connected generator. In each instance, the dotted curves are for steam superheated 100°F above saturation temperature, the solid curves for saturated steam at the throttle. The generator efficiency is shown dotted. The curves A and B are for an exhaust pressure of 4 in. Hg abs. (26 in. vacuum), C and D for atmospheric exhaust, E and F for an exhaust at 5 psig.

236. Performance of Steam Engines.

A set of typical performance curves is shown in Fig. 191. Naturally, the numerical values of the various items depicted by these curves vary widely. Some steam rate curves are nearly flat, an indication that the efficiency does not vary greatly with the load. Some steam rate curves move steeply upwards on each side of the point of minimum steam consumption. An engine with this type of curve would not be economical where the load was variable and where the engine seldom operated at the load corresponding to maximum efficiency. Recall in passing that the steam rate in itself is not a measure of the relative efficiency of two or more engines, unless the engines all operate on the same intake and exhaust pressures and temperatures. However, the brake steam-rate curve indicates the point of maximum efficiency as far as useful delivered work is concerned. The actual shaft work of a steam engine is often measured by a hydraulic brake or a prony brake (§ 116).

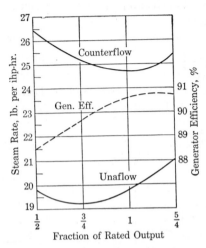

The variation of steam rates under varying operating conditions is shown in Fig. 192. The curves have been plotted for three exhaust pressures, and for each of these exhaust pressures, the steam rate is shown when the steam is initially saturated (solid curves) and when it is initially superheated 100° (dotted curves). A comparison of the economy of a counterflow and a unaflow engine is shown in Fig. 193.

Fig. 193. Comparison of Steam Rates. These curves are drawn from data furnished by the Skinner Engine Company for a throttle pressure of 125 psig, exhaust to atmosphere, and saturated steam at the throttle. Each engine drives a 250-kw generator, the rated load. Recall that the thermal efficiency is inversely proportional to the steam rate, that maximum thermal efficiency is at the point of minimum steam rate. Then observe that the counterflow has its maximum efficiency at about 100% of rated load. The unaflow engines often have their maximum efficiency between ½ and ¾ of rated load, but are more efficient at full load than a similar-size counterflow at full load.

237. Closure. Steam engines are not manufactured in the quantities that they formerly were. Internal combustion engines present formidable competition in the same horsepower range; also, small geared turbines have a lower initial cost, though perhaps a higher heat rate. However, situations still arise where the reciprocating steam engine is the most economical and most satisfactory answer to a particular problem. It should not be ignored where steam is needed for other purposes and where the power obtained would be more or less a by-product.

SELECTED REFERENCES

Croft, T., *Steam Engine Principles and Practice*, McGraw-Hill.
Skinner Engine Co., *The Universal Unaflow*.
Thurston, R. H., *A Manual of the Steam Engine*, John Wiley.

PROBLEMS

NOTE. *Sketch a Ts diagram wherever applicable and also an energy diagram.*

341. A double-acting, 12x15-in. steam engine receives steam at 205 psia and 400°F and exhausts at 5 psia. While it is running at 200 rpm, the following indicator cards are obtained: area head end, 2.17 sq. in.; area crank end, 2.34 sq. in.; length of each card, 3 in.; scale of indicator spring, 100 lb.; piston rod diameter, 1.5 in. During this test, it was found that the mechanical efficiency was 86% and the steam rate was 23 lb./bhp-hr. Calculate (a) the ihp of each cylinder end and the total, (b) the indicated work and thermal efficiency, (c) the rate of flow of steam (total).

Ans. (a) 127.7 ihp total, (b) 128.6 Btu/lb., 11.9%, (c) 2530 lb./hr.

342. An 11x13-in. steam engine receives steam at 135 psia and 400°F and exhausts to a condenser at 120°F. At a speed of 220 rpm, indicator cards are obtained as follows: area head end, 1.6 sq in.; area crank end, 1.61 sq. in.; length of each card, 3 in.; scale of indicator spring, 80 lb.; piston rod diameter, 2 in. A prony brake with a brake arm of 63 in. shows a net load of 232 lb. While these data were obtained, the steam rate was 20.5 lb./bhp-hr., average. Determine (a) the bhp, (b) the ihp, (c) the mechanical efficiency, (d) the brake work and thermal efficiency, (e) the indicated thermal efficiency, (f) the heat rate.

Ans. (a) 51, (b) 57.7, (c) 88.3%, (d) 10.95%, (e) 12.4%, (f) 23,250 Btu/bhp-hr.

343. An ideal incomplete expansion engine uses 3050 lb./hr. of steam and expands it from 370 psia and 520°F to release at 50 psia; exhaust is at 118°F. On the basis of 1 lb. of steam, determine (a) the work and power, (b) the steam rate, (c) the thermal efficiency, (d) the mep, (e) the enthalpy h_e of the ideal exhaust.

Ans. (a) 281.6 hp, (b) 10.82 lb. per hp-hr., (c) 20%, (d) 162.3 psi, (e) 1027.9 Btu/lb.

344. An incomplete expansion engine uses saturated steam at 85.3 psig, with release at 27.31 psia and exhaust at 215°F. Steam consumption is 1000 lb. per hr.; indicated engine efficiency, 72%; mechanical efficiency, 88%. (a) On the basis of 1 lb. of steam, compute the work, thermal efficiency, and quality of the exhaust of the ideal engine. Compute (b) the indicated work, thermal efficiency and ihp; (c) the brake work; (d) the approximate enthalpy of the actual exhaust; (e) the lost work with respect to W_I.

Ans. (a) 12.25%, 90.5%, (b) 8.82%, 36.4 ihp, (c) 81.4 Btu/lb., (d) 1094.8 Btu/lb., (e) 36 Btu/lb.

345. Steam at 160 psia and 500°F is supplied to an incomplete expansion engine for which release is at 30 psia and exhaust at 15 psia. During a full-load test, it was found that $w_b = 22.3$ lb. per bhp-hr. and $\eta_m = 80\%$. (a) For the corresponding ideal engine, calculate the work, steam rate, and efficiency. (b) For the actual engine, determine the brake thermal efficiency, indicated engine efficiency, indicated mep, and heat rate (on both bhp and ihp).

Ans. (a) 14.22 lb./hp-hr., 16.4%, (b) 10.45%, 79.6%, 57.9 psi, 24,400 Btu/bhp-hr., 19,500 Btu/ihp-hr.

346. The indicated steam rate of a compound steam engine is 15.8 lb./ihp-hr. while the rate of steam flow is 2760 lb./hr., and the actual enthalpy of the exhaust at 104°F is 1033.2 Btu/lb. The mechanical efficiency is 85%; the brake engine efficiency is 60%; the electric generator efficiency is 92%. (a) If the initial pressure is 150 psia, what is the initial state of the steam? Compute (b) the brake and combined thermal efficiencies, (c) the work and efficiency of the corresponding ideal engine, (d) the output of the generator (kw).

Ans. (b) 12.2%, 11.2%, (c) 228.3 Btu/lb., 20.35%, (d) 102 kw.

347–350. These numbers may be used for other problems.

15

THE REVERSED CYCLE

238. Introduction. The "reversed" thermodynamic cycle, arranged to "pump" heat from one temperature to a higher temperature, serves many useful purposes in a technological age. In addition to its well-known uses in preserving foods, in manufacturing ice, and in conditioning air for summer comfort, the refrigeration cycle has many other industrial applications, as in making "cold rubber" (to improve wearing quality), in oil refinery processes, in the treatment of steel, and in the manufacture of chemicals. The reversed cycle is also used for heating buildings, and in this application it is popularly called a *heat pump*. In a technical sense, *heat pump* is a general name for all reversed cycles.

239. The Reversed Carnot Cycle. At the outset, since the Carnot cycle is quite revealing in a general way, we should review the material of § 137 and refresh ourselves on the principles of the reversed cycle. First, suppose that the cycle is to be used for refrigeration. In Fig. 194, the refrigerant,

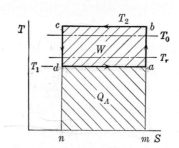

Fig. 194. Reversed Carnot
Cycle, Refrigeration.

which is the system, is isentropically compressed ab from a cold temperature T_1 to a temperature T_2 above that of some naturally available heat sink T_o. The system then discharges heat at some constant temperature T_2 along bc. At some state c, an isentropic expansion cd lowers the temperature of the refrigerant to T_1, which is below the temperature of the body to be cooled, say a refrigerator at T_r, so that now heat may flow from the refrigerator to the refrigerant, thus cooling the refrigerator. The substance receives heat along the path *da*, whence the cycle repeats. As described, the cycle is internally reversible. It approaches external reversibility and a true Carnot cycle as the temperature differences $T_2 - T_o$ and $T_r - T_1$ approach zero.

If the reversed cycle is used for heating, Fig. 195, the working substance undergoes the same sequence of operations, the only change being in the temperatures. For heating, the temperature T_2 must be above the room temperature T_r so that heat will flow from the refrigerant to the room, heat-

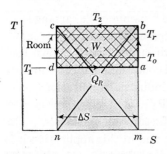

Fig. 195, Carnot Cycle for Heating.

ing it. Also, the source of heat is now some naturally available heat reservoir (the air, a well, or lake, etc.) at temperature T_o which is higher than the temperature T_1 after the refrigerant has had its isentropic expansion *cd*. Heat thus flows from this reservoir into the system.

In each of these systems, the input is the work W, represented by the rectangular area *abcd*;

$$(a) \qquad W = (T_2 - T_1)\Delta S \text{ Btu,}$$

as a positive number, where $\Delta S = S_a - S_d = S_b - S_c$. We know that work done *on* the system is conventionally given a negative sign. However, in the applications of the reversed cycles, it is convenient to ignore the negative sign because of its nuisance aspect. The output of the refrigeration cycle is refrigeration, which is the heat added to the system, represented by the area *ndam*, Fig. 194;

$$(b) \qquad Q_A = T_1(S_a - S_d) = T_1\Delta S \text{ Btu.}$$

The output of the heating cycle is the heat delivered to the space to be heated, which is heat rejected, represented by the area *mbcn*, Fig. 195;

$$(c) \qquad Q_R = T_2(S_b - S_c) = T_2\Delta S \text{ Btu,}$$

as a positive number. By comparing Figs. 194 and 195, we see that the heats Q_A and Q_R are correctly expressed by (b) and (c) in either case. The coefficients of performance COP, § 137, are (output/input)

$$(60) \quad \gamma_r = \frac{\text{Refrigeration}}{\text{Work}} = \frac{Q_A}{W} \quad \text{and} \quad \gamma_h = \frac{\text{Heating effect}}{\text{Work}} = \frac{Q_R}{W},$$

[USED FOR COOLING]   [WARMING]

in general terms. For the Carnot cycle, the COP's are, from (a), (b), and (c),

$$(d) \quad \gamma_r = \frac{Q_A}{W} = \frac{T_1}{T_2 - T_1} \quad \text{and} \quad \gamma_h = \frac{Q_R}{W} = \frac{T_2}{T_2 - T_1},$$

[COOLING]   [WARMING]

applicable to the *Carnot or other reversible cycle only*. The coefficient of performance as given by (**d**) is the highest possible for all cycles operating between the temperatures T_1 and T_2. Other *ideal* cycles which we shall study will have a lower COP.

240. Conclusions from the Carnot Cycle. There are certain conclusions of general validity which can be drawn from the Carnot cycle.

1. It is desirable that the work W to activate the cycle be a minimum, since it comes from an outside source and must be paid for.

2. The work will be reduced as the temperature T_2 is lowered. (a) In a refrigerating cycle, Fig. 194, the lowest temperature T_o that is attainable by a natural coolant, such as the atmosphere or a lake, is the most economical. There is thus a natural lower limit for T_2 set by T_o; in practice, T_2 is some 5–20°F greater than T_o. (b) In a warming cycle, Fig. 195, T_2 must be some 10–20°F or more above the room temperature. Thus, if it is desired to keep a room at 70°F, the refrigerant must be at, say, 90°F or more. Smaller temperature differences than mentioned could be used, but as the temperature difference decreases, the surface area needed in the heat exchanger increases in order to maintain the same rate of heat flow, thereby increasing the cost of the heat exchanger. In practice, it is a matter of getting an economical balance.

3. The work will be reduced as the temperature T_1 is increased. (a) In a refrigerating cycle, Fig. 194, it is therefore economical of work to carry on the desired refrigeration at as high a temperature as practicable. To freeze water, temperatures below 32°F are essential; but to cool air for comfort air conditioning, much higher temperatures may be used. (b) In a warming cycle, Fig. 195, the temperature T_1 must be below some naturally available temperature, and there is nothing which can be done about this except to explore the possibilities of finding bodies which remain relatively warm during the winter. The presence of warm springs is very helpful. Deep wells or the earth itself may provide natural sources of heat at temperatures higher than winter atmospheric temperatures.

4. For particular temperature limits, the heat exchanges should take place at constant temperature for the most effective use of the work. In the case of vapor refrigerants, § 242, the refrigerant will be at a constant temperature during much of the heat transfer process; but this is not true when a gas is the refrigerant.

241. Definitions and Ratings. The Btu is too small a unit to be convenient in rating commercial refrigerating plants. The larger unit used in refrigerating practice is defined as the number of Btu required to freeze 1 ton of water at 32°F into ice at 32°F. The heat of fusion of ice is very nearly 144 Btu/lb.; therefore, to freeze 2000 lb., there must be abstracted (2000)(144) = 288,000 Btu. This unit, precisely 288,000 Btu, is the definition of a **standard ton** of refrigeration.

To specify *capacity*, we must know how long it takes to perform a particular amount of refrigeration. One **standard commercial ton** of refrigeration is defined as 288,000 Btu absorbed at a uniform rate during 24 hours. When the engineer speaks of a *ton* of refrigeration, he generally means a standard commercial ton. Thus, on hourly and minute bases, a ton of refrigeration is

(e) $$\frac{288,000}{24} = 12,000 \text{ Btu/hr.} \quad \text{and} \quad \frac{12,000}{60} = 200 \text{ Btu/min.}$$

To say that a plant is a 10-ton plant is the same thing as saying that the capacity of the plant is (10)(200) = 2000 Btu/min. of refrigeration.

A common method of expressing the actual efficiency of a compression system is to give the horsepower used per commercial ton of refrigeration. This number, which is not a dimensionless number, is obtained of course by testing the actual machine. A relation between the horsepower per ton and the coefficient of performance is easily obtained from the definition of the coefficient of performance. Let the refrigeration be given as N tons $= 200N$ Btu/min. Let the horsepower required for this N tons of refrigeration be represented by hp; then, the corresponding work is $42.4hp$ Btu/min. Thus, the coefficient of performance for refrigeration is

(f) $$\gamma = \frac{\text{Refrigeration}}{\text{Work}} = \frac{200N}{42.4hp},$$

from which $W = (\text{refrigeration})/\gamma$; and the horsepower per ton of refrigeration is

(g) $$\frac{hp}{N} = \frac{200}{42.4\gamma} = \frac{4.72}{\gamma}.$$

This expression may be used for either actual or ideal cycles.

242. Vapor Compression System. The most common method of securing refrigeration is by a vapor compression system, so-called because the working substance is a vapor and is carried from the low-temperature region to the high-temperature region by compressing it. The devices necessary to carry out the vapor cycle are simple and are represented diagrammatically in Fig. 196, which should be compared with Fig. 197. In the ideal case, all flow is of course without friction, except that through the expansion valve, and all processes except those in the condenser and cold room are adiabatic. Figure 198 shows the reversed idealized vapor cycle on the Ts plane with

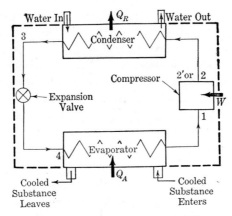

Fig. 196.　Compression System for Vapors.

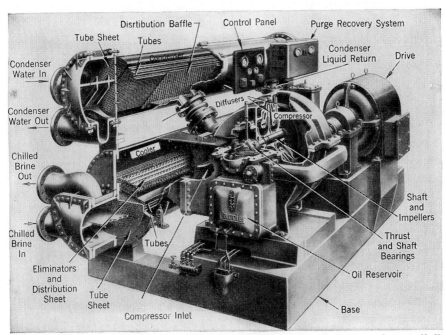

Fig. 197.　Refrigerating Unit. This illustration shows a compact design of a unit, in which the refrigerant is Carrene. Observe the use of a centrifugal compressor, which is partly sectioned. The condenser water heats up as it passes through the condenser and it may be handled as is circulating water for a steam condenser. The chilled brine is led to the point where a cooling effect is desired and is returned to the cooler (evaporator) after it has picked up some heat.

numbers corresponding to those on Fig. 196.   The compressor may be either
a centrifugal or a reciprocating machine.   The compression process is
actually nearly adiabatic 1-2′, Fig. 198, and ideally isentropic 1-2, $s_1 = s_2$.
At discharge from the compressor, the *saturation* temperature t_f corresponding to the pressure p_2 *must be* above the temperature of the available heat
sink, in order that *the substance may reject heat to a naturally available
receiver of heat.*   In commercial installations, the heat rejected during condensation is carried away by circulating water, as in a condenser; but in the
domestic refrigerator, circulating air absorbs the rejected heat Q_R.   The
condenser removes the superheat, if any (from state 2, Fig. 198), the latent
heat of evaporation, and it generally subcools the liquid a small amount, say

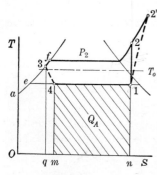

from f to 3, Fig. 198.   The *expansion valve,* or
throttling valve, is used to regulate, either
manually or automatically, the flow or refrigerant.   The throttling process 3-4, $h_3 = h_4$,
results in a very wet mixture at 4, Fig. 198.
In the domestic refrigerator, Fig. 200, the evaporator is located in the space to be cooled, which
might in general be called, the cold room.   On
the other hand, in making ice, the common
practice is first to cool brine by direct contact
with the evaporator and then to circulate the
brine around cans containing the water to be

Fig. 198.   Refrigeration Cycle.

frozen into ice.   Similarly, in some air-conditioning systems, water is refrigerated first and then the cold water is used to cool the air.   In any case,
the refrigerant receives heat Q_A along the process 4-1, Fig. 198, and this heat
is the refrigeration.

To get the work of the compressor, apply the energy equation with
$\Delta K = 0$ and $Q = 0$ (or balance the energy diagram of Fig. 196), and find

(h) $W = h_2 - h_1$ or $W = h_{2'} - h_1$ Btu/lb.
                           [ISENTROPIC]   [IRREVERSIBLE, $Q = 0$]

as a positive number.   The cold room, or *evaporator* as it is generally called
in a vapor system, is a typical heat exchanger, § 154; so we have ($h_3 = h_4$)

(i) $Q_A = h_1 - h_4 = h_1 - h_3$ Btu/lb.,

which is the refrigeration of this ideal cycle.   We have used $h_3 = h_4$ because
h_3 is found directly from vapor tables corresponding to the temperature t_3.
Since the *condenser* is another heat exchanger, we find for the ideal cycle

(j) $Q_R = h_2 - h_3$ Btu/lb.

as a positive number. We should note that equation (**j**) gives the heating effect in a warming cycle. The ideal coefficient of performance (COP) for refrigeration is

(**k**) $CO_{Ref} = \gamma = \dfrac{\text{Refrigeration}}{\text{Work}} = \dfrac{h_1 - h_4}{h_2 - h_1} = \dfrac{h_1 - h_3}{h_2 - h_1}.$

243. Displacement of the Compressor. For a particular refrigerating capacity, the size of a reciprocating compressor depends upon the number of pounds of refrigerant that must be circulated per unit of time to obtain the desired refrigerating effect and upon the specific volume of the substance at the intake pressure of the compressor. Suppose the plant is to have a capacity of N tons; then the rate of refrigeration is $200N$ Btu/min. Now if the refrigeration per pound of refrigerant is $h_1 - h_4$ Btu, Fig. 198, then the mass of refrigerant circulated is

(**l**) $$w = \frac{\text{Btu/min.}}{\text{Btu/lb.}} = \frac{200N}{h_1 - h_4} \text{ lb./min.}$$

The condition of the refrigerant at 1, Fig. 198, is known or assumed, so that the specific volume v_1 may be determined from refrigerant tables. Evidently $(w \text{ lb./min.})(v_1 \text{ cu. ft./lb.})$ is the needed displacement volume V_D cfm for 100% volumetric efficiency. Review § 79 again. If the volumetric efficiency is η_v, we have

(**m**) $$V_D = \frac{wv_1}{\eta_v} = \frac{v_1}{\eta_v}\left(\frac{200N}{h_1 - h_4}\right) \text{ cfm.}$$

Practical values of the volumetric efficiency should usually fall within the range 65–85%. The factors affecting volumetric efficiency in vapor compressors are much the same as those discussed in § 79. Also, the types of rotary compressors used are as described in § 91. Most of the discussion of Chapter 6 applies to refrigerant compressors, except as an ideal gas is postulated.

244. Example. An ammonia compressor receives wet vapor at 10°F and compresses it to a saturated state at 190 psia. The temperature at the expansion valve is 85°F. The compressor is double acting, 12x14 in., it runs at 200 rpm, and its volumetric efficiency at normal operating conditions is 78%. Let the compression efficiency be $\eta_c = W/W' = 80\%$. For the ideal cycle, determine (a) the coefficient of performance γ, (b) the tons of refrigeration N, and (c) the horsepower per ton. On the basis of the actual fluid work, determine (d) γ', (e) N', (f) hp/N (actual), and (g) the temperature at $2'$, Fig. 199, if the actual compression is adiabatic.

SOLUTION.   From the NH_3 tables of the U. S. Bureau of Standards (see Tables XI and XII, Appendix, and the footnote on p. 183), we find the following for state 1 at 10°F, state 2 at 190 psia, and state 3 at 85°F:

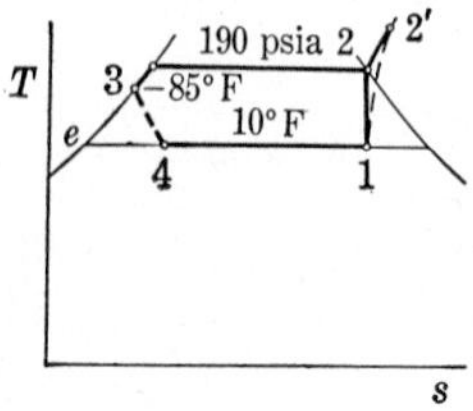

Fig. 199.

$$h_{f1} = 53.8 \qquad s_{g1} = 1.3157 \qquad h_{g2} = h_2 = 632.4$$
$$h_{fg1} = 561.1 \qquad v_{f1} = 0.02446 \qquad s_{g2} = s_2 = 1.1802$$
$$s_{f1} = 0.1208 \qquad v_{g1} = 7.304 \qquad h_3 = h_4 = 137.8$$

From $s_1 = s_2$, we get

$$1.1802 = 0.1208 + 1.1949x_1, \qquad \text{or} \qquad x_1 = 88.7\%.$$
$$h_1 = 53.8 + (0.887)(561.1) = 551.5 \text{ Btu/lb.}$$
$$v_1 = 0.0244 + (0.887)(7.28) = 6.48 \text{ cu. ft./lb.}$$

(a) For $W = h_2 - h_1 = 632.4 - 551.5 = 80.9$ Btu/lb. and the refrigeration $Q_A = h_1 - h_4 = 551.5 - 137.8 = 413.7$ Btu/lb., we have

$$\gamma = \frac{Q_A}{W} = \frac{413.7}{80.9} = 5.11.$$

(b) The displacement in cfm, for $2n$ diagrams per minute in a double-acting compressor, is

$$V_D = \frac{\pi D^2}{4} L(2n) = \frac{\pi(144)(14)(2 \times 200)}{(4)(1728)} = 366 \text{ cfm.}$$

For $\eta_v = 78\%$, the volume V_1' "drawn in" per minute is $V_1' = (0.78)(366)$ cfm, and for $v_1 = 6.48$ cu. ft./lb., the mass of refrigerant circulated per minute is

$$w = \frac{V_1'}{v_1} = \frac{(0.78)(366)}{6.48} = 44.1 \text{ lb./min.}$$

Thus the total refrigeration is $(44.1)(413.7)$ Btu/min.   Dividing this value by 200 Btu/min-ton gives

$$N = \frac{(44.1)(413.7)}{200} = 91.2 \text{ tons.}$$

(c) The horsepower for 44.1 lb./min. of refrigerant is

$$hp = \frac{(44.1)(80.9)}{42.4} = 84.2 \text{ hp}$$

and the horsepower per ton is $84.2/91.2 = 0.942$.

(d) The actual work of the fluid is $W' = W/\eta = 80.9/0.80 = 101.1$ Btu/lb. and for other conditions the same,

$$\gamma' = \frac{Q_A}{W'} = \frac{413.7}{101.1} = 4.08.$$

(e) For the amount of refrigerant circulated remaining the same as in the ideal cycle (the horsepower of the motor must be greater than before), the tons of refrigerant are the same as before, 91.2 tons.

(f) The actual fluid horsepower is the ideal hp divided by the compression efficiency, or $hp' = 84.2/0.80 = 105$ hp; thus

$$\frac{hp'}{N} = \frac{105}{91.2} = 1.152 \text{ hp/ton.}$$

Including mechanical and other losses, the actual bhp per ton will be somewhat greater than this value.

(g) For an adiabatic steady flow compression 1-2', the work as a positive number is $h_{2'} - h_1 = (h_2 - h_1)_s/0.80$, or

$$h_{2'} = h_1 + \frac{h_2 - h_1}{0.80} = 551.5 + \frac{80.9}{0.80} = 652.6 \text{ Btu/lb.}$$

In the complete tables at 190 psia and $h = 652.6$, we find the temperature at 2' as $t_{2'} = 122.4°\text{F}.$

245. Refrigerants. Table IV shows a comparison of some characteristics of popular refrigerants. Some of the desirable qualities of a refrigerant are:

1. Refrigerants are preferably nontoxic, so that in case of leakage no one is in danger of injury. This attribute is of paramount importance in air-conditioning systems and home refrigerators, for example, but toxic refrigerants are tolerable in commercial installations where reasonable precautions are taken. The Carrenes, Freons (trade names), and carbon dioxide are not toxic, but the others in Table IV are, in more or less degree. Methyl chloride is not only toxic but is practically odorless; where this refrigerant is used, a warning agent (acrolein) which is irritating to the eyes and nose should be added.

2. Refrigerants should be economical, both in initial cost and in mainte. nance. Maintenance problems include: controlling leakage (there is less trouble with leakage of large molecules than of small ones); providing adequate lubrication (the refrigerant should not react with the oil to destroy its lubricating qualities); and avoiding corrosion (the refrigerant should not corrode the materials which it contacts). Also the refrigerant should be readily available for recharging the system when necessary.

3. Refrigerants should be nonflammable. A number of hydrocarbons have been and are used as refrigerants, examples of which in Table IV are butane and propane. These and others (ammonia, methyl chloride, etc.) constitute a fire and explosion hazard. The other refrigerants in Table IV are nonflammable.

4. Refrigerants should have a high latent heat at the evaporator temperature (see Fig. 108, p. 184) and a low specific volume. The type and size of compressor are functions of these physical traits. If the latent heat is high (see NH_3, Table IV), much refrigeration is done by each pound of substance circulated; if in addition the specific volume is low, the volume of substance to be circulated and therefore the size of compressor and passage-

ways are small. Notice that when the ideal displacement volume V_D is small, reciprocating compressors are feasible; when V_D is large (Carrene 1, $F11$, and $F113$), centrifugal compressors (which can be run at high speed) become necessary. If, for example, Carrene 1 were compressed in a reciprocating machine, the compressor would have to be $74.5/3.44 = 21.6$ times larger than a NH_3 compressor (same speed) for the same refrigerating capacity.

Table IV. *CHARACTERISTICS OF REFRIGERANTS*

The pressures (Pres.) are saturation pressures in psia; Q_A, w, and V_D correspond to the case where the fluid leaves the evaporator as saturated vapor (state 1, Fig. 199 is on the saturated vapor line) and for the liquid entering the throttling valve at 86°F, which is a typical condenser temperature. The displacement is for 100% volumetric efficiency; the condenser and evaporator temperatures are 86°F and 5°F, respectively. Under "Type of Compressor": Rec. = reciprocating; Rot. = rotary (Fig. 51); Cen. = centrifugal.

NOTES: (a) An azeotropic mixture of Freon 12 and $C_2H_4F_2$. (b) Dichloromethane; also called methylene chloride. (c) Trichloromonofluoromethane. (d) Dichlorodifluoromethane. (e) Monochlorodifluoromethane. (f) Trichlorotrifluoroethane. (g) Dichlorotetrafluoroethane.

	Formula	Pres. at 5°F	Pres. at 86°F	Q_A Btu/lb.	w lb./min-ton	V_D cfm/ton	Type of Compressor
Ammonia	NH_3	34.3	169.2	474.4	0.42	3.44	Rec.
Butane	C_4H_{10}	8.2	41.6	123.5	1.62	16.2	Rec., Rot.
Carbon dioxide	CO_2	332.2	1045.7	56.7	3.53	0.94	Recip.
Carrene 1 (b)	CH_2Cl_2	1.16	10.6	134.1	1.49	74.5	Rot., Cen.
Carrene 7 (a)	(a)	31.1	128.1	59.8	3.34	6.2	Rec., Rot.
Freon 11 (c)	CCl_3F	2.93	18.3	67.5	2.96	36.4	Rot., Cen.
Freon 12 (d)	CCl_2F_2	26.5	107.9	51.1	3.92	5.8	Rec., Rot.
Freon 22 (e)	$CHClF_2$	43.0	174.5	69.3	2.89	3.59	Rec.
Freon 113 (f)	$C_2Cl_3F_3$	0.98	7.9	53.67	3.72	100.5	Cen.
Freon 114 (g)	$C_2Cl_2F_4$	6.8	36.7	43.1	4.64	19.6	Rot.
Methyl chloride	CH_3Cl	21.2	94.7	150.3	1.33	5.95	Rec., Rot.
Sulfur dioxide	SO_2	11.8	66.4	141.4	1.41	9.08	Rec., Rot.
Propane	C_3H_8	41.9	156.2	123	1.63	4.1	Rec.

5. Refrigerants should have low saturation pressures at normal operating temperatures. The cost of design, manufacture, and operation is involved. High pressures, as in the case of CO_2, mean heavy parts and thick-walled pipes. (A compensating factor in the case of CO_2 is the small V_D required per ton of refrigeration.) Also, it is preferable that the sat-

uration pressure at the evaporator temperature be slightly above atmospheric pressure, in order to be sure of no leakage of air into the system. Carrene 1 and Freon 113 have saturation pressures below atmospheric even at the *condenser* temperature of 86°F. Since an evaporator temperature of 5°F is relatively low for many purposes of refrigeration, a higher evaporator temperature may be permissible and may result in some of the refrigerants being at or above atmospheric pressure in the evaporator; for example, butane is approximately at atmospheric pressure when the saturation temperature is at 30°F, Freon 114 at 39°F, and sulfur dioxide at 14°F. Also important is a low *pressure ratio* p_2/p_1, because of the effect of this ratio on the work necessary for compression.

6. While the foregoing attributes are perhaps the most significant, there are miscellaneous other characteristics which are desirable: good thermal conductivity for rapid heat transfer, wetting ability, inertness (the refrigerant should not react in any way with the materials it touches), stability (the refrigerant should not break down into different matter of smaller molecules), low viscosity (for ease of movement), high critical temperature, and a high dielectric strength (in hermetically sealed units where the refrigerant contacts the motors). Also, it stands to reason that the refrigerant should not solidify at any temperature in its cycle.

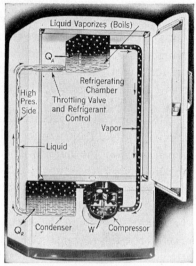

Courtesy Frigidaire Division, General Motors

Fig. 200. Domestic Refrigerator. The system is the working substance, Freon 12; Q_A comes from inside box; Q_R is delivered to the surroundings; W is the fluid work, the electrical energy to drive the rotary compressor minus the mechanical and electrical losses. Motors for household units are usually about $\frac{1}{6}$ to $\frac{1}{4}$ hp; at 1750 rpm.

The traditional refrigerants are still widely used: *ammonia* is used in industrial and commercial refrigeration; carbon dioxide, because of its low critical temperature at 87.8°F, is used principally in the northern latitudes and for low temperature refrigeration (solid CO_2, known as dry ice, is widely used for cooling purposes); sulfur dioxide is extensively used in industrial applications because of its advantageous thermodynamic traits, but it is toxic.

The "newer" refrigerants, for example, the Freons, often designated by the letter F and a number, as $F12$, appeared when physical chemists found that chlorine or fluorine atoms could be substituted for hydrogen atoms in certain hydrocarbon molecules (the methane and ethane series). When substances evolved which were neither flammable nor toxic and had saturation temperatures and pressures suitable for refrigerants, they were found to be more desirable in many situations than the traditional refrigerants. They are extensively used and can be manufactured with nearly any desired property, though not necessarily with all the properties desired. For household refrigerators, Fig. 200, and air conditioning, $F11$, $F12$, $F114$, and Carrene 7 are commonly used.

A significant commercial advantage of the line of newer refrigerants is that a manufacturer may use the same compressor for different capacities by changing the refrigerant and installing a different size of motor. For example, for a particular displacement, a greater refrigerating effect is obtained from $F22$ than from $F12$; greater power is also required for the $F22$.

246. Absorption Systems of Refrigeration. There are several systems of refrigeration known under the general heading of *absorption systems*. The reason for the name will be made clear by describing the operation. An ammonia-water system, in which the refrigerant is *ammonia*, is shown diagrammatically in Fig. 201, and a system using a lithium-bromide solution in water, with water as the refrigerant, is outlined in Fig. 202. In the NH_3-H_2O system, the strength of the solution is in terms of the refrigerant NH_3; the solvent is the water. In the lithium-bromide system, the strength of the solution is in terms of the solvent. Thus, a strong salt solution is a good solvent for the refrigerant H_2O; a weak NH_3 solution is a good solvent for the refrigerant NH_3. This contrary use of the words *strong* and *weak* with respect to the refrigerant is confusing unless you think carefully. It will be worth while to compare the two systems. First, starting with Fig. 201 and the condenser at A, NH_3 vapor (refrigerant) is condensed to liquid, throttled through an expansion valve BC, and it does refrigeration (receives heat during its evaporation) in the evaporator. After leaving the evaporator (or cold room), the refrigerant (NH_3 in this one) enters an **absorber,** which contains a substance that will absorb the refrigerant. In this case, the absorbent is water and the NH_3 goes into solution. Strong solutions of ammonia, called **strong liquid** (or *liquor*), being lighter, rise to the top of the absorber. Thus the strong liquid which has little capacity left for absorbing NH_3 is pumped to the generator where it is heated. The heating causes evaporation, and more NH_3 evaporates than H_2O, because hot H_2O can contain less NH_3 in solution than cold H_2O. For this reason, it is desirable to keep the absorber cool. The absorption process releases heat (it is exothermic and the latent heat of the NH_3 must be carried away), which accounts for the circulation of cooling water indicated in Fig. 201. That part of the solution which has relatively little NH_3 in it is called a *weak liquid;* it tends toward the bottom of the absorber. Returning to the generator, we note that after NH_3 has been evaporated from solution, the remaining liquid is a *weak liquid* and can be returned to the absorber for further duty. However, it is also hot, so it is only natural that the return be through the heat exchanger. The heat from the weak liquid passes to the strong liquid, which has to be heated in the generator anyway. The heat transferred in the exchanger is just so much steam saved in the regenerator, besides reducing the rejected heat in the absorber. The purpose of the

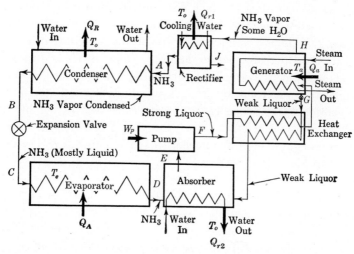

Fig. 201. *Ammonia-Water Absorption System of Refrigeration.* **As the reader knows, each piece of apparatus may be analyzed separately as a steady flow device.**

rectifier, Fig. 201, is to cool the vapors from the generator enough to condense most of the H_2O, so that mostly vaporous NH_3 enters the condenser and starts the cycle over. The condensate in the rectifier, a strong solution, 'is returned to the generator. In practice, the rectifier is likely to be a part of the condenser, and the same cooling water picks up heat Q_R and Q_{r1}, Fig. 201. The heat Q_{r2} is small compared to Q_a, Q_R, and Q_A.

The coefficient of performance as defined in (a) does not apply to these cycles, because the significant energy supplied to the cycle to keep it going is Q_a in the generator. Thus a suitable performance factor for such cycles is the Btu of refrigeration (output) divided by the heat transferred in the generator (input); or if the energy to drive the pumps is accounted for, the denominator is increased by the amount of these works; that is, the performance factor η_p is, Fig. 201,

(n)
$$\eta_p = \frac{Q_A}{Q_a} \quad \text{or} \quad \eta_p = \frac{Q_A}{Q_a + \Sigma W},$$

where ΣW may include the pump works of one or more of the pumps, according to the desired accuracy. Sometimes in practice, performance factors are expressed in pounds of steam supplied to the system per ton of refrigeration.*

There is a basic objection to using ammonia in an air conditioning machine because it is toxic. Moreover, the ammonia absorption system is expensive in initial cost, and in operating cost unless very low-cost heat is available for the generator. The low efficiency of the NH_3-H_2O system is due in large part to concomitant and unavoidable evaporation in the generator of the absorbent H_2O which does no refrigeration. Thus, if a solid absorbent, which would not evaporate, were used, a higher efficiency could be expected. Perhaps you have observed during humid weather that table salt, sodium chloride, becomes so damp it cannot be shaken from the dispenser. This happens because sodium chloride is a good absorber of the H_2O and has taken it from the air. Thus, table salt and H_2O could be used in an absorption refrigerating system as described below for a different salt, lithium bromide (and H_2O). Before studying Fig. 202, you should fix in mind the various fluid circuits in order to avoid confusion. The numbered points refer to Fig. 202.

1. *The steam circuit to the generator.* Low pressure steam (say, 12 psig) passes through the generator tubes (14, Fig. 202) and the heat flow evaporates the refrigerant (water) in the generator, just as in Fig. 201. The heat is Q_a.

2. *Condenser-water circuit.* This water passes first through the absorber tubes 21 (compare with Fig. 201), picking up the heat from the process of absorption (the latent heat of H_2O plus that evolved by the exothermic absorption), then it goes through the condenser tubes, 22, Fig. 202, where it causes the vapor from the evaporator to condense; this is rejected heat, Q_R. This condenser water usually completes its circuit through a cooling tower (§ 264), returning to this unit after having been recooled by atmospheric air.

3. *The refrigerating circuit*, consisting of the solution (absorbent) and the refrigerant (water). The vapor from the evaporation in the generator is condensed in the condenser where the temperature may perhaps be 95°F (0.81 psia) with 85°F cooling water. This condensate (refrigerant) moves to the evaporator via connection 24, Fig. 202, through a throttling valve (or a loop) which maintains the pressure differential between the condenser vessel and the evaporator vessel; $h_{23} = h_5$. The evaporator and the absorber are intimately connected (in the same vessel in Fig. 202), so that the solution can absorb the H_2O which "flashes" into steam as it enters the

---

* For properties of NH_3-H_2O solutions, see *Refrigerating Data Book*, by the Am. Soc. of Refrig. Eng.

evaporator at 5.   To hasten the absorption process, a pump 18 picks up
solution from the bottom of the absorber, via 17, and discharges it in a spray
to the absorber through nozzles 19.   That part of the H_2O entering the
evaporator at 5 which does not evaporate is cooled because it is the source
of energy needed to evaporate the fraction which "flashes" into steam;

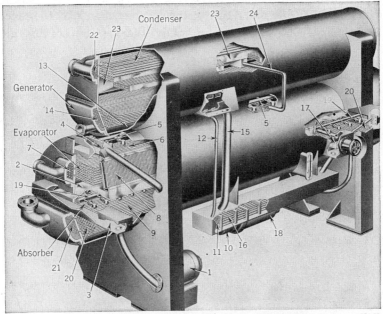

Courtesy Carrier Corp., Syracuse, N. Y.

Fig. 202. · *Absorption Refrigeration with Salt Solution.*   The salt is lithium
bromide.   The evaporator pump 1 picks up primary water from pan 2,
discharges it (via 3) through the header and spray nozzles 5.   The cold
water passing over tubes 6 receives heat from the chilled water in the tubes.
The vapor formed at 5 passes through eliminators 8, thence to be absorbed
by the solution 9.   A solution pump 10 moves weak solution from the bottom
of absorber, through the heat exchanger tubes 11 to the generator 13 (via 12).
Steam in the generator tubes 14 concentrates the solution by evaporating
some water.   The strong solution returns to the absorber via 15, the heat
exchanger 16, and the valve 17.   Another solution pump 18 takes strong
solution from the bottom of the absorber to the header 19, where it is
sprayed in order to expose more surface for the absorption of steam.   This
spray passes over the tube bundle 20, through which condenser water circulates to pick up the heat that is a consequence of the absorption.

$\Delta h = 0$.   The temperature of this cooled water depends upon the temperature maintained in the evaporator, say 40°F (or about 0.122 psia).   There
must be enough brine solution to absorb the steam at the rate at which it
forms while the H_2O flows into the evaporator.   The 40°F water may now
be used for refrigeration in systems where such a temperature is appropriate,
as in an air conditioning system.

4. *The chilled-water circuit.* The cold water produced in the evaporator could be passed through coils about which air could be circulated for cooling. However, the usual arrangement is to use this primary cold water to produce so-called *chilled water.* The chilled water passes through tubes 7, Fig. 202, which are steadily sprayed at 5 with primary cold water. By way of illustration, the chilled water may leave the evaporator at 45°F, pick up its heat (refrigerating load), and return to the evaporator at 55°F, to be recooled by the primary cold water. Now study the caption to Fig. 202.

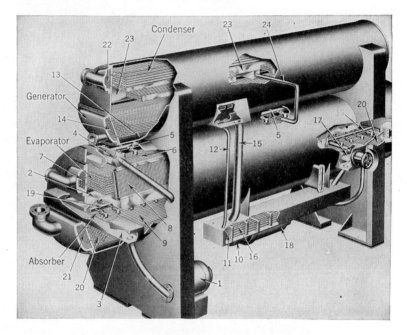

Fig. 202.   Repeated.

There are other substances used in absorption systems; examples are methylene chloride as the refrigerant and dimethyl ether of tetraethylene glycol as the absorbent; water as the refrigerant and lithium-chloride brine as the absorbent.

247. Reversed Cycle for Heating. When the reversed cycle is used for heating, it is popularly called a *heat pump.* As usual, the Carnot cycle furnishes a simple means of understanding the flow of energy in a vapor compression system and provides the highest conceivable standard of performance, § 239. A heat pump makes it possible to use work for heating without being too lavish with available energy. If the COP is 4, it means that four times the work input to the system is delivered for heating. For example, if 10 kw are used in a resistance coil for heating, the heat obtained is (10)(3412) = 34,120 Btu/hr.; if used in a heat pump with a COP of 4, the heat obtained is (4)(34,120) = 136,480 Btu/hr.

There are several commercial machines available which are designed to operate as air conditioners in both summer and winter—cooling the inside air during the summer and heating it during the winter, by merely throwing a switch. See Fig. 203. During the cooling season, the outside coil *B* acts as the condenser, receiving the discharge from the compressor. The coil *A* is the evaporator and it cools the air from the house which flows over it. For heating, the coils *A* and *B* swap functions; the coil *A* becomes the

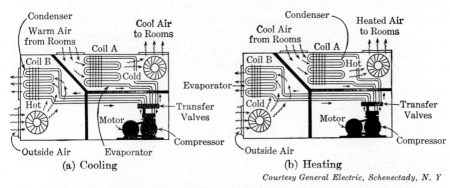

Fig. 203.   *Heat Pump for Heating and Cooling.*

condenser, adding heat to the house via air which circulates over it; the coil *B* is the evaporator, picking up heat from the outside.

It is not often that the reversed-cycle machine is an economical means of heating alone; but where refrigeration is needed for other purposes, such as air conditioning, it will be easier to justify its use. Favorable factors include: low rates of electricity, a mild climate, the availability of relatively warm water as a source of heat in winter, and in a negative way, expensive heating fuels. The unit operates more efficiently if the summer condenser, coil *B*, is cooled by water. In small installations, the extra cost of water may more than offset the loss of efficiency which goes along with air cooling the condenser.

248. Closure. As usual in chapters dealing with a specialty, only the basic elements of refrigeration are given here. For more detail, one must refer to books and current literature devoted to the subject.

Have you observed the difference between the implications of the words *reversed cycle* and *reversible cycle*? Any cycle in which the temperature at which heat is received is lower than the temperature at which heat is discharged is a reversed cycle. A reversible cycle is one which is reversible externally and internally and has the highest conceivable COP (and efficiency) for the stated temperature limits.   Reread §§ 137 and 138.

SELECTED REFERENCES

Am. Soc. of Refrig. Eng., *Refrigerating Data Book*.
Barger and Rohsenow, *A comparison of refrigerants when used in vapor compression cycles over an extended temperature range*, ASME paper, 56-SA-6.
Jennings and Lewis, *Air Conditioning and Refrigeration*, International Textbook.
Jordan and Priester, *Refrigeration and Air Conditioning*, Prentice-Hall.
Macintire and Hutchinson, *Refrigeration Engineering*, John Wiley.
Moyer and Fittz, *Refrigeration*, McGraw-Hill.
Penrod, E. B., *A review of some heat pump installations*, Mech. Eng., Vol. 69, p. 639.
Raber and Hutchinson, *Refrigeration and Air Conditioning Engineering*, John Wiley.
Sparks, N. R., *Theory of Mechanical Refrigeration*, McGraw-Hill.
Stevens, L. R., Jr., *A systematic study of air cycles for aircraft-cooling applications*, ASME paper, 56-SA-11.
Woolrich and Bartlett, *Handbook of Refrigerating Engineering*, Van Nostrand.

PROBLEMS

351. An ideal refrigeration cycle operates on NH$_3$ with an evaporator temperature of $-10°F$. The final compression state is saturated vapor at 90°F and there is no subcooling of the liquid before it enters the expansion valve (at 90°F). For 1 lb., find (a) the refrigeration, (b) the net work, (c) the heat rejected in the condenser. Also find (d) the COP, (e) the amount of NH$_3$ to be circulated, (f) the hp/ton, (g) the displacement of the compressor (100% volumetric efficiency) for a capacity of 15 tons.
   Ans. (b) 100.9 Btu/lb., (d) 3.84, (e) 0.516 lb./min., (f) 1.228, (g) 77.2 cfm.

352. The same as **351** except that the refrigerant is Freon 12.
   Ans. (b) 12.84 Btu/lb., (d) 3.47, (e) 4.48 lb./min., (f) 1.36, (g) 127 cfm.

353. A refrigeration cycle operates on NH$_3$ with the refrigerant entering the compressor as saturated vapor; evaporator temperature, 10°F; condenser pressure, 120 psia; temperature just before expansion valve, 60°F; capacity,

20 tons; volumetric efficiency, 80%. For the ideal cycle, determine (a) the lb. NH$_3$/min., (b) the COP, (c) the displacement needed, (d) the horsepower. Let the actual state at the end of compression be 120 psia and 180°F and let the other states remain as given. Determine (e) the compression efficiency, (f) the actual hp/ton and COP, (g) the heat rejected in the condenser.
   Ans. (a) 7.91 lb./min., (b) 7.48, (c) 72.1 cfm, (d) 12.6, (e) 79.2%, (f) 0.795 hp/ton, 5.93, (g) 4690 Btu/min.

354. Liquid NH$_3$ enters an expansion valve at 86°F. The pressure in the evaporator is 28 psia. At the end of isentropic compression, $p_2 = 200$ psia and $t_2 = 140°F$. The volumetric efficiency is 82% and the capacity is to be 200 tons. Compute the needed compressor displacement. *Ans.* 1040 cfm.

355. What is the refrigerating capacity of a 9x9-in., twin-cylinder, single-acting compressor that turns at 190 rpm and has a volumetric efficiency of 85% when the liquid temperature before the expansion valve is 90°F and saturated vapor at 10°F enters the compressor (a) if the refrigerant is NH_3, (b) if the refrigerant is $F12$? Find the isentropic compressor horsepower in each case if the NH_3 is compressed to 180 psia and the $F12$ to 115 psia. (These values are arbitrarily chosen to fit the tables given in this text and are approximately comparable.)

Ans. (a) 34.5 tons, 33.2 hp, (b) 20 tons, 19.7 hp.

356. The temperature of a refrigerant at the expansion valve is 80°F; the evaporator is at 40°F. The substance leaves the evaporator, entering the compressor, as saturated vapor only. The cooling capacity is to be 25 tons. For comparsion purposes, consider the volumetric efficiency of the double-acting compressor as 100%; let $L/D = 1$; let $n = 150$ rpm. Compute the required displacement in cfm and the bore D and stroke L when the refrigerant is (a) NH_3, (b) SO_2, (c) CO_2, (d) $F12$, (e) H_2O. Are all the answers reasonable? [For CO_2: $h_{g40} = 98.4$, $h_{f80} = 35.6$ Btu/lb., $v_{g40} = 0.145$ cu. ft./lb. For SO_2: $h_{g40} = 185.37$, $h_{f80} = 40.05$ Btu/lb., $v_{g40} = 2.887$ cu. ft./lb.]

Ans. (a) 40.5 cfm, 6.66x6.66 in. (b) 9x9, (c) 4.39x4.39, (d) 8.02x8.02, (e) 44.3x44.3 in.

357. The following data were obtained from a 10½x18-in., horizontal, double-acting, NH_3 compressor, running at 205 rpm: discharge state, 170 psia and 230°F; intake state, 40 psia and 30°F; liquid temperature at expansion valve, 82°F; ihp of compressor, 107; volumetric efficiency, 81.7%; mechanical efficiency, 90.5%; refrigeration, measured at the brine coils, 100 tons. (a) Compute the lb./min. of refrigerant and the refrigeration by the refrigerant. How much less refrigeration is done by the brine than in the evaporator? (b) What is the actual bhp/ton and the COP based

on bhp? (c) Apply the energy equation to the compressor and estimate the net heat transferred from the NH_3 in the compressor.

Ans. (a) 40.9 lb./min., 100.75 tons, (b) 4.03, 1.17 bhp/ton, (c) 507 Btu/min.

358. A reversed vapor compression cycle is to be used for heating. The maximum demand is expected to be 600 cfm of 40°F outside air heated to 85°F. The temperature in the evaporator is to be 25°F, and the Freon 12 refrigerant is pumped to 150 psia, having entered the compressor as saturated vapor. Liquid enters the expansion valve at 100°F. (a) What rate of refrigerant circulation is needed? Also determine (b) the horsepower input for an actual/ideal work ratio of 70%, (c) the actual COP, (d) the cost of heating at 2 cents/kw-hr., first, when the heat is obtained from the reversed cycle and second, when the heat is obtained from an electrical heating element.

Ans. (a) 8.71 lb./min., (b) 1.64 hp, (c) 4.04, (d) 2.45, 18.1 ¢/hr.

359. The inhabitants of another planet feel comfortable at a temperature of about 200°F and feel cold at 150°F. To keep their habitations warm, they have invented the heat pump and use H_2O as the refrigerant. Let the refrigerant in the outside environment be evaporating at 130°F and let condensation in the inside heating coils occur at 220°F. Compression ends on the saturated vapor line and the water enters the expansion valve at 210°F. The heat needed is 4630 Btu/min. For an ideal cycle, determine (a) the COP, (b) the rate of circulation of refrigerant, (c) the compressor displacement for a volumetric efficiency of 80%.

Ans. (a) 7.26, (b) 4.75 lb./min., (c) 844 cfm.

360-370. These numbers may be used for other problems.

✍ *16*

MIXTURES

249. Introduction. Since you have already worked problems with air as the working substance and since air is a mixture of gases, you already know how to handle mixtures of ideal gases—given the appropriate characteristics (R, c_p, c_v, etc.) of the mixture. Mixtures in which one component may condense or evaporate (we call them mixtures of vapors and gases), such as atmospheric air from which H_2O may condense on a cold window pane, are not so easily handled. We shall touch on a few simple principles of mixtures and briefly on atmospheric air which is a mixture of dry air and water vapor.

250. Avogadro's Law. According to Avogadro, an Italian (1776–1856): *All ideal gases at a particular pressure and temperature have the same number of molecules in a given volume* (Avogadro's law). Since the molecular weight is an index to the mass of the molecule, it follows that the density ρ, say in lb. per cu. ft., is proportional to the mass of the molecule; or

(**a**) $$\frac{\rho_x}{\rho_y} = \frac{M_x}{M_y},$$

where ρ_x and ρ_y are the densities and M_x and M_y are the molecular weights of the gases X and Y, respectively. As the densities are inversely proportional to the specific volumes, $\rho_x/\rho_y = M_x/M_y = v_y/v_x$, or

(**b**) $$M_x v_x = M_y v_y.$$

We have shown that the molecular weight *times* the specific volume for gas X *is equal* to the product of these numbers for gas Y, the gases being at the *same* pressure and temperature. Since gases X and Y may be any two gases, it follows from Avogadro's law that the product Mv must be the same for all ideal gases at any particular temperature and pressure.

You recall that a mol of a substance is M lb. (or M gm.), where M is the molecular weight. To distinguish between M lb. and M gm., we speak of a pound mol, meaning M lb., and a gram mol, meaning M gm. Since both mols are commonly used in this country, always specify which is meant.

We shall deal entirely with pound mols from here on, so that for our present purposes, we may think of the units of M as

(c) $M \rightarrow$ lb./mol.

If there are N mols, the total mass is NM lb.

251. Universal Gas Constant. Multiply both sides of the characteristic equation of an ideal gas, $pv = RT$, by the molecular weight M, and get $pMv = MRT$, or

(d) $MR = \dfrac{p(Mv)}{T}.$ $\left[\text{from } \dfrac{p_1 Mv_1}{T_1} = \dfrac{p_2 Mv_2}{T_2} \right]$

Since Mv is the same for all ideal gases and since the volume Mv varies inversely with the pressure p (Boyle's law) and directly as the temperature T (Charles' law), it follows that the product MR must also be the *same for all ideal gases*. This product MR is called the universal gas constant and may be represented by the symbol $\overline{R}$. Its value is generally taken as 1545 ft-lb./mol-°R;

(e) $\overline{R} = MR = 1545$ ft-lb./mol-°R   and $R = \dfrac{1545}{M}.$

The specific gas constant R is often conveniently found from (e) either for a single gas or a mixture of gases. A mixture of gases is considered to have an equivalent molecular weight; thus, air is said to have a molecular weight of 28.97 (use 29 on the slide rule).

252. Mixtures of Gases. The individual gases or vapors in a mixture are called **constituents** or **components.** The description of the mixture is given by a **volumetric analysis** or by a **gravimetric analysis.** Sometimes one analysis is useful, sometimes the other; hence, we must be able to convert from one to another with ease.

The *volumetric analysis* expresses the amounts of the components in the mixture by the percentages of the total volume which each component would occupy if the various gases were placed in separate compartments at the pressure p_m and temperature T_m of the mixture. That is, in Fig. 204, imagine gases X, Y,

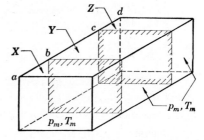

Fig. 204. **Total Volume is V_m. When $V_m = 1$ cu. ft., the volume of gas X is B_x; of gas Y, B_y; of gas Z, B_z.**

and Z separated by partitions at b and c, each one at pressure p_m and temperature T_m. Thus, each one occupies a certain percentage or fraction of the entire volume, represented by B_x, B_y, and B_z (the symbol B suggesting *bulk*). Now if the partitions are removed and the gases mix, we say that the volumetric percentages of the gases X, Y, and Z are B_x, B_y, and B_z.

It is important to note that if the vessel in Fig. 204 contains 1 mol of the total mixture, the mols of gases X, Y, and Z are B_x, B_y, and B_z. That is, the volumetric fraction B_x is the number of mols of gas X in a mixture which totals 1 mol; $B_x + B_y + B_z = 1$. The volumetric percentage B_x is the number of mols of X in a mixture which totals 100 mols; $B_x + B_y + B_z = 100$.

The *gravimetric analysis* describes the mixture by giving the percentages *by weight* (mass) of each constituent. For example, the gravimetric percentage or fraction of gas X is

(f)
$$G_x = \frac{\text{Mass of gas } X}{\text{Total mass of the mixture}}.$$

For a mixture of gases X, Y, and Z, the gravimetric analysis is $G_x\%$ of X, $G_y\%$ of Y, and $G_z\%$ of Z, each expressed as a percentage of the mass; G also stands for the fractional part of unit mass.

To convert from volumetric to gravimetric analysis, or vice versa, we note that B mols times M lb./mol is the mass in pounds (B mols $\times$ M lb./mol); and G (lb./unit mixture)/(M lb./mol) is mols and mols are proportional to volume. Let there be three gases, for example, with a volumetric composition of B_x, B_y, and B_z. Then in tabulated form, we have

$$M_x B_x = \text{lb. gas } X; \qquad\qquad M_x B_x/(\Sigma MB) = G_x;$$
$$M_y B_y = \text{lb. gas } Y; \qquad\qquad M_y B_y/(\Sigma MB) = G_y;$$
$$\underline{M_z B_z = \text{lb. gas } Z;} \qquad\qquad M_z B_z/(\Sigma MB) = G_z;$$
$$\Sigma MB = \text{lb. of mixture.}$$

If the gravimetric composition is given, we have

$$G_x/M_x = \text{mols gas } X; \qquad\qquad (G_x/M_x)/(\Sigma G/M) = B_x;$$
$$G_y/M_y = \text{mols gas } Y; \qquad\qquad (G_y/M_y)/(\Sigma G/M) = B_y;$$
$$\underline{G_z/M_z = \text{mols gas } Z;} \qquad\qquad (G_z/M_z)/(\Sigma G/M) = B_z;$$
$$\Sigma G/M = \text{mols of mixture.}$$

253. Dalton's Law of Partial Pressures. It was John Dalton (1766–1844) who first stated that the total pressure p_m exerted by a mixture of gases (or vapors) is the sum of the pressures which each gas (or vapor) would exert were it to occupy the vessel alone. The pressure which one gas in a mixture exerts is called its *partial pressure*. Thus, if p_x, p_y, and p_z represent respectively the partial pressures of the mixed gases X, Y, and Z, Dalton's law states

(68)
$$p_m = p_x + p_y + p_z + \cdots$$
$$[T_m = T_x = T_y = T_z, \qquad V_m = V_x = V_y = V_z]$$

The characteristic equation of an ideal gas in terms of the number of mols is $pV = 1545NT$. Applying this equation to a component X and to the mixture, we get

(g) $$p_x V_m = 1545 N_x T_m \quad \text{and} \quad p_m V_m = 1545 N_m T_m.$$

By division with equations (g), we have

$$\frac{p_x V_m}{p_m V_m} = \frac{1545 N_x T_m}{1545 N_m T_m} \quad \text{or} \quad \frac{p_x}{p_m} = \frac{N_x}{N_m} = B_x.$$

In the foregoing, we used the following principles: If the mixture is in internal thermal equilibrium, *all gases are at the same temperature T_m; each gas occupies the same volume V_m*. We recognized that the number of mols of X divided by the total number of mols N_m is the volumetric percentage; and we have arrived at the quite useful relation that the volumetric fraction B is equal to the ratio of the partial pressure divided by the total pressure; or

(h) $$p_x = B_x p_m, \qquad p_y = B_y p_m, \qquad p_z = B_z p_m,$$

true for ideal gases and useful for actual gases.

254. Properties of Mixtures. The equivalent molecular weight M_m of a mixture is given by

(i) $$M_m = B_x M_x + B_y M_y + B_z M_z + \cdots = \Sigma BM \text{ lb./mol,}$$

where the B's are the fractional parts of 1 mol of mixture ($\Sigma B = 1$ mol) and the M's are the molecular weights of the components. Then the specific gas constant R_m is obtained from (e);

(j) $$R_m = \frac{1545}{M_m} \text{ ft-lb./lb-°R.}$$

The specific heat of a mixture of gases is

(k) $$c_m = G_x c_x + G_y c_y + G_z c_z + \cdots = \Sigma Gc \text{ Btu/lb-°R,}$$

where the G's are the fractional parts of 1 lb. of mixture ($\Sigma G = 1$ lb.) and the c's (Btu/lb.-°R) are specific heats. The internal energy of a mixture is the sum of the internal energies of the components:

(l) $$u_m = G_x u_x + G_y u_y + G_z u_z + \cdots = \Sigma Gu \text{ Btu/lb.,}$$

where the G's are as defined for (k) and, for example, u_x is the internal energy of 1 lb. of gas X. Equations analogous to (l) may be written for enthalpy h_m and entropy s_m.

255. Mixtures of Vapors and Gases. Before proceeding with mixtures containing condensing or evaporating components, let us review certain important points to keep in mind.

1. The volume of any constituent (at its partial pressure and t_m) is the volume of the mixture.

2. The pressure of a mixture is the sum of the partial pressures of the constituents (Dalton's law).

3. The volumetric fraction of a constituent in a mixture times the total pressure p_m is the partial pressure of the constituent; $p_x = B_x p_m$.

4. The density of a mixture is the sum of the densities of the constituents: $\rho_m = \rho_x + \rho_y + \rho_z + \cdots$.

5. The number of mols of each gas is proportional to its volumetric fraction or percentage.

6. The mixture is assumed to be in internal equilibrium; all parts at the same temperature.

Although there are many vapor-gas mixtures of concern to the engineer, such as the air-gasoline mixture from the carburetor and the products of combustion of a hydrocarbon fuel, we shall confine our discussion to the air-water mixture. The same principles apply to the others.

The noncondensing components of a mixture will be called dry gas, abbreviated "dg." or dry air "da." The condensable component is called the vapor, abbreviated "v."

256. Dew Point. Imagine a container A, Fig. 205(b), in which there is superheated vapor (say H_2O), state 1, Fig. 205(a). If this container is

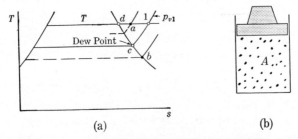

(a)   (b)

Fig. 205.   Dew Point and Relative Humidity.

placed in colder surroundings so that heat flows outward, the superheated vapor is cooled at, say, constant pressure, path 1-c. If heat is further rejected after arrival at state c, where the vapor is saturated, some of the vapor will condense. The state c is the condensation point or **dew point** at constant pressure with respect to the initial state 1. Thus, any superheated vapor has a dew point which depends on the initial state and the process by which the saturated vapor line is reached. If the vapor is cooled below temperature c, condensation occurs and the pressure of the vapor decreases [a decreasing weight on the piston of Fig. 205(b)].

In atmospheric air, the H_2O is generally superheated steam. If this air is cooled at a total constant pressure, the steam cools at constant pressure (all components of the mixture being taken as ideal gases). Some temperature is eventually reached below which condensation of the H_2O in the air occurs; this temperature is said to be the *dew point of the air*, but from the previous paragraph we see that it is the dew point of the H_2O in the air. As explained later, we have means of determining the partial pressure p_{v1} of the H_2O vapor in the air. Knowing p_{v1}, we find the dew point from the vapor tables by looking up the saturation temperature corresponding to p_{v1}; and that is it.

If atmospheric air is cooled at constant total pressure below its dew point c, say to state b, where the temperature is t_b, some of the vapor necessarily condenses, but the vapor which remains at t_b is saturated and at a pressure lower than p_{v1}; the vapor pressure p_{vb} is the saturation pressure corresponding to the temperature t_b. During cooling below the dew point at constant total pressure, the partial pressures do not remain constant. If p_m is the total pressure of the mixture and p_v is the vapor pressure, the pressure of the dry gas p_g is taken as $p_g = p_m - p_v$.

We shall generally assume that the liquid formed by cooling a gas-vapor mixture below its dew point settles out, which it will do, given time, and that the vapor left is saturated vapor. (Atmospheric mists contain small bits of liquid H_2O, which means that the vapor is wet vapor.)

257. Relative Humidity. Consider again the container A, Fig. 205, with superheated vapor in it. Suppose a small amount of liquid is injected and the system is manipulated in such a way as to maintain constant temperature. (This can be done by letting the system come into thermal equilibrium with a constant environment and then giving it time to do so again after additional liquid has been injected.) Perhaps the first injection is such an amount that it all vaporizes and the final equilibrium state is a. If just the right amount of liquid is introduced and vaporized at constant temperature, the equilibrium state becomes saturated vapor at d. What the foregoing discussion suggests is that a saturated vapor state can be reached at constant temperature (and increasing pressure) by evaporating more liquid into the space A, Fig. 205. The ratio of the vapor pressures at 1 and d, p_{v1}/p_{vd}, is called the **relative humidity** ϕ. Notice that the relative humidity of any superheated vapor can therefore be expressed as the actual pressure of the vapor *divided by* the saturation pressure corresponding to the temperature of the vapor.

Returning to a gas-vapor mixture, we conclude that if additional liquid is vaporized into the mixture (at constant temperature t_m and total pressure p_m), the vapor becomes less superheated, its partial pressure increases, and, if the process is continued, the vapor in the gas becomes saturated vapor.

In applying these notions to atmospheric air, we say that air which contains saturated steam (state d, c, b, or any other on the saturated vapor curve) is **saturated air,** but we mean that the *steam* is saturated. However, such air (or other gas) is "saturated" with steam (or other vapor) in the sense that *there cannot be an increase in the amount of steam (or vapor) in the air (or gas) as long as the total pressure and temperature of the mixture remain the same.*

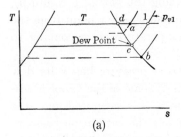

(a)

Fig. 205.   Repeated.

The partial pressure of the steam in the air is ordinarily a fraction of a pound per square inch (0.5069 psia for "saturated air" at 80°F; less, if the "air" is not saturated; see your steam tables). At such low pressures, the molecules are so far apart that they exert a negligible force on one another and occupy negligible space; thus the steam acts very much like an ideal gas

$$pv \approx RT, \qquad pV \approx N\bar{R}T = 1545NT, \qquad \text{and} \qquad p \approx \rho RT,$$

where N is the number of mols. We shall find the density $\rho = 1/v$ of convenience in this chapter. Thus for the vapor at states 1 and d, we have $p_{v1}/p_{vd} \approx \rho_{v1}R_vT/(\rho_{vd}R_vT)$, and the relative humidity is

$$(69) \qquad\qquad \phi = \frac{p_{v1}}{p_{vd}} \approx \frac{\rho_{v1}}{\rho_{vd}} = \frac{v_{vd}}{v_{v1}},$$

where the subscripts refer to Fig. 205.

258. Humidity Ratio. We shall find it convenient to base calculations on a unit mass of dry gas (dg.), because the mass of the vapor and therefore of the mixture often varies; but the mass of dry gas remains constant. Thus a convenient term is the *mass of vapor per pound of dry gas,* called the *humidity ratio* ω in connection with air-steam mixtures; $\omega = w_v/w_g$. (The name may be extended to include other mixtures.) This value can be found from

$$(\mathbf{m}) \qquad\qquad \omega = \frac{\rho_v}{\rho_g} = \frac{\text{lb. v./cu. ft.}}{\text{lb. dg./cu. ft.}} = \frac{\text{lb. v.}}{\text{lb. dg.}}$$

in which $\rho_g = p_g/(R_gT_g)$, where p_g is the *partial* pressure of the dry gas; $p_g = p_m - p_v$. The density of saturated vapor is $\rho_v = 1/v_v$, in which v_v is taken from vapor tables.

When the vapor is in a state approximating an ideal gas, we may use $\rho = p/(RT)$ in equation $(\mathbf{m})$ to get

$$(\mathbf{n}) \qquad\qquad \omega = \frac{\rho_v}{\rho_g} = \frac{(p_v)(R_gT_g)}{(R_vT_v)(p_g)} = \frac{p_vR_g}{p_gR_v} = \frac{p_vR_g}{R_v(p_m - p_v)} \frac{\text{lb. v.}}{\text{lb. dg.}},$$

where, for internal equilibrium, $T_g = T_v$, and where the partial pressure of the gas is equal to the pressure of the mixture minus the pressure of the vapor, $p_g = p_m - p_v$. Equation (n) may be applied to gas-vapor mixtures in any state, provided the partial pressure of the vapor is low. If equation (n) is applied to an air-steam mixture, we use $R_a = R_g = 53.3$ and $R_v = 1545/18 = 85.7$ for H_2O whose molecular weight is approximately 18, and find

(o) $$\omega = \frac{53.3 p_v}{85.7 p_a} = \frac{0.622 p_v}{p_m - p_v} \quad \text{or} \quad p_v = \frac{p_m \omega}{0.622 + \omega}$$

[AIR-STEAM MIXTURE ONLY]

where ω is lb. v./lb. dg.

259. Wet-Bulb Temperature. The relative humidity of atmospheric air, that is, the relative amount of steam in the air, is easily found via an experimental determination of a *wet-bulb temperature* t_w. The actual temperature of the air is called the *dry-bulb temperature* t_d, because it is of course read from a thermometer whose bulb is dry. The instrument used for the purpose of determining t_w is called a *psychrometer,* of which there are several types. The commonest one is a sling psychrometer, which consists of two thermometers attached to a handle so that they may be easily whirled about the axis of the handle. One thermometer is dry and gives the air temperature; the other has on its bulb a wet gauze and is called a wet-bulb thermometer. The temperature t_w indicated by the wet-bulb thermometer depends upon the rate of evaporation of moisture from the wet gauze. The heat necessary to evaporate this moisture is supplied by the air passing over the gauze. Consequently, this air (and water) is cooled below the atmospheric temperature, the amount by which it is cooled, $t_d - t_w$, being called the *wet-bulb depression.*

The rate of evaporation of the water depends in part on the amount of steam already in the air. If the air is saturated, none of the water on the gauze evaporates because the air is already a saturated mixture with respect to the steam; the wet-bulb and dry-bulb temperatures are the same. The less "moisture" (steam) carried by the air, the more that must be evaporated in order to result in saturation; hence, the rate of evaporation being greater, the wet-bulb temperature will be lower. The higher the relative humidity, the slower the rate of evaporation and the higher the wet-bulb temperature. With the wet-bulb and dry-bulb temperatures, we may enter a *psychrometric chart,* Fig. 206, and find the amount of steam in the air, the relative humidity, and other useful information.

260. Partial Pressure of Steam in Air. The basic approach to the partial pressure of the vapor in air is via an adiabatic saturation process and the corresponding energy balance, but to cover this is likely to take too much time for a short course. Using this approach, W. H. Carrier developed an expression, with the help of some reasonable approximations for atmospheric air, as follows:

$$(p) \qquad p_v = p_{vw} - \frac{(p_m - p_{vw})(t_d - t_w)}{2830 - 1.44t_w} \text{ psi,} \qquad \text{[CARRIER'S EQUATION]}$$

where p_v is the partial pressure of the water vapor in the air, p_{vw} is the vapor pressure at the wet-bulb temperature (corresponding to t_w in steam tables),

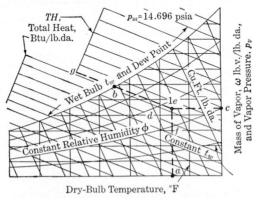

Fig. 206. *Form of Psychrometric Chart.* This chart may be entered with various data. Suppose the wet- and dry-bulb temperatures are known; find the wet-bulb temperature at b, the dry-bulb at a, and follow constant temperature lines until they meet at state 1. Move to right or left to c and read values of ω and p_{v1}; estimate the volume between the lines d and e; estimate ϕ between lines e and f; follow constant wet bulb to g and read value of total heat. See working chart at rear.

p_m is the atmospheric pressure (the barometer reading in psi), $t_d°$F is the dry-bulb temperature, and $t_w°$F is the wet-bulb temperature.

261. Enthalpy of Superheated Steam at Low Pressure. Since steam tables do not give enthalpies of superheated steam at pressures below 1 psia, another means of obtaining it is needed. Having observed that the steam in the air may be treated as an ideal gas with little error, we recall that the enthalpy of an ideal gas is a function of temperature only (§ 47). Thus, the easiest way to determine the enthalpy of superheated steam at pressures below 1 psia is to use the enthalpy of saturated steam at the same temperature. In Fig. 207, for instance,

$$(q) \qquad\qquad h_{v1} = h_{gb} \text{ Btu/lb. v.}$$

This same principle may be applied to other vapors when the vapor pressure is low.

There is another property which is commonly used in air conditioning called **total heat** TH, defined by*

(r) $$TH = h_{aw} + \omega_w h_{gw} = 0.24 t_w + \omega_w h_{gw} \text{ Btu/lb. da.,}$$

where h_{gw} is the enthalpy of saturated steam and ω_w is the humidity ratio, both at the wet-bulb temperature t_w; h_{aw} is the enthalpy of air at t_w. This property is useful because the change of total heat $\Delta TH \approx \Delta H$, and therefore ΔTH is approximately the transferred heat in a steady flow process with $W = 0$ and $\Delta K = 0$. Moreover, since the *total heat is a function of the wet bulb-temperature only*, it can be included on a psychrometric chart without complication (Fig. 206).

262. Example. The dry- and wet-bulb temperatures of air are found to be $t_d = 83°F$ and $t_w = 68°F$. The barometer is $p_m = 29.4$ in Hg. Determine (a) the partial pressure of the vapor, (b) the humidity ratio, (c) the relative humidity, (d) the dew point, (e) the density of the air, (f) the density of dry air at the same p_m and t_d. Refer to Fig. 207. (Steam table values are from Keenan and Keyes.)

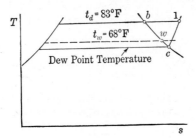

Fig. 207.

SOLUTION. (a) Let the state be represented by 1, Fig. 207. From the steam tables at $t_w = 68°F$, we get $p_{vw} = 0.339$ psia. Then $p_m = (0.491)(29.4) = 14.44$ psia; $p_m - p_{vw} = 14.44 - 0.339 = 14.101$ psia. Using these values in Carrier's equation (p), we have

$$p_{v1} = p_{vw} - \frac{(p_m - p_{vw})(t_d - t_w)}{2830 - 1.44 t_w}$$

$$= 0.339 - \frac{(14.1)(15)}{2830 - (1.44)(68)} = 0.2615 \text{ psia.}$$

(b) The humidity ratio is given by (o) as

$$\omega_1 = \frac{0.622 \, p_v}{p_m - p_v} = \frac{(0.622)(0.2615)}{14.1} = 0.0115 \text{ lb. v./lb. da.,}$$

or $(0.0115)(7000) = 80.5$ grains v./lb. da.

* There is some confusion in the language here. This property is sometimes incorrectly called *enthalpy*. It is the enthalpy of a saturated mixture only.

(c) As defined by equation (69), the relative humidity is

$$\phi = \frac{p_{v1}}{p_{vb}} = \frac{0.262}{0.5588} = 46.9\%,$$

where $p_{vb} = 0.5588$ is the saturation pressure corresponding to the dry-bulb temperature $t_d = 83°F$.

(d) The vapor pressure at c, $p_{vc} = p_{v1} = 0.262$ psia. The saturation temperature corresponding to this pressure is found in the steam tables as 60.6°F, the *dew point*.

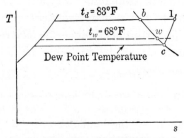

Fig. 207. Repeated.

(e) The density of the mixture is the sum of the densities of the constituents; $\rho_m = \rho_a + \rho_v$. The pressure and density of the dry air in state 1, Fig. 207, are

$$p_{a1} = p_m - p_{v1} = 14.44 - 0.262 = 14.18 \text{ psia.}$$

$$\rho_{a1} = \frac{p_{a1}}{R_a T_a} = \frac{(14.18)(144)}{(53.3)(543)} = 0.0706 \text{ cu. ft./lb.}$$

From equation (69), we get the density of the vapor at 1 as

$$\rho_{v1} = \phi \rho_{vb} = \frac{\phi}{v_{gb}} = \frac{0.469}{577.4} = 0.00081 \text{ lb./cu. ft.,}$$

where $v_{gb} = 577.4$ cu. ft./lb. is the volume of saturated vapor at state b, Fig. 207.

$$\rho_m = \rho_{a1} + \rho_{v1} = 0.0706 + 0.00081 = 0.07141 \text{ lb./cu. ft.}$$

(f) For dry air at 29.4 in. Hg = 14.44 psia and 83°F, the density is

$$\rho_a = \frac{p_a}{R_a T_a} = \frac{(14.44)(144)}{(53.3)(543)} = 0.0719 \text{ lb./cu. ft.}$$

It is interesting to note that dry air at a particular temperature and pressure is heavier than atmospheric air at the same temperature and pressure, $0.0719 > 0.07141$. For practice, the student should *check the foregoing answers by a psychrometric chart*, noting that the chart is constructed for a $p_m = 14.696$ psia.

263. Example—Constant Total Pressure (Steady Flow). An atmospheric air mixture in state 1 has the following properties: $p_m = 29.92$ in. Hg, $t_d = 100°F$, $\omega_1 = 0.0295$ lb. v./lb. da. This air is cooled to 60°F, state 2, Fig. 208, and then heated to 85°F, state 3. (a) Determine the relative humidity of the original mixture. (b) How much moisture is deposited during the cooling to 60°F? (c) How

much heat is removed during cooling.   (d) For a flow of 100,000 cfm, how many
tons of refrigeration are ideally required?   (e) What is the volume of the original
100,000 cfm after cooling?   (f) What is the relative humidity of the air in state 3,
Fig. 208?

NOTE.   The events of this problem are fairly typical of the events in summer
air conditioning of habitations.   Since the various answers may be obtained with
the aid of a psychrometric chart, the reader should use the chart and check all
results.

SOLUTION.   (a) To find the relative humidity, first find the partial pressure p_{v1}
of the vapor from equation (o);

$$p_{v1} = \frac{\omega_1 p_m}{0.622 + \omega_1} = \frac{(0.0295)(14.7)}{0.622 + 0.0295} = 0.666 \text{ psia.}$$

From the steam tables, we find $p_{vb} = 0.9492$ psia for 100°F and then

$$\phi = p_{v1}/p_{vb} = 0.666/0.9492 = 70.2\%.$$

(b) The condensed H_2O is obtained by subtracting ω_2 from ω_1.   To get an idea
of where state 2 for the H_2O is, we enter the steam tables and find the dew point c,
Fig. 208, corresponding to $p_{v1} = 0.666$ as $t_c = 88.4°F$.   Thus, the air has been

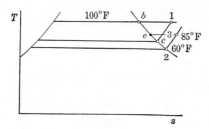

Fig. 208.

cooled below the dew point and H_2O has been condensed.   At 60°F, $p_{v2} = 0.2563$
psia is taken from the tables; then from equation (o) we get

$$\omega_2 = \frac{0.622 p_{v2}}{p_m - p_{v2}} = \frac{(0.622)(0.2563)}{14.7 - 0.2563} = 0.01105 \text{ lb. v./lb. da.}$$

The condensation is therefore

$$\omega_1 - \omega_2 = 0.0295 - 0.01105 = 0.01845 \text{ lb. v./lb. da.}$$

(For the 100,000 cfm, this condensation amounts to

$$(6770)(0.01845)/(8.4 \text{ lb./gal. } H_2O) = 14.85 \text{ gpm,}$$

which is equivalent to 892 gal./hr.   See part (d) for computation of 6770 lb./min.).

(c) The heat transferred at constant pressure or in a steady flow process where
$W = 0$ and $\Delta K = 0$ is $Q = \Delta h$.   The enthalpy of the vapor in the original air is
$h_{v1} = h_{gb} = 1105.2$ Btu/lb. v. at 100°F; or

$$H_{v1} = \omega_1 h_{v1} = (0.0295)(1105.2) = 32.6 \text{ Btu/lb. da.}$$

At state 2, the enthalpy of the H_2O should account for the condensed steam; that is,

$$H_{v2} = \omega_2 h_{g2} + (\omega_1 - \omega_2) h_{f2}$$
$$= (0.01105)(1088) + (0.01845)(28.06)$$
$$= 12 + 0.518 = 12.518 \text{ Btu/lb. da.,}$$

where h_{g2} and h_{f2} correspond to a temperature of $t_2 = 60°F$. Now the heat rejected by 1 lb. of dry air is $\Delta h = c_p(t_2 - t_1)$ and the heat rejected by the vapor is $H_{v2} - H_{v1}$; hence, we have

$$Q = \Delta h_m = c_p(t_2 - t_1) + H_{v2} - H_{v1}$$
$$= 0.24(60 - 100) + 12.518 - 32.6 = -29.7 \text{ Btu/lb. da.}$$

The heat removed per pound of original mixture is $29.7/1.0295 = 28.85$ Btu/lb. mixture. This value of Q should be closely approximated by ΔTH (see the psychrometric chart).

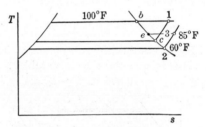

Fig. 208.   Repeated.

(d) If there are 100,000 cfm of atmospheric air, there are also 100,000 cfm of dry air and 100,000 cfm of vapor. The mass of 100,000 cfm of dry air flowing is

$$w_a = \frac{p_{a1} V_{a1}}{R_a T_1} = \frac{(14.7 - 0.666)(144)(100,000)}{(53.3)(560)} = 6770 \text{ lb./min.}$$

The total amount of heat transferred is therefore $w_a \Delta h_m = (6770)(29.7) = 201,000$ Btu/min. Since 1 ton of refrigeration is equivalent to 200 Btu/min., the ideal amount required is $201,000/200 = 1005$ tons, enough for a fair-sized structure.

(e) The volume of the mixture after it has cooled is the volume of dry air, or

$$V_{m2} = V_{a2} = \frac{w_a R_a T_2}{p_{a2}} = \frac{(6770)(53.3)(520)}{(14.44)(144)} = 90,300 \text{ cfm.}$$

Checking this value, using the steam, we get ($6770\omega_2$ lb. v.)

$$(\omega_2 v_{g2} \text{ cu. ft. v./lb. da.})(w_a \text{ lb. da.}) = (0.01105)(1206.7)(6770) = 90,300 \text{ cfm.}$$

(f) The partial pressure of the steam remains constant during the heating from 2 to 3; so $p_{v3} = p_{v2} = 0.2563$ psia. Saturated steam at $85°F$ has a pressure of $p_{ve} = 0.5959$ psia. The relative humidity at 3 is

$$\phi_3 = \frac{p_{v3}}{p_{ve}} = \frac{0.2563}{0.5959} = 43\%.$$

264. Cooling Water with Air. Since large quantities of cooling water are needed for condensers of all kinds (steam, refrigerant, etc.) it becomes

economical in the absence of a river or large lake to cool the condenser water
and recirculate it.　Such cooling is done by having some of the water evaporate into the air; some of the heat needed to evaporate the water comes from

Fig. 209.　Spray Pond.

Fig. 210.　Atmospheric Cooling Tower.
The air enters between the louvres, which
slope downward toward the inside.　Sloping in this manner, they reduce the
amount of water which might be blown
away.

the water itself, leaving the water cooler.　Simple spraying of water into the
air accomplishes this purpose, as in the spray pond of Fig. 209.

Cooling towers are used for the same purpose and operate on the same
principle.　They may be built, Fig. 210, so that the natural movement of
the atmospheric air through the cooling tower causes the evaporation of

some of the condenser water, thereby cooling the remainder. The water to be cooled is sprayed into the tower near the top. If the amount of water blown away in the type of cooling tower of Fig. 210 is excessive, other types may be advisable.

Fig. 211. Induced-Draft Cooling Tower.
Forced-draft or induced-draft fans on cooling towers increase capacity.

In cooling towers which do not depend on the natural circulation of air, the air may be moved by induced-draft fans, Fig. 211, or by forced-draft fans, which would be located at the bottom of the tower. Capacity is greatly increased by the use of fans. Also, fans make it possible to govern the rate of cooling in accordance with the needs, to some extent, by regulating the amount of air blown through the tower. The power required for

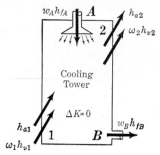

Fig. 212. Energy Diagram for Cooling Tower.

induced draft is greater than for forced draft; however, the undesired recirculation of the discharged, nearly saturated air is more likely to occur with forced draft, an event which would reduce the capacity of the tower.

Figure 212 shows entering and departing energy quantities, with the tower as a steady flow system. Entering at 1 is unsaturated atmospheric air.   This air picks up moisture and leaves at 2 in a nearly saturated condition and usually, but not necessarily, at a higher temperature than that at 1.   Depending upon the size and design of the cooling tower, the relative humidity at state 2 should be greater than 90% and approach 100%.   The hot condenser water enters at A, is cooled by partial evaporation to a lower temperature, and leaves at B.   Assuming no incidental transfer of heat or other changes of energy (since the actual system is not surrounded by an adiabatic surface, a small error is involved in this assumption), we get, Fig. 212,

(s) $$h_{a1} + \omega_1 h_{v1} + w_A h_{fA} = h_{a2} + \omega_2 h_{v2} + w_B h_{fB} \text{ Btu/lb. da.,}$$

where

ω_1 = pounds of vapor per pound of dry air at 1,
h_{v1} = the specific enthalpy of the superheated vapor in the atmosphere,
w_A = pounds of water entering per pound of dry air,
h_{fA} = the specific enthalpy of this water at temperature t_A,
ω_2 = pounds of vapor per pound of dry air in the departing air; $\omega_2 > \omega_1$,
h_{v2} = the specific enthalpy of vapor at state 2, sometimes assumed to be saturated,
$w_B = w_A - (\omega_2 - \omega_1)$ = pounds of departing water per pound of dry air., obtained from a mass balance of the H_2O,
h_{fB} = the specific enthalpy of water at temperature t_B.

The unknown in equation (s) is usually w_A, the pounds of condenser water that can be handled by 1 lb. of dry air.   The amount of air needed will depend upon the condition of the atmospheric air.   The higher the wet-bulb temperature, the smaller the amount of water that can be cooled, other conditions remaining the same.   In using equation (s) to estimate the air requirements, substitute $w_A - (\omega_2 - \omega_1)$ for w_B and let

$$h_{a2} - h_{a1} = c_p(t_2 - t_1) = 0.24(t_2 - t_1).$$

These substitutions give

(t) $$w_A = \frac{0.24(t_2 - t_1) + \omega_2(h_{v2} - h_{fB}) - \omega_1(h_{v1} - h_{fB})}{h_{fA} - h_{fB}} \text{ lb. } H_2O/\text{lb. da.,}$$

wherein algebraic signs must be carefully regarded.   The subscripts are in accordance with the symbols of Fig. 212.   Observe that $1/w_A$ lb. da./lb. H_2O is the mass of dry air needed to cool 1 lb. of water in the steady flow system defined by equation (t).   Knowing the total amount of condenser water to be circulated, we may compute the required amount of air for cooling purposes.   The water that must be added to the cooling-water system from time to time to compensate for that carried away, $\omega_2 - \omega_1$, is called the *make-up water.*

265. Cooling Air with Water.   In air conditioning, it is not uncommon to cool and dehumidify the air by passing it through a spray of cold water.

If the water is cold enough, the air may be cooled below its dew point and as a consequence lose moisture, so that when it is reheated to room temperature, its relative humidity is at a comfortable value. The energy quantities involved in applying the law of conservation of energy are of the same nature as those for the cooling tower, Fig. 212. There are w_A lb. of water entering and w_B lb. of water departing. However, the water is

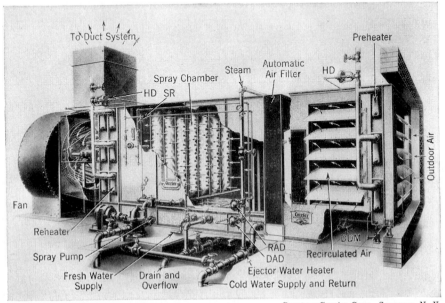

Fig. 213. *Dehumidifier and Air Washer.* Observe at the right the dampers for controlling the amount of recirculated air and the amount of fresh outdoor air. The preheater (at right) heats the air passing to the spray chamber or washer. By regulating the amount of preheat, we may also regulate the dew point of the air leaving the spray chamber during the *heating* season. The air is filtered; then, during the *cooling* season, it is cooled in the spray chamber to the proper dew-point temperature, after which it may or may not be necessary to reheat it. The centrifugal fan forces the air to the duct system.

By *air conditioning* is meant the proper regulation of (1) the temperature of the air, (2) the humidity, and (3) the motion and distribution of the air. These are the minimum functions of an air-conditioning system. It is desirable also for the system (4) to clean the air.

warmer on leaving than on entering, since in this case, the water is the coolant. Moreover, if dehumidification occurs, the mass of water departing w_B is greater than the mass entering, w_A. The mass balance for the H_2O is

$$\omega_1 + w_A = \omega_2 + w_B \text{ lb. } H_2O/\text{lb. da.}$$

Equations (s) and (t) are applicable to the case of cooling air with water, and equation (t) gives the pounds of water needed to cool 1 lb. of dry air and the moisture that it carries with it; hence, the mass of water needed per pound of atmospheric air is $w_A/(1 + \omega_1)$. The signs of certain terms are not the same for the cooling tower and the dehumidifier, but it is only necessary to give due regard to the algebraic sign obtained.

Figure 213 shows an air-conditioning unit. The cooling process in the example of § 263 may be brought about in the manner described in this article.

266. Closure. The degree of ease with which one learns to handle mixtures of gases and vapors is intimately dependent upon one's comprehension of the laws which govern an ideal gas alone and the laws which govern a vapor alone. However, there are certain characteristics of the mixture and certain new terms that must be mastered. The units of this chapter should be handled with particular care because they are often helpful in pointing the way to a solution of a problem.

If air is saturated, the dew-point, wet-bulb, and dry-bulb temperatures are the same. The partial pressure of the vapor in the mixture is the saturation pressure corresponding to the dew point, not wet-bulb temperature; and, if no condensation or evaporation occurs, the partial pressure remains constant as long as the total pressure remains constant.

SELECTED REFERENCES

Carrier, Cherne, Grant, *Modern Air Conditioning, Heating and Ventilating*, Pitman.
Faires, V. M., *Thermodynamics*, Macmillan.
Goodman, William, *Air Conditioning Analysis*, Macmillan.
Greene, A. M., Jr., *Principles of Heating, Ventilating, and Air Conditioning*, John Wiley.
Guide of the Amer. Soc. of Heat. and Air Cond. Eng.
Jennings and Lewis, *Air Conditioning and Refrigeration*, International Textbook.
Jordan and Priester, *Refrigeration and Air Conditioning*, Prentice-Hall.
Raber and Hutchinson, *Refrigeration and Air Conditioning Engineering*, John Wiley.

PROBLEMS

NOTE. *In solving problems on air-steam mixtures, check algebraic solutions by a psychrometric chart (in rear of book) wherever applicable, thereby becoming familiar with the commercial manner of obtaining a solution as well as with the basic theory (which latter objective is of course the principal aim of the engineer). If the student will sketch the processes of all problems on the plane of the psychrometric chart, he will assuredly obtain a better understanding of the events.*

371. A mixture of 1 lb. CO and 3 lb. N_2 is in a tank at 30 psia and 80°F. Determine (a) the partial pressure of each gas, (b) the volume of the tank, (c) the volume that each gas would occupy if it were separated from the other gases but at 30 psia and 80°F. (d) If these gases are separated by a partition as in (c) and the partition is removed, what is the net change in entropy after the gases have diffused to equilibrium?

Ans. (a) 7.5, 22.5 psia, (b) 27.5 cu. ft., (c) 6.88, 20.62 cu. ft., (d) +0.159 Btu/°R.

372. The dry products of combustion of a coal have the following volumetric composition: 11% CO_2, 3.5% O_2, 85.5% N_2. Calculate (a) the gravimetric analysis, (b) the equivalent molecular weight, (c) the mixture's specific gas constant, (d) the partial pressure of each constituent for $p_m = 14.7$ psia, (e) the specific heat at constant pressure for the mixture, (f) the molar specific heat C_p using the result in (e) and checking by use of the volumetric analysis.

Ans. (a) 16.2, 3.75, 80.05%, (b) 29.9, (c) 51.7, (d) 1.616, 0.514, 12.57 psia, (e) 0.24, (f) 7.17.

373. The specific humidity of atmospheric air at 96°F is 0.022 lb. H_2O/lb. da. Find (a) the partial pressure of the vapor, (b) the relative humidity, (c) the dew point.

Ans. (a) 0.502 psia, (b) 59.7%, (c) 79.7°F.

374. Air at a pressure of 29.92 in. Hg abs. and 85°F d.b. has a relative humidity of 65%. Find (a) the partial pressures of the dry air and the vapor, (b) the humidity ratio, (c) the dew point, (d) the volume of mixture per pound of dry air.

Ans. (a) 0.387, 14.313 psia, (b) 0.01685, (c) 72°F, (d) 14.1 cu. ft.

375. Calculate the vacuum in a condenser (referred to 29.92 in. Hg) when there is 0.15 lb. v./lb. da. (v. = steam) and when the temperature in the condenser is 120°F. *Ans.* 26.15 in. Hg.

376. The state of the atmosphere is defined by 27.6 in. Hg abs., 72°F d.b., 58° w.b. (a) Compute the vapor pressure (Carrier's equation). Determine (b) the relative humidity, (c) the humidity ratio, (d) the dew point. (e)

What is the density of the atmospheric air? What would be the density of dry air at the same total pressure? Which is heavier? (f) Check this solution by the psychrometric chart. Show sketch of your solution.

Ans. (a) 0.1705 psia, (b) 43.9%, (c) 0.00791 lb. v./lb. da., (d) 48.8°F, (e) 0.06864, 0.069 lb./cu. ft.

377. Atmospheric air at 29.92 in. Hg abs. and 80°F d.b. has a relative humidity of 50%. Find (a) the partial pressure of the da., (b) the humidity ratio, (c) the volume of 1 lb. of mixture, (d) the amount of H_2O condensed, (e) the heat rejected when the mixture is cooled at constant total pressure to 50°F.

Ans. (a) 14.45, (b) 0.01093, (c) 13.7, (d) 0.003305 lb./lb. da., (e) 10.86 Btu/lb.

378. Atmospheric air (29.92 in. Hg) is heated at constant pressure from 36°F and 60% relative humidity to 75°F (typical home heating). (a) What is the relative humidity in state 2? (b) How much moisture must be added to the air in the second state to bring its relative humidity to 40% (state 3)? Convert to gal./hr. for 10,000 cfm of atmospheric air (not typical of home heating to bring in this much outside air continuously). Name all states in your solution on your Ts diagram. (c) What is the dew point of the air in state 1? in state 2? in state 3?

Ans. (a) 14.5%, (b) 27 gal./hr., (c) $DP_3 = 49$°F.

379. The following processes are typical of those in summer air conditioning. Atmospheric air, at 90°F d.b., $\phi = 70\%$, and barometer of 28.5 in. Hg, is cooled in a steady flow process to 50°F (state 2), after which it is reheated (perhaps by heat flow into the building) to 73°F d.b. (state 3), all at constant total pressure. Determine (a) ϕ_2 and ω_2. (b) How much moisture is removed from the air? Determine (c) Q_{1-2} (including h_f at state 2), (d) the change of total heat, ΔTH_{1-2}, from the psychrometric chart. Is ΔTH a reasonable approximation of ΔH for engineering purposes? (e) What is the relative humidity in state 3?

Ans. (a) 100%, 0.00801, (b) 101 gr./lb. da., (c) −25.64 Btu/lb. da., (d) −25.84 Btu/lb. da., (e) 44.3%.

380. Solve the following problem, which is typical of summer air conditioning, by chart only. Atmospheric air at 100°F and 70% relative humidity (state 1) is cooled to 60°F (state 2) and delivered to a room where a temperature of 80°F (state 3) is maintained. The air remains at atmospheric pressure. Find (a) ω_1 and TH_1, (b) ω_2 and ω_3, (c) TH_2, (d) the condensed H_2O, (e) the approximate heat transferred between states 1 and 2.

Ans. (a) 206 gr., 56.6 Btu/lb. da., (b) 78 gr., (c) 26.5 Btu/lb. da., (d) 128 gr./lb. da., (e) 30.1 Btu/lb. da.

381. It is desired to process atmospheric air at state 1, 92°F and 60% relative humidity, to state 2, 75°F and 40% relative humidity. Sketch the necessary processes on the Ts plane, using refrigeration, and solve by chart only. (a) To what temperature must the atmospheric air be cooled? (b) How much moisture is removed? (c) What are the wet-bulb temperatures at states 1 and 2?

Ans. (a) 49°F, (b) 0.01245 lb./lb. da., (c) 80°F, 59.5°F.

382. A cooling tower cools condensing water from 102°F to 80°F. Atmospheric conditions are: barometer, 29.92 in. Hg; 80°F d.b.; $\phi = 50\%$. This air leaves the cooling tower at 96°F d.b. and $\phi = 90\%$. Show an energy diagram of the tower and write the equa-

tion for the energy balance. Determine (a) the mass of condenser water cooled, lb./lb. da., (b) the volume of atmospheric air required to cool 50,000 lb./hr. of water, (c) the amount of make-up needed per hour.

Ans. (a) 1.278, (b) 9025 cfm, (c) 892 lb./hr.

383. An air-conditioned auditorium requires 5000 cfm of free air and is to be maintained at 75°F and 50% relative humidity (state 2). At the maximum operating condition, the outside air is expected to be 96°F d.b. and 85°F w.b. (state 1). The free air is cooled in a spray of cold water until the humidity ratio reaches the desired value. It is then delivered to the auditorium, and the heating of this cooled air to the inside conditions is balanced by the heat flow into the building. (Assume that there is no addition of moisture during the heating process.) Find (a) p_{v1} from Carrier's equation, (b) ω_1, ω_2, and the H_2O condensed, (c) the dew point for state 2, (d) the heat extracted from the air (ΔH), (e) the tons of refrigeration needed. (f) Make an energy diagram of the cooling operation (air and cooling water), write the energy-balance equation, and find the amount of water delivered to the spray if it enters at 40°F and leaves at 54°F.

Ans. (a) 0.5385 psia, (b) 35.4 gal. per hr. condensed, (c) 55.3°F, (d) 25.46 Btu/lb. da., (e) 43.6, (f) 74.8 gpm.

384. An air washer uses refrigerated water to cool and dehumidify air. The amount of cold water entering is 2.55 lb./lb. da. at 38°F; water leaves at 48°F; $\omega_1 = 0.0214$ lb. v./lb. da.; $\omega_2 = 0.00762$ lb. v./lb. da. Make an energy diagram of the cooling water as the system and find the heat transferred.

Ans. 25.7 Btu/lb. da.

385–390. These numbers may be used for other problems.

FUELS AND COMBUSTION

267. Solid Fuels. We have observed from our study of steam generators that the fuels used may be solid, liquid, or gaseous. Among solid fuels, we find coal, including lignite (§ 268), wood, peat, and several manufactured combustibles such as coke, charcoal, and briquets.

Peat, semicarbonized vegetable matter formed by the partial decomposition of various plants in water, is little used in this country. Until it is dried, it has a very high moisture content. *Lignite,* a brownish sort of coal in a state between peat and bituminous coal, exists in great quantity. *Coke,* mostly carbon and ash, is made by heating bituminous coal in little or no air and driving out the volatile matter (which becomes coke-oven gas). *Charcoal,* made from wood by distilling the volatile products, has many special uses, but it is not often used in power plants.

268. Analysis of Coal. A relatively simple and common commercial analysis is called the *proximate analysis.* This analysis shows the percentages of moisture, volatile matter, fixed carbon, and ash. If appropriate, the sulfur content may be determined. The test procedure for these determinations has been carefully worked out and standardized.* The amount of moisture depends upon the immediately preceding history of the coal, whether it is freshly mined, whether it has dried in air, whether it has been rained on, etc. It is determined from the loss of weight of a sample which has been dried for an hour in a standardized oven at about 225°F. The volatile matter consists mostly of hydrocarbons (chemically of the form C_xH_y), and it is driven off at high temperature with no air present. The ash is the residue after complete combustion, and the fixed carbon is taken as 100% minus the sum of the percentages of moisture, volatile matter, and ash. The *ultimate analysis,* which is more elaborate, gives the moisture and ash (and sulfur) as in the proximate analysis, but it details the other elements as percentages *by weight* of carbon, hydrogen, oxygen, and nitrogen. This gravimetric breakdown permits a theoretical computation of the flue-gas analysis for complete combustion for comparison purposes.

* ASME Test Code for Solid Fuels.

The analyses of coal are sometimes stated on moisture-free or ash-free bases. These bases are computed from the foregoing analyses by simple arithmetic.

269. Kinds of Coal. Various ways of classifying coal have been devised. (See ASTM Specification D388-38.) The names below are accepted practice but the analyses are only typical.

1. *Meta-anthracite,* the highest rank of anthracite, found in Rhode Island, contains a minimum of volatile matter and a maximum of fixed carbon. Typical analysis, dry basis (moisture free): volatile matter, 1.2%; fixed carbon, 90.7%; ash, 8.1%; typical moisture as received, 2.8%.

2. *Anthracite coal,* found in Pennsylvania, is hard and burns without smoke. It is low in volatile matter, high in carbon. Typical analysis, dry basis: volatile matter, 3.4%; fixed carbon, 87.2%; ash, 9.4%; moisture as received, 3.3%.

3. *Semianthracite coal,* also hard, burns with very little smoke. Typical analysis, dry basis: volatile matter, 13%; fixed carbon, 74.6%; ash, 12.4%; moisture as received, 2.4%.

4. *Semibituminous coal* does not result in much smoke and is not as hard as the anthracites. Observe the increase in volatile matter. Typical analysis, dry basis: volatile matter, 16%; fixed carbon, 79.1%; ash, 4.9%; moisture as received, 3.6%.

5. *Bituminous coal* has still more volatile matter, which results in considerable smoke if incompletely burned. (Some unburned volatile matter is invisible as it leaves the stack, so that the absence of smoke is not necessarily indicative of complete combustion.) The volatile matter varies between wide limits and the coal is relatively soft. Some bituminous coals are good coking coals, some are not. Most of the coal used in this country is bituminous. It resists weathering excellently. Typical analysis, dry basis: volatile matter, 34.3%; fixed carbon, 59.2%; ash, 6.5%; moisture as received, 1.4%.

6. *Subbituminous coal,* sometimes called black lignite, slacks on exposure to weather and usually has a relatively high initial moisture content. It pulverizes easily. Typical analysis, dry basis: volatile matter, 42.8%; fixed carbon, 54.4%; ash, 2.8%; moisture as received, 17%.

7. *Lignite,* brown in color with a woody structure, also has a high initial moisture content (30–45%) and slacks on exposure more readily than subbituminous. It is widely used in regions, mostly west of the Mississippi, where better coals are not plentiful. With properly designed equipment, it burns very well. Typical analysis as mined: moisture, 33%; volatile matter, 30%; fixed carbon, 30%; ash, 7%.

8. *Cannel coal,* not falling in any particular system of classification, is bituminous but has an extra high hydrogen content. It is used for the manufacture of gas.

Any of the foregoing fuels can be burned in properly designed furnaces with practically no smoke. The references to smoking apply in particular to small hand-stoked furnaces. The use made of these various coals is largely determined by economic considerations. Since coal is bulky, its cost rapidly increases as the distance of shipment increases. Thus, anthracite, for example, is seldom used at great distances from those regions where anthracite is mined, mostly in Pennsylvania. In general, the best coals are found in the eastern part of the country.

270. Liquid Fuels. The most important commercial liquid fuels are petroleum and the products obtained from it. Others used under favorable economic conditions include alcohol and coal tar (from distillation of coal). Fuel oil, which is a complex mixture of hydrocarbons, varies in grade from very light oils, for use in household and other small heating units, to heavy oils which have to be heated to reduce viscosity before they can be readily sprayed into the furnace. In addition to fuel oil, petroleum yields gasoline, kerosene, and lubricating oils. Moreover, in the refining processes, petroleum coke, a solid residue of 90–95% fixed carbon useful as a fuel, is sometimes obtained. Fuel oil is also made by the hydrogenation of coal. A typical ultimate analysis of a No. 2 fuel oil is: 12.5% H_2, 87.2% C, 0.3% S, 0.02% N_2. Most crude oils will contain 10-14% H_2.

271. Gaseous Fuels. Where available, *natural gas* is usually the cheapest gaseous fuel. Its principal constituent is methane (CH_4), although some of the California gases (and some others, too) contain up to one third by volume of ethane (C_2H_6). A typical Oklahoma natural gas has a volumetric composition of 84.1% CH_4, 6.7% C_2H_6, 0.8% CO_2, 8.4% N_2. The ultimate analysis of the same gas is 20.85% H_2, 64.84% C, 12.9% N_2, 1.41% O_2.

Producer gas, made in a gas producer, is the outcome of the incomplete combustion of wood, coal, or coke, principally of bituminous coal. Commonly, steam is blown through the fuel bed. Because of the incomplete combustion, CO is formed, and because of the breakdown of the steam molecule (H_2O), hydrogen is formed. Thus, the principal constituents which have heating value are carbon monoxide (CO) and hydrogen (H_2). A typical analysis would approximate 25% CO, 3% CH_4, 13% H_2, 5% CO_2; remainder, nitrogen and miscellaneous gases.

Blast-furnace gas is given off during the operation of a blast furnace, wherein the iron ore is smelted, the first step in the manufacture of steel.

Since it has heating value, it is used locally in gas engines and in various furnaces. A typical analysis would show by volume about 13% CO_2, 27% CO, 2% H_2, the remainder being mostly nitrogen with a small amount of methane (CH_4).

Coke-oven gas is a by-product of the manufacture of coke by the destructive distillation of coal. Since coke is a fuel for blast furnaces, coke-oven gas is often available at steel mills. A characteristic heating value of coke-oven gas is 540 Btu/cu. ft. Inasmuch as it has a higher heating value than blast-furnace gas, it is often mixed with blast-furnace gas to produce a richer fuel where both gases are available. A typical analysis would show by volume about 6% CO, 57% H_2, 27% CH_4, the balance being smaller amounts of miscellaneous gases.

Except as available as a by-product, manufactured gases are generally too expensive for use in the generation of power, but they are commonly used for domestic purposes in cities.

272. Combustion. As it is commonly understood, combustion is a rapid oxidation of a substance accompanied by the release of considerable energy and by a substantial increase in temperature of the substances in the reaction. It is a complex phenomenon of which our knowledge is incomplete. As in other specialized phases of applied thermodynamics, such as internal combustion engines, refrigeration, etc., we shall do no more than lay an elementary foundation.

We shall approach all combustion reactions in the same general manner, an approach involving a single technique. This plan will facilitate the learning process. In practice, where repetition is involved, it is usually possible to simplify the computations, for example by deriving special equations, equations which a technician could easily use, thereby leaving the engineer free for more valuable activities. Once you have learned the basic idea of obtaining combustion equations, one problem is as easy as another, though some will be longer than others.

We shall for convenience attach special meanings to two words as follows. By *ideal* combustion or combustion in *ideal* air, we shall mean what the chemist calls the stoichiometric air; the amount of air involved is exactly that needed to furnish the necessary oxygen for complete theoretical combustion. We also speak of it as "100% air." By *theoretical* combustion or a *theoretical* reaction, we shall mean combustion as defined by a simple, balanced chemical equation for the specified conditions, in any amount of air—deficiency, excess, or ideal—and the *theoretical* amount of air is that amount which satisfies any theoretical chemical equation.

The names of a few of the more common hydrocarbons together with their chemical formulas are given in Table XIII, Appendix.   Commercial petroleum fuels are mixtures of hydrocarbons; for example, hexadane, $C_{16}H_{34}$, is found in fuel oil, but also in many others; regular and premium grades of gasoline have *an average* molecule of the approximate form $(CH_2)_x$, that is, there are two atoms of hydrogen for each atom of carbon, yet gasoline contains octane, heptane, etc.

A review of the discussion of fuels shows that the combustible elements are *carbon* (free, combined with hydrogen, or incompletely combined with oxygen), *hydrogen* (free or combined), and *sulfur*.   Even though the burning of sulfur releases heat, it is an undesirable component because its presence results in the formation of corroding acids.   If the sulfur content of a fuel is too high, the cost of maintaining and replacing equipment using this fuel may be so great as to make it uneconomical to use the fuel at all.

273. Composition of Air.   Atmospheric air has a volumetric composition of 20.99% oxygen, 78.03% nitrogen, somewhat less than 1% argon, with small quantities or traces of several inert gases such as water vapor, carbon dioxide, helium, hydrogen, and neon.   For engineering calculations, it is usually accurate enough to include all inert gases as nitrogen and use the analysis 21% oxygen 79% nitrogen, by volume.   Thus, we may say that in 100 mols of air, there are approximately 21 mols of N_2 and 79 mols of N_2, or

(**a**) $$\frac{79}{21} = 3.76 \frac{\text{mols } N_2}{\text{mols } O_2} \quad \text{or} \quad 3.76 \frac{\text{cu. ft. } N_2}{\text{cu. ft. } O_2},$$

a useful number to memorize for the current study.   The approximate gravimetric composition of air is

$$23.1\% \ O_2, \ 76.9\% \ N_2, \text{ by weight,}$$

or there are $76.9/23.1 = 3.32$ lb. N_2/lb. O_2.

274. Combustion of Hydrogen.   We may use hydrogen as an illustration of the information which can be obtained from the equation of the chemical reaction.   We recall at the outset that the coefficient of the chemical equation stands for the number of molecules in each reaction, which is the same thing as saying that it is proportional to the number of mols of each element or constituent, or to the volumes of each when each one is a gas at the same pressure and temperature (Avogadro's law).   The reader can no doubt write the equation for the combustion of hydrogen and on this account may pass over the detailed explanation below.   However, the method of procedure for the more complicated problems is being explained in this simple case, so study it carefully.   If hydrogen is burned in the ideal amount of air we might first write

(b) $H_2 + a\,O_2 + 3.76a\,N_2 \longrightarrow b\,H_2O + 3.76a\,N_2,$

in which 1 molecule (or mol) of fuel (H_2) is shown, a molecules (or mols) of O_2 (amount unknown), $3.76a$ molecules (or mols) of N_2 from equation (a). We know that the reaction results in some amount (b molecules or mols) of H_2O and that the N_2 survives the reaction unchanged at $3.76a$ molecules (or mols). The coefficients a and b are obtained by using the law of conservation of mass; that is, there must be the *same mass of each of the elements on both sides of the equation.* This simple principle is the basis of balancing all chemical equations. In applying the law, we write what we call material balances. In this case, we would make a hydrogen balance and an oxygen balance. The mass of hydrogen in the first term is proportional to the number of atoms of hydrogen, which is the product of the coefficient 1 and the number of atoms in the molecule 2, as shown by the subscript. On the right-hand side of the equation, the total number of atoms of hydrogen is $2b$, the product of the coefficient b of the H_2O term and the subscript 2 on the H element. By the conservation of mass, there must be the same number of hydrogen atoms before and after the reaction; hence

(c)   Hydrogen balance: $2 = 2b,$ or $b = 1.$

Considering the oxygen, we see that there are $2a$ atoms on the left-hand side of (b) and b atoms on the right-hand side. Since the number is the same, we have

(d)   Oyxgen balance: $2a = b = 1,$ or $a = \dfrac{1}{2}.$

With a and b known, the chemical equation for the theoretical combustion of hydrogen in ideal air can now be written

(e) $H_2 + \dfrac{1}{2}\,O_2 + 1.88\,N_2 \longrightarrow H_2O + 1.88\,N_2.$

In the case of gaseous substances at a certain pressure and temperature, the coefficients of the terms in the chemical equation are proportional to volumes; thus, from (e), we write

1 mol $H_2 + \dfrac{1}{2}$ mol $O_2 + 1.88$ mols N_2 *react to* 1 mol $H_2O + 1.88$ mols $N_2,$

or

1 cu. ft. $H_2 + \dfrac{1}{2}$ cu. ft. $O_2 + 1.88$ cu. ft. $N_2 \longrightarrow 1$ cu. ft. $H_2O + 1.88$ cu. ft. $N_2;$

[ALL GASEOUS AND AT SAME p AND T]

and to make it easy to write, we do it this way:

$$\text{Relative volumes: } 1 + \frac{1}{2} + 1.88 \longrightarrow 1 + 1.88.$$

What these coefficients tell us is that, for example, it takes $\frac{1}{2}$ cu. ft. O_2 or 2.38 $(= 0.5 + 1.88)$ cu. ft. of air to burn completely 1 cu. ft. of H_2O; that the volume of the **reactants** (on the left-hand side) is greater than the volume of the **products** (on the right-hand side), or 3.88 cu. ft. reduce to 2.88 cu. ft. after the reaction when the volumes are measured *at the same pressure and temperature* and *when the H_2O is a vapor.* If the products are cooled to normal atmospheric temperature, most of the H_2O condenses. The volume occupied by a liquid is negligible compared to that occupied by a gas, so that the volume of liquid H_2O is ignored. Thus, with volumes measured at a low temperature, we could say that 3.88 cu. ft. of reactants reduce to about 1.88 cu. ft. of products in this particular case. Also note that the volumetric analysis of the reactants is easy to find; $1/3.88 = 32.5\%$ H_2 by volume, for example.

Now returning to equation (e), we may write the values of the relative masses involved. The mass of 1 mol H_2 is 2 lb., where in combustion computations we generally use approximate whole-number atomic weights, which are sufficiently accurate for most computations. The mass of $\frac{1}{2}$ mol O_2 is $(\frac{1}{2}$ mol$)(32$ lb./mol$) = 16$ lb. The mass of 1.88 mols N_2 is $(1.88)(28)$ $= 52.6$ lb. The mass of 1 mol H_2O is $(1)(2 + 16) = 18$ lb. In the same order in which the terms appear in (e), we have the

$$\text{Relative mass: } 2 + 16 + 52.6 = 18 + 52.6,$$
$$\text{Per pound } H_2: 1 + 8 + 26.3 = 9 + 26.3.$$

Since mass in conserved, there must be the same mass on each side of the equation (always make this check—we have 35.3 lb. on each side). From the mass relationships, we can say that it takes 8 lb. O_2 or 34.3 lb. air to burn 1 lb. H_2. The air/fuel (A/F) and the fuel/air (F/A) ratios are

$$\text{A/F} = 34.3 \text{ lb. air/lb. fuel,} \qquad \text{F/A} = 0.0291 \text{ lb. fuel/lb. air.}$$

We see also that there result 9 lb. H_2O for each pound of hydrogen burned.

275. Combustion of Carbon in Deficient Air. Fuels may be burned in more or less than the ideal amount of air. Suppose, by way of illustration, that this example be the combustion of carbon in deficient air, say 80% of ideal. First, we need to know what the complete reaction is, namely to CO_2, and second, how much air is required for ideal combustion. For the ideal requirement, consider the oxygen only (nitrogen varies directly with the oxygen):

$$C + O_2 \longrightarrow CO_2$$
$$\text{Mols: } 1 + 1 \longrightarrow 1.$$

We see that it takes 1 mol O_2 to burn 1 mol C to CO_2. Therefore, 80% of ideal air means that only 0.8 mol O_2 is available.

Now note that carbon is a solid; as such, it occupies negligible volume. Consequently, a mol of C (12 lb.) is *not* proportional to volume. Next, consider what the products of combustion may be. No doubt, some unburned carbon passes out in practice, but theoretically we assume that each carbon atom finds some oxygen. Thus with a deficiency of air, the products consist of CO_2, CO, and N_2. Knowing that there is 0.8 mol O_2, the given condition, we write

$$C + 0.8\ O_2 + (0.8)(3.76)\ N_2 \longrightarrow a\ CO_2 + b\ CO + (0.8)(3.76)\ N_2.$$
$$\text{Carbon balance: } 1 = a + b;$$
$$\text{Oxygen balance: } 1.6 = 2a + b.$$

Solving the material balance equations simultaneously, we get $a = 0.6$ and $b = 0.4$. The *theoretical* combustion is then represented by

(f)
$$C + 0.8\ O_2 + 3.01\ N_2 \longrightarrow 0.6\ CO_2 + 0.4\ CO + 3.01\ N_2$$

Mols:	$1 + 0.8$	$+ 3.01$	$\longrightarrow 0.6$	$+ 0.4$	$+ 3.01.$
Relative volumes:	$0 + 0.8$	$+ 3.01$	$\longrightarrow 0.6$	$+ 0.4$	$+ 3.01.$
Relative mass:	$12 + 25.6$	$+ 84.28$	$= 26.4$	$+ 11.2$	$+ 84.28.$
Mass/lb. C:	$1 + 2.133$	$+ 7.02$	$= 2.2$	$+ 0.933$	$+ 7.02.$

From the foregoing, we see that with 80% ideal air, 1 mol of carbon produces 0.6 mol CO_2 and 0.4 CO. We may also say, for example, that under the specified conditions there is 0.933 lb. CO/lb. C. None of the products is likely to condense; hence, a volume of reactants of 3.81 cu. ft. increases to 4.01 cu. ft. of products (same t and p). Compare with the change of volume during the combustion of hydrogen, which was a *decrease*. The volume of products may be less than, equal to, or greater than the volume of the reactants (at specified t and p). From the relative volumes, a volumetric analysis of reactants and products can be computed. From the masses, gravimetric analyses may be made.

276. Combustion of Carbon Monoxide in Excess Air. Let the next example be one of excess air in the combustion of CO. The ideal oxygen would be that required to produce complete combustion to CO_2;

$$CO + \tfrac{1}{2}\ O_2 \longrightarrow CO_2.$$

Let the amount of oxygen be arbitrarily 1 mol/mol CO (100% excess air, we say). Then the theoretical combustion will use all of the CO and there will be O_2 in the products. Hence, we may write

$$CO + O_2 + 3.76 \, N_2 \longrightarrow a \, CO_2 + b \, O_2 + 3.76 \, N_2.$$

Carbon balance: $1 = a$,   or $a = 1.$
Oxygen balance: $1 + 2 = 2a + 2b$, or $b = \frac{1}{2}.$

The theoretical equation becomes

(g)

	CO	+ O_2	+ 3.76 N_2	$\longrightarrow$	CO_2	+ $\frac{1}{2}$ O_2	+ 3.76 N_2.
Mols:	1	+ 1	+ 3.76	$\longrightarrow$	1	+ $\frac{1}{2}$	+ 3.76.
Relative volumes:	1	+ 1	+ 3.76	$\longrightarrow$	1	+ $\frac{1}{2}$	+ 3.76.
Relative masses:	28	+ 32	+ 104.94	=	44	+ 16	+ 104.94.
Mass/pound CO:	1	+ 1.14	+ 3.76	=	1.57	+ 0.571	+ 3.76.

The air-fuel ratio is thus $1.14 + 3.76 = 4.9$ lb. air/lb. fuel. The detail of inserting unknown coefficients a, b, etc., into the foregoing equations is not so important in these easy situations, but it is good practice in preparation for more difficult problems.

277. Combustion of a Hydrocarbon. What may be given in the case of a hydrocarbon is the chemical formula, as C_8H_{18}, or the ultimate analysis, as 84.2% C, 15.8% H_2 (other elements are present, but only sulfur would burn). In any case, it must be known whether combustion occurs with ideal air or with excess or deficient air. With this knowledge, we decide upon the products obtained in a theoretical reaction. If ideal air or more is supplied, we assume that the H_2 is burned to H_2O and the C is burned to CO_2. An excess of O_2 appears as O_2 in the products.

If there is deficient air, we assume for theoretical combustion that all of the H_2 burns to H_2O, because the affinity of oxygen for hydrogen is strong, and that the C burns to CO and CO_2, usually in unknown proportions. Follow the plan of § 275 in this case. If any sulfur (atomic weight = 32) is present, assume that it reacts to sulfur dioxide (SO_2). (Some of it reacts to SO_3 and then to sulfuric acid in the presence of H_2O.)

If the chemical formula for the hydrocarbon is known, the percentage of C and H_2 in the fuel can be computed. Thus, 1 mol of C_8H_{18} has a mass of

$$8 \times 12 + 18 = 114 \text{ lb., molecular weight,}$$

of which $8 \times 12 = 96$ lb. is C and 18 lb. is H_2; therefore, $96/144 = 84.2\%$ C, and $18/144 = 15.8\%$ C, gravimetric.

In the opposite direction, a chemical formula can be obtained from the ultimate analysis. For example, let there be $G_C = 80\%$ C and $G_H = 20\%$ H_2. The equivalent mols G/M for each are $80/12 = 6.67$ and $20/1 = 20$, which numbers are proportional to the number of atoms of C and H_2, respectively.   Equivalent hydrocarbons would be

$$C_{6.67}H_{20} \quad \text{or} \quad CH_3 \quad \text{or} \quad C_2H_6$$

or any one where the number of H_2 *atoms* is $20/6.67 = 3$ times the number of C atoms; designated $(CH_3)_x$. Notice that the molecular weight of $C_{6.67}H_{20}$ is 100.

One of the products of combustion of a hydrocarbon is H_2O. Therefore in working with volumes, one must know whether the H_2O is liquid or vapor. (See § 284). For present purposes, we shall assume that the temperature is above 150°F, which is likely to be above the temperature at which condensation starts, or below, say 80°F, which will cause most of the H_2O to condense. Moreover, if a normally liquid fuel is involved, as octane (C_8H_{18}), one must decide whether to count it as a liquid with negligible volume, or as a vapor conforming to Avogadro's law.

278. Example—Combustion of Octane. If gaseous C_8H_{18}, indicated by C_8H_{18} (*g*), is burned in ideal air, what volume of air at 140°F and 14 psia is required? Determine the relative volumes and masses of the constituents of the reactants and of the products, and compute the air-fuel ratio.

SOLUTION. The equation for C_8H_{18} would be easy to balance directly, but it is probably a good idea to continue with the regulation plan of analysis. Thus, the products are known to be some quantity of H_2O, CO_2, and N_2. The preliminary equation is

$$C_8H_{18} \, (g) + a \, O_2 + 3.76 \, a \, N_2 \longrightarrow b \, H_2O + c \, CO_2 + 3.76 \, a \, N_2.$$

The material balances give

$$\begin{array}{lll} \text{C:} \;\; 8 = c, & \text{or} & c = 8. \\ \text{H}_2\text{:} \; 18 = 2b, & \text{or} & b = 9. \\ \text{O}_2\text{:} \; 2a = b + 2c, & \text{or} & a = 12.5. \end{array}$$

Then, if the final temperature is low enough to have condensed the H_2O to liquid, indicated by H_2O (*l*), we get $[(3.76)(12.5) = 47]$

(h) $$C_8H_{18}(g) + 12.5 \, O_2 + 47 \, N_2 \longrightarrow 9 \, H_2O(l) + 8 \, CO_2 + 47 \, N_2$$

Mols:	1	$+ 12.5$	$+ 47$	$\longrightarrow 9$	$+ 8$	$+ 47$
Relative volume:	1	$+ 12.5$	$+ 47$	$\longrightarrow 0$	$+ 8$	$+ 47$
Relative mass:	114	$+ 400$	$+ 1316$	$= 162$	$+ 352$	$+ 1316$
Mass/pound fuel:	1	$+ 3.51$	$+ 11.54$	$= 1.42$	$+ 3.09$	$+ 11.54.$

The air/fuel ratio is $3.51 + 11.54 = 15.05$ lb. air/lb. fuel. At this stage, the volume of air may be computed in several different ways. Knowing that 15.05 lb. air/lb. fuel are required, we get $(140°F + 460 = 600°R)$

$$V_a = \frac{wRT}{p} = \frac{(15.05)(53.3)(600)}{(14)(144)} = 239 \text{ cu. ft./lb. fuel.}$$

279. Example—Finding Air Required and Products from Gravimetric Analysis of Fuel. The common practice with coal and other solid fuels is to define it by an ultimate analysis. Whenever a gravimetric analysis is given, convert to mols of each element; that is, if G is a percentage number,

$$(G_x \text{ lb.}/100 \text{ lb. fuel})/(M_x \text{ lb./mol}) = G_x/M_x \text{ mols}/100 \text{ lb. fuel.}$$

Given the ultimate analysis of an Illinois coal as follows, dry basis:

G	67.34% C,	4.67% H_2	8.47% O_2	1.25% N_2	4.77% S	13.5% Ash
G/M	5.61 C,	2.33 H_2	0.265 O_2	0.045 N_2	0.149 S	

The second line is obtained by dividing each G by the corresponding M of the element and the numbers are now *mols per* 100 lb. *of dry fuel*. Since the coefficients in the chemical equation are mols, we may write

$$[5.61 \text{ C} + 2.33 \text{ H}_2 + 0.265 \text{ O}_2 + 0.045 \text{ N}_2 + 0.149 \text{ S}] + a \text{ O}_2 + 3.76a \text{ N}_2$$
$$\longrightarrow b \text{ CO}_2 + c \text{ H}_2\text{O} + d \text{ SO}_2 + (3.76a + e) \text{ N}_2,$$

where the quantities within the brackets are for 100 lb. of dry fuel. The material balances are

C: $5.61 = b$,	or		$b = 5.61$.
N_2: $2(0.045 + 3.76a) = 2(3.76a + e)$,	or		$e = 0.045$.
H_2: $2.33 \times 2 = 2c$,	or		$c = 2.33$.
S: $0.149 = d$,	or		$d = 0.149$.
O_2: $(0.265 \times 2) + 2a = 2b + c + 2d$,	or		$a = 6.66$.

Now the chemical equation can be written showing the theoretical number of mols (or molecules) of each constituent for combustion in ideal air.

(i) $[5.61 \text{ C} + 2.33 \text{ H}_2 + 0.265 \text{ O}_2 + 0.045 \text{ N}_2 + 0.149 \text{ S}] + 6.66 \text{ O}_2 + 25.04 \text{ N}_2$
$$\longrightarrow 5.61 \text{ CO}_2 + 2.33 \text{ H}_2\text{O} + 0.149 \text{ SO}_2 + 25.09 \text{ N}_2.$$

It is a good idea to keep the elements of the fuel separate, by using brackets, and then there is no chance of confusing the oxygen and nitrogen of the fuel with the entering air. The mols of air are $6.66 + 25.04 = 31.7$ mols per 100 lb. of dry fuel; and at $M = 29$ lb./mol for air, we get

$$31.7 \times 29 = 919.3 \text{ lb. air}/100 \text{ lb. dry fuel, or } 9.19 \text{ lb. air/lb. dry fuel.}$$

Now that we have the theoretical chemical equation, almost any desired ratio is easily found. As before, the mols and relative volumes of each constituent would be indicated (carbon, sulfur, and coal are solids, zero volume), and the relative masses would be written down. Note that the relative masses are pounds per 100 lb. of dry coal.

Coal *as received* or *as fired* contains moisture, H_2O. If there is a considerable quantity of moisture in the coal, as in many low-grade coals, this is a serious matter, because some of the heating value of the combustible elements is necessarily used to evaporate the H_2O, and the latent heat of evaporation goes out of the stack as a loss. To get the air/fuel ratio for coal as fired, let the moisture content of the coal in the foregoing example be 12%. Then, there is 88% of dry coal, or 0.88 lb. dry fuel/lb. wet fuel (as fired). Thus,

$$\left(9.19 \, \frac{\text{lb. air}}{\text{lb. dry fuel}}\right) \left(0.88 \, \frac{\text{lb. dry fuel}}{\text{lb. as fired}}\right) = 8.1 \text{ lb. air/lb. fuel as fired.}$$

As previously mentioned, the sulfur content is frequently neglected in computations such as these. Moreover, the nitrogen in the fuel is usually a small quantity and as such it would not be missed in slide rule calculations. On the other hand, the practice is to include the oxygen, letting it count toward the oxygen required for combustion, as in the above example.

280. Analyzing the Products of Combustion. From the analysis of the products of combustion, we can determine approximately the actual amount of air supplied. There are various devices in use, of which Fig. 214, an

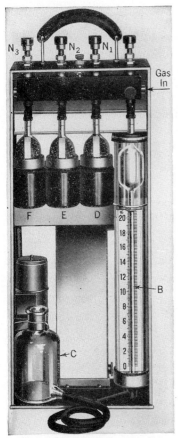

Orsat apparatus, is an example. The Orsat determines the percentages of CO_2, CO, and O_2 in the dry products (even though the test sample may be saturated with H_2O). Since the products from an internal combustion engine contain methane (CH_4) and hydrogen (H_2), these constituents can be (1) ignored, (2) determined by more complete test, or (3) estimated. Experience suggests

Fig. 214. Flue-Gas Analyzer. The bottle C containing water is connected to the burette B by a rubber tube. Raising and lowering the bottle causes the water to flow into and out of the burette. In operation, the air in the burette and the adjoining passages is first driven out by displacing it with the water in C. A sample of flue gas is then drawn into the burette B. During these preliminary operations, the needle valves N_1, N_2, and N_3 to the solution containers D, E, and F have been closed. With valve N_1 open, the sample of flue gas in the burette is forced into container D by raising bottle C. A solution of potassium hydroxide in D absorbs the carbon dioxide of the flue gas, leaving the other constituents unaffected. Remaining gas is returned to the burette by lowering C, and the loss of volume is noted. Successively, the gas is then forced into E, where a solution of pyrogallic acid in a solution of potassium hydroxide absorbs the oxygen, and into F, where a solution of cuprous chloride in ammonia absorbs the carbon monoxide. The remaining gas is assumed to be all nitrogen, or an estimation of other products is made.

Courtesy Ellison-Draft Gage Co., Chicago

that the amount of CH_4 is about 0.22% of the volume of dry exhaust gas and that the amount of free H_2 by volume is about half of the volumetric percentage of CO.*

From the products analysis, we can construct the corresponding theoretical chemical equation or obtain part of it, depending on what is known

* NACA report No. 476, 616.

about the fuel.   There are pitfalls and inevitable sources of error, such as unburned fuel in the ash and/or in the smoke.   (Smoke, what we see, *is* unburned fuel.)   Various situations arise in practice, which had best be covered by example.

Ordinarily, power plants keep a continuous record of the CO_2 in the flue gas, using a CO_2 recorder.   The amount of CO_2 is taken as an indicator of the efficiency of combustion on the theory that the more complete the combustion, the greater the percentage of CO_2 for a certain amount of excess air. However, an Orsat check on the other constituents is necessary from time to time, because under certain conditions an increase of CO_2 will be indicated (with decreasing excess air) when the loss due to incomplete combustion actually increases.   In a particular case, the optimum amount of CO_2 in the products should be determined from a test and this optimum value is not likely to be the maximum amount of CO_2 that the products can show.

281. Example—Known Percentage of Carbon in Fuel.   The analyses of the fuel and of the products may be complete, in which case several material balances may be made.   However, the more accurate estimate of the air is likely to be obtained from the carbon balance; hence, the amount of carbon *burned* is the only essential information needed with respect to the fuel if its free oxygen and nitrogen contents are negligibly small.

A flue-gas analysis of the dry products of the coal in the example of § 279 is made and found to be 15% CO_2, 3.5% O_2, and 0.2% CO, with the remainder assumed to be nitrogen, 81.3% N_2; all by volume of dry gases.   What excess or deficiency of air is supplied?

SOLUTION.   From § 279, we have the following mols of the elements per 100 lb. of dry fuel (for example, 67.34% C is $67.34/12 = 5.61$ mols C/100 lb.):

$$5.61 \text{ C}, \quad 2.33 \text{ H}_2, \quad 0.265 \text{ O}_2, \quad 0.045 \text{ N}_2, \quad 0.149 \text{ S}.$$

Considering *only the carbon*, we find the partial chemical equation is

$$a \text{ [5.61 C]} + \cdots \longrightarrow 15 \text{ CO}_2 + 0.2 \text{ CO} + 3.5 \text{ O}_2 + 81.3 \text{ N}_2 + \cdots .$$
[100 LB. DRY F]   [GIVEN PRODUCTS]

The dry product analysis is known and is written as given.   We do not know how much carbon was required to produce the CO_2 and CO in the 100 mols of products; therefore, a coefficient a is applied to the 5.61 mols of C.   A carbon balance gives

$$\text{C: } 5.61a = 15 + 0.2, \quad \text{or} \quad a = 2.71.$$

Noting that $5.61a = (5.61)(2.71) = 15.2$, we find

$$[15.2 \text{ C}] + \cdots \longrightarrow 15 \text{ CO}_2 + 0.2 \text{ CO} + 3.5 \text{ O}_2 + 81.3 \text{ N}_2 + \cdots .$$

It is customary to assume that the nitrogen measures the amount of air, provided there is none in the fuel, since it passes through the reaction unaffected.   The number of mols of O_2 which accompanied 81.3 mols N_2 are $81.3/3.76 = 21.6$ mols O_2.   Thus, the total mols of air are $81.3 + 21.6 = 102.9$ mols air.   The mass of air per lb. of carbon burned is

$$\frac{(102.9 \text{ mols})(29 \text{ lb./mol})}{(15.2 \text{ mols})(12 \text{ lb./mol})} = 16.36 \text{ lb. air/lb. C burned.}$$

If all the carbon in the fuel is burned and if the moisture content of the coal as fired is 12% [1 − 0.12 = 0.88 lb. dry fuel/lb. fuel as fired (f.a.f.)], we have the actual air as

$$\left(16.36 \frac{\text{lb. air}}{\text{lb. C}}\right)\left(0.6734 \frac{\text{lb. C}}{\text{lb. dry fuel}}\right)\left(0.88 \frac{\text{lb. dry fuel}}{\text{lb. as fired}}\right) = 9.7 \frac{\text{lb. air}}{\text{lb. as fired}},$$

versus 8.1 lb. air for ideal combustion.   The excess is (9.7 − 8.1)/8.1 $\doteq$ 19.8%.

282. Allowance for Unburned Carbon.   When the amount of unburned carbon is known, it can be included in the computations.   Suppose that samples of the *refuse,* which is the total discharge from the grate and is equal to the carbon plus ash, have been tested and found to consist of a certain fraction by weight of carbon; that is, the pounds of C per pound of refuse.   The solution is outlined as follows:

$$1 - (\text{lb. C/lb. refuse}) = \text{lb. ash/lb. refuse.}$$

$$\left(\frac{\text{lb. C in refuse}}{\text{lb. refuse}}\right) \div \left(\frac{\text{lb. ash in refuse}}{\text{lb. refuse}}\right) = \frac{\text{lb. C in refuse}}{\text{lb. ash}}.$$

$$\left(\frac{\text{lb. ash}}{\text{lb. dry fuel}}\right) \times \left(\frac{\text{lb. C in refuse}}{\text{lb. ash}}\right) = \frac{\text{lb. C in refuse}}{\text{lb. dry fuel}}.$$

This value subtracted from the total carbon in a pound of fuel will be the carbon burned.

Using data of the previous example and assuming that the refuse contains 10.6% C (0.106 lb. C/lb. refuse), we have 1 − 0.106 = 0.894 lb. ash/lb. refuse and, with 13.5% ash in the dry fuel, § 279,

$$(0.135)\left(\frac{0.106}{0.894}\right) = 0.016 \text{ lb. C unburned/lb. dry fuel.}$$

Burned carbon is then 0.6734 − 0.016 = 0.6574 lb. C burned/lb. dry fuel.

283. Example—Composition of Fuel Unknown.   This type of problem is typically one involving hydrocarbons C_xH_y of unknown composition, but it can be applied to other fuels.   However, unless the fuel has very small amounts of O_2, N_2, and S, this approach, which assumes that the fuel contains only carbon and hydrogen, is subject to significant error.

The *dry* exhaust from an automotive engine at 1 atm pressure has a volumetric analysis as follows: 12.5% CO_2, 3.1% O_2, 0.3% CO, which is the information obtained from the Orsat.   (There should also be about 0.22% CH_4 and 0.15% H_2— see § 280.   These quantities may be included in the computations if desired, but we shall omit them to shorten the presentation.)   Assume that the remainder of the exhaust is $N_2 = 84.1\%$.   (a) Set up the theoretical combustion equation, finding values of x and y in C_xH_y. Determine (b) the air/fuel ratio, (c) the partial pressure of the H_2O in the hot exhaust.

SOLUTION. The products analysis shows no H_2O, but *we must not forget to include it because it is sure to be there.* Since there is assumed to be no O_2 in the fuel, the O_2 on the left-hand side of the chemical equation is that which accompanies the N_2 in the air; $84.1/3.76 = 22.4$ mols O_2.

$$C_xH_y + 22.4\ O_2 + 84.1\ N_2 \longrightarrow 12.5\ CO_2 + 3.1\ O_2 + 0.3\ CO + 84.1\ N_2 + a\ H_2O.$$

The material balances:

$$
\begin{array}{lll}
C: x = 12.5 + 0.3, & \text{or} & x = 12.8 \\
O_2: (2)(22.4) = (2)(12.5) + (2)(3.1) + 0.3 + a, & \text{or} \quad a = 13.3 \\
H_2: y = 2a = (2)(13.3), & \text{or} & y = 26.6
\end{array}
$$

Thus, *provided* all of the carbon and hydrogen did burn, the fuel is represented by $C_{12.8}H_{26.6}$, or it is a mixture of hydrocarbons for which the ratio $y/x = 26.6/12.8$ is an average value. The chemical equation tells no more. The balanced equation then is

$$C_{12.8}H_{26.6} + 22.4\ O_2 + 84.1\ N_2$$
$$\longrightarrow 12.5\ CO_2 + 3.1\ O_2 + 0.3\ CO + 84.1\ N_2 + 13.3\ H_2O.$$

(b) The "molecular weight" of $C_{12.8}H_{26.6}$ is $(12)(12.8) + 26.6 = 180.2$ lb./mol fuel. Since the mols of air per mol of fuel are $22.4 + 84.1 = 106.5$ mols air/mol fuel, we have the air/fuel (A/F) ratio as

$$A/F = \frac{(106.5)(29)}{180.2} = 17.1 \text{ lb. air/lb. fuel.}$$

(c) The partial pressure is obtained from the volumetric percentage. In hot gases, the H_2O is not condensed and its percentage is

$$B_{H_2O} = 13.3/(12.5 + 3.1 + 0.3 + 84.1 + 13.3) = 11.8\%.$$
$$p_{H_2O} = (0.118)(14.7) = 1.73 \text{ psia.}$$

284. Heats of Combustion. After a chemical reaction occurs within a system, heat either flows into or out of the system. The chemist calls this heat, as measured in certain ways, the *heat of reaction.* The kind of reaction in which we are interested at the moment is one from which heat flows outward, and, in particular, the combustion reaction. In a general way, we speak of this energy as the **heat of combustion** or the **heating value.** This is not a unique number but depends upon the circumstances under which it is obtained.

One of these circumstances is the bomb calorimeter, Fig. 215, used for solid and liquid fuels. A carefully measured quantity of fuel is placed in the calorimeter, ignited by an electric fuse, and burned in the oxygen-filled bomb. The heat rejected by the constant volume system in the bomb in cooling back to the original temperature, when corrected to the standard condition of 77°F, is one of the heating values of the fuel. Another heating value is obtained from the steady flow or constant pressure calorimeter, Fig. 216, through which the fuel and air flow at essentially constant pressure.*

We have noticed that water vapor (steam) appears in the products of combustion whenever the fuel contains hydrogen. When the products are cooled well below the temperature at the dew point of this vapor, most of it condenses, giving up heat in an amount depending on the amount of H_2O condensed. If all of the vapor formed by combustion is condensed when the products have reached the initial test temperature, the corresponding

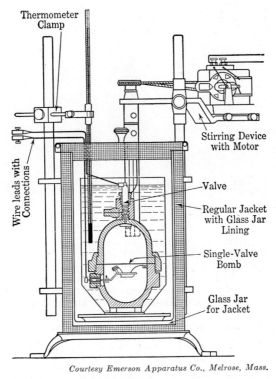

Thermometer Clamp

Stirring Device with Motor

Valve

Regular Jacket with Glass Jar Lining

Single-Valve Bomb

Glass Jar for Jacket

Wire leads with Connections

Courtesy Emerson Apparatus Co., Melrose, Mass.

Fig. 215.   Bomb Calorimeter.

heating value is termed the **higher** or **gross heating value** or the **higher heat of combustion**, q_h. The **lower heating value** or the **lower heat of combustion** q_l is the higher value minus the latent heat of the condensed water vapor. A fuel without H_2 does not have a higher and a lower heating value because all of the other products remain gaseous at test temperatures.

If a small amount of water is placed in the bomb, the gases in it become saturated with vapor, so that all of the vapor *due to combustion* condenses. The result is the *higher* heating value q_h, Btu/lb. fuel. The lower heating

* The difference between these heating values is usually small and is often ignored in some types of engineering calculations.

value of q_l is obtained by subtracting the internal energy of evaporation of the H_2O at the standard temperature of 77°F. However, the heating values given in Table XIII, Appendix, are for the constant pressure combustion.

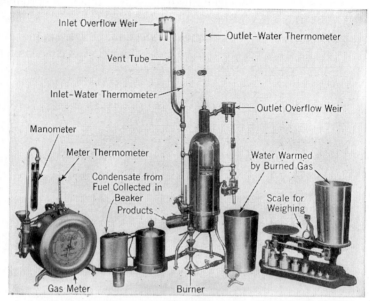

Fig. 216. *Calorimeter, Constant Pressure Burning.* The observations in operating this calorimeter include: a measured amount of gas, temperatures of inlet and outlet water from which the heat is computed, the mass of water accepting this heat, the inlet gas temperature, the temperature of the products (exhaust), the mass of condensate from the hydrogen of the fuel (in condensate beaker). All readings are corrected in accordance with the calibration of the instruments, and corrections may be made for atmospheric pressure, temperature, and humidity to reduce the results to standard conditions—77°F(25°C), 29.92-in. barometer.

The relation between the higher and lower heating values at constant pressure is

(j) $$q_l = q_h - 1050.4w_w \text{ Btu/lb. fuel}$$

where w_w lb. H_2O/lb. fuel is the mass of H_2O formed during combustion [which is (9)(mass of hydrogen in fuel), § 274]. If accuracy of heating values is important, see a more detailed discussion.*

The heating values of coals vary widely. Since an approximate heating value is often advantageous, Dulong's empirical formula may be used if the ultimate analysis is known:

(k) $$q_h = 14,500\,C + 62,000(H - O/8) + 4000\,S \text{ Btu/lb.,} \qquad \text{[COAL]}$$

* For example, Faires, *Thermodynamics*, Macmillan.

where C, H (for hydrogen), O (for oxygen), and S are the gravimetric percentages of each of these elements in the fuel.

285. Dissociation. At low temperatures, the reactions depicted by the combustion equations are completed virtually as shown. However, at high temperatures, one or more of the products may break up into its elements; that is, the reaction proceeds in both directions at once, thus

$$H_2 + \tfrac{1}{2} O_2 \rightleftarrows H_2O, \quad \text{and} \quad CO + \tfrac{1}{2} O_2 \rightleftarrows CO_2,$$

a phenomenon called **dissociation.** At a low temperature, say 1000°F, dissociation or the reverse reaction occurs but at such a low rate as to be negligible. Above, say, 3500°F, the amount of CO in the products starts to increase significantly with temperature, and the fact of incomplete combustion at higher temperatures cannot be ignored. Similarly, dissociation of the H_2O molecule becomes important above some 4500°F.

The amount of dissociation at any temperature, as measured, say, by the amount of CO and H_2 molecules in the products, can be predicted (computed). For a particular fuel system, there is a condition of the system wherein the rate of the forward reaction is equal to the rate of the reverse reactions, in which case there is no change in the concentrations of the various substances. This condition is spoken of as **chemical equilibrium** or **reaction equilibrium,** and when it is reached the temperature of the mixture will not rise further. Thus, temperatures computed to be above about 3500°F for hydrocarbon fuels are higher than actual temperatures unless dissociation was taken into account.

The foregoing is not to imply that combustion remains incomplete, since, if energy is removed by heat transfer or work done, the temperature tends to fall and more of the fuel reacts to CO_2 or H_2O. In an internal combustion engine, combustion may be practically complete shortly after the expansion stroke begins.

286. Energy Balance on a Steam Generator. The reader now has a background for understanding the details of an energy balance on a steam generator, which is usually computed on the basis of 1 lb. of fuel or as a percentage of the higher heating value of the fuel (see Fig. 117, p. 195). The following items may be accounted for:

1. Heat transferred to the H_2O. This item is sometimes broken down into two parts as in Fig. 117: the heat to evaporate the water and the heat to superheat the steam. The computation is made by equation (b), § 158, or from $Q = w_{bo.}(h_2 - h_1)$, where $w_{bo.}$ lb. steam/lb. fuel (not lb./hr.) is the mass of steam, h_2 is the enthalpy of the departing steam, and h_1 is the enthalpy of the entering water.

2. Loss due to H_2O formed by the burning of hydrogen in the fuel. As a rule, we purposely do not try to reduce the temperature of the products below the dew point of the H_2O because of the corrosion problem. The amount of this loss is

(1) $$E_1 = w_{w1}(h_1 - h_2) = 9w_{H_2}(h_1 - h_2) \text{ Btu/lb. fuel,}$$

where w_{w1} lb./lb. fuel is the mass of H_2O *formed during combustion* (w_{H_2} is the mass of hydrogen per pound of fuel), h_1 is the enthalpy of the steam in the products at the temperature of the combustion products as they leave the last heating surface, and h_2 is the enthalpy of water at, say, the reference temperature of the heating value, 77°F. This loss is designated as "Due to H_2O of Combustion" in Fig. 117.

3. Loss due to water in the fuel. If the fuel is coal, it generally is wet in its as-fired condition. This water is evaporated during combustion and departs as steam in the products. Thus, this loss is similar to that in item 2 and is computed from

(m) $$E_2 = w_{w2}(h_1 - h_2) \text{ Btu/lb. fuel,}$$

where w_{w2} lb./lb. fuel is the free moisture in the fuel as fired, h_1 and h_2 are as defined under item 2.

4. Loss due to the energy of the dry products leaving the last heating surface (sometimes called sensible heat). Measured above the standard heating-value temperature, this loss is

(n) $$E_3 = w_{dg}(h_{p1} - h_{p2}) = w_{dg}c_p(t_1 - 77) \text{ Btu/lb. fuel,}$$

where w_{dg} lb./lb. fuel is the mass of dry products, t_1 is the exit temperature of the gases from the last heating surface, and the average value of c_p is about 0.24 Btu/lb-°R.

5. Loss due to heating the H_2O in the air supplied for combustion. This loss is small and often neglected. If the humidity ratio of the air is ω lb. v./lb. da., § 258, and if w_{da} is the pounds of dry air per pound of fuel, then ωw_{da} lb. v./lb. of fuel enters the furnace with the air. If this vapor has an average $c_p = 0.47$ Btu/lb-°R, then the magnitude of the loss is

(o) $$E_4 = \omega w_{da}.0.47(t_1 - 77) \text{ Btu/lb. fuel,}$$

as measured above the same datum as before. The sum of items 4 and 5 is labeled "Loss, Theoretical Air and Its Moisture" plus "Loss in Excess Air and Its Moisture" in Fig. 117.

6. Loss from carbon in the refuse. See § 282 for a method of getting

w_{cr} lb. C in refuse/lb. fuel.   Then this mass times the heating value of carbon (Table XIII) is the loss:

(p) $$E_5 = w_{cr}(14,087) \text{ Btu/lb. fuel.}$$

7. Loss due to incomplete combustion of gases in the products.   This loss may be estimated by computing the heat which would be released if the components in the products were completely burned.   For example, for the CO in the products, we can use

(q) $$E_6 = \left(\frac{\text{lb. CO in prod.}}{\text{lb. C in prod.}}\right)\left(\frac{\text{lb. C in prod.}}{\text{lb. fuel}}\right)\left(\text{ht. val. of CO}\right) \text{Btu/lb. fuel.}$$
$$\qquad\qquad\quad [\text{A}] \qquad\qquad\quad [\text{B}] \qquad\qquad\quad [\text{C}]$$

Term [A] is obtained from the products analysis; for example,

$$\frac{\text{lb. CO}}{\text{lb. C}} = \frac{28\,CO}{12(CO + CO_2)},$$

where CO and CO_2 are the volumetric percentages (mols) of these components in the products.   Term [B] is simply the pounds of carbon *burned* per pound of fuel (that is, allow for carbon in the refuse, § 282).   Term [C] is 434.6 Btu/lb. CO, obtained from Table XIII.

8. Unaccounted for losses are obtained by subtracting the sum of items 1–7 above from the higher heating value of the fuel.   Unaccounted for losses will include radiation, heat given off from the hot ashes, energy losses due to leaks, unburned carbon in chimney ash, etc.

A base of other than 77°F may be used, but, if so, the heating values should theoretically be corrected to the base used.   The test codes permit the use of certain approximations for some of the foregoing losses.

287. Stokers.   For those interested, we shall close this chapter with a brief and limited discussion of fuel-burning equipment.   A stoker is a device to feed coal into a furnace.   The type of stoker to be used naturally depends upon the particulars involved in the installation, such as the kind of fuel, the kind of furnace, the draft pressure needed (which is not only different for different types of stokers but is affected by air heaters and economizers), the variability (or stability) of the load, and the overall cost involved. Where the costs are significant, the choice of stoker should be made only after a careful study of all economic factors, direct and indirect.

(*a*) *Traveling grates.*   A traveling grate, illustrated in the furnace of Fig. 119, p. 197, is an endless arrangement of grate bars or links, which moves slowly and continuously during operation.   The rate of movement and the thickness of the fuel bed can be regulated in accordance with the load.   The details of the construction vary with the manufacturer.   Fuels

Drive Sprocket

Courtesy Babcock & Wilcox Co., New York

Fig. 217.   Detail of a Chain Grate.

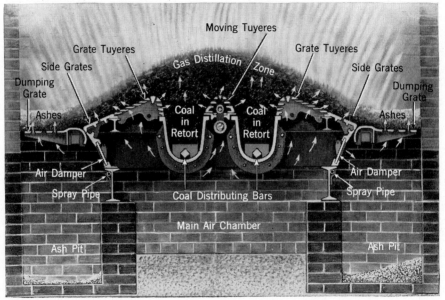

Courtesy Detroit Stoker Co., Detroit

Fig. 218. Grate for Underfeed Stoker. View from Front. There is a ram for each retort. Since the hottest coal is on top in underfeed furnaces, the heating surfaces of the boiler get the maximum benefit from radiant heat. In this type, the burning fuel gradually works sidewise and reaches the dumping grates as ash, whence it is dropped to the ash pit. Secondary air for combustion is admitted through openings (not shown here) in the furnace walls or in the front of the furnace above the fuel bed.

used with traveling grates include: free-burning, noncoking bituminous coals; lignite; anthracite (to Nos. 3 and 4 buckwheat); and coke breeze. The primary air for combustion enters via compartments under the top surface of the grate.

In one construction of a traveling grate, there is a cast-iron grate bar that extends from one side of the grate to the other, on which small elements, called *keys*, are mounted side by side and overlapping. The assembly of one grate bar and the row of keys constitutes a *unit* of the grate. The bars are then attached to driving chains which run over sprockets at the ends of the grate. The sprockets drive the grate. Another construction is to build it up as a series of links, the links being arranged and assembled in a manner similar to a silent-chain power drive, as in Fig. 217. Traveling

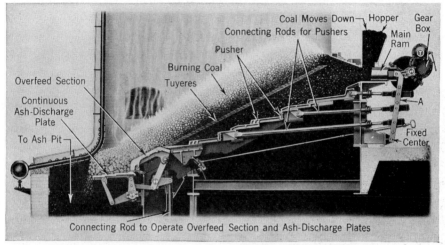

Connecting Rod to Operate Overfeed Section and Ash-Discharge Plates

Courtesy American Engineering Co., Philadelphia

Fig. 219. *Longitudinal Section of a Multiple-Retort Underfeed Stoker.* With more than two retorts, the ash discharges at the rear and the grate slopes downward from the front. This view is a section through the center of a retort. This type of stoker is adaptable to boiler capacities of about 20,000 to 500,000 kB/hr. It is clear from this picture how the pushers (or secondary rams) distribute the coal. They operate at the same time as the main ram through the connecting link *A*. The ash is continuously discharged. The ash discharge plate is moved through the linkage shown by a hydraulically (oil) operated piston, which also gives intermittent motion to the overfeed section of the grate. The purpose of the overfeed section is to keep the coal moving, break it up, and aid in getting all carbon burned.

grate stokers are utilized for capacities from about 15,000 to 200,000 lb./hr. steam, occasionally for larger units.

(b) **Underfeed stokers.** In underfeed stokers, coal is pushed into the bottom of a **retort,** Fig. 218, by either a conveyor type of screw or by rams, Fig. 219. This type is made with single or multiple retorts. The single and double ones usually have horizontal retorts as in Fig. 218 with ash disposal to the side. In the multiple jobs, Fig. 219, the retorts slope downward from front toward rear with the ash dump in the rear. The primary air enters through **tuyeres,** Fig. 218, which are passageways in the grate for air. Forced draft is essential for the operation of underfeed stokers because of the great thickness of the fuel bed. The single- or double-retort stokers are made for steam capacities of from 1000 to 40,000 lb./hr.; multiple retorts from about 15,000 to 200,000 lb/hr., perhaps more.

(c) *Spreader stokers.* Spreader stokers, Fig. 220, have been developed into a highly satisfactory device, operating efficiently and flexibly with a wide range of fuels. With dumping grates, they come in capacities of some 1000 to 125,000 lb./hr. of steam, and with continuous discharge grates, Fig. 220, from 30,000 to perhaps 400,000 lb./hr. of steam. In this stoker, a rotating element throws the coal into the furnace in such a fashion that it is deposited more or less evenly on a horizontal grate. The finer particles of coal are burned before they reach the bed; the combustion of the heavier pieces is completed on the grate. Forced draft, which as usual can be regulated to suit the load, is used with spreader stokers.

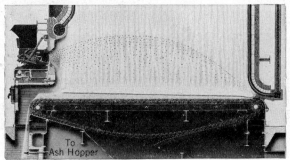

Courtesy Detroit Stoker Co., Detroit

Fig. 220. Spreader Stoker. Combustible in the ash should be less than 2% of the refuse.

In relation to the capacity figures given for the foregoing stokers, we might note that oil and gas burners are used for any capacity from the smallest to the largest, pulverized coal firing is used largely in capacities above 35,000 lb./hr. of steam, and stationary grates up to a capacity of about 15,000 lb./hr.

288. Firing Pulverized Fuel. Pulverized coal may be burned alone or in combination with oil or gas. Pulverization results in more rapid combustion of the coal, because of the greater surface area exposed to flame per pound of coal and the more intimate mixing of coal and air. The amount of excess air required is less, due to thorough mixing of coal and air, than in methods of firing previously described. By way of comparison, the optimum percentage of excess air is likely to be within the following ranges:

Pulverized coal, 15–20%;   Fuel oil, 5–20%;
Underfeed coal stoker, 20–50%;   Natural gas, 5–12%.

In the case of pulverized coal, the rate of combustion can be more quickly changed to care for changes in the load on the boiler. Coupled with a greater capacity for a particular size of furnace is the advantage of being able to use cheap grades of coal. These and other advantages have made

Raw Coal Feed

Fine Coal and Air Out

Damper

Rotating Classifier
Coal Here

Stationary Ring

Rotating Ring

Hot Primary Air In

Fan Housing

Springs Regulate Pressure

Pyrites Trap

Bevel Gear

V-Belt Drive

Courtesy Babcock & Wilcox Co., New York

Fig. 221. Rolling-Ball Pulverizer. The fineness of the grind is controlled by pressure on the grinding rings and balls, the pressure being regulated by the adjustment of the force of the springs. The air inside is under the pressure used at the furnace burners, so that the fuel and air flow directly into the furnace from the pulverizer. When preheated air is used, the expected arrangement, no external drier for the coal is needed. The hot primary air dries the coal. The lower ring rotates, the upper is stationary. Coal ground fine enough to be lifted by the air passes up through the classifier, which whirls the stream, thus causing particles above a certain size to be thrown out by centrifugal force. Pieces of metal and pyrites pass through the spring-loaded ball race, due to centrifugal force, and move around outside the periphery of the lower ring until they are dumped in the pyrites trap. The amount of coal fed can be changed by the damper control on the primary air supplied, the air being measured by a venturi, for example. Through a suitable mechanism, a reduction in the primary air results in a reduction in the coal fed.

the use of pulverized coal quite advantageous in many localities. The danger of explosion of coal-dust-laden air must be guarded against.

Notice the location of the pulverizers in Figs. 114 and 120. In units burning pulverized coal, nothing of the firing equipment appears in the furnace except the ends of the burners through which the coal and air pass. This practically limits the upkeep of the firing system to the pulverizer and

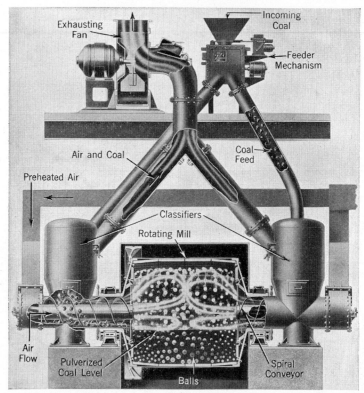

Courtesy Foster Wheeler Corp., New York

Fig. 222. Ball Mill Pulverizer. The mill consists of a rotating drum
which contains a number of small steel balls. The coal is fed into this
drum by the spiral conveyors, which in turn receive it from a feeder
mechanism at a controlled rate. As the drum rotates, the cascading
action of the steel balls pulverizes the coal. Fine coal, entrained in a
stream of air, is carried out of each end of the mill as shown, flowing
counter to the incoming coal. Coarser particles of coal are rejected in
the classifiers and returned to the mill. Preheated air is supplied,
drying the coal, and the fan shown aids in exhausting the air and coal
from the unit to the burners. The electrically driven feeder is controlled through a mechanism actuated by the level of pulverized coal
in the mill. The fine coal seals off an aperture as the level rises,
uncovers it as the level falls.

its related equipment, although there may be some difficulties with fly ash
and with greater deposits on tubes.

Pulverizers are available in several different types and designs. A
design using the rolling principle of crushing is shown in Fig. 221. The mill
shown in Fig. 222 is called a ball-mill pulverizer. Not illustrated is an
impact pulverizer which employs paddles to break up the coal by pounding
it. Pulverization may be preceded by crushing in a coal crusher in order to
have small pieces of coal fed to the pulverizer.

The burners may be so located as to direct the jet horizontally into the furnace from a wall location; they may be located to direct the jet downward, or they may be located at the corners of the furnace to direct the jets tangent to an imaginary circle in the center of the furnace. The last method is called *tangential firing,* a method which has been refined to provide tilting burners.

To understand the usefulness of tilting burners, Fig. 223, we first recall that the turbine is designed for a particular initial condition of the steam, a certain temperature and pressure. Its efficiency decreases whenever the

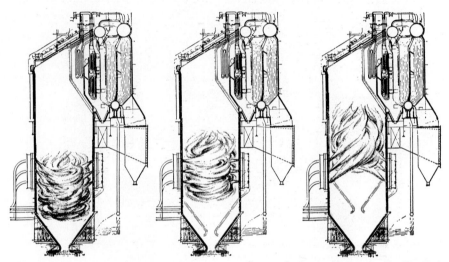

Courtesy Combustion Engineering Co., New York

Fig. 223. *Tangential Firing, Tilting Burners.* A typical tangentially fired furnace. The view in (a) shows the burners tilted downward **30°**, the position for heavy firing conditions; in (b), the burners are horizontal; and in (c), they are tilted **30°** upward, the position for lighter firing conditions. Observe the vortex effect produced in this type of firing. The superheater coils are located below and to the left of the steam drums. With the burners tilted upward, there is as complete combustion as in the other positions and no noticeable increase in fly ash.

entering steam has properties different from these design conditions. Now if the load on the turbine decreases, the load on the steam generator also decreases. Hence, the rate of firing the furnace must be decreased, which results in a lowering of the average temperature of the gases which pass over the superheater. Thus, the temperature of the superheated steam is reduced and the turbine which receives it does not operate at its maximum efficiency. The tilting burners are a means of combating this temperature drop of the superheated steam. If the load is reduced, the burners are tilted upward and the gases, reaching the superheater in less time, are hotter than they would be otherwise and tend to maintain the temperature of the

delivered steam.   (This argument is for that construction in which the superheater is above the burners.)   If the load is increased, more fuel is fired,
the burners are tilted downward, more time elapses before the gases reach
the superheater, and these gases, having had more time to give up energy by
radiation to the radiant heating surfaces than if the firing had been horizontal, will not increase the superheated steam temperature unduly.*   See
also §§ 164 and 170 for other means of controlling steam temperature.

289. Firing Gas and Oil.   The furnace design for gas and oil fuels is
much the same as for pulverized coal.   Less excess air is needed for gas than

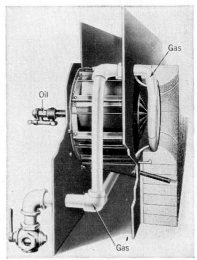

Courtesy Babcock & Wilcox Co., New York

Courtesy Babcock & Wilcox Co., New York

Fig. 224.   Oil Burner with Blower.
This is a mechanical-atomizing oil
burner with a self-contained, turbine-
driven blower.

**Fig. 225.   Combination Oil and Gas
Burner.**   The gas supply line, in the
foreground, leads to an annular ring.
The jets of gas are emitted from many
small orifices in this ring.

for oil, and less is needed for oil than for coal.   Decreasing excess air tends
to raise the efficiency of the boiler—but the greater percentage of hydrogen
in oil and (still greater in) gas tends to reduce the efficiency as computed on
the basis of the higher heating value.   Either oil or gas (usually, natural
gas) makes an excellent fuel from the standpoint of cleanliness, capacity,
and flexibility.

Because of these advantages and its high heating value per cubic foot,
oil is widely used as a fuel in the transportation field, especially in steamships

* For a more complete discussion, see Powell, *Tilting burners provide flexible furnace
performance,* in Combustion, June, 1945.

and locomotives.   Many stationary power plants in areas close to sources of natural gas are finding that this gas is the most economical fuel.

The burners for gas are designed to produce turbulence, with good mixing of fuel and air in the furnace as the result.   Oil burners are primarily designed to atomize the oil, break it up into fine particles so that a good mixture of air and fuel is attainable.   An oil heater may be used to heat the oil before it goes to the atomizer, in order to reduce its viscosity.   Oil burners are generally either mechanical atomizing or steam atomizing.   In steam atomizing, a fast-moving jet of steam strikes the oil, reducing it to small particles.   In mechanical atomizing, the oil is under pressure and it leaves through an orifice with a whirling motion and in the shape of a hollow cone. The air for combustion, also with a whirling motion, enters the furnace through openings around the oil orifice.   There are many designs of oil and gas burners, examples of which are seen in Figs. 224 and 225.

290. Closure.   The combustion phenomenon is being given much research study because of the need of greater knowledge of it in connection with rockets, jets, gas turbines, and internal combustion engines.   Since new facts and near facts are being uncovered almost daily, one needs to refer to current technical publications for information—true of course in any field where scientists and engineers are working creatively.

In processes of the hot products of combustion, it is desirable to allow for the variation of specific heats because otherwise the error may be substantial.   The gas tables (Keenan and Kaye) are very helpful in reducing tedious integrations.   See our Tables VI and VII, Appendix.   Notice that Table VII gives enthalpy in Btu per mol.   To get h Btu/lb., divide the table value $\bar{h}$ by the molecular weight M of the substance.   To get internal energy in Btu per mol, subtract the $p\bar{v}/J$ in the last column from $\bar{h}$.

SELECTED REFERENCES

Hersey, Eberhardt, and Hottel, *Thermodynamic properties of the working fluid in internal combustion engines*, SAE Jour., Vol. 39, p. 409.
Hottel, Williams, and Satterfield, *Thermodynamic Charts for Combustion Processes*, Parts I and II, John Wiley.
Jost, W. (translated by H. O. Croft), *Explosion and Combustion Processes in Gases*, McGraw-Hill.
Lewis and von Elbe, *Combustion Flames and Explosions*, Academic Press.
Various technical papers of Bur. of Mines, NACA, and Bur. of Standards.

PROBLEMS

NOTE.   *Be sure to include a chemical equation with balanced masses in each solution, even in the simplest problems, showing all mass balances.*

391. Ethyl alcohol (C_2H_6O) is completely burned in ideal air. (a) Set up the chemical equation and determine the relative masses and volumes. Compute (b) the air/fuel ratio, (c) the needed volume of air at 65°F and 14.7 psia, (d) the volumetric and gravimetic percentages of H_2O in the products, (e) the partial pressure of the H_2O vapor in products, (f) the volume of products at 300°F.

Ans. (b) 8.955, (c) 118.2 cu ft. per lb. fuel, (d) 18.42, 11.8%, (e) 2.71 psia, (f) 196 cu. ft./lb. fuel.

392. Benzene (C_6H_6) is to be burned in air. (a) What are the percentages of C and H_2 in the fuel? For each of the following situations, balance the theoretical chemical equation, find the relative masses and volumes, determine the air/fuel ratio and the lb. CO_2 per pound of products: (b) burned in ideal air, (c) burned in 10% excess air, (d) burned in 90% ideal air with complete combustion of the hydrogen.

Ans. (a) 92.3% C, 7.69% H_2, (b) $A/F = 13.2$, 0.238 lb. CO_2/lb. prod., (c) 14.52, 0.218, (d) 11.88, 0.197.

393. Set up the chemical equation for the combustion of ethane (C_2H_6) in ideal air and find the relative masses and volumes. Determine (a) the A/F ratio, (b) the gravimetric analysis of the products, (c) the volumetric analysis of the hot products (gaseous H_2O), (d) the volumetric analysis of the cold products (liquid H_2O), (e) the equivalent molecular weight and gas constant of the hot products. (f) What are the percentages by weight of carbon and hydrogen in the fuel?

Ans. (a) 16, (b) 17.24% CO_2, (c) 11% CO_2, (d) 13.19% CO_2, (e) 28.1, 55, (f) 80% C, 20% H_2.

394. The same as **393** except that there is a 10% deficiency of air. Assume that only carbon is incompletely burned, but at least to CO.

Ans. (a) 14.4, (b) 12.38% CO_2 (c) 7.72% CO_2, (d) 9.4% CO_2, (e) 27.45, 56.25.

395. (a) Set up the chemical equation for the ideal combustion of propane (C_6H_8) in air. Show mass balances and obtain relative masses and volumes. Compute (b) the percentages by weight of carbon and hydrogen in the fuel, (c) the A/F ratio, (d) the gravimetric and volumetric percentages of H_2O in the hot products, (e) the lower heating value per pound of the original air-fuel mixture, (f) the partial pressure of the H_2O in the hot products if the total pressure is 15 psia. What is the dew point corresponding to this pressure? (g) What is the volume of the products at 40°F (all H_2O formed by combustion is condensed)?

Ans. (b) 81.8% C, 18.2% H_2, (c) 15.59, (d) 9.88, 16.1%, (e) 804 Btu/lb., (f) 2.41 psia, 133°F, (g) 176.5 cu. ft. per lb. fuel.

396. The ultimate analysis of a coal as fired is: 79.8% C, 5.07% H_2, 6.82% O_2, 1.53% N_2, 0.65% S, 3.13% ash, 3% moisture. (a) What is the gravimetric analysis of the ash-free and moisture-free coal? (b) Set up the combustion equation for ideal air including all constituents except the ash and moisture. (c) Set up the combustion equation as above but omit also the N and S. From this equation, determine the lb. air/lb. C; then the lb. air/lb. fuel as fired and lb. air/lb. dry coal. (d) What is the A/F (as-fired) ratio with 40% excess air? (e) What are the lb. N_2/lb. CO_2 in the products?

Ans. (a) 5.4% H_2, (c) 13.23 lb. air per lb. C, 10.95 lb. a./lb. d.c., (d) 14.8 lb. a./lb. f., (e) 2.77.

397. A gas has the following gravimetric composition: 90.5% CH_4, 9.5% C_2H_6. For combustion with ideal air, compute (a) the A/F ratio, (b) the mass of each of the products per lb. fuel, (c) the volumetric analysis of the hot products, (d) the partial pressure of the N_2 for $p_m = 14.7$ psia, (e) the volume of products from 1 lb. of fuel at 14.7 psia and 1000°F.

Ans. (a) 17.12, (b) 2.76 lb. CO_2/lb. f., (c) 9.63% CO_2, (d) 10.5 psia, (e) 695 cu. ft.

398. The gravimetric analysis of a fuel oil, which is being consumed at the rate of 5 tons/hr., is: 85.5% C, 12.2% H_2, 2.3% N_2. (a) Balance a chemical equation for 20% excess air and find the A/F ratio. Also compute (b) the volume of air required, cfm at 14.7 psia and 60°F, (c) the volume of products at 14.7 psia and 370°F, (d) the partial pressure of the N_2 and the pounds of N_2 in products per min., (e) the values of x and y in C_xH_y (omitting N_2).

Ans. (a) 16.85, (b) 36,800 cfm, (c) 61,800 cfm, (d) 11.03 psia, 2134 lb. per min., (e) $C_{7.29}H_{12.5}$.

399. The dry exhaust of an internal combustion engine shows the following volumetric composition: 12.5% CO_2, 4.2% O_2, 0.3% CO, 83% N_2. If the fuel contains only carbon and hydrogen, balance the chemical equation and determine (a) the A/F ratio, (b) the lb. C/lb. of dry products, (c) the lb. O_2 in dry products per lb. fuel.

Ans. (a) 17.4, (b) 0.051, (c) 3.33.

400. A bituminous coal has the following ultimate analysis: 72% C, 4.4% H_2, 1.6% S, 3.6% O_2, 1.4% N_2, 8% H_2O, 9% ash. On a certain test, the following volumetric composition of the dry flue gases was obtained by Orsat: 15.2% CO_2, 3.6% O_2, 0.3% CO, 80.9% N_2. (a) With this Orsat analysis, set up a chemical equation considering only the carbon burned and find the A/F ratio. Let the N_2 be a measure of the amount of air. (b) During the foregoing combustion, the refuse showed

10.6% C. What is the corrected A/F ratio? (c) What ideal air is required and what is the percentage excess (if any)? Ignore the S, N_2, and H_2O in the fuel. (d) What is the approximate higher heating value of this coal?

Ans. (a) 11.5, (b) 11.32, (c) 17.3% excess, (d) 12,950 Btu/lb.

401. The ultimate analysis (always gravimetric) of a crude oil is 87.1% C and 12.9% H_2. A certain test of the products of combustion gave the following volumetric percentages: 12% CO_2, 4.6% O_2, 0.3% CO, 83.1% N_2—dry analysis. Show all mass balances. Determine (a) the ideal amount of air required for complete combustion, lb. per lb. fuel, (b) the actual air/fuel ratio and the percentage of excess or deficiency. Using the balanced chemical equation for the actual combustion, compute (c) the fraction by weight of H_2O in the products and the lb. H_2O per lb. fuel, (d) the partial pressure of the nitrogen in the hot products for $p_m = 14.7$ psia, (e) the volume of the products at 440°F, cu. ft./lb. of fuel, and the volume of the nitrogen, (f) the equivalent molecular weight of the *dry* products and the specific gas constant R. (g) If the higher heating value of the fuel is 20,000 Btu/lb. f., what is the lower heating value?

Ans. (a) 14.45 lb. a./lb. f., (b) 18.1, 24.6% excess, (c) 1.16 lb. H_2O/lb. fuel, (d) 11 psia, (e) 431 cu. ft./lb. f., (f) 30.08, 51.4, (g) 18,780.

402. The dry exhaust from an automotive engine has a volumetric analysis as follows: 12.5% CO_2, 3.1% O_2, 0.3% CO, and 84.1% N_2. Assume that the fuel contains only hydrogen and carbon. (a) Set up the combustion equation and determine the "equivalent fuel"; that is, x and y in C_xH_y. (b) What is the air/fuel ratio. What are (c) the volumetric percentages of H_2O and CO_2

in the hot products, (d) the partial pressure of the N_2 if the total pressure is 14.7 psia, (e) the volume of hot products at 3000°R from 1 lb. of fuel, (f) the fraction by weight of carbon in the fuel. (g) If the higher heating value of this fuel is 20,200 Btu/lb., what is the lower heating value?

Ans.   (b) 17.05, (c) 11.72%, 11.07%, (d) 10.9 psia, (e) 1380 cu. ft./lb. f., (f) 0.854, (g) 18,800.

403. In a steam generator, 85% of the higher heating value of the fuel is transferred to steam and water in accordance with the data and results of problem **400.** This problem is to compute an energy balance given the following additional data: exit temperature of flue gases, 345°F; use $q_h = 12,800$ Btu/lb. as obtained by test. Use the solution of problem **400** as the basis of other necessary computations. Ignore the moisture in the atmospheric air.

Ans. $E_2 = 463$, $E_4 = 760$ Btu/lb.f.

404–410. These numbers may be used for other problems.

✐ *18*

PUMPS AND FANS

291. Introduction. Both pumps and fans serve fundamentally the same purpose: to move a fluid from here to there, sometimes accompanied by a significant increase of pressure, sometimes not. *Pumping* usually implies that a liquid is being moved, unless the context indicates otherwise; whereas fans are used only for moving gases. The situation in which gases undergo a significant increase in pressure is covered in Chapter 6. Hence, this chapter will consider the movement of gases with only small changes in pressure and the movement of liquids in a general way.

Courtesy American-Marsh Pumps, Inc.,
Battle Creek, Mich.

Fig. 226. Duplex Pump.

Courtesy Foster Wheeler Corp., New York

Fig. 227. Vertical Centrifugal Circulating Pump. This pump, a 72-in. size, has the shaft in a vertical position.

292. Pumps. A pump is one of the oldest of machines, so ancient that it was originally operated only by man and animal power. All kinds of fluids are pumped. In a power plant, the two principal uses are to pump the feedwater into the boiler, Figs. 226 and 228, and the condenser water through the condenser, Fig. 227. Reciprocating and centrifugal pumps are the most common types (but see Figs. 231 and 232).

Reciprocating pumps are traditional in boiler feed systems, and are common in small- and medium-sized plants.   They are usually of the duplex type, Fig. 226, but simplex pumps (one water cylinder) and triplex pumps (three water cylinders) are used.   With two pumping cylinders, as in the duplex, the flow of water is steadier.   In Fig. 226, the water cylinders are on the right, the steam cylinders on the left.   The air chamber, projecting upward on the right, also aids in maintaining a steadier discharge pressure. Reciprocating pumps may be favored for a high discharge pressure and a relatively small quantity of liquid; also, because of their flexibility, when the

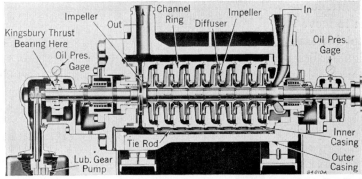

Fig. 228.   Multistage Centrifugal Pump.   A single-suction feedwater pump with diffusers, manufactured for discharge pressures to 3000 psia and higher; capacity to 2800 gpm at 800°F water.   Up to about 1400 psia, the outer casing is cast steel; above 1400 psia, it is forged steel.   The annular area between the inner and outer casings is filled with water at the discharge pressure, reducing temperature inequalities.   The channel ring assemblies are held together by tie rods for handling purposes. See Fig. 229.   All of the impellers are shown in section except the last one (on left).

quantity output is quite variable.   Many reciprocating pumps have plungers rather than pistons.

Centrifugal pumps are used in a wide range of sizes, but are practically universal for large quantities of liquid, for example, circulating pumps, Fig. 227.   They are used as boiler feed pumps and are designed to pump to the maximum pressures used in power plants.   To reach the high pressures, the liquid passes through several centrifugal stages; Fig. 228 shows a multistage centrifugal pump for feedwater.

Characteristics of centrifugal pumps include: a good efficiency at the optimum load but a rapidly decreasing efficiency for load variations of more than about ±20%, which means that they are particularly appropriate when the quantity delivered is nearly constant; a steady discharge pressure; high speed and therefore small size for a particular capacity.   Also this type of pump is designed to handle some solid matter (as dirt) in the liquid.   As explained in some detail for centrifugal fans, § 299, a centrifugal pump has certain unique operating characteristics (see Fig. 234 and § 294) and these characteristics must be suitable for the job to be done.

The centrifugal pump operates much as the centrifugal blower, Fig. 53, § 91, in that first the speed of the fluid is greatly increased, thus increasing its kinetic energy.   Then the fluid passes through diffuser passages, § 190, and the kinetic energy is used to pump the fluid to a higher pressure (approaching the stagnation pressure).   See Fig. 229; but more commonly

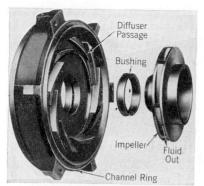

Courtesy Ingersoll-Rand Co., New York

Fig. 229. Diffuser and Impeller. Some of the parts of a channel ring assembly for the pump of Fig. 228 are shown. The fluid enters axially near the shaft and departs from the impeller in a radial direction, thence through diffuser passages, thence to the next stage. Compare with Fig. 228.

Fig. 230. Volute Passage for Centrifugal Pump.

used is a volute casing only, Fig. 230, which provides an increasingly larger passageway about the impellers to the discharge line.

Maintaining a vacuum in a condenser involves not only the removal of the condensate but also the removal of the air which leaks in.   The air and some vapor may be removed by a separate pump, usually a centrifugal pump or ejector, in which case another pump, the condensate pump, removes liquid only.

There are too many other types of pumps to try to illustrate all of them here.   The *steam injector*, § 191, while sometimes used as a feedwater pump, has a very low thermal efficiency.   It is sometimes advantageous as a pump for abrasive solutions when the pressure range is small.   Liquid pumps are also made with rotating lobes as in Fig. 50, § 91, and with vanes as in Fig.

51.   Other rotary pumps include the gear pump, Fig. 231, which operates
on the same idea as the pump of Fig. 50, and the screw pump, Fig. 232.

293. Work for Liquid Pumps.   For the pump work in steam cycle
analysis, § 214, we chose to use the simple expression $W_p = (p_2 - p_1)v$
ft-lb./lb. on the assumption that the changes of kinetic and potential energies were zero.   The other assumptions, $Q = 0$ and incompressibility

Roller Bearings

*Courtesy Commercial Shearing & Stamping Co.,
Youngstown, O.*

Fig. 231.   Gear Pump. The principle of
operation is the same as that described for
the two-lobe blower (pump), Fig. 50.   The
liquid filling the tooth spaces is carried
from the inlet side to the discharge side,
and the meshing teeth prevent a back flow.
The volumetric efficiency may average as
high as 95% for accurately made pumps,
with close fits.   One manufacturer makes
this type of pump in capacities up to about
50 gpm at 1000 psi and 1800 rpm; speed
range to 3000 rpm; discharge pressure to
1500 psi.   Gear pumps may be built in
tandem on one shaft, driven by a single
source of power.   Gear pump styles include an internal gear and pinion.

$(v = C)$, will not be changed, but
ΔK and ΔP might be significant.
For the conditions stated and a reversible process, equation (14), p.
30, yields

(a) $-v(p_2 - p_1) = K_2 - K_1 +$
$\qquad\qquad P_2 - P_1 + W$ ft-lb./lb.

In this equation, let the specific volume $v = 1/\rho$, the reciprocal of the
density.   Then you might note that
if we ignore the difference between
the pound mass, which is implicit in
all terms of this equation, and the
pound force, each term is in units of
feet.   That is, as you perhaps have
done in fluid mechanics, we may
think of each term as a *head;*
$\Delta P = \Delta z$ ft., which is evident;

$\Delta K = \Delta v^2/(2g_o)$
$\qquad \longrightarrow (\text{ft.}^2/\text{sec.}^2)/(\text{ft./sec.}^2) = \text{ft.};$

$pv = \dfrac{p}{\rho} \longrightarrow \dfrac{(\text{lb./ft.}^2)}{(\text{lb./ft.}^3)} = \text{ft.}$

Solving for the pump work, $W = H_t$ the total head, and changing signs of
the heads so that the work is positive, we get, for constant ρ and frictionless
flow,

$$(70) \qquad H_t = \left(\frac{p_2}{\rho} - \frac{p_1}{\rho}\right) + \left(\frac{v_2^2}{2g_o} - \frac{v_1^2}{2g_o}\right) + \quad (z_2 - z_1) \quad \text{ft-lb./lb.,}$$

$\qquad\qquad\quad$ [PRESSURE $\qquad\qquad$ [VELOCITY $\qquad\qquad$ [GRAVITATIONAL
$\qquad\qquad\qquad$ HEAD] $\qquad\qquad\qquad$ HEAD] $\qquad\qquad\qquad$ HEAD]

where $v^2/(2g_o)$ or its change is termed the **velocity head** (compare with
§ 193), p/ρ or its change is the **pressure head,** z or its change is the *potential
energy head* (**gravitational head**), and the sum of the pressure and gravita-

tional heads, $\Delta z + \Delta(p/\rho)$, is called the **static head.** It will be worth your while to review §§ 192 and 193 for comparisons now. Equation (70) is applicable to any liquid (whose volume remains virtually constant); the corresponding energy diagram is depicted in Fig. 233. The actual pump

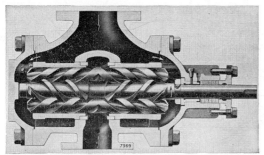

Courtesy DeLaval Steam Turbine Co., Trenton, N. J.

Fig. 232. Positive Displacement, Screw-Type Pump. Liquid flows into the open thread spaces of the outside idler screws, is trapped there when the corresponding thread of the middle screw meshes, and is then forced towards the middle (in this model), whence it is discharged. This series is used for pressures to 150 psig and for temperatures to 250°F; pumping vegetable oils, fuel oils, lubricants, etc. Another similar screw pump uses only two screws, which are driven by timing gears to maintain the relative position of the rotors.

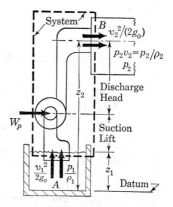

Fig. 233. Energy Diagram for Isentropic Pumping of Liquid. If a pressure gage is located on the discharge side and close to the pump, the reading could be (and is) used for p_2 and the *discharge head* omitted; at this location, the pressure gage measures the total static head, including frictional head.

must do some additional work in overcoming friction, which is usually added to equation (70) as a *frictional head;* thus

(b) $\qquad H'_t = \dfrac{\text{Actual total}}{\text{head}} = \dfrac{\text{Static}}{\text{head}} + \dfrac{\text{Velocity}}{\text{head}} + \dfrac{\text{Frictional}}{\text{head}}.$

This practice of using *heads* is convenient because the frictional losses in pipe lines (through valves, elbows, etc.) as found in handbooks and other places is usually a head in feet. Considering equation (70), or (b), from the energy viewpoint, we see that the units are ft-lb./lb., foot-pounds of work per pound of substance. Hence if H_t or H'_t is multiplied by the mass w lb./min., we get the total work per minute, wH_t ft-lb./min. Converted to horsepower, the work done on the liquid, called water horsepower, or more appropriately, *liquid horsepower,* is then

(c) $\qquad\qquad\qquad \text{Liquid } hp = \dfrac{wH_t}{33,000},$

where the head H_t is in feet; w and H_t are both for the same fluid.

294. Performance of Pumps. The *pump efficiency* η_p is the output work divided by the shaft work input. The output work is that done on the fluid, wH_t or as given by (c). Thus,

(d)
$$\eta_p = \frac{W_{out}}{W_{in}} = \frac{hp_{out}}{hp_{in}}.$$

The probable range of efficiencies is wide, smaller pumps and higher-head pumps tending toward lower efficiencies; the peak of the efficiency curve, Fig. 234, may be anywhere from 40–90%. In an electric drive, the overall

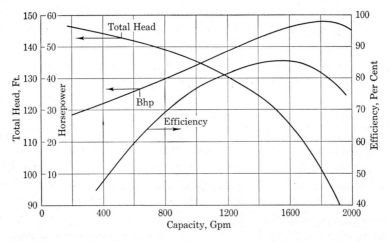

Fig. 234. Typical Performance Curves of a Centrifugal Pump. Test values are for a constant speed of 1750 rpm; 6x8 in. (discharge diameter by intake diameter) with a 12-in. impeller wheel. If this pump is to operate near its point of maximum efficiency, the total head must be about 110–125 ft. and the corresponding capacity is around 1500 gpm. Suppose that the head were increased (by partially closing a valve, for instance) until the output becomes 800 gpm, then the horsepower and the efficiency both decrease. The maximum head is about 148 ft., but as this head is approached, the delivery and efficiency approach zero. In a general way, efficiencies are smaller for smaller impeller wheels. (Data courtesy Goulds Pumps, Inc., Seneca Falls, N. Y.)

efficiency would be easiest to measure because then the denominator of (d) is the input of electricity to the motor. If the pump is driven by a steam engine or steam turbine, we often use a thermal efficiency where the numerator (output) is the work done on the fluid as before and the denominator is the energy E_c chargeable against the steam drive (§ 202); $E_c = h_1 - h_{f2}$ where h_1 is the enthalpy of the entering steam and h_{f2} is the enthalpy of water at the exhaust temperature.

omit

(e)
$$e = \frac{wH_t/J}{(h_1 - h_{f2})w_s},$$

where w_s is the pounds of steam per minute entering the steam drive.   The curves of Fig. 234 are typical of the performance of centrifugal pumps running at a constant speed.

The *quantity* of incompressible liquid delivered by a centrifugal pump *is directly proportional to speed; $w \propto n$*, where w is the mass delivered and n is rpm.   Since kinetic energy $v^2/(2g_o)$ is one of the *head* terms in (70), it follows that the total head H_t can be expressed as some number N times the velocity head; $H_t = N[\Delta v^2/(2g_o)]$, which is to say that *the head varies as the square of the speed; $H_t \propto v^2$ or $H_t \propto n^2$* (because $v = r\omega$, where r is the radius and ω is the angular velocity in radians per unit of time, $\omega = 2\pi n$).   From equation (c), we see that power is proportional to wH_t; but w is proportional to n and H_t is proportional to n^2.   Hence power is proportional to $n \times n^2$ or *power is proportional to the cube of the speed; hp $\propto n^3$*.   Suppose, for example, that it is decided to increase the delivery of a certain pump a small amount, say 10%.   This objective would be accomplished by increasing the pump's speed 10% or 0.1.   As a consequence of this, the total head pumped would be $1.1^2 = 1.21$ times the original head, a 21% increase; and the power required (for the same efficiency) would be $1.1^3 = 1.331$ times the original power, or an increase of 33%.   It does not necessarily follow that the original motor can carry a 33% larger load without damage.

As for reciprocating compressors, pumps have a volumetric efficiency η_v, which is defined as the actual mass drawn in and discharged divided by the mass that would occupy the displacement volume at intake conditions (see §§ 79 and 129).   In more common usage for pumps is the pump *slip* which is $1 - \eta_v$;

$$\text{Slip} = 1 - \eta_v,$$

a value which can be found by test.

295. Example.   A 20,000-kw turbo-generator uses 8 lb./kw-hr. of steam and operates through a pressure range from 850 to 1 psia.   The condensate enters the pump through a suction line whose internal area is 28.9 sq. in.; it leaves through a line whose area is 20 sq. in.   The condensate is pumped directly into the boiler through a total lift of 70 ft.   (a) What is the required ideal horsepower?   (b) Suppose the pump is designed to operate against a head 10% greater than ideal to overcome friction and to be certain of ready flow into the boiler.   If its efficiency is 70%, what actual horsepower is needed?

SOLUTION.   (a) If there is saturated water at 1 psia, the specific volume from Table IX is $v = 0.01614$ cu. ft./lb., or $\rho = 1/0.01614$ lb./cu. ft.   The amount of water handled at rated load is $w = (20,000 \text{ kw})(8 \text{ lb./kw-hr.}) = 160,000$ lb./hr. or 2667 lb./min. or 44.4 lb./sec.   From the continuity of mass $w = Av\rho$, we get the speeds

$$v_1 = \frac{w}{A\rho} = \frac{(44.4)(0.01614)}{28.9/144} = 3.56 \text{ fps}, \qquad v_2 = \frac{(44.4)(0.01614)}{20/144} = 5.16 \text{ fps},$$

from which the velocity head is

$$H_v = \frac{v_2{}^2 - v_1{}^2}{2g_o} = \frac{5.16^2 - 3.56^2}{64.4} = 0.217 \text{ ft.}$$

The pressure head is $(v = 1/\rho)$

$$H_p = v(p_2 - p_1) = (0.01614)(144)(850 - 1) = 1973 \text{ ft.}$$

For a potential energy head of 70 ft., the total head is

$$H_t = 0.217 + 1973 + 70 = 2043 \text{ ft.,}$$

where we consider the velocity head as negligible. Keep in mind too that H_t is the work per pound (ft-lb./lb.). The ideal horsepower, sometimes called the ideal water horsepower, is

$$hp = \frac{wH_t}{33,000} = \frac{(2667)(2043)}{33,000} = 165 \text{ hp.}$$

(b) A 10% increase in head with the same mass flow would require $(1.1)(165)$ = 181.5 hp. For a pump efficiency of 70%, the actual horsepower is

$$hp = \frac{181.5}{0.70} = 259 \text{ hp.}$$

In this example, not only is the velocity head negligible, but the gravity head, 70 ft., nearly is. However, if the discharge pressure were 85 psia instead of 850 psia, the 70 ft. would constitute a significant part of the total head. Also, while the frictional head in so short a line would be quite small compared to the total head (perhaps of the order of 1 or 2 ft.), this head in a long transport line might be the largest one. The point is that all heads must be investigated to be sure that nothing significant is omitted. Finally, we might note that while the pump power is a good many horsepower (equivalent to about 193 kw), it is relatively small compared to the 20,000 kw of the plant.

296. Fans. Strange as it may seem, the approach used for pumps is appropriate for fans. The reason is that, since fans change the pressure only a small amount, the gas being "fanned" changes volume insignificantly; that is, $v \approx C$ for practical purposes. Moreover, the other assumption of § 293, to wit, $Q = 0$, is valid. Now if the process is ideal (isentropic), these assumptions yield equation (70) no matter what the fluid. Thus the fan work per pound of gas is (p_1 and p_2 psf are static pressures, § 193)

(f) $$H_t = \frac{p_2}{\rho_2} - \frac{p_1}{\rho_1} + \frac{v_2{}^2 - v_1{}^2}{2g_o} + z_2 - z_1 \text{ ft. (or ft-lb./lb.)}$$

where we have used ρ_1 and ρ_2 for ρ. If the head is measured in feet, it must be feet of the substance being transported; if air is being moved, p/ρ and $v^2/(2g_o)$ would each be feet of air. It is likely that the gravity head Δz is insignificant in the case of forced transport (certainly in the absence of a high chimney). In any event, the pressure gage 2 can be placed near the discharge of the fan so that Δz would be irrelevant. For the technical terms, refer to §§ 192 and 193, in which $W = 0$. Now if the stagnation pressures at the entrance and exit sections of the fan are determined, p_{o1} and p_{o2} psf, the velocity head is automatically accounted for; and if $\Delta z = 0$, we get for constant density

$$\text{(g)} \qquad H_t = \underbrace{\frac{p_2 - p_1}{\rho}}_{\text{[STATIC HEAD]}} + \underbrace{\frac{v_2{}^2 - v_1{}^2}{2g_o}}_{\text{[VELOCITY HEAD]}} = \frac{p_{o2} - p_{o1}}{\rho} \text{ ft. (or ft-lb./lb.).}$$

Recall that the difference between the impact (stagnation) pressure and the static pressure is called the *velocity pressure;* if this pressure is measured in inches or feet of fluid, as is p/ρ, it is also called the *velocity head.* Logically, the power for operation against the total head is given by equation (c) above, repeated for convenience;

$$\text{(c)} \qquad\qquad \text{Gas (Air) hp} = \frac{wH_t}{33,000},$$

where w lb./min. is the mass of gas flowing and H_t ft. is the head measured by a column of the same gas. The height of a column of one fluid corresponding to a particular pressure may be converted to the equivalent height of another fluid by the ratios of their densities (for all practical purposes); that is, these heights are inversely proportional to the densities. Thus, suppose the head is H_w in. H$_2$O at 80°F; the density of the water is $\rho_w = 1/v_f$, where v_f is taken from the steam tables at 80°F. If the corresponding height H_a of a column of air is desired, obtain the air density from $\rho_a = p/(RT)$ at 80°F; then for H_w in feet,

$$\text{(h)} \qquad\qquad H_a = \frac{H_w \rho_w}{\rho_a} \text{ ft. air;}$$

or feet of any other gas if ρ_a is the density of the other gas. Usually in gas flow, the pressures are measured in inches of water; for example, the *static head* (or pressure head) is $H_{ws} = p/\rho$ in. H$_2$O. Converting the inches to feet and using equation (h) will produce the head in feet of the gas concerned.

In dealing with differences in pressures, we note that the difference of gage pressures is the same as the difference of absolute pressures. The manometers read inches of water gage, which is conveniently abbreviated as follows: 5 in. wg. "Standard" air in fan work is at 70°F and has a density of 0.075 lb./cu. ft.

The *fan efficiency* η_f is the work (or hp) done on the gas *divided by* the input shaft work (or hp). This is stated in the same way as the pump efficiency; however, it is common to use either of two efficiencies for fans:

one called the *total efficiency* in which the numerator is the horsepower corresponding to the total head,

(i)
$$\eta_f = \frac{wH_t/33{,}000}{\text{input hp}};$$
[TOTAL EFFICIENCY]

the other, often used where the velocity head is not significant, called the *static efficiency*, in which the numerator is the horsepower corresponding to the static head ($= \Delta p/\rho = H_s$ ft.),

(j)
$$\eta_f = \frac{wH_s/33{,}000}{\text{input hp}}.$$
[STATIC EFFICIENCY]

In these equations, w lb./min. is the mass rate of flow of the gas. Fan efficiencies may be as low as 40% at the point of optimum operation, but something between 60–80%, and sometimes greater, is more to be expected.

297. Example. In a 40,000-kw steam plant, the air required for the furnace is 340,000 lb./hr. The air enters the forced-draft fans from the atmosphere (14.7 psia and 80°F). It is expected that a Pitot tube traverse in the discharge duct near the fan will show a total (stagnation) pressure of 7 in. wg. and a static pressure of 6.5 in. wg. (a) Convert the total and static heads to feet of air, and find the velocity head. (b) What is the average velocity in the duct? (c) What cross-sectional area of duct is needed? (d) What horsepower is required for an overall fan (total) efficiency of 70%?

SOLUTION. (a) The density of the gage water at 80°F is $\rho_w = 1/0.01608$ (Table VIII) and the density of the atmospheric air is

$$\rho_a = \frac{p}{RT} = \frac{(14.7)(144)}{(53.3)(540)} = 0.0737 \text{ lb./cu. ft.}$$

The heads in feet of air are, equation (h):

$$\text{Total head, } H_t = \frac{H_w \rho_w}{\rho_a} = \frac{7}{(12)(0.01608)(0.0737)} = 492 \text{ ft. air.}$$

$$\text{Static head, } H_s = \frac{6.5}{(12)(0.01608)(0.0737)} = 457 \text{ ft. air.}$$

$$\text{Velocity head, } H_t - H_s = 492 - 457 = 35 \text{ ft. air.}$$

(b) After the fan, the velocity head is $v_2{}^2/(2g_o) = 35$ ft., from which

$$v_2 = (2g_o \times 35)^{1/2} = [(2)(32.2)(35)]^{1/2} = 47.5 \text{ fps.}$$

(c) At 80°F, the volume of air is $V = w/\rho$ [lb./(lb./cu. ft.)]. For $w = 340{,}000$ lb./hr. or $w = 340{,}000/3600 = 94.5$ lb./sec.,

$$V = \frac{w}{\rho} = \frac{94.5}{0.0737} = 696 \text{ cu. ft./sec.,}$$

which is equal to the area times the average velocity, Av, or

$$A = \frac{V}{v} = \frac{696}{47.5} = 14.65 \text{ sq. ft.,}$$

the area of the duct.

(d) Since the air enters from the dead state, $v_1 = 0$, and the total head produced by the fan is 492 ft. Therefore, for $\eta_f = 70\%$ and $w = 340,000/60 = 5667$ lb./min.,

$$hp = \frac{\text{air hp}}{0.70} = \frac{wH_t}{(0.70)(33,000)} = \frac{(5667)(492)}{(0.70)(33,000)} = 121 \text{ hp.}$$

298. Types of Fans. The rotary blowers, § 91, can be operated as fans. Usually however, fans are axial-flow fans, as in the ordinary household fan, which is a propeller type, or as in Fig. 235; or they are centrifugal fans, of which there are many variations. The axial-flow fans are suitable for low heads. The motor may drive the fan by belting, but, in Fig. 235, it is inside

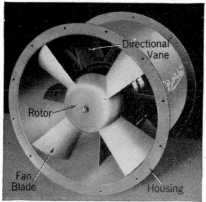

Courtesy Buffalo Forge Co., Buffalo, N. Y.

Fig. 235. Axial-Flow Fan. The motor in this particular unit is inside the housing, directly connected to the fan shaft. Behind the fan blades are seen some stationary vanes, which serve the purpose of "removing" the whirling motion given to the gas stream by the fan blades. It is intended for ventilating systems where the static pressure head is from ¼ to 1½ in. wg.

Courtesy Clarage Fan Co., Kalamazoo, Mich.

Fig. 236. Centrifugal Fan. Used for draft fan where static pressure head is 7–30 in. wg. This unit is double width and has double inlet (axially from both ends).

the housing, directly connected to the fan shaft. Behind the fan blades, Fig. 235, are seen some stationary vanes which serve the purpose of "removing" the whirling motion (turbulence) produced by the fan blades, thereby improving the operating efficiency. With such guide vanes, the fan is called a *vaneaxial fan.*

The general operation of a centrifugal fan, Fig. 236, is the same as described for centrifugal blowers and pumps; the air enters the center of the rotor and is speeded up in the blades by centrifugal force (and also the pressure builds up in a radial direction), then it passes through a diffuser section, which is the space between the rotor and the casing. The shape of the casing to produce the diffuser effect, called a *scroll,* is theoretically a

logarithmic spiral.   Some of the velocity head at the blade tip is converted into static head in the scroll.

In a centrifugal fan, there may be many small (long and narrow) blades
or a few larger blades as in Fig. 236.   In either case the blades may be curved
forward, straight and radial, or curved backward.   The effects of these
curvatures are suggested by Fig. 237, in which it is assumed that each blade
has the same absolute or tangential speed at the tip of the blade v_b, and
that a particle of air (or gas) has the same speed relative to the blade $v_{a/b}$, in
each.   (The velocity polygons could as well be drawn on the assumption of
the same absolute air velocities v_a.)   Perhaps you recall the relative velocity
rule from mechanics,

(**k**) $$v_a = v_b \leftrightarrow\!\!\!+ v_{a/b},$$

which is to say that the absolute velocity of the air v_a is equal to the *vector*
sum of the absolute velocity of the blade v_b and the velocity of the air with

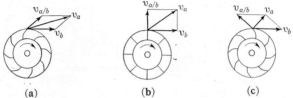

(a)   (b)   (c)

**Fig. 237.   Effect of Blade Curvature.   (a) Forward curved
blades; (b) radial blades; (c) backward curved blades.**

respect to the blade $v_{a/b}$.   The direction of the relative velocity $v_{a/b}$ as it
leaves the blade is tangent to the blade at the tip.   We notice that the forward curved blades, Fig. 237(a), result in the largest absolute air velocity
v_a for a given blade speed v_b (and rpm); that the backward curved blades
give the smallest v_a.   One conclusion from this is that for a particular v_a,
the rotor turns slower for forward curve than for backward curve.   There
is sometimes an advantage related to speed; perhaps to have a fan directly
connected to an 1800-rpm electric motor, backward curves are necessary to
avoid excessive air velocity v_a.   The kinetic energy corresponding to this
velocity is not efficiently used for compression in a diffuser section and a
better efficiency may be obtained with a lower v_a and more of the desired
pressure increase occurring in the blades.   In some applications, there is
another advantage to the backward curve: a fan with such blades will not
overload the motor (it is just a characteristic as learned from tests, Fig. 238),
whereas when other blade shapes are used, the power required to turn the
fan at constant speed continues to increase as the static pressure decreases
(if something happens so that the "load" goes off the fan, the motor might
burn out—if it is not designed for the load).

299. Performance of Fans.   Like people, fans have their peculiarities and they are not necessarily what you would expect.   Let a particular fan be turned at constant speed.   Then the static pressure has a definite relation to the volume (cfm) of air being moved.   In each of the charts of Fig. 238, this relationship is defined by the "static pressure" curve.   The static pressure typically reaches a maximum at some low percentage of the maximum capacity and decreases.   Suppose by way of illustration that 100% abscissa is 10,000 cfm and 100% pressure is 10 in. wg.   If the air required

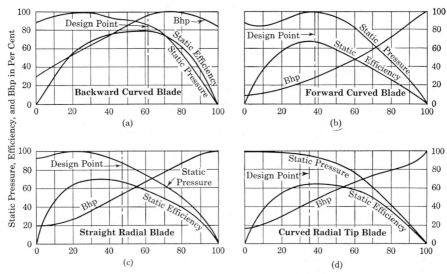

Fig. 238.   Performance of Centrifugal Fans.   The abscissa represents the percentage of maximum output, output measured in cfm, say.   The design point for the type fan in (a) is approximately 60% of output at zero head.   A set of these curves applies to all fan sizes of a particular design of fan (all sizes conform to the theory of similitude). After Fig. 26-4, *Combustion Engineering,* by Combustion Engineering-Superheater, Inc.

by the system is 6000 cfm, then the static pressure developed by the backward-curved-blade fan, Fig. 238(a), is about 8.7 in. wg.   If the resistance of the system is not such as to build up this pressure, dampers must be adjusted until this pressure of 8.7 in. wg. is obtained in order to have a flow of 6000 cfm.   In short, each fan has characteristic curves at a particular speed and they do not change with changes in the system being served. Thus, it is essential that if a constant speed fan is used, it must be chosen to match the system requirements.

Many systems require varying output; for example, a forced-draft fan should deliver about half as much air when the boiler is operating at half load as when it is at full load.   Considering the same fan as before, Fig. 238(a), a half-load requirement would be 3000 cfm.   Corresponding to 30%

abscissa, we find the static pressure to be 10 in. wg., and 3000 cfm will not flow from this fan at the given fan speed unless the static pressure is 10 in. wg. The simplest way to provide regulation is to introduce additional resistance to the system, either after the fan, called damper regulation, or before the fan, called inlet vane control and somewhat more efficient than the damper. While the damper is the most wasteful of power, it is a cheap control, easily made automatic.

The most efficient (and most expensive in initial cost) control is by varying the speed of the fan. The means of doing this include magnetic couplings, hydraulic couplings, variable speed a-c motors, variable speed steam turbines, and mechanical variable speed drives. A two-speed motor, which is less expensive than a variable speed motor, is often used as a satis-factory compromise. The relationships between speed, capacity, pressure, and power as given for pumps, § 294, also hold closely for centrifugal fans; namely, the capacity (cfm) of a particular fan varies directly as the speed n, the static pressure varies as the square of the speed n^2, and the required power varies as the cube of the speed n^3. Thus if the requirements in capacity are reduced by half and the fan speed is halved, then the pressure must be $\frac{1}{4}$ of its previous value, and the power would be $(\frac{1}{2})^3 = \frac{1}{8}$ of its previous value.

There are an indefinite number of conclusions which can be drawn from the curves of Fig. 238 together with the rules of the speed-pressure-power relations. You might try to see how many conclusions you can draw. The interested reader will refer to more complete works on the subject, and the engineer concerned with the selection of fans will do the same and also get help from the specialists employed by fan manufacturers.

300. Draft for Furnaces. *Draft* is generally taken as the difference between atmospheric pressure and the pressure of the gas at some point inside the steam-generator-chimney system when the gas is at a pressure below atmospheric. If the gage pressure is positive at some point, as when forced draft is used, there is no "draft" in the technical sense at that point. The gas pressure varies along the path of flow and it is customary to measure this pressure at various points by draft gages, Figs. 239 and 240. If it is desired to measure the gas pressure at more than three places, as is often the case, more than three units can be combined, as in Fig. 239. A pressure drop occurs through the fuel bed, through the furnace proper, through air heaters and economizers, etc. The sum of all of these pressure drops plus the drops in breeching and stack is the static pressure differential to be over-come or the amount of draft required in order to have flow.

As we have noticed in the descriptions of steam generators, forced draft and/or induced draft are commonly used. The general name for a fan-produced draft is *mechanical draft,* as opposed to natural draft (§ 301).

Forced draft alone produces a pressure in the furnace greater than atmospheric, with the resultant possibility of leakage of noxious gases into the boiler room, unless the setting is built air-tight (which is more costly). Induced draft alone may lower the pressure in the furnace so much below atmospheric that air leakage will reduce the efficiency of operation. The

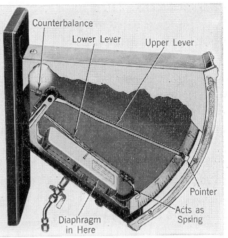

Counterbalance
Lower Lever   Upper Lever
Pointer
Acts as Spring
Pointer   Diaphragm in Here

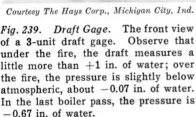

UNDER FIRE   OVERFIRE   LAST PASS

Pointer

Courtesy The Hays Corp., Michigan City, Ind.   *Courtesy The Hays Corp., Michigan City, Ind.*

Fig. 239. Draft Gage. The front view of a 3-unit draft gage. Observe that under the fire, the draft measures a little more than +1 in. of water; over the fire, the pressure is slightly below atmospheric, about −0.07 in. of water. In the last boiler pass, the pressure is −0.67 in. of water.

Fig. 240. Mechanism in Draft Gage. This view shows the mechanism inside the draft gage of Fig. 239. The pressure acts on a diaphragm inside of the box. Changes in pressure cause the lower lever to move. Its movement is magnified to a much larger movement of the upper lever, the outer end of which forms the pointer.

combination of forced and induced draft makes it possible to have any desirable pressure in the furnace—usually slightly below atmospheric. Even if mechanical draft is used, a stack or chimney is ordinarily provided to discharge the products of combustion high enough so that they will not be a nuisance to residents of the vicinity and will not damage vegetation or property.

301. Natural Draft. Natural draft is provided by a chimney and is the term used when no fans (or jet pumps) are used. It is estimated by using Archimedes' principle of buoyance. The hot gases in the stack are lighter than the cold outside air, and they tend to be pushed up by a force equal to the difference between the weights of a chimney full of atmospheric air and a chimney full of stack gases. For 1 sq. ft. of cross section, the weight of gas is $z\gamma$, where γ is the specific weight (lb./cu. ft.) and is conveniently taken as $z\rho$ (approximately when gravity is not standard), where z is the height of the column of gas whose average density is ρ lb./cu. ft. Thus, the theoretical draft provided by the chimney (stack draft) is

(1) $\Delta p = z(\rho_a - \rho_g)$ psf   or $\Delta p = 0.192z(\rho_a - \rho_g)$ in. H_2O,

where ρ_a $(= p/(RT)$ is the density of the atmospheric air, ρ_g is the density of the stack gases, z ft. is the effective stack height, and 0.192 is in. H_2O per psf. Equation (1) can be obtained by an energy diagram. Let the datum of potential energy be the bottom of the stack; then $z_2 = z =$ stack height.

Most of the difference in density is due to temperature, so for the computations for (1), the pressures are effectively equal for gas and air, taken as the barometric pressure. The temperature of the gas is highest at the bottom of the stack, and due to heat loss and leakage of air inward, it decreases as the gas moves up. Use the average temperature T_g, which can be taken as the arithmetic average of top and bottom temperatures. Charts are available for estimating the top temperature.* Also, since the stack gases are mostly nitrogen, there is not too much error in using the same value of $R = 53.3$ ft-lb./lb-°R for both the air and chimney gas. Thus with p and R the same for both, we get

(m) $$\rho_a - \rho_g = \frac{p}{RT_a} - \frac{p}{RT_g} = \frac{p}{53.3}\left(\frac{1}{T_a} - \frac{1}{T_g}\right);$$

where p is the barometric pressure in psf. If the barometer is in inches of Hg as usual, we can use $(0.491)(144)(p_a)$, where p_a in. Hg is the barometer reading, and then substitute the result obtained from (m) into (1), to find the *stack draft* as (with the approximations stated)

(n) $$\Delta p = \frac{(0.192)(0.491)(144)p_a z}{53.3}\left(\frac{1}{T_a} - \frac{1}{T_g}\right)$$

$$= 0.255 p_a z \left(\frac{1}{T_a} - \frac{1}{T_g}\right) \text{ in. } H_2O,$$

$$[\Delta p \text{ IN. } H_2O; \; p_a \text{ IN. HG}]$$

where T_a and T_g are the absolute temperatures of the surrounding air and chimney gas, respectively. We note that the amount of natural draft generated by the stack depends upon atmospheric conditions and upon the temperature of the flue gases. The use of economizers and air heaters results in cooler flue gases, and the cooler gases result in a smaller draft. Probably some 15-30% of the total head from (n) is velocity head.

* *Steam*, by Babcock and Wilcox Co.

302. Example. Investigate the possibility of using a chimney in obtaining the 7-in. wg. pressure differential of the example of § 297 (which is only part of the pressure differential needed in such a steam generator), if the gases have an average temperature of 440°F and the atmosphere is at 28 in. Hg and 40°F.

SOLUTION. The required stack height from equation (**n**) is (440°F = 900°R and 40°F = 500°R)

$$z = \frac{\Delta p}{0.255 p_a \left(\dfrac{1}{T_a} - \dfrac{1}{T_g}\right)} = \frac{7}{(0.255)(28)\left(\dfrac{1}{500} - \dfrac{1}{900}\right)} = 1100 \text{ ft.,}$$

which is rather high. Considering that there might be an equal pressure loss cared for by the induced-draft fan and considering that the stack effectiveness is likely of the order of 80% (actual stack needed = 1100/0.8 = 1375 ft.), it would seem that natural draft alone is out of the question for such large steam generators.

303. Closure. While the pump work and the fan work associated with a steam power plant are each a small percentage of the plant's output, these works, as the examples show, are individually large enough to be worth the best engineering design and construction. In the highest pressure plants being planned, the pump work significantly affects the overall thermal efficiency; for the best thermal efficiency, the pumps must be carefully designed and operated.

Since a given centrifugal pump or fan can do so much and no more, it is wise to choose one which has somewhat more capacity than one thinks will be needed, but not too much more because the needed static pressure may have to be obtained by arbitrary resistances in the lines which mean more work. Especially for fans, the performance on the job may be much different from that on the test block, most likely poorer, because the setup for the tests are favorable, with straight ducts for intake and for discharge. Experts in this area can make good estimates of what the difference between test block and actual performances might be.

SELECTED REFERENCES

Babcock and Wilcox Co., *Steam*.
Baumeister, T., Jr., *Fans*, McGraw-Hill.
Church, A. H., *Centrifugal Pumps and Blowers*, John Wiley.
Daugherty, R. L., *Hydraulics*, McGraw-Hill.
de Lorenzi, O., *Combustion Engineering*, Combustion Engineering-Superheater Co.
Keller and Marks, *The Theory and Performance of Axial Flow Fans*, McGraw-Hill.
Kristal and Annett, *Pumps*, McGraw-Hill.
Stepanoff, A. J., *Turboblowers: Theory, Design and Application of Centrifugal and Axial Flow Compressors and Fans*, John Wiley.
Wilson, W. E., *Positive Displacement Pumps and Fluid Motors*, Pitman.

PROBLEMS

[handwritten marginalia: 1 gal = 231 in³; 7.48 gal/ft³]

411. A centrifugal pump picks up water from a tank at atmospheric pressure and delivers 500 gpm at 60°F into a line in which the velocity is 8.02 fps; the water is raised through an elevation of 50 ft. through passages whose total frictional head is 50 ft. and into a vessel wherein the pressure is 196.2 psig. In this operation, the power consumed by the driving motor is 100 hp. What are the water horsepower and the overall efficiency of the pump?   *Ans.* ~~65.7%~~.

[handwritten: $H_T = 534$ ft H₂O   e = 69.8%]

412. A boiler feedwater pump with an efficiency of 55% picks up 2000 lb. per min. of water at 0.949 psia and pumps it (a) to 300 psia, (b) to 3000 psia. The changes of ΔK and Δz are negligible. For each case, compute the static heads, the ideal and actual works (in hp), and the friction head. (c) What actual horsepower is computed for part (b) when the density at state 2 is found from Table IX?

Ans. (a) 2.32, 697 ft., 42.1, 76.5 hp, 570 ft., (b) 2.32, 6970 ft., 422, 768 hp, 5712 ft., (c) 760 hp.

413. Gear pumps are frequently used to provide power for hydraulic systems. A manufacturer of such a pump specifies an output of 19.3 gpm of oil, whose density is 53.4 lb./cu. ft., against a pressure head of 1100 psi. The velocity head is negligible. The brake input is 14 bhp at 1200 rpm; 1½-in. gears. (a) What is the efficiency of this pump? (b) If the efficiency of the hydraulic motor in which this oil is used is 70%, what is the overall efficiency? Would this appear to be a competitive system for large amounts of power?   *Ans.* (a) 73.3%, (b) 51.2%.

414. A 20,000-kw turbo-generator unit requires 16,750 gpm of circulating water for the condenser. The inlet from a lake is at the same level as the outlet to the lake. The water is raised 15 ft. in passing through the condenser. In the pipe line, its velocity is 6 fps. The frictional head loss in the condenser is 15 ft. and in the pipe lines, 30 ft. of water. If the efficiency of the circulating pump is 80%, what shaft horsepower is required?   *Ans.* 240.

415. A pump moves 100 gpm of oil which weighs 56 lb./cu. ft. A pressure gage at the level of the center line of the intake reads a vacuum of 1 in. Hg, and at the center line of the discharge, the static pressure is 9 in. Hg gage. The oil is picked up from a pond and delivered into a 2-in. line. (a) What is the velocity head and the static head? (b) For a pump efficiency of 45%, what horsepower is required?

Ans. (a) 1.68, 12.63 ft., (b) 0.722 hp.

416. A handbook gives the following equation for the "water" horsepower:

$$whp = \frac{(G)(\text{head in ft.})(\text{sp. gr.})}{3960} \text{ hp,}$$

where sp. gr. = specific gravity, G = gallons per minute, based on 85°F water. Starting with a fundamental equation in the text, show that this equation is true (or nearly so).

417. A forced-draft fan delivers 50,000 cfm of air at 80°F to a furnace against a static head of 6.5 in. H_2O. The velocity in the discharge duct is 40 fps. The overall efficiency is 68%. (a) Compute the static and velocity heads in feet of air. (b) Increase this head by 15% as a safety factor and compute the air horsepower and the power required of the motor.

Ans. (a) 457, 24.9 ft., (b) 67.8 kw (motor).

418. The resistances for an induced-draft fan that handles 7700 lb./min.

of gases at 350°F are: draft loss in furnace, 0.1; in boiler and superheater, 5; in air heater, 2; in flues, 0.45, all in in. H₂O at 80°F. To be on the safe side, these resistances should be increased by 20%. For a total overall fan efficiency of 72%, what horsepower is required? (For the purpose of computing horsepower, it is reasonable to assume that these gases have the properties of air.)   *Ans.* 310 hp.

419. A manufacturer's catalog gives the output of a fan at maximum efficiency as 20,750 cfm of standard air (0.075 lb./cu. ft.) at a velocity 3200 fpm against a static pressure of 8 in. H₂O at 60°F; *bhp* = 34.6. Compute the velocity and static heads in feet of air and the total and static efficiencies.
        Ans. 44.2, 554 ft., 81.5%, 75.5%.

420. The barometer is 28.5 in. Hg and the atmospheric temperature is 100°F. An 80-ft. stack contains flue gases at an average temperature of 440°F. Let R for stack gases be the same as that for air and compute the density of the air, the density of the gases, and the stack draft.
        Ans. 0.0676, 0.0421 lb./cu. ft., 0.392 in. H₂O.

421. It is desired to determine the height of chimney for a boiler delivering 2000 bo. hp. The following draft losses have been estimated: furnace, 0.1; through boiler, 0.7; through breeching and turns, 0.2, each in in. wg. The average stack temperature is to be taken as 600°F; outside air temperature, 60°F; standard atmospheric pressure. Increase the computed draft by 25% as a factor of safety and to care for the friction loss in the stack itself.
        Ans. 168 ft.

Note. *There are not 421 problems in this book. See blank numbers at the end of each chapter.*

MISCELLANEOUS EQUIPMENT

304. Introduction. This chapter covers a few odds and ends which may be of interest to the reader, principally matters and activities related to water and especially as the water is used for the generation of steam.

305. Troubles from Impure Feedwater. Raw (untreated) water contains impurities in varying amounts, depending upon the source of the water. In some cases, the raw water may be used directly as feedwater without resulting troubles; yet a water which may prove satisfactory in a small boiler operating at low capacity may give trouble in a boiler operating at a relatively high capacity. Improper water results in one or more of the following events: (1) deposits of scale, (2) foaming, (3) priming, (4) corrosion, and (5) embrittlement.

Deposits of *scale* result from solids in solution or in suspension and they reduce the rate of heat transfer, sometimes being responsible for burned-out tubes. *Foaming,* caused by a scum of oil and vegetable matter on the surface of the water in the boiler shell or by excessive alkalinity of the boiler feed, is occurring when a mass of bubbles forms on the surface of the water and many particles of water are being projected into the steam space. It is one but not the sole cause of priming. A boiler is *priming* when relatively large quantities of water are passing out with the steam. This water is a hazard to pipe lines and apparatus. *Corrosion* is a transformation of the metal, as by oxidation. *Embrittlement,* which occurs when certain impurities are present, is a phenomenon which manifests itself in cracks in, and failure of, riveted boiler joints.

Since the impurities which are responsible for the foregoing ills are of varying kinds and amounts, it is only natural that no single treatment would serve equally well for all waters. Some impurities are not difficult to eliminate. In each case, the water should be analyzed by a competent chemist. With a known analysis, a suitable treatment may be prescribed.

306. Impurities in Water. Raw water as taken from rivers, lakes, etc., may contain a considerable amount of mud and other solids in suspension. If such impurities are troublesome, the raw water should be passed through a filter, or the suspended solids should be coagulated and settled in a sedimentation tank.　Filtering with a coagulant will remove organic matter, bacteria, iron in suspension, and other suspended and colloidal impurities.

In varying degrees, raw water contains dissolved minerals, which are the source of scale deposits when the water is heated.　These dissolved, scale-forming materials, which include magnesium bicarbonate, calcium bicarbonate, calcium sulfate, magnesium sulfate, and magnesium chloride, are removed or are replaced by less objectionable salts by chemical processes. It is these minerals which give water the property called *hardness;* the harder the water, in general, the greater the quantity of mineral matter in solution. The hardness is measured by the amount of these calcium and magnesium salts expressed in grains per gallon (7000 grains per lb.).

So-called noncondensable gases, gases which do not condense at the temperatures ordinarily encountered in raw water, are corrosive agents and are invariably carried in the water.　The most objectionable gas is usually oxygen, with carbon dioxide second.　As an outcome of oxygen, ferric hydroxide (rust) is formed if the container is steel.　The process of rust formation speeds up as the temperature increases and as the oxygen content increases, so that in the case of hot feedwater, corrosion from oxygen may be a serious matter.　Carbon dioxide results in corrosive action, too, especially in the presence of dissolved oxygen.　The CO_2 combines with the water to form carbonic acid, a corroding agent under certain conditions for ferrous metals, nickel alloys, and copper alloys.　Infrequently, ammonia is found in raw water.　It reacts with water to form ammonium hydroxide (NH_4OH), an alkali which corrodes copper alloys, commonly found in valves, tubes, and other fittings.

307. *pH* Value of the Water.　Another important factor related to corrosion is the *pH* value of the water, a quantitative measure of the acidity or alkalinity of the solution.　Both acids and alkalies dissociate when combined with water.　The acids dissociate to form positive hydrogen ions (H^+), and the alkalies form negative hydroxyl ions (OH^-).　The total concentration of ions, the sum of the H^+ ions and the OH^- ions, is always the same.　When the number of H^+ ions is equal to the number of OH^- ions, the water is neutral (pure) and the *pH* value is 7.　When *pH* is greater than 7, the OH^- ions exceed the H^+ ions and the water is alkaline.　When *pH* is less than 7, the H^+ ions exceed the OH^- ions and the water is acid.　The smaller the *pH* is, when below 7, the greater the acidity.

In absolute measure, the hydrogen ion concentration is expressed in grams per liter.　The logarithm to the base 10 of the reciprocal of this absolute measure is the *pH* value, which ranges from zero to 14.

When the pH is between 9.3 and 10.5 (alkaline), a range in which boiler water is sometimes maintained, a protective film may be formed on the surface of the metal to retard corrosion. If the pH changes to some value outside of this range, the protective film disappears. Except for this phenomenon (if the oxygen content remains constant), the corrosion rate increases rapidly as the water becomes more acid ($pH < 7$) and decreases somewhat as it becomes more basic. Thus, we see that while oxygen is a corrosive agent, its effects are retarded by a regulation of pH. Since excessive alkalinity may result in priming or embrittlement, there is a limit to improvement by this means. However, the oxygen is not difficult to remove.

308. Chemical Treatment. The particular chemical treatment to be used depends upon the analysis of the water. Hence, our discussion will only be illustrative of available treatments. A class of material very commonly used for softening water is called zeolite. There are a number of different zeolites, natural and synthetic, each having the characteristic ability to exchange its sodium (or hydrogen) for calcium and magnesium in compounds which make the water hard. For examples, consider the following reactions:

$$\begin{array}{llll}
\text{Calcium} & \text{Sodium} & \text{Sodium} & \text{Calcium} \\
\text{bicarbonate} + \text{zeolite} \rightarrow & \text{bicarbonate} + & \text{zeolite;}
\end{array}$$

$$\begin{array}{llll}
\text{Calcium} & \text{Sodium} & \text{Sodium} & \text{Calcium} \\
\text{sulfate} + \text{zeolite} \rightarrow & \text{sulfate} + & \text{zeolite;}
\end{array}$$

$$\begin{array}{llll}
\text{Magnesium} & \text{Sodium} & \text{Sodium} & \text{Magnesium} \\
\text{bicarbonate} + \text{zeolite} \rightarrow & \text{bicarbonate} + & \text{zeolite;}
\end{array}$$

$$\begin{array}{llll}
\text{Magnesium} & \text{Sodium} & \text{Sodium} & \text{Magnesium} \\
\text{sulfate} + \text{zeolite} \rightarrow & \text{sulfate} + & \text{zeolite.}
\end{array}$$

Observe that in each case the magnesium or calcium in the sulfate or bicarbonate on the left side of the equation is replaced by the sodium from the zeolite. Since a particular quantity of zeolite originally contains a particular amount of sodium, this sodium is gradually used in the water-softening process until there is no sodium left in the zeolite. Fortunately, the exchange can be made in the opposite direction; so the zeolite is *regenerated* by circulating through it a sodium chloride (common salt) solution. The sodium in the salt is exchanged for the calcium and magnesium in the zeolite. Thus, the operation of a zeolite softener is interrupted from time to time for regeneration. See Fig. 241.

Since the chemical reaction produces either sodium bicarbonate or sodium sulfate in the examples above, the soft outgoing water may contain an excessive quantity of sodium salts, especially if the raw water is very hard.   In consequence, the water may be so strongly basic that foaming and priming occur.   In short, after passing through the softener, the water may need other treatments, not only to reduce its *pH* value, but also to deaerate or to decarbonate it.

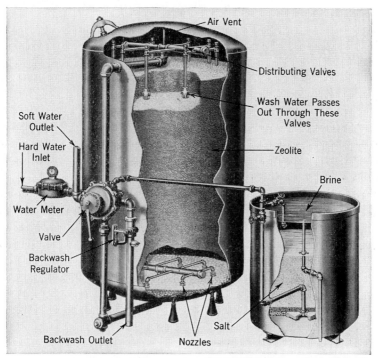

Air Vent

Distributing Valves

Wash Water Passes Out Through These Valves

Soft Water Outlet

Hard Water Inlet

Zeolite

Brine

Water Meter

Valve

Backwash Regulator

Backwash Outlet   Salt

Nozzles

Courtesy Elgin Softener Corp., Elgin, Ill.

Fig. 241.   Zeolite Softener. The hard water passes through a meter, which is generally equipped with an automatic alarm to warn for time to regenerate, and is sprayed through the distributing valves over the zeolite. The water passes through the zeolite and through a bed of sand on gravel at the bottom, thence through the nozzles and out of the softener. When regeneration is needed, the multiport valve is set first for the backwash. Then water enters at the bottom, washes out foreign material, and loosens up the bed of zeolite. After the backwash, brine sprayed on top of the zeolite seeps through, regenerating it. The brine tank also has a bed of sand and gravel at the bottom for filtering purposes.

This softening treatment reduces the blowoff (§ 313) necessary and the frequency of cleaning out scale.   Water softening is used also for purposes other than treating feedwater.   Many industrial processes require soft water.   In some localities, water softening is practically a necessity for laundries.

309. Deaeration.   Deaeration is used to eliminate or reduce the quantity of gases carried by the water.   Physical phenomena which are utilized for this purpose are:

1. At high temperature, the solubility of these gases in water is much reduced. For example, in air and at atmospheric pressure, water at 80°F may contain eight times as much oxygen as at 200°F. Thus, since deaeration is ordinarily carried on at elevated temperatures, this process is often combined with that of feedwater heating. The feedwater heater of Fig. 128, § 167, is also a deaerator.

2. The solubility of a gas in a liquid is proportional to the absolute partial pressure of that gas on the liquid. For example, water in air at 80°F may contain some 5.5 times more oxygen when the pressure is 25 psia than when it is 5 psia. To take advantage of this phenomenon, the water being treated is surrounded by an atmosphere of steam (also useful for feedwater heating), which reduces the partial pressure of the gases to a low value.

3. The gases will leave the water easier and quicker if the water is broken into small units (thin sheets). In this event, the gases may escape by traveling a minimum distance.

The removal of CO_2 is not so simple. That which is uncombined is largely eliminated by deaeration, but much CO_2 is frequently in chemical combinations, bicarbonates and carbonates. There is a natural balance between free CO_2, bicarbonates, and carbonates, so that when the free CO_2 is removed, the bicarbonate tends to reestablish the free form and the carbonate to decompose to the bicarbonate form. It takes time for these transformations to occur. Moreover, water of low pH contains a greater percentage of its CO_2 in the free form. These properties of CO_2 and water mixtures are utilized when it becomes necessary to remove CO_2.

310. Feedwater Regulators. Manual control of the flow of feed-water is feasible and is used in some small installations. In central station practice, automatic regulation is the rule, with three basic types of regulators employed.

In the *float type,* a float chamber is connected to the top and bottom of the steam drum, so that the level of water in the chamber is the same as that in the boiler drum. As the water level changes, the float moves up or down, and in doing so, it operates a balanced feed valve through a suitable linkage. The feed valve regulates the flow of water, increasing the flow when the level drops, decreasing it when the level rises.

The *thermo-pressure type* consists of an inclined tube inside a larger finned tube with a jacket between them. The inside tube is connected to the steam and water space of the steam drum, so that the level of water in it is the same as the level in the boiler. The jacket or annular space between the tubes is connected to a diaphragm type of feed valve and the jacket with this connection is a closed system containing water. At a steady output from the boiler, the hot steam in the upper part of the inside tube transfers heat to the water in the jacket, which in turn transfers the same amount of heat to the atmosphere through the outside finned tube, with the result that the opening of the feed valve remains constant. If the output increases, the water level drops and more hot steam enters the inside tube and transfers more heat to the water in the jacket than is dissipated by the finned tube. As a result, the pressure in the jacket increases, which causes the feed valve to open wider. If there is a decrease in load, the water level rises and the opposite train of events occurs.

In the *thermo-expansion type,* there is an inclined metallic tube so connected to the drum that the water level in the tube is the same as that in the drum (see the *thermostat* in Fig. 242). The water in the lower part of the tube is cold, just a little above room temperature. The steam is hot. The lower end of the tube is fixed and the upper end is connected to a bell crank. If the water level falls, there will be an increase of steam in the tube which consequently expands, since its average temperature increases. This expansion moves the bell crank and connecting links which actuate the feed valve through a pilot valve.

A regulator that operates by virtue of a change in water level alone is not satisfactory on high-capacity boilers where the load may fluctuate suddenly. Such steam generators have relatively low water capacities, and therefore not much reserve. If, for example, the load suddenly increases, there is a rapid rush of steam from the drum, the pressure drops a little, and the water boils violently. Since there are more steam bubbles *in* the water, the water swells and the water line rises when there is actually less liquid in the drum. Thus, a regulator operating from the water level alone gives the wrong initial response, both for increasing and decreasing loads. Of course, if the drain continues, the water level will go down after the swell, and the feed valve will be opened wider. The consequent fluctuation of water level may be dangerous in some cases. For more sensitive control, some regulators are partially actuated by the rate of steam flow, an example of which is the Copes Flowmatic in Fig. 242.

311. Safety Valves. It is conventional safety practice to include some sort of pressure release device on vessels or containers wherein the pressure varies. As might be expected, safety valves are required by law on boilers. There are many variations in the details of their design, but all of them are preloaded so that a certain boiler pressure is expected to open (pop) them. Weight loading of the valve, either directly or on a lever, is not permitted by the ASME *Code;* hence, spring loading is generally used. Figure 243 is an example of a safety valve. The valve should close after the pressure has

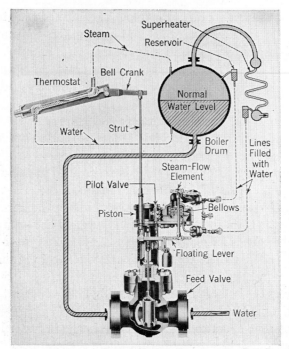

Courtesy Northern Equipment Co., Erie, Pa.

Fig. 242. Copes Flowmatic Feedwater Regulator.
The action of the thermostat in this control is as
described for the thermo-expansion type of regulator.
In this case, the strut from the bell crank attaches to
a floating lever, which, at its other end, is connected
through a linkage to the steam-flow element. This
steam-flow element consists of a brass bellows in a
chamber. The upper side of the bellows is subjected
to boiler pressure and the lower side is subjected to
the pressure at the outlet from the superheater plus
the pressure exerted by a spring in order to equalize
the pressures. See Fig. 118 for information about the
pressure drop through the superheater. An increase
or decrease in steam flow results in an increase or
decrease in pressure drop through the superheater,
causing the bellows and spring to compress or expand proportionately. The movement is transmitted
through the external linkage shown to the floating
lever. The movement of the floating lever operates
the pilot valve, which admits a fluid (air, oil, or water
at 50 to 100 psi) to the proper side of the piston which
directly controls the feed valve.

dropped somewhat below the popping pressure and it should not chatter during either the opening or closing. A minimum of two safety valves is required on each boiler, and one for the superheater.

Another safety device, sometimes used when the pressure is below 225 psi, is the *fusible plug,* which is a hollow bronze or steel bushing with the central hole filled with tin. The tin has a melting point of about 450°F,

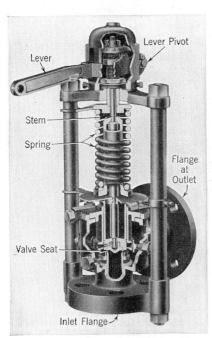

Courtesy Foster Engineering Co., Newark, N. J.

Fig. 243. Safety Valve. When the valve opens a little, the pressure is exerted over a larger area. This force, together with that arising from the change of momentum of the steam as it flows out, produces the total force which results in quick opening.

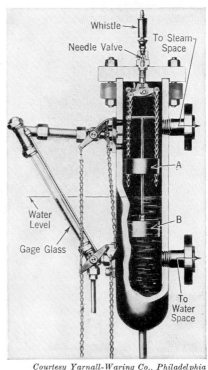

Courtesy Yarnall-Waring Co., Philadelphia

Fig. 244. Hi-Lo Alarm.

between the temperatures of the steam and hot gases. The plugs are placed at the lowest water level considered as a warning point. When the water level falls below the plug, the tin melts out and steam escapes through the hole, giving warning.

312. Water Level Indicators. The simplest of water level indicators consists of a gage glass and test cocks, as seen in Fig. 119. Larger systems require more elaborate devices. In Fig. 244, the inclined glass can be seen

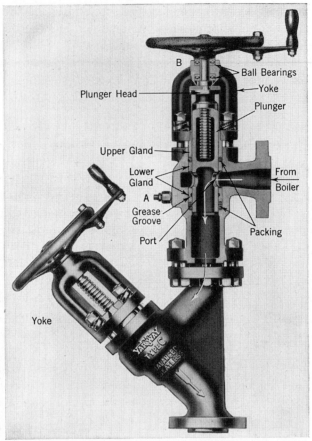

Courtesy Yarnall-Waring Co., Philadelphia

Fig. 245. *Blowoff Valves.* This is a sleeve plunger type of valve. The upper valve is shown in the open position, while the lower one, with the same internal construction, is in the closed position. The upper valve is closed by turning the hand wheel, which causes the plunger to move down closing off the port in the lower gland. With continued tightening, the shoulder on the plunger contacts the upper gland, pushing it down, squeezing the packing against the adjacent walls, making a tight shutoff. The valve is lubricated through alemite fittings at *A* and *B*.

and a whistle gives warning for both high water and low water. As shown, the water is at normal level, and the whistle warning is closed. The warning is operated by the two cylindrically shaped weights *A* and *B* as they act through the linkage at the top, the basis being Archimedes' principle that the buoyant force on a body is equal to the weight of fluid displaced. The valve opens when the lower weight *B* "weighs" more than it does in this position relative to *A*. Hence, when the water rises over the upper weight

A, its *weight* (as measured by a spring scale) is *reduced* and the valve to the whistle opens. When the water drops below the lower weight B, its *weight* is *increased* and the valve opens. In large units, these devices are equipped with remote indicators; the operator may be in another building.

313. Blowoff Valves. Blowoff valves are always placed at the bottom of the lowest drum, called the *mud drum*, or at the lowest point to which water circulates. In this location, they are opened, sometimes several times a day, sometimes once in several days, to wash out sediment and dirt which gradually accumulate at the lowest level. Blowoff also serves the purpose of keeping down the boiler concentration of mineral solids, a concentration that gradually builds up from the addition of make-up water. They are used in pairs, Fig. 245. The valve next to the boiler should be opened last and closed first, consequently taking most of the wear. Since the outside or *sealing valve* is thus operated under no pressure and no flow, it stays in good condition. Intermittent blowoffs usually discharge into the sewer.

Sometimes, when conditions warrant, valves are used at the water level of the steam drum. In this location, it is called a *surface blow* and it is intended to clean the boiler of scum from oil or grease, which acts as an insulator on tubes and therefore may be the cause of tube failure from burning.

Arrangements for a continuous and automatic blowoff, instead of an intermittent and manual one, are available. In this system, the adiabatic (throttling) flow of water from high pressure to low pressure results in the evaporation of some of the water (according to the law $h_1 = h_2$). The steam so formed may be used to heat the feedwater in a feedwater heater and the remaining hot water used for the same purpose in a heat exchanger. Thus, the thermal loss from the blowoff may be kept at a minimum.

314. Other Valves. Valves for ordinary service in opening and closing lines are usually either **globe valves,** Fig. 246, or **gate valves,** Fig. 247. For various reasons, valves are made of various materials, including iron, steel, bronze, stainless steel, etc. In Fig. 246, the packing nut, the gland, and the packing provide means of preventing leakage about the stem or spindle. The valve is closed by contact between the disk and the seat ring, both of which may be reground or replaced after wear or other damage. The ordinary domestic faucet is a globe valve.

Turning the hand wheel of a gate valve, Fig. 247, causes the wedge-shaped gate to open or close the passageway. The seat rings of cast bronze are renewable. The packing prevents leakage about the spindle. With gate valves wide open, the flow is straight through with a minimum of fluid friction, which is not true for the globe valve. In the largest sizes, gate valves are power operated.

Most plants have need of steam at less than boiler pressure. In some cases, such steam may be obtained by extraction at the desired pressure from the prime mover. Frequently, all or part of such lower-pressure steam is

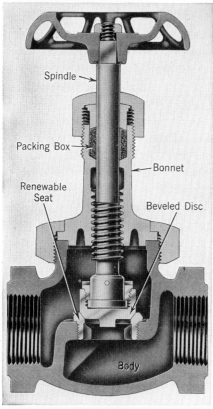

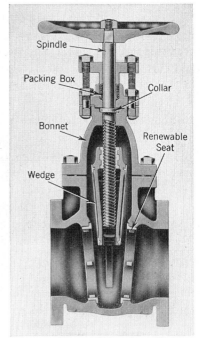

Courtesy Jenkins Bros., New York

Courtesy Jenkins Bros., New York

Fig. 246. Globe Valve. Valve with iron body; limited to use for steam at 150 lb./sq. in. and 450°F.

Fig. 247. Iron-Body Gate Valve.

obtained by throttling through a reducing valve. The valves are available in many different designs, of which Fig. 248 is illustrative. This valve is shown closed at the seat. In operation, the reduced pressure p_2 exists on the lower side of the *diaphragm*. The reduced pressure p_2 on the valve plus the force of the spring balances the high pressure p_1. A particular spring and adjustment cause throttling to a certain pressure. For this valve, any one of four different springs may be used, making it possible to reduce the pressure to any value up to 85 psig when the initial pressure is not greater than 250 psia. The discharge pressure is automatically maintained about constant as follows: since the pressure under the diaphragm is p_2, the spring pushes the diaphragm down and opens the valve wider when p_2 decreases, allowing a greater flow and tending to build up the pressure p_2; if p_2 increases, this pressure pushes the diaphragm upwards, tending to close the valve and to reduce the flow so that pressure p_2 falls. Reducing valves are used for air, water, and other fluids. Although the reducing valve is often the most economical method of obtaining low-pressure steam, it should be remembered that a throttling process destroys available energy, § 209.

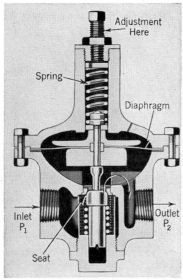

Courtesy Clark Mfg. Co., Cleveland

Fig. 248.   Reducing Valve.

Other common valves include needle and butterfly valves, illustrated with carburetors, Fig. 83, and quarter-turn plug valves. The plug valve consists of a plug with a drilled hole. If the plug is turned so that the hole lines up with the pipe or tube, the valve is open. A quarter turn places the hole at right angles with the flow, closing the valve. This is a light-service item.

315. Separators. It is often desirable to remove some of the entrained moisture, oil, or other impurities of flowing steam in order to avoid damage to equipment or to increase the efficiency of a process. The steam, for example, may be the wet discharge of a steam engine enroute to a steam heating system. Or, in order that the steam be nearly free of moisture as it enters an engine or turbine, a separator may be placed just ahead of the throttle valve. A common type of separator, Fig. 249, contains a baffle which faces the line of flow. The steam (or air, etc.), striking the baffle, is suddenly deflected. The particles of entrained water or oil or solid, due to their greater mass and inertia, strike the baffle and fall to the bottom of the separator. The water may be removed from the separator by traps, § 316 or it may be drained manually.

There are several other types of separators, one of which is shown in Fig. 250. The steam entering at the top is given a swirling motion by the helical

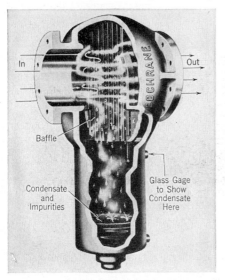

Fig. 249. Cochrane Separator. **This model is used on horizontal lines carrying live steam, exhaust steam, or compressed air, for removing oil and water. The steam (or air) passes through the separator by going around the sides of the baffle.**

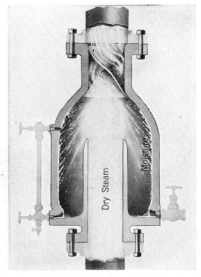

Fig. 250.   Centrifugal Separator.

surface shown. Centrifugal force then causes the heavier particles of water (or oil or any solid matter) to fly to the sides of the vessel, while steam of the order of 99% dry passes through the lower central outlet. Separators may be necessary following a desuperheater, § 170, because of water carried out of the desuperheater in the stream.

316. Traps. Traps are used to collect and automatically discharge the condensed vapor (liquid) in heating systems, steam lines, evaporators, separators, and other heat exchangers, and they are also designed to vent air which may have collected in the system. Let a steam line be used as an illustration. The trap is so located that water from the condensation of the steam in the line flows by gravity to it. Ordinarily, the rising level of water in the trap eventually causes a valve to open (through some simple mechanism).   In order for water to leave the trap, it is necessary for the pressure in the trap, which is the same as the line pressure, to be greater than the pressure in the discharge region.   If a pipe, or other space, below atmospheric pressure is to be trapped, a special arrangement of valves will allow liquid to collect in the trap at line vacuum pressure.   At the proper liquid level, the region of vacuum pressure is closed off and another valve opens to the atmosphere.   The atmospheric pressure in the trap allows the liquid to flow out by gravity.   At a certain low water level, the valves operate to isolate the trap from the atmosphere and connect it to the vacuum pressure region.

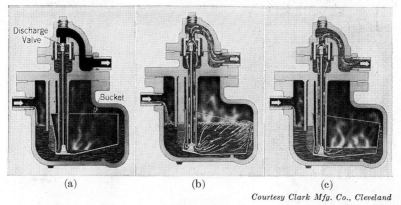

(a)   (b)   (c)

Courtesy Clark Mfg. Co., Cleveland

Fig. 251. Open Bucket Steam Trap. In (a), bucket is floating, closing valve; condensate is entering, no discharge. In (b), condensate has spilled over into and filled the bucket, causing it to drop and open the discharge valve; steam pressure pushes liquid out. In (c), most of the liquid in the bucket has been discharged, no more liquid is flowing into it, and it is about to move up, buoyed by the water, and close the discharge valve.

By the same arrangement of valves, the trap may be discharged to a high pressure region, instead of to the atmosphere.

The open bucket trap and its operation are shown in Fig. 251.   The pictures of the inverted bucket steam trap of Fig. 252 not only show the operation of the trap as a liquid discharger, but also its action in venting air. Another common type of trap not illustrated is one in which a float is attached to the end of a lever.   As the liquid level moves up and down, the float moves up and down, and through the lever it opens and closes the vent valve.   A sleeve-valve type with a float is so designed that, for a steady flow, it will stabilize in one position with the valve opened just wide enough to pass the condensate continuously, rather than intermittently as in Figs. 251 and 252.

317. Soot Blowers and Tube Cleaners. Deposits of any kind on heat transfer surfaces reduce the rate of heat flow from the hotter to the colder

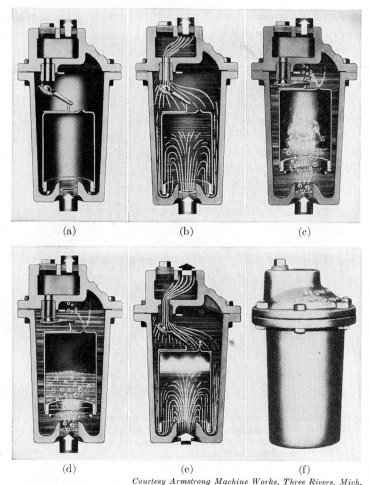

(a)   (b)   (c)

(d)   (e)   (f)

Courtesy Armstrong Machine Works, Three Rivers, Mich.

Fig. 252. Inverted Bucket Steam Trap. When units have been idle, they and the lines leading to them fill with air. In (a), steam is off, the trap is empty, the valve is open. In (b), steam has been turned on, air ahead of the condensate has been pushed out, the trap fills with water and additional water flows out the discharge until steam reaches the trap as in (c). In (c), the steam fills the bucket, which therefore floats and closes the discharge valve. In (d), steam in the bucket condenses and is vented (see bubbles at top of bucket) as more condensate enters, gradually filling the bucket with water. In (e), the bouyant steam has been replaced by water and the bucket moves down opening the discharge valve. When the bucket refills with steam, the valve closes, with the cycle starting over in normal operation at (c). The view in (f) shows the external appearance.

fluid.   Tubes and other surfaces exposed to the products of combustion will collect a layer of soot, which should be removed from time to time in order to maintain the capacity of the heat transfer element.   One method of cleaning is by the use of soot blowers.   These instruments may be manually operated devices or they may be installed as part of the equipment.   The cleaning agent is steam issuing from nozzles.   Care must be taken that impinging steam does not erode the metal surfaces.

The scale which forms on the insides of tubes may be removed either by cutting it out or pounding it out.   Both the cutting and hammering devices

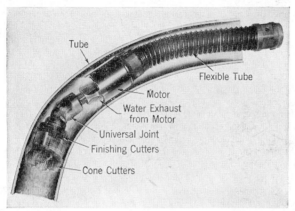

Courtesy Elliott Co., Jeanette, Pa.

Fig. 253.   Water-Driven Tube Cleaner.   The "motor" which drives the revolving cutters is a small water turbine.   The assembly shown is especially for curved tubes.   The universal joint is unnecessary in a straight-tube cleaner.   The cutters are carried on a hinged arm in such a manner that centrifugal action throws the cutters against the inside of the tube.

are in common use.   Figure 253 illustrates a revolving cutter type, driven by water, preferably in this design, at a pressure of 150 psi for maximum power. Steam and compressed air are also used in driving tube cleaners.

318. Closure.   This could go on indefinitely since a modern power plant, or any large plant using thermodynamic principles, is a complex thing. However, this sampling suggests the nature of some of the essential devices which the outsider seldom thinks about.   Also, the thermodynamic discussions could continue, but the interested reader will desire to, and the engineer concerned with thermodynamic applications will be determined to, pursue the study in more complete works.

STP

$1 \text{ } \# \text{mole} = 359.046 ft^3$

$T_{STP} = 491.69°R$

$P_{STP} = 14.70 \text{ } psia$

APPENDIX

Table V. *CHARACTERISTIC CONSTANTS FOR GASES*

(a) For the gases marked (a), the values of c_p are instantaneous values at $540°R = 80°F$ taken from spectroscopic data. Then c_v was found from $c_v = c_p - R/J$, and k from c_p/c_v. These values are for zero pressure, but they are suitably accurate for ordinary computations at ordinary pressures.

(b) For the gases marked (b), the values of c_p and k were taken from the *International Critical Tables*, Vol. V, for standard atmospheric pressure and 15°C (59°F). Then c_v was computed from $c_v = c_p/k$.

The gas constant R for each gas was computed from $R = p/(\rho T)$, where $\rho = 1/v$ was taken from the *International Critical Tables*, Vol. III, for standard atmospheric pressure and 32°F. M = molecular weight; c_p and c_v are in Btu/lb-°R. To obtain C_v Btu/mol, use $C_v = C_p - 1.986$.

Gas		M	c_p	c_v	k	C_p	R	MR
Air	(a)	28.970	0.24	0.1715	1.4	6.95	53.3	1545
Carbon monoxide (CO)	(a)	28.010	0.2487	0.1779	1.398	6.97	55.1	1543
Hydrogen (H$_2$)	(a)	2.016	3.421	2.4354	1.405	6.9	767	1546
Nitric oxide (NO)	(a)	30.008	0.2378	0.1717	1.384	7.14	51.4	1542
Nitrogen (N$_2$)	(a)	28.016	0.2484	0.1776	1.4	6.96	55.1	1543
Oxygen (O$_2$)	(a)	32	0.2193	0.1573	1.394	7.02	48.25	1544
Argon (A)	(b)	39.95	0.125	0.0749	1.668	4.99	38.7	1544
Helium (He)	(b)	4.003	1.25	0.754	1.659	5.00	386	1544
Carbon dioxide (CO$_2$)	(a)	44.01	0.202	0.157	1.29	8.89	34.9	1536
Hydrogen sulfide (H$_2$S)	(a)	34.08	0.328	0.270	1.21	11.18	44.8	1523
Nitrous oxide (N$_2$O)	(a)	44.02	0.211	0.166	1.27	9.29	34.9	1536
Sulfur dioxide (SO$_2$)	(a)	64.06	0.154	0.123	1.25	9.87	23.6	1512
Acetylene (C$_2$H$_2$)	(a)	26.04	0.409	0.333	1.23	10.65	58.8	1529
Ethane (C$_2$H$_6$)	(a)	30.07	0.422	0.357	1.18	12.69	50.8	1524
Ethylene (C$_2$H$_4$)	(a)	28.05	0.374	0.304	1.23	10.49	54.7	1532
Isobutane (C$_4$H$_{10}$)	(a)	58.12	0.420	0.387	1.09	24.4	25.8	1499
Methane (CH$_4$)	(a)	16.04	0.533	0.409	1.30	8.55	96.2	1539
Propane (C$_3$H$_8$)	(a)	44.09	0.404	0.360	1.12	17.81	34.1	1504

405

Table VI. *PROPERTIES OF AIR AT LOW PRESSURES (ONE POUND)*

Reproduced from Keenan and Kaye, *Gas Tables*, with permission of authors and publisher, John Wiley.

$T°R$	h Btu/lb.	p_r	u Btu/lb.	v_r	ϕ Btu/lb-°R	$T°R$	h Btu/lb.	p_r	u Btu/lb.	v_r	ϕ Btu/lb-°R
360	85.97	0.3363	61.29	396.6	0.50369	1460	358.63	50.34	258.54	10.743	0.84704
380	90.75	0.4061	64.70	346.6	0.51663	1480	363.89	53.04	262.44	10.336	0.85062
400	95.53	0.4858	68.11	305.0	0.52890	1500	369.17	55.86	266.34	9.948	0.85416
420	100.32	0.5760	71.52	270.1	0.54058	1520	374.47	58.78	270.26	9.578	0.85767
440	105.11	0.6776	74.93	240.6	0.55172	1540	379.77	61.83	274.20	9.226	0.86113
460	109.90	0.7913	78.36	215.33	0.56235	1560	385.08	65.00	278.13	8.890	0.86456
480	114.69	0.9182	81.77	193.65	0.57255	1580	390.40	68.30	282.09	8.569	0.86794
500	119.48	1.0590	85.20	174.90	0.58233	1600	395.74	71.73	286.06	8.263	0.87130
520	124.27	1.2147	88.62	158.58	0.59173	1620	401.09	75.29	290.04	7.971	0.87462
540	129.06	1.3860	92.04	144.32	0.60078	1640	406.45	78.99	294.03	7.691	0.87791
560	133.86	1.5742	95.47	131.78	0.60950	1660	411.82	82.83	298.02	7.424	0.88116
580	138.66	1.7800	98.90	120.70	0.61793	1680	417.20	86.82	302.04	7.168	0.88439
600	143.47	2.005	102.34	110.88	0.62607	1700	422.59	90.95	306.06	6.924	0.88758
620	148.28	2.249	105.78	102.12	0.63395	1720	428.00	95.24	310.09	6.690	0.89074
640	153.09	2.514	109.21	94.30	0.64159	1740	433.41	99.69	314.13	6.465	0.89387
660	157.92	2.801	112.67	87.27	0.64902	1760	438.83	104.30	318.18	6.251	0.89697
680	162.73	3.111	116.12	80.96	0.65621	1780	444.26	109.08	322.24	6.045	0.90003
700	167.56	3.446	119.58	75.25	0.66321	1800	449.71	114.03	326.32	5.847	0.90308
720	172.39	3.806	123.04	70.07	0.67002	1820	455.17	119.16	330.40	5.658	0.90609
740	177.23	4.193	126.51	65.38	0.67665	1840	460.63	124.47	334.50	5.476	0.90908
760	182.08	4.607	129.99	61.10	0.68312	1860	466.12	129.95	338.61	5.302	0.91203
780	186.94	5.051	133.47	57.20	0.68942	1880	471.60	135.64	342.73	5.134	0.91497
800	191.81	5.526	136.97	53.63	0.69558	1900	477.09	141.51	346.85	4.974	0.91788
820	196.69	6.033	140.47	50.35	0.70160	1920	482.60	147.59	350.98	4.819	0.92076
840	201.56	6.573	143.98	47.34	0.70747	1940	488.12	153.87	355.12	4.670	0.92362
860	206.46	7.149	147.50	44.57	0.71323	1960	493.64	160.37	359.28	4.527	0.92645
880	211.35	7.761	151.02	42.01	0.71886	1980	499.17	167.07	363.43	4.390	0.92926
900	216.26	8.411	154.57	39.64	0.72438	2000	504.71	174.00	367.61	4.258	0.93205
920	221.18	9.102	158.12	37.44	0.72979	2020	510.26	181.16	371.79	4.130	0.93481
940	226.11	9.834	161.68	35.41	0.73509	2040	515.82	188.54	375.98	4.008	0.93756
960	231.06	10.610	165.26	33.52	0.74030	2060	521.39	196.16	380.18	3.890	0.94026
980	236.02	11.430	168.83	31.76	0.74540	2080	526.97	204.02	384.39	3.777	0.94296
1000	240.98	12.298	172.43	30.12	0.75042	2100	532.55	212.1	388.60	3.667	0.94564
1020	245.97	13.215	176.04	28.59	0.75536	2150	546.54	233.5	399.17	3.410	0.95222
1040	250.95	14.182	179.66	27.17	0.76019	2200	560.59	256.6	409.78	3.176	0.95868
1060	255.96	15.203	183.29	25.82	0.76496	2250	574.69	281.4	420.46	2.961	0.96501
1080	260.97	16.278	186.93	24.58	0.76964	2300	588.82	308.1	431.16	2.765	0.97123
1100	265.99	17.413	190.58	23.40	0.77426	2350	603.00	336.8	441.91	2.585	0.97732
1120	271.03	18.604	194.25	22.30	0.77880	2400	617.22	367.6	452.70	2.419	0.98331
1140	276.08	19.858	197.94	21.27	0.78326	2450	631.48	400.5	463.54	2.266	0.98919
1160	281.14	21.18	201.63	20.293	0.78767	2500	645.78	435.7	474.40	2.125	0.99497
1180	286.21	22.56	205.33	19.377	0.79201	2550	660.12	473.3	485.31	1.9956	1.00064
1200	291.30	24.01	209.05	18.514	0.79628	2600	674.49	513.5	496.26	1.8756	1.00623
1220	296.41	25.53	212.78	17.700	0.80050	2650	688.90	556.3	507.25	1.7646	1.01172
1240	301.52	27.13	216.53	16.932	0.80466	2700	703.35	601.9	518.26	1.6617	1.01712
1260	306.65	28.80	220.28	16.205	0.80876	2750	717.83	650.4	529.31	1.5662	1.02244
1280	311.79	30.55	244.05	15.518	0.81280	2800	732.33	702.0	540.40	1.4775	1.02767
1300	316.94	32.39	227.83	14.868	0.81680	2850	746.88	756.7	551.52	1.3951	1.03282
1320	322.11	34.31	231.63	14.253	0.82075	2900	761.45	814.8	562.66	1.3184	1.03788
1340	327.29	36.31	235.43	13.670	0.82464	2950	776.05	876.4	573.84	1.2469	1.04288
1360	332.48	38.41	239.25	13.118	0.82848	3000	790.68	941.4	585.04	1.1803	1.04779
1380	337.68	40.59	243.08	12.593	0.83229	3500	938.40	1829.3	698.48	0.7087	1.09332
1400	342.90	42.88	246.93	12.095	0.83604	4000	1088.26	3280	814.06	0.4518	1.13334
1420	348.14	45.26	250.79	11.622	0.83975	4500	1239.86	5521	931.39	0.3019	1.16905
1440	353.37	47.75	254.66	11.172	0.84341	5000	1392.87	8837	1050.12	0.20959	1.20129
						6000	1702.29	20120	1291.00	0.11047	1.25769
						6500	1858.44	28974	1412.87	0.08310	1.28268

Table VII. ENTHALPY (BTU/MOL) OF GASES AT LOW PRESSURE

Reproduced from Keenan and Kaye, *Gas Tables*, with permission of authors and publisher, John Wiley. Values of $\bar{h}$ are in Btu/mol; $\bar{R} = 1.986$ Btu/mol-°R; 536.69°R = 459.69 + 77°F.

Temp. °R	N₂ 28.016	O₂ 32	H₂O 18.016	CO₂ 44.01	H₂ 2.016	CO 28.01	Prods. 400% Ideal	Prods. 200% Ideal	$p\bar{v}/J$ = $\bar{R}T$
500	3,472.2	3,466.2	3,962.0	3,706.2	3,386.1	3,472.1	3,486.7	3,511.2	993
520	3,611.3	3,606.1	4,122.0	3,880.3	3,523.3	3,611.2	3,627.4	3,653.7	1,033
536.69	3,727.3	3,723.0	4,255.8	4,027.5	3,638.1	3,727.3	3,744.6	3,772.7	1,067
540	3,750.3	3,746.2	4,282.4	4,056.8	3,660.9	3,750.3	3,768.0	3,796.3	1,072
560	3,889.5	3,886.6	4,442.8	4,235.8	3,798.8	3,889.5	3,909.2	3,939.4	1,112
580	4,028.7	4,027.3	4,603.7	4,417.2	3,937.1	4,028.7	4,050.4	4,082.7	1,152
600	4,167.9	4,168.3	4,764.7	4,600.9	4,075.6	4,168.0	4,191.9	4,226.3	1,192
700	4,864.9	4,879.3	5,575.4	5,552.0	4,770.2	4,866.0	4,901.7	4,947.7	1,390
800	5,564.4	5,602.0	6,396.9	6,552.9	5,467.1	5,568.2	5,617.5	5,676.3	1,589
900	6,268.1	6,337.9	7,230.9	7,597.6	6,165.3	6,276.4	6,340.3	6,413.0	1,787
1000	6,977.9	7,087.5	8,078.9	8,682.1	6,864.5	6,992.2	7,072.1	7,159.8	1,986
1100	7,695.0	7,850.4	8,942.0	9,802.6	7,564.6	7,716.8	7,812.9	7,916.4	2,185
1200	8,420.0	8,625.8	9,820.4	10,955.3	8,265.8	8,450.8	8,563.4	8,683.6	2,383
1300	9,153.9	9,412.9	10,714.5	12,136.9	8,968.7	9,194.6	9,324.1	9,461.7	2,582
1400	9,896.9	10,210.4	11,624.8	13,344.7	9,673.8	9,948.1	10,095.0	10,250.7	2,780
1500	10,648.9	11,017.1	12,551.4	14,576.0	10,381.5	10,711.1	10,875.6	11,052.2	2,979
1600	11,409.7	11,832.5	13,494.9	15,829.0	11,092.5	11,483.4	11,665.6	11,859.6	3,178
1700	12,178.9	12,655.6	14,455.4	17,101.4	11,807.4	12,264.3	12,464.3	12,678.6	3,376
1800	12,956.3	13,485.8	15,433.0	18,391.5	12,526.8	13,053.2	13,271.7	13,507.0	3,575
1900	13,741.6	14,322.1	16,427.5	19,697.8	13,250.9	13,849.8	14,087.2	14,344.1	3,773
2000	14,534.4	15,164.0	17,439.0	21,018.7	13,980.1	14,653.2	14,910.3	15,189.3	3,972
2100	15,334.0	16,010.9	18,466.9	22,352.7	14,714.5	15,463.3	15,740.5	16,042.4	4,171
2200	16,139.8	16,862.6	19,510.8	23,699.0	15,454.4	16,279.4	16,577.1	16,902.5	4,369
2300	16,951.2	17,718.8	20,570.6	25,056.3	16,199.8	17,101.0	17,419.8	17,769.3	4,568
2400	17,767.9	18,579.2	21,645.7	26,424.0	16,950.6	17,927.4	18,268.0	18,642.1	4,766
2500	18,589.5	19,443.4	22,735.4	27,801.2	17,707.3	18,758.8	19,121.4	19,520.7	4,965
2600	19,415.8	20,311.4	23,839.5	29,187.1	18,469.7	19,594.3	19,979.7	20,404.6	5,164
2700	20,246.4	21,182.9	24,957.2	30,581.2	19,237.8	20,434.0	20,842.8	21,293.8	5,362
2800	21,081.1	22,057.8	26,088.0	31,982.8	20,011.8	21,277.2	21,709.8	22,187.5	5,561
2900	21,919.5	22,936.1	27,231.2	33,391.5	20,791.5	22,123.8	22,581.4	23,086.0	5,759
3000	22,761.5	23,817.7	28,386.3	34,806.6	21,576.9	22,973.4	23,456.6	23,988.5	5,958
3100	23,606.8	24,702.5	29,552.8	36,227.9	22,367.7	23,826.0	24,335.5	24,895.3	6,157
3200	24,455.0	25,590.5	30,730.2	37,654.7	23,164.1	24,681.2	25,217.8	25,805.6	6,355
3300	25,306.0	26,481.6	31,918.2	39,086.7	23,965.5	25,539.0	26,102.9	26,719.2	6,554
3400	26,159.7	27,375.5	33,116.0	40,523.6	24,771.9	26,399.3	26,991.4	27,636.4	6,752
3500	27,015.9	28,273.3	34,323.5	41,965.2	25,582.9	27,261.8	27,882.9	28,556.8	6,951
3600	27,874.4	29,173.9	35,540.1	43,411.0	26,398.5	28,126.6		29,479.9	7,150
3700	28,735.1	30,077.5	36,765.4	44,860.6	27,218.5	28,993.5		30,406.0	7,348
3800	29,597.9	30,984.1	37,998.9	46,314.0	28,042.8	29,862.3		31,334.8	7,547
3900	30,462.8	31,893.6	39,240.2	47,771.0	28,871.1	30,732.9		32,266.2	7,745
4000	31,329.4	32,806.1	40,489.1	49,231.4	29,703.5	31,605.2		33,199.6	7,944
4100	32,198.0	33,721.6	41,745.4	50,695.1	30,539.8	32,479.1			8,143
4200	33,068.1	34,639.9	43,008.4	52,162.0	31,379.8	33,354.4			8,341
4300	33,939.9	35,561.1	44,278.0	53,632.1	32,223.5	34,231.2			8,540
4400	34,813.1	36,485.0	45,553.9	55,105.1	33,070.9	35,109.2			8,738
4500	35,687.8	37,411.6	46,835.9	56,581.0	33,921.6	35,988.6			8,937
4600	36,563.8	38,341.4	48,123.6	58,059.7	34,775.7	36,869.3			9,136
4700	37,441.1	39,273.6	49,416.9	59,541.1	35,633.0	37,751.0			9,334
4800	38,319.5	40,208.6	50,715.5	61,024.9	36,493.4	38,633.9			9,533
4900	39,199.1	41,146.1	52,019.0	62,511.3	37,356.9	39,517.8			9,731
5000	40,079.8	42,086.3	53,327.4	64,000.0	38,223.3	40,402.7			9,930
5100	40,961.6	43,029.1	54,640.3	65,490.9	39,092.8	41,288.6			10,129
5200	41,844.4	43,974.3	55,957.4	66,984.0	39,965.1	42,175.5			10,327
5300	42,728.3	44,922.2	57,278.7	68,479.1	40,840.2	43,063.2			10,526
5400	43,612.9	45,872.1	58,603.9	69,975.9	41,717.7	43,951.8			10,724

407

Table VIII. SATURATED STEAM: TEMPERATURES*

Values for 1# H₂O (handwritten) *DATUM PLANE – 32° F* (handwritten)

TEMP. FAHR.	ABS. PRESS.	SPECIFIC VOLUME			ENTHALPY			ENTROPY		
	Lb. / Sq. In.	Sat. Liquid	Evap.	Sat. Vapor	Sat. Liquid	Evap.	Sat. Vapor	Sat. Liquid	Evap.	Sat. Vapor
t	p	v_f	v_{fg}	v_g	h_f	h_{fg}	h_g	s_f	s_{fg}	s_g
32°	0.08854	0.01602	3306	3306	0.00	1075.8	1075.8	0.0000	2.1877	2.1877
35	0.09995	0.01602	2947	2947	3.02	1074.1	1077.1	0.0061	2.1709	2.1770
40	0.12170	0.01602	2444	2444	8.05	1071.3	1079.3	0.0162	2.1435	2.1597
45	0.14752	0.01602	2036.4	2036.4	13.06	1068.4	1081.5	0.0262	2.1167	2.1429
50	0.17811	0.01603	1703.2	1703.2	18.07	1065.6	1083.7	0.0361	2.0903	2.1264
60°	0.2563	0.01604	1206.6	1206.7	28.06	1059.9	1088.0	0.0555	2.0393	2.0948
70	0.3631	0.01606	867.8	867.9	38.04	1054.3	1092.3	0.0745	1.9902	2.0647
80	0.5069	0.01608	633.1	633.1	48.02	1048.6	1096.6	0.0932	1.9428	2.0360
90	0.6982	0.01610	468.0	468.0	57.99	1042.9	1100.9	0.1115	1.8972	2.0087
100	0.9492	0.01613	350.3	350.4	67.97	1037.2	1105.2	0.1295	1.8531	1.9826
110°	1.2748	0.01617	265.3	265.4	77.94	1031.6	1109.5	0.1471	1.8106	1.9577
120	1.6924	0.01620	203.25	203.27	87.92	1025.8	1113.7	0.1645	1.7694	1.9339
130	2.2225	0.01625	157.32	157.34	97.90	1020.0	1117.9	0.1816	1.7296	1.9112
140	2.8886	0.01629	122.99	123.01	107.89	1014.1	1122.0	0.1984	1.6910	1.8894
150	3.718	0.01634	97.06	97.07	117.89	1008.2	1126.1	0.2149	1.6537	1.8685
160°	4.741	0.01639	77.27	77.29	127.89	1002.3	1130.2	0.2311	1.6174	1.8485
170	5.992	0.01645	62.04	62.06	137.90	996.3	1134.2	0.2472	1.5822	1.8293
180	7.510	0.01651	50.21	50.23	147.92	990.2	1138.1	0.2630	1.5480	1.8109
190	9.339	0.01657	40.94	40.96	157.95	984.1	1142.0	0.2785	1.5147	1.7932
200	11.526	0.01663	33.62	33.64	167.99	977.9	1145.9	0.2938	1.4824	1.7762
210°	14.123	0.01670	27.80	27.82	178.05	971.6	1149.7	0.3090	1.4508	1.7598
212	14.696	0.01672	26.78	26.80	180.07	970.3	1150.4	0.3120	1.4446	1.7566
220	17.186	0.01677	23.13	23.15	188.13	965.2	1153.4	0.3239	1.4201	1.7440
230	20.780	0.01684	19.365	19.382	198.23	958.8	1157.0	0.3387	1.3901	1.7288
240	24.969	0.01692	16.306	16.323	208.34	952.2	1160.5	0.3531	1.3609	1.7140
250°	29.825	0.01700	13.804	13.821	218.48	945.5	1164.0	0.3675	1.3323	1.6998
260	35.429	0.01709	11.746	11.763	228.64	938.7	1167.3	0.3817	1.3043	1.6860
270	41.858	0.01717	10.044	10.061	238.84	931.8	1170.6	0.3958	1.2769	1.6727
280	49.203	0.01726	8.628	8.645	249.06	924.7	1173.8	0.4096	1.2501	1.6597
290	57.556	0.01735	7.444	7.461	259.31	917.5	1176.8	0.4234	1.2238	1.6472
300°	67.013	0.01745	6.449	6.466	269.59	910.1	1179.7	0.4369	1.1980	1.6350
310	77.68	0.01755	5.609	5.626	279.92	902.6	1182.5	0.4504	1.1727	1.6231
320	89.66	0.01765	4.896	4.914	290.28	894.9	1185.2	0.4637	1.1478	1.6115
330	103.06	0.01776	4.289	4.307	300.68	887.0	1187.7	0.4769	1.1233	1.6002
340	118.01	0.01787	3.770	3.788	311.13	879.0	1190.1	0.4900	1.0992	1.5891
350°	134.63	0.01799	3.324	3.342	321.63	870.7	1192.3	0.5029	1.0754	1 5783
360	153.04	0.01811	2.939	2.957	332.18	862.2	1194.4	0.5158	1.0519	1 5677
370	173.37	0.01823	2.606	2.625	342.79	853.5	1196.3	0.5286	1.0287	1.5573
380	195.77	0.01836	2.317	2.335	353.45	844.6	1198.1	0.5413	1.0059	1.5471
390	220.37	0.01850	2.0651	2.0836	364.17	835.4	1199.6	0.5539	0.9832	1.5371
400°	247.31	0.01864	1.8447	1.8633	374.97	826.0	1201.0	0.5664	0.9608	1.5272
410	276.75	0.01878	1.6512	1.6700	385.83	816.3	1202.1	0.5788	0.9386	1.5174
420	308.83	0.01894	1.4811	1.5000	396.77	806.3	1203.1	0.5912	0.9166	1.5078
430	343.72	0.01910	1.3308	1.3499	407.79	796.0	1203.8	0.6035	0.8947	1.4982
440	381.59	0.01926	1.1979	1.2171	418.90	785.4	1204.3	0.6158	0.8730	1.4887
450°	422.6	0.0194	1.0799	1.0993	430.1	774.5	1204.6	0.6280	0.8513	1.4793
460	466.9	0.0196	0.9748	0.9944	441.4	763.2	1204.6	0.6402	0.8298	1.4700
470	514.7	0.0198	0.8811	0.9009	452.8	751.5	1204.3	0.6523	0.8083	1.4606
480	566.1	0.0200	0.7972	0.8172	464.4	739.4	1203.7	0.6645	0.7868	1.4513
490	621.4	0.0202	0.7221	0.7423	476.0	726.8	1202.8	0.6766	0.7653	1.4419
500°	680.8	0.0204	0.6545	0.6749	487.8	713.9	1201.7	0.6887	0.7438	1.4325
600	1542.9	0.0236	0.2432	0.2668	617.0	548.5	1165.5	0.8131	0.5176	1.3307
700°	3093.7	0.0369	0.0392	0.0761	823.3	172.1	995.4	0.9905	0.1484	1.1389
705.4	3206.2	0.0503	0	0.0503	902.7	0	902.7	1.0580	0	1.0580

*Steam tables, abridged from *Thermodynamic Properties of Steam* by Joseph H. Keenan and Frederick G. Keyes. Copyright, 1937, by Joseph H. Keenan and Frederick G. Keyes. Published by John Wiley & Sons, Inc., New York.

408

Subscripts: (handwritten)

f – means "of saturated liquid" (handwritten)

g – " " " vapor " (handwritten)

fg – " change in from liquid to vapor, (handwritten)

Table IX. *SATURATED STEAM: PRESSURES*

Abs. Press. Lb. Sq. In.	Temp. Fahr.	Specific Volume		Enthalpy			Entropy			Internal Energy	
		Sat. Liquid	Sat. Vapor	Sat. Liquid	Evap.	Sat. Vapor	Sat. Liquid	Evap.	Sat. Vapor	Sat. Liquid	Sat. Vapor
p	t	v_f	v_g	h_f	h_{fg}	h_g	s_f	s_{fg}	s_g	u_f	u_g
1.0	101.74	0.01614	333.6	69.70	1036.3	1106.0	0.1326	1.8456	1.9782	69.70	1044.3
2.0	126.08	0.01623	173.73	93.99	1022.2	1116.2	0.1749	1.7451	1.9200	93.98	1051.9
3.0	141.48	0.01630	118.71	109.37	1013.2	1122.6	0.2008	1.6855	1.8863	109.36	1056.7
4.0	152.97	0.01636	90.63	120.86	1006.4	1127.3	0.2198	1.6427	1.8625	120.85	1060.2
5.0	162.24	0.01640	73.52	130.13	1001.0	1131.1	0.2347	1.6094	1.8441	130.12	1063.1
6.0	170.06	0.01645	61.98	137.96	996.2	1134.2	0.2472	1.5820	1.8292	137.94	1065.4
7.0	176.85	0.01649	53.64	144.76	992.1	1136.9	0.2581	1.5586	1.8167	144.74	1067.4
8.0	182.86	0.01653	47.34	150.79	988.5	1139.3	0.2674	1.5383	1.8057	150.77	1069.2
9.0	188.28	0.01656	42.40	156.22	985.2	1141.4	0.2759	1.5203	1.7962	156.19	1070.8
10	193.21	0.01659	38.42	161.17	982.1	1143.3	0.2835	1.5041	1.7876	161.14	1072.2
14.696	212.00	0.01672	26.80	180.07	970.3	1150.4	0.3120	1.4446	1.7566	180.02	1077.5
15	213.03	0.01672	26.29	181.11	969.7	1150.8	0.3135	1.4415	1.7549	181.06	1077.8
20	227.96	0.01683	20.089	196.16	960.1	1156.3	0.3356	1.3962	1.7319	196.10	1081.9
25	240.07	0.01692	16.303	208.42	952.1	1160.6	0.3533	1.3606	1.7139	208.34	1085.1
30	250.33	0.01701	13.746	218.82	945.3	1164.1	0.3680	1.3313	1.6993	218.73	1087.8
35	259.28	0.01708	11.898	227.91	939.2	1167.1	0.3807	1.3063	1.6870	227.80	1090.1
40	267.25	0.01715	10.498	236.03	933.7	1169.7	0.3919	1.2844	1.6763	235.90	1092.0
45	274.44	0.01721	9.401	243.36	928.6	1172.0	0.4019	1.2650	1.6669	243.22	1093.7
50	281.01	0.01727	8.515	250.09	924.0	1174.1	0.4110	1.2474	1.6585	249.93	1095.3
55	287.07	0.01732	7.787	256.30	919.6	1175.9	0.4193	1.2316	1.6509	256.12	1096.7
60	292.71	0.01738	7.175	262.09	915.5	1177.6	0.4270	1.2168	1.6438	261.90	1097.9
65	297.97	0.01743	6.655	267.50	911.6	1179.1	0.4342	1.2032	1.6374	267.29	1099.1
70	302.92	0.01748	6.206	272.61	907.9	1180.6	0.4409	1.1906	1.6315	272.38	1100.2
75	307.60	0.01753	5.816	277.43	904.5	1181.9	0.4472	1.1787	1.6259	277.19	1101.2
80	312.03	0.01757	5.472	282.02	901.1	1183.1	0.4531	1.1676	1.6207	281.76	1102.1
85	316.25	0.01761	5.168	286.39	897.8	1184.2	0.4587	1.1571	1.6158	286.11	1102.9
90	320.27	0.01766	4.896	290.56	894.7	1185.3	0.4641	1.1471	1.6112	290.27	1103.7
95	324.12	0.01770	4.652	294.56	891.7	1186.2	0.4692	1.1376	1.6068	294.25	1104.5
100	327.81	0.01774	4.432	298.40	888.8	1187.2	0.4740	1.1286	1.6026	298.08	1105.2
110	334.77	0.01782	4.049	305.66	883.2	1188.9	0.4832	1.1117	1.5948	305.30	1106.5
120	341.25	0.01789	3.728	312.44	877.9	1190.4	0.4916	1.0962	1.5878	312.05	1107.6
130	347.32	0.01796	3.455	318.81	872.9	1191.7	0.4995	1.0817	1.5812	318.38	1108.6
140	353.02	0.01802	3.220	324.82	868.2	1193.0	0.5069	1.0682	1.5751	324.35	1109.6
150	358.42	0.01809	3.015	330.51	863.6	1194.1	0.5138	1.0556	1.5694	330.01	1110.5
160	363.53	0.01815	2.834	335.93	859.2	1195.1	0.5204	1.0436	1.5640	335.39	1111.2
170	368.41	0.01822	2.675	341.09	854.9	1196.0	0.5266	1.0324	1.5590	340.52	1111.9
180	373.06	0.01827	2.532	346.03	850.8	1196.9	0.5325	1.0217	1.5542	345.42	1112.5
190	377.51	0.01833	2.404	350.79	846.8	1197.6	0.5381	1.0116	1.5497	350.15	1113.1
200	381.79	0.01839	2.288	355.36	843.0	1198.4	0.5435	1.0018	1.5453	354.68	1113.7
250	400.95	0.01865	1.8438	376.00	825.1	1201.1	0.5675	0.9588	1.5263	375.14	1115.8
300	417.33	0.01890	1.5433	393.84	809.0	1202.8	0.5879	0.9225	1.5104	392.79	1117.1
350	431.72	0.01913	1.3260	409.69	794.2	1203.9	0.6056	0.8910	1.4966	408.45	1118.0
400	444.59	0.0193	1.1613	424.0	780.5	1204.5	0.6214	0.8630	1.4844	422.6	1118.5
450	456.28	0.0195	1.0320	437.2	767.4	1204.6	0.6356	0.8378	1.4734	435.5	1118.7
500	467.01	0.0197	0.9278	449.4	755.0	1204.4	0.6487	0.8147	1.4634	447.6	1118.6
550	476.94	0.0199	0.8424	460.8	743.1	1203.9	0.6608	0.7934	1.4542	458.8	1118.2
600	486.21	0.0201	0.7698	471.6	731.6	1203.2	0.6720	0.7734	1.4454	469.4	1117.7
650	494.90	0.0203	0.7083	481.8	720.5	1202.3	0.6826	0.7548	1.4374	479.4	1117.1
700	503.10	0.0205	0.6554	491.5	709.7	1201.2	0.6925	0.7371	1.4296	488.8	1116.3
800	518.23	0.0209	0.5687	509.7	688.9	1198.6	0.7108	0.7045	1.4153	506.6	1114.4
900	531.98	0.0212	0.5006	526.6	668.8	1195.4	0.7275	0.6744	1.4020	523.1	1112.1
1000	544.61	0.0216	0.4456	542.4	649.4	1191.8	0.7430	0.6467	1.3897	538.4	1109.4
1200	567.22	0.0223	0.3619	571.7	611.7	1183.4	0.7711	0.5956	1.3667	566.7	1103.0
1400	587.10	0.0231	0.3012	598.7	574.7	1173.4	0.7963	0.5491	1.3454	592.7	1095.4
1500	596.23	0.0235	0.2765	611.6	556.3	1167.9	0.8082	0.5269	1.3351	605.1	1091.2
2000	635.82	0.0257	0.1878	671.7	463.4	1135.1	0.8619	0.4230	1.2849	662.2	1065.6
3000	695.36	0.0346	0.0858	802.5	217.8	1020.3	0.9731	0.1885	1.1615	783.4	972.7
3206.2	705.40	0.0503	0.0503	902.7	0	902.7	1.0580	0	1.0580	872.9	872.9

Table X. *SUPERHEATED STEAM*

ABS. PRESS.		TEMPERATURE—DEGREES FAHRENHEIT									
Lb./Sq. In. (Sat.Temp.)		200°	300°	400°	500°	600°	700°	800°	900°	1000°	1100°
1 (101.74)	v	392.6	452.3	512.0	571.6	631.2	690.8	750.4	809.9	869.5	929.1
	h	1150.4	1195.8	1241.7	1288.3	1335.7	1383.8	1432.8	1482.7	1533.5	1585.2
	s	2.0512	2.1153	2.1720	2.2233	2.2702	2.3137	2.3542	2.3923	2.4283	2.4625
5 (162.24)	v	78.16	90.25	102.26	114.22	126.16	138.10	150.03	161.95	173.87	185.79
	h	1148.8	1195.0	1241.2	1288.0	1335.4	1383.6	1432.7	1482.6	1533.4	1585.1
	s	1.8718	1.9370	1.9942	2.0456	2.0927	2.1361	2.1767	2.2148	2.2509	2.2851
10 (193.21)	v	38.85	45.00	51.04	57.05	63.03	69.01	74.98	80.95	86.92	92.88
	h	1146.6	1193.9	1240.6	1287.5	1335.1	1383.4	1432.5	1482.4	1533.2	1585.0
	s	1.7927	1.8595	1.9172	1.9689	2.0160	2.0596	2.1002	2.1383	2.1744	2.2086
14.696 (212.00)	v		30.53	34.68	38.78	42.86	46.94	51.00	55.07	59.13	63.19
	h		1192.8	1239.9	1287.1	1334.8	1383.2	1432.3	1482.3	1533.1	1584.8
	s		1.8160	1.8743	1.9261	1.9734	2.0170	2.0576	2.0958	2.1319	2.1662
20 (227.96)	v		22.36	25.43	28.46	31.47	34.47	37.46	40.45	43.44	46.42
	h		1191.6	1239.2	1286.6	1334.4	1382.9	1432.1	1482.1	1533.0	1584.7
	s		1.7808	1.8396	1.8918	1.9392	1.9829	2.0235	2.0618	2.0978	2.1321
40 (267.25)	v		11.040	12.628	14.168	15.688	17.198	18.702	20.20	21.70	23.20
	h		1186.8	1236.5	1284.8	1333.1	1381.9	1431.3	1481.4	1532.4	1584.3
	s		1.6994	1.7608	1.8140	1.8619	1.9058	1.9467	1.9850	2.0212	2.0555
60 (292.71)	v		7.259	8.357	9.403	10.427	11.441	12.449	13.452	14.454	15.453
	h		1181.6	1233.6	1283.0	1331.8	1380.9	1430.5	1480.8	1531.9	1583.8
	s		1.6492	1.7135	1.7678	1.8162	1.8605	1.9015	1.9400	1.9762	2.0106
80 (312.03)	v			6.220	7.020	7.797	8.562	9.322	10.077	10.830	11.582
	h			1230.7	1281.1	1330.5	1379.9	1429.7	1480.1	1531.3	1583.4
	s			1.6791	1.7346	1.7836	1.8281	1.8694	1.9079	1.9442	1.9787
100 (327.81)	v			4.937	5.589	6.218	6.835	7.446	8.052	8.656	9.259
	h			1227.6	1279.1	1329.1	1378.9	1428.9	1479.5	1530.8	1582.9
	s			1.6518	1.7085	1.7580	1.8029	1.8443	1.8829	1.9193	1.9538
120 (341.25)	v			4.081	4.636	5.165	5.683	6.195	6.702	7.207	7.710
	h			1224.4	1277.2	1327.7	1377.8	1428.1	1478.8	1530.2	1582.4
	s			1.6287	1.6869	1.7370	1.7822	1.8237	1.8625	1.8990	1.9335
140 (353.02)	v			3.468	3.954	4.413	4.861	5.301	5.738	6.172	6.604
	h			1221.1	1275.2	1326.4	1376.8	1427.3	1478.2	1529.7	1581.9
	s			1.6087	1.6683	1.7190	1.7645	1.8063	1.8451	1.8817	1.9163
160 (363.53)	v			3.008	3.443	3.849	4.244	4.631	5.015	5.396	5.775
	h			1217.6	1273.1	1325.0	1375.7	1426.4	1477.5	1529.1	1581.4
	s			1.5908	1.6519	1.7033	1.7491	1.7911	1.8301	1.8667	1.9014
180 (373.06)	v			2.649	3.044	3.411	3.764	4.110	4.452	4.792	5.129
	h			1214.0	1271.0	1323.5	1374.7	1425.6	1476.8	1528.6	1581.0
	s			1.5745	1.6373	1.6894	1.7355	1.7776	1.8167	1.8534	1.8882
200 (381.79)	v			2.361	2.726	3.060	3.380	3.693	4.002	4.309	4.613
	h			1210.3	1268.9	1322.1	1373.6	1424.8	1476.2	1528.0	1580.5
	s			1.5594	1.6240	1.6767	1.7232	1.7655	1.8048	1.8415	1.8763
220 (389.86)	v			2.125	2.465	2.772	3.066	3.352	3.634	3.913	4.191
	h			1206.5	1266.7	1320.7	1372.6	1424.0	1475.5	1527.5	1580.0
	s			1.5453	1.6117	1.6652	1.7120	1.7545	1.7939	1.8308	1.8656
240 (397.37)	v			1.9276	2.247	2.533	2.804	3.068	3.327	3.584	3.839
	h			1202.5	1264.5	1319.2	1371.5	1423.2	1474.8	1526.9	1579.6
	s			1.5319	1.6003	1.6546	1.7017	1.7444	1.7839	1.8209	1.8558
260 (404.42)	v				2.063	2.330	2.582	2.827	3.067	3.305	3.541
	h				1262.3	1317.7	1370.4	1422.3	1474.2	1526.3	1579.1
	s				1.5897	1.6447	1.6922	1.7352	1.7748	1.8118	1.8467
300 (417.33)	v				1.7675	2.005	2.227	2.442	2.652	2.859	3.065
	h				1257.6	1314.7	1368.3	1420.6	1472.8	1525.2	1578.1
	s				1.5701	1.6268	1.6751	1.7184	1.7582	1.7954	1.8305
350 (431.72)	v				1.4923	1.7036	1.8980	2.084	2.226	2.445	2.622
	h				1251.5	1310.9	1365.5	1418.5	1471.1	1523.8	1577.0
	s				1.5481	1.6070	1.6563	1.7002	1.7403	1.7777	1.8130
400 (444.59)	v				1.2851	1.4770	1.6508	1.8161	1.9767	2.134	2.290
	h				1245.1	1306.9	1362.7	1416.4	1469.4	1522.4	1575.8
	s				1.5281	1.5894	1.6398	1.6842	1.7247	1.7623	1.7977

Table X. *SUPERHEATED STEAM* (*Continued*)

ABS. PRESS.		TEMPERATURE—DEGREES FAHRENHEIT										
Lb./Sq. In. (Sat.Temp.)		500°	550°	600°	620°	640°	660°	680°	700°	800°	900°	1000°
450 (456.28)	v	1.1231	1.2155	1.3005	1.3332	1.3652	1.3967	1.4278	1.4584	1.6074	1.7516	1.8928
	h	1238.4	1272.0	1302.8	1314.6	1326.2	1337.5	1348.8	1359.9	1414.3	1467.7	1521.0
	s	1.5095	1.5437	1.5735	1.5845	1.5951	1.6054	1.6153	1.6250	1.6699	1.7108	1.7486
500 (467.01)	v	0.9927	1.0800	1.1591	1.1893	1.2188	1.2478	1.2763	1.3044	1.4405	1.5715	1.6996
	h	1231.3	1266.8	1298.6	1310.7	1322.6	1334.2	1345.7	1357.0	1412.1	1466.0	1519.6
	s	1.4919	1.5280	1.5588	1.5701	1.5810	1.5915	1.6016	1.6115	1.6571	1.6982	1.7363
550 (476.94)	v	0.8852	0.9686	1.0431	1.0714	1.0989	1.1259	1.1523	1.1783	1.3038	1.4241	1.5414
	h	1223.7	1261.2	1294.3	1306.8	1318.9	1330.8	1342.5	1354.0	1409.9	1464.3	1518.2
	s	1.4751	1.5131	1.5451	1.5568	1.5680	1.5787	1.5890	1.5991	1.6452	1.6868	1.7250
600 (486.21)	v	0.7947	0.8753	0.9463	0.9729	0.9988	1.0241	1.0489	1.0732	1.1899	1.3013	1.4096
	h	1215.7	1255.5	1289.9	1302.7	1315.2	1327.4	1339.3	1351.1	1407.7	1462.5	1516.7
	s	1.4586	1.4990	1.5323	1.5443	1.5558	1.5667	1.5773	1.5875	1.6343	1.6762	1.7147
700 (503.10)	v		0.7277	0.7934	0.8177	0.8411	0.8639	0.8860	0.9077	1.0108	1.1082	1.2024
	h		1243.2	1280.6	1294.3	1307.5	1320.3	1332.8	1345.0	1403.2	1459.0	1513.9
	s		1.4722	1.5084	1.5212	1.5333	1.5449	1.5559	1.5665	1.6147	1.6573	1.6963
800 (518.23)	v		0.6154	0.6779	0.7006	0.7223	0.7433	0.7635	0.7833	0.8763	0.9633	1.0470
	h		1229.8	1270.7	1285.4	1299.4	1312.9	1325.9	1338.6	1398.6	1455.4	1511.0
	s		1.4467	1.4863	1.5000	1.5129	1.5250	1.5366	1.5476	1.5972	1.6407	1.6801
900 (531.98)	v		0.5264	0.5873	0.6089	0.6294	0.6491	0.6680	0.6863	0.7716	0.8506	0.9262
	h		1215.0	1260.1	1275.9	1290.9	1305.1	1318.8	1332.1	1393.9	1451.8	1508.1
	s		1.4216	1.4653	1.4800	1.4938	1.5066	1.5187	1.5303	1.5814	1.6257	1.6656
1000 (544.61)	v		0.4533	0.5140	0.5350	0.5546	0.5733	0.5912	0.6084	0.6878	0.7604	0.8294
	h		1198.3	1248.8	1265.9	1281.9	1297.0	1311.4	1325.3	1389.2	1448.2	1505.1
	s		1.3961	1.4450	1.4610	1.4757	1.4893	1.5021	1.5141	1.5670	1.6121	1.6525
1100 (556.31)	v			0.4532	0.4738	0.4929	0.5110	0.5281	0.5445	0.6191	0.6866	0.7503
	h			1236.7	1255.3	1272.4	1288.5	1303.7	1318.3	1384.3	1444.5	1502.2
	s			1.4251	1.4425	1.4583	1.4728	1.4862	1.4989	1.5535	1.5995	1.6405
1200 (567.22)	v			0.4016	0.4222	0.4410	0.4586	0.4752	0.4909	0.5617	0.6250	0.6843
	h			1223.5	1243.9	1262.4	1279.6	1295.7	1311.0	1379.3	1440.7	1499.2
	s			1.4052	1.4243	1.4413	1.4568	1.4710	1.4843	1.5409	1.5879	1.6293
1400 (587.10)	v			0.3174	0.3390	0.3580	0.3753	0.3912	0.4062	0.4714	0.5281	0.5805
	h			1193.0	1218.4	1240.4	1260.3	1278.5	1295.5	1369.1	1433.1	1493.2
	s			1.3639	1.3877	1.4079	1.4258	1.4419	1.4567	1.5177	1.5666	1.6093
1600 (604.90)	v				0.2733	0.2936	0.3112	0.3271	0.3417	0.4034	0.4553	0.5027
	h				1187.8	1215.2	1238.7	1259.6	1278.7	1358.4	1425.3	1487.0
	s				1.3489	1.3741	1.3952	1.4137	1.4303	1.4964	1.5476	1.5914
1800 (621.03)	v					0.2407	0.2597	0.2760	0.2907	0.3502	0.3986	0.4421
	h					1185.1	1214.0	1238.5	1260.3	1347.2	1417.4	1480.8
	s					1.3377	1.3638	1.3855	1.4044	1.4765	1.5301	1.5752
2000 (635.82)	v					0.1936	0.2161	0.2337	0.2489	0.3074	0.3532	0.3935
	h					1145.6	1184.9	1214.8	1240.0	1335.5	1409.2	1474.5
	s					1.2945	1.3300	1.3564	1.3783	1.4576	1.5139	1.5603
2500 (668.13)	v							0.1484	0.1686	0.2294	0.2710	0.3061
	h							1132.3	1176.8	1303.6	1387.8	1458.4
	s							1.2687	1.3073	1.4127	1.4772	1.5273
3000 (695.36)	v								0.0984	0.1760	0.2159	0.2476
	h								1060.7	1267.2	1365.0	1441.8
	s								1.1966	1.3690	1.4439	1.4984
3206.2 (705.40)	v									0.1583	0.1981	0.2288
	h									1250.5	1355.2	1434.7
	s									1.3508	1.4309	1.4874

Table XI. SATURATED AMMONIA*

Pressure psi abs. p	Temp. of t	Volume		Enthalpy			Entropy	
		Liquid v_f	Vapor v_g	Liquid h_f	Evap. h_{fg}	Vapor h_g	Liquid s_f	Vapor s_g
5.0	−63.11	0.02271	49.31	−24.5	612.8	588.3	−0.0599	1.4857
10.0	−41.34	0.02319	25.81	− 1.4	598.5	597.1	−0.0034	1.4276
15.0	−27.29	0.02350	17.67	13.6	588.8	602.4	0.0318	1.3938
15.98	−25.0	0.02357	16.66	16.0	587.2	603.2	0.0374	1.3886
18.30	−20.0	0.02369	14.68	21.4	583.6	605.0	0.0497	1.3774
19.7	−17.20	0.02375	13.70	24.4	581.6	606.0	0.0560	1.3710
20.0	−16.64	0.02378	13.50	25.0	581.2	606.2	0.0578	1.3700
20.88	−15.0	0.02381	12.97	26.7	580.0	606.7	0.0618	1.3664
21.0	−14.78	0.02382	12.90	27.0	579.8	606.8	0.0623	1.3659
23.74	−10.0	0.02393	11.50	32.1	576.4	608.5	0.0738	1.3558
24.7	− 8.40	0.02397	11.086	33.8	575.2	609.0	0.0772	1.3525
25.0	− 7.96	0.02398	10.96	34.3	574.8	609.1	0.0787	1.3515
26.92	− 5.0	0.02406	10.23	37.5	572.6	610.1	0.0857	1.3454
28.0	− 3.40	0.02410	9.853	39.3	571.4	610.7	0.0895	1.3421
30.0	− 0.57	0.02418	9.236	42.3	569.3	611.6	0.0962	1.3364
30.42	0.0	0.02419	9.116	42.9	568.9	611.8	0.0975	1.3352
34.27	5.0	0.02432	8.150	48.3	565.0	613.3	0.1092	1.3253
34.7	5.52	0.02433	8.067	48.9	564.6	613.5	0.1104	1.3243
35.0	5.89	0.02434	7.991	49.3	564.3	613.6	0.1113	1.3236
37.7	9.07	0.02443	7.452	52.8	561.8	614.6	0.1187	1.3175
38.51	10.0	0.02446	7.304	53.8	561.1	614.9	0.1208	1.3157
40.0	11.66	0.02451	7.047	55.6	559.8	615.4	0.1246	1.3125
43.14	15.00	0.02460	6.562	59.2	557.1	616.3	0.1323	1.3062
48.21	20.0	0.02474	5.910	64.7	553.1	617.8	0.1437	1.2969
50.0	21.67	0.02479	5.710	66.5	551.7	618.2	0.1475	1.2939
53.73	25.00	0.02488	5.334	70.2	548.9	619.1	0.1551	1.2879
73.32	40.0	0.02533	3.971	86.8	536.2	623.0	0.1885	1.2618
100.0	56.05	0.02584	2.952	104.7	521.8	626.5	0.2237	1.2356
107.6	60.0	0.02597	2.751	109.2	518.1	627.3	0.2322	1.2294
120.0	66.02	0.02618	2.476	116.0	512.4	628.4	0.2452	1.2201
124.3	68.00	0.02625	2.393	118.3	510.5	628.8	0.2494	1.2170
128.8	70.0	0.02632	2.312	120.5	508.6	629.1	0.2537	1.2140
130.0	70.53	0.02634	2.291	121.1	508.1	629.2	0.2548	1.2132
150.0	78.81	0.02664	1.994	130.6	499.9	630.5	0.2724	1.2009
153.0	80.0	0.02668	1.955	132.0	498.7	630.7	0.2749	1.1991
166.4	85.0	0.02687	1.801	137.8	493.6	631.4	0.2854	1.1918
169.2	86.00	0.02691	1.772	138.9	492.6	631.5	0.2875	1.1904
174.8	88.00	0.02698	1.716	141.2	490.6	631.8	0.2917	1.1875
180.0	89.78	0.02706	1.667	143.3	488.7	632.0	0.2954	1.1850
180.6	90.0	0.02707	1.661	143.5	488.5	632.0	0.2958	1.1846
186.6	92.00	0.02715	1.609	145.8	486.4	632.2	0.3000	1.1818
190.0	93.13	0.02720	1.581	147.2	485.2	632.4	0.3024	1.1802
200.0	96.34	0.02732	1.502	150.9	481.8	632.7	0.3090	1.1756
205.0	97.90	0.02738	1.466	152.7	480.1	632.8	0.3122	1.1734
214.7	100.90	0.02751	1.400	156.2	476.9	633.1	0.3180	1.1690
247.0	110.00	0.02790	1.217	167.0	466.7	633.7	0.3372	1.1566

*Extracted by permission from Tables of Thermodynamic Properties of Ammonia, U. S. Bureau of Standards Bulletin No. 142.

Table XII. SUPERHEATED AMMONIA*

Temp. °F.	Absolute Pressure, psi. (Saturation temperature in italics)								
	15 −27.29°			20 −16.64°			25 −7.96°		
	v	h	s	v	h	s	v	h	s
Sat.	17.67	602.4	1.3938	13.50	606.2	1.3700	10.96	609.1	1.3515
−20	18.01	606.4	1.4031	.....	.....	.....	.....	.....	.....
−10	18.47	611.9	.4154	13.74	610.0	1.3784	.....	.....	.....
0	18.92	617.2	1.4272	14.09	615.5	1.3907	11.19	613.8	1.3616
10	19.37	622.5	.4386	14.44	621.0	.4025	11.47	619.4	.3738
20	19.82	627.8	.4497	14.78	626.4	.4138	11.75	625.0	.3855
30	20.26	633.0	.4604	15.11	631.7	.4248	12.03	630.4	.3967
40	20.70	638.2	.4709	15.45	637.0	.4356	12.30	635.8	.4077
50	21.14	643.4	1.4812	15.78	642.3	1.4460	12.57	641.2	1.4183
60	21.58	648.5	.4912	16.12	647.5	.4562	12.84	646.5	.4287
70	22.01	653.7	.5011	16.45	652.8	.4662	13.11	651.8	.4388
80	22.44	658.9	.5108	16.78	658.0	.4760	13.37	657.1	.4487
90	22.88	664.0	.5203	17.10	663.2	.4856	13.64	662.4	.4584
100	23.31	669.2	1.5296	17.43	668.5	1.4950	13.90	667.7	1.4679
110	23.74	674.4	.5388	17.76	673.7	.5042	14.17	673.0	.4772
120	24.17	679.6	.5478	18.08	678.9	.5133	14.43	678.2	.4864
130	24.60	684.8	.5567	18.41	684.2	.5223	14.69	683.5	.4954
140	25.03	690.0	.5655	18.73	689.4	.5312	14.95	688.8	.5043
150	25.46	695.3	1.5742	19.05	694.7	1.5399	15.21	694.1	1.5131
160	25.88	700.5	.5827	19.37	700.0	.5485	15.47	699.4	.5217
170	26.31	705.8	.5911	19.70	705.3	.5569	15.73	704.7	.5303
180	26.74	711.1	.5995	20.02	710.6	.5653	15.99	710.1	.5387
190	27.16	716.4	.6077	20.34	715.9	.5736	16.25	715.4	.5470
200	27.59	721.7	1.6158	20.66	721.2	1.5817	16.50	720.8	1.5552
220	28.44	732.4	.6318	21.30	732.0	.5978	17.02	731.6	.5713
240	.....	.....	.....	21.94	742.8	.6135	17.53	742.5	.5870
260	.....	.....	.....	.....	.....	.....	18.04	753.4	.6025
	30 −0.57°			35 5.89°			40 11.66°		
Sat.	9.236	611.6	1.3364	7.991	613.6	1.3236	7.047	615.4	1.3125
10	9.492	617.8	1.3497	8.078	616.1	1.3289	.....	.....	.....
20	9.731	623.5	.3618	8.287	622.0	.3413	7.203	620.4	1.3231
30	9.966	629.1	.3733	8.493	627.7	.3532	7.387	626.3	.3353
40	10.20	634.6	.3845	8.695	633.4	.3646	7.568	632.1	.3470
50	10.43	640.1	1.3953	8.895	638.9	1.3756	7.746	637.8	1.3583
60	10.65	645.5	.4059	9.093	644.4	.3863	7.922	643.4	.3692
70	10.88	650.9	.4161	9.289	649.9	.3967	8.096	648.9	.3797
80	11.10	656.2	.4261	9.484	655.3	.4069	8.268	654.4	.3900
90	11.33	661.6	.4359	9.677	660.7	.4168	8.439	659.9	.4000
100	11.55	666.9	1.4456	9.869	666.1	1.4265	8.609	665.3	1.4098
110	11.77	672.2	.4550	10.06	671.5	.4360	8.777	670.7	.4194
120	11.99	677.5	.4642	10.25	676.8	.4453	8.945	676.1	.4288
130	12.21	682.9	.4733	10.44	682.2	.4545	9.112	681.5	.4381
140	12.43	688.2	.4823	10.63	687.6	.4635	9.278	686.9	.4471
150	12.65	693.5	1.4911	10.82	692.9	1.4724	9.444	692.3	1.4561
160	12.87	698.8	.4998	11.00	698.3	.4811	9.609	697.7	.4648
170	13.08	704.2	.5083	11.19	703.7	.4897	9.774	703.1	.4735
180	13.30	709.6	.5168	11.38	709.1	.4982	9.938	708.5	.4820
190	13.52	714.9	.5251	11.56	714.5	.5066	10.10	714.0	.4904
200	13.73	720.3	1.5334	11.75	719.9	1.5148	10.27	719.4	1.4987
220	14.16	731.1	.5495	12.12	730.7	.5311	10.59	730.3	.5150
240	14.59	742.0	.5653	12.49	741.7	.5469	10.92	741.3	.5309
260	15.02	753.0	.5808	12.86	752.7	.5624	11.24	752.3	.5465
280	15.45	764.1	.5960	13.23	763.7	.5776	11.56	763.4	.5617
300	.....	.....	.....	.....	.....	.....	11.88	774.6	.5766

* Extracted by permission from Tables of Thermodynamic Properties of Ammonia, U. S. Bureau of Standards Bulletin No. 142.

Table XII. *SUPERHEATED AMMONIA* (*Continued*)

Temp. °F.	Absolute Pressure, psi. (Saturation temperature in italics)								
	110 *61.21°*			**120** *66.02°*			**140** *74.79°*		
	v	*h*	*s*	*v*	*h*	*s*	*v*	*h*	*s*
Sat.	*2.693*	*627.5*	*1.2275*	*2.476*	*628.4*	*1.2201*	*2.132*	*629.9*	*1.2068*
70	2.761	633.7	1.2392	2.505	631.3	1.2255	.....	.....	.....
80	2.837	640.5	.2519	2.576	638.3	.2386	2.166	633.8	1.2140
90	2.910	647.0	.2640	2.645	645.0	.2510	2.228	640.9	.2272
100	2.981	653.4	1.2755	2.712	651.6	1.2628	2.288	647.8	1.2396
110	3.051	659.7	.2866	2.778	658.0	.2741	2.347	654.5	.2515
120	3.120	665.8	.2972	2.842	664.2	.2850	2.404	661.1	.2628
130	3.188	671.9	.3076	2.905	670.4	.2956	2.460	667.4	.2738
140	3.255	677.8	.3176	2.967	676.5	.3058	2.515	673.7	.2843
150	3.321	683.7	1.3274	3.029	682.5	1.3157	2.569	679.9	1.2945
160	3.386	689.6	.3370	3.089	688.4	.3254	2.622	686.0	.3045
170	3.451	695.4	.3463	3.149	694.3	.3348	2.675	692.0	.3141
180	3.515	701.2	.3555	3.209	700.2	.3441	2.727	698.0	.3236
190	3.579	707.0	.3644	3.268	706.0	.3531	2.779	704.0	.3328
200	3.642	712.8	1.3732	3.326	711.8	1.3620	2.830	709.9	1.3418
210	3.705	718.5	.3819	3.385	717.6	.3707	2.880	715.8	.3507
220	3.768	724.3	.3904	3.442	723.4	.3793	2.931	721.6	.3594
230	3.830	730.0	.3988	3.500	729.2	.3877	2.981	727.5	.3679
240	3.892	735.7	.4070	3.557	734.9	.3960	3.030	733.3	.3763
250	3.954	741.5	1.4151	3.614	740.7	1.4042	3.080	739.2	1.3846
260	4.015	747.2	.4232	3.671	746.5	.4123	3.129	745.0	.3928
270	4.076	752.9	.4311	3.727	752.2	.4202	3.179	750.8	.4008
280	4.137	758.7	.4389	3.783	758.0	.4281	3.227	756.7	.4088
290	4.198	764.5	.4466	3.839	763.8	.4359	3.275	762.5	.4166
300	4.259	770.2	1.4543	3.895	769.6	1.4435	3.323	768.3	1.4243
320	.....	.....	.....	.....	.....	.....	3.420	780.0	.4395
	100 *82.64°*			**180** *89.78°*			**200** *96.34°*		
Sat.	*1.872*	*631.1*	*1.1952*	*1.667*	*632.0*	*1.1850*	*1.502*	*632.7*	*1.1756*
90	1.914	636.6	1.2055	1.668	632.2	1.1853	.....	.....	.....
100	1.969	643.9	1.2186	1.720	639.9	1.1992	1.520	635.6	1.1809
110	2.023	651.0	.2311	1.770	647.3	.2123	1.567	643.4	.1947
120	2.075	657.8	.2429	1.818	654.4	.2247	1.612	650.9	.2077
130	2.125	664.4	.2542	1.865	661.3	.2364	1.656	658.1	.2200
140	2.175	670.9	.2652	1.910	668.0	.2477	1.698	665.0	.2317
150	2.224	677.2	1.2757	1.955	674.6	1.2586	1.740	671.8	1.2429
160	2.272	683.5	.2859	1.999	681.0	.2691	1.780	678.4	.2537
170	2.319	689.7	.2958	2.042	687.3	.2792	1.820	684.9	.2641
180	2.365	695.8	.3054	2.084	693.6	.2891	1.859	691.3	.2742
190	2.411	701.9	.3148	2.126	699.8	.2987	1.897	697.7	.2840
200	2.457	707.9	1.3240	2.167	705.9	1.3081	1.935	703.9	1.2935
210	2.502	713.9	.3331	2.208	712.0	.3172	1.972	710.1	.3029
220	2.547	719.9	.3419	2.248	718.1	.3262	2.009	716.3	.3120
230	2.591	725.8	.3506	2.288	724.1	.3350	2.046	722.4	.3209
240	2.635	731.7	.3591	2.328	730.1	.3436	2.082	728.4	.3296
250	2.679	737.6	1.3675	2.367	736.1	1.3521	2.118	734.5	1.3382
260	2.723	743.5	.3757	2.407	742.0	.3605	2.154	740.5	.3467
270	2.766	749.4	.3838	2.446	748.0	.3687	2.189	746.5	.3550
280	2.809	755.3	.3919	2.484	753.9	.3768	2.225	752.5	.3631
290	2.852	761.2	.3998	2.523	759.9	.3847	2.260	758.5	.3712
300	2.895	767.1	1.4076	2.561	765.8	1.3926	2.295	764.5	1.3791
320	2.980	778.9	.4229	2.637	777.7	.4081	2.364	776.5	.3947
340	3.064	790.7	.4379	2.713	789.6	.4231	2.432	788.5	.4099

Table XIII. *HEATING VALUE OF FUELS AT CONSTANT PRESSURE*

All heating values $-h°_{rp}$ are for a reference state at 77°F, or essentially so, and are for complete combustion to the most stable state, except C to CO. Values for substances marked with an asterisk * are for academic use only, because the compositions and heating values of the substances vary markedly. However, given the ultimate analysis of dry coal, etc., the heating value is approximated by a sum of the values for the elements. Meanings of symbols: in choosing a heating value, use (s), (l), or (g) to indicate the phase of the fuel: (s) = solid; (l) = liquid; (g) = gas. Unless otherwise indicated, choose the heating value according to the natural state of the fuel; for example, benzene is normally a liquid—therefore, use values opposite (l). (a) Lower heating value for H_2O not condensed. (b) Higher heating value for H_2O condensed. In every case, the CO_2 is in a gaseous state.

Fuel	Formula	M	$-h°_{rp}$ Btu/lb. Fuel, Solid or Liquid		$-h°_{rp}$ Btu/lb. Fuel, Gaseous Fuel	
			Lower (a) $q°_l$	Higher (b) $q°_h$	Lower (a) $q°_l$	Higher (b) $q°_h$
SOLID (s)						
Anthracite coal*			13,330	13,540		
Bituminous coal*			13,100	13,600		
Carbon (to CO_2)	C	12.01	14,086.8			
Carbon (to CO)	C	12.01	3,990			
Coke, beehive			12,450	12,530		
Lignite*			6,700	7,350		
Sulfur	S	32.06	3,980			
Wood, air-dried oak*			8,000			
NORMALLY LIQUID (l)						
Benzene	C_6H_6	78.108	17,259	17,986	17,446	18,172
n-Decane	$C_{10}H_{22}$	142.276	19,020	20,483	19,175	20,638
n-Dodecane	$C_{12}H_{26}$	170.328	18,966	20,410	19,120	20,564
Ethyl alcohol	C_2H_6O	46.068	11,929	13,161		
Fuel oil*			18,500	19,700		
Gasoline*			18,800	20,200		
n-Heptane	C_7H_{16}	100.198	19,157	20,668	19,314	20,825
n-Hexadecane	$C_{16}H_{34}$	226.432	18,898	20,318	19,052	20,472
Kerosene*			18,500	19,900		
Methyl alcohol	CH_4O	32.042	9,078	10,259		
n-Octane	C_8H_{18}	114.224	19,100	20,591	19,256	20,746
Octene	C_8H_{16}	112.208	19,000	20,350	19,157	20,506
n-Pentane	C_5H_{12}	72.146	19,340	20,914	19,499	21,072
NORMALLY GAS (g)						
Acetylene	C_2H_2	26.036			20,734	21,460
Blast-furnace gas*					1,100	1,120
n-Butane	C_4H_{10}	58.120	19,508	21,134	19,665	21,293
Carbon Monoxide	CO	28.01			4,343.6	
Cyanogen [to CO_2 and N_2]	C_2N_2	80.052			5,890	
Ethane	C_2H_6	30.068			20,416	22,304
Ethene	C_2H_4	28.052			20,276	21,625
Hydrogen	H_2	2.016			51,571.4	60,957.7
Methane	CH_4	16.042			21,502	23,861
Natural gas*					20,500	23,000
n-Pentane	C_5H_{12}	72.146	19,340	20,914	19,499	21,072
Propane	C_3H_8	44.094			19,929	21,846
Refinery gas*					19,600	21,400

Table XIV. SATURATION PROPERTIES OF FREON 12*

Temp. °F	Abs. Pres. psi	Volume cu. ft./lb.		Enthalpy Btu/lb.			Entropy Btu/lb-°R	
t	p	v_f	v_g	h_f	h_{fg}	h_g	s_f	s_g
−10	19.19	0.01091	1.973	6.37	69.82	76.19	0.01462	0.16989
0	23.85	0.01103	1.609	8.52	68.75	77.27	0.01932	0.16888
1	24.36	0.01104	1.577	8.74	68.64	77.38	0.01979	0.16878
10	29.34	0.01116	1.324	10.68	67.65	78.33	0.02395	0.16798
20	35.74	0.01130	1.099	12.86	66.52	79.38	0.02851	0.16719
30	43.15	0.01144	0.919	15.06	65.36	80.42	0.03301	0.16648
40	51.67	0.01159	0.774	17.27	64.16	81.43	0.03745	0.16586
50	61.39	0.01175	0.655	19.51	62.93	82.44	0.04184	0.16530
60	72.43	0.01191	0.558	21.77	61.64	83.41	0.04618	0.16479
70	84.89	0.01209	0.478	24.05	60.31	84.36	0.05048	0.16434
80	98.87	0.01228	0.411	26.36	58.92	85.28	0.05475	0.16392
90	114.49	0.01248	0.355	28.71	57.46	86.17	0.05900	0.16353
100	131.86	0.01269	0.308	31.10	55.93	87.03	0.06323	0.16315

Table XV. PROPERTIES OF SUPERHEATED FREON 12*

Saturation properties in italics

Temp. °F	80 PSIA (*66.21°F*)			100 PSIA (*80.76°F*)		
	v	h	s	v	h	s
	0.5068	*84.00*	*0.16450*	*0.4067*	*85.35*	*0.16389*
70	0.5127	84.64	0.16571			
80	0.528	86.32	0.16885			
90	0.543	87.98	0.17190	0.419	86.96	0.16685
100	0.557	89.64	0.17489	0.431	88.69	0.16996
110	0.572	91.24	0.17782	0.444	90.41	0.17300

Temp. °F	115 PSIA (*90.31°F*)			150 PSIA (*109.45°F*)		
	0.3537	*86.20*	*0.16352*	*0.2697*	*87.80*	*0.16281*
100	0.365	87.94	0.16665			
110	0.376	89.71	0.16978	0.271	87.91	0.16299
120	0.387	91.46	0.17283	0.280	89.80	0.16629
130	0.398	93.20	0.17581	0.289	91.66	0.16947

* Copyright 1955 and 1956, E. I. du Pont de Nemours & Co., Inc. Reprinted by permission.

Table XVI. *USEFUL CONSTANTS*

Abbreviations: atm = atmospheres, cal = calorie, cm = centimeter, gm = gram, gmol = gram-mol, kcal = kilo-calorie, kg = kilogram, kJ = kilo-joule, km = kilometer, kw = kilowatt, m = meter, mol = lb. mol, wt = watt; others as usual. $2.3 \log_{10} N = \log_e N = \ln N$.

LINEAR

$12 \dfrac{\text{in.}}{\text{ft.}}$	$0.394 \dfrac{\text{in.}}{\text{cm}}$	$30.48 \dfrac{\text{cm}}{\text{ft.}}$	$5280 \dfrac{\text{ft.}}{\text{mi.}}$
$3 \dfrac{\text{ft.}}{\text{yd.}}$	$2.54 \dfrac{\text{cm}}{\text{in.}}$	$3.28 \dfrac{\text{ft.}}{\text{m}}$	$1.609 \dfrac{\text{km}}{\text{mi.}}$

AREA

$43{,}560 \dfrac{\text{ft}^2}{\text{acre}}$	$144 \dfrac{\text{in.}^2}{\text{ft}^2}$	$10.76 \dfrac{\text{ft}^2}{\text{m}^2}$	$640 \dfrac{\text{acres}}{\text{mi}^2}$	$6.45 \dfrac{\text{cm}^2}{\text{in.}^2}$

VOLUME

$1728 \dfrac{\text{in.}^3}{\text{ft}^3}$	$7.481 \dfrac{\text{gal.}}{\text{ft}^3}$	$8 \dfrac{\text{pt.}}{\text{gal.}}$	$28{,}320 \dfrac{\text{cm}^3}{\text{ft}^3}$
$231 \dfrac{\text{in.}^3}{\text{gal.}}$	$1.244 \dfrac{\text{ft}^3}{\text{bushel}}$	$43{,}560 \dfrac{\text{ft}^3}{\text{acre-ft.}}$	$3531 \dfrac{\text{ft}^3}{\text{m}^3}$

ANGULAR

$6.2832 \dfrac{\text{rad.}}{\text{rev.}}$	$57.3 \dfrac{\text{deg.}}{\text{rad.}}$	$9.549 \dfrac{\text{rpm}}{\text{rad./sec}}$

TIME

$60 \dfrac{\text{sec.}}{\text{min.}}$	$3600 \dfrac{\text{sec.}}{\text{hr.}}$	$60 \dfrac{\text{min.}}{\text{hr.}}$	$24 \dfrac{\text{hr.}}{\text{day}}$

SPEED

$1.152 \dfrac{\text{mph}}{\text{knot}}$	$88 \dfrac{\text{fpm}}{\text{mph}}$	$0.6818 \dfrac{\text{mph}}{\text{fps}}$	$1.467 \dfrac{\text{fps}}{\text{mph}}$

FORCE, PRESSURE, MASS

$2000 \dfrac{\text{lb.}}{\text{ton}}$	$1000 \dfrac{\text{lb.}}{\text{kip}}$	$2.205 \dfrac{\text{lb.}}{\text{kg}}$	$33.9 \dfrac{\text{ft. H}_2\text{O (60°F)}}{\text{atm}}$	$0.49 \dfrac{\text{psi}}{\text{in. Hg (60°F)}}$
$16 \dfrac{\text{oz.}}{\text{lb.}}$	$7000 \dfrac{\text{grains}}{\text{lb.}}$	$453.6 \dfrac{\text{gm}}{\text{lb.}}$	$13.6 \dfrac{\text{in. H}_2\text{O}}{\text{in. Hg}}$	$0.0361 \dfrac{\text{psi}}{\text{in. H}_2\text{O (60°F)}}$
$32.174 \dfrac{\text{lb.}}{\text{slug}}$	$444{,}800 \dfrac{\text{dynes}}{\text{lb.}}$	$980.7 \dfrac{\text{dynes}}{\text{gm}}$	$29.92 \dfrac{\text{in. Hg (32°F)}}{\text{atm}}$	

ENERGY AND POWER

$860 \dfrac{\text{cal(IT)}}{\text{wt-hr.}}$	$33{,}000 \dfrac{\text{ft-lb.}}{\text{hp-min.}}$	$2544 \dfrac{\text{Btu}}{\text{hp-hr.}}$	$3412.1 \dfrac{\text{Btu}}{\text{kw-hr.}}$	$1.341 \dfrac{\text{hp}}{\text{kw}}$	$1000 \dfrac{\text{joules}}{\text{kJ}}$
$1 \dfrac{\text{Joule}}{\text{wt-sec.}}$	$10^7 \dfrac{\text{ergs}}{\text{joule}}$	$1800 \dfrac{\text{Btu/lb.mol}}{\text{kcal/gmol}}$	$1.356 \dfrac{\text{joules}}{\text{ft-lb.}}$	$1.055 \dfrac{\text{kJ}}{\text{Btu}}$	$4.1868 \dfrac{\text{kJ}}{\text{kcal}}$
$778.172 \dfrac{\text{ft-lb.}}{\text{Btu}}$	$550 \dfrac{\text{ft-lb.}}{\text{hp-sec.}}$	$42.4 \dfrac{\text{Btu}}{\text{hp-min.}}$	$0.746 \dfrac{\text{kw}}{\text{hp}}$	$252 \dfrac{\text{cal}}{\text{Btu}}$	$3600 \dfrac{\text{kJ}}{\text{kw-hr.}}$
	$737.562 \dfrac{\text{ft-lb.}}{\text{kw-sec.}}$				

UNIVERSAL GAS CONSTANT

$1545.32 \dfrac{\text{ft-lb.}}{\text{mol-°R}}$	$0.730 \dfrac{\text{atm-ft}^3}{\text{mol-°R}}$	$0.00078 \dfrac{\text{hp-hr.}}{\text{mol-°R}}$
$1.986 \dfrac{\text{Btu}}{\text{mol-°R}}$ and $\dfrac{\text{cal}}{\text{gmol-°K}}$	$10.73 \dfrac{\text{psia-ft}^3}{\text{mol-°R}}$	$82.06 \dfrac{\text{atm-cm}^3}{\text{gmol-°K}}$

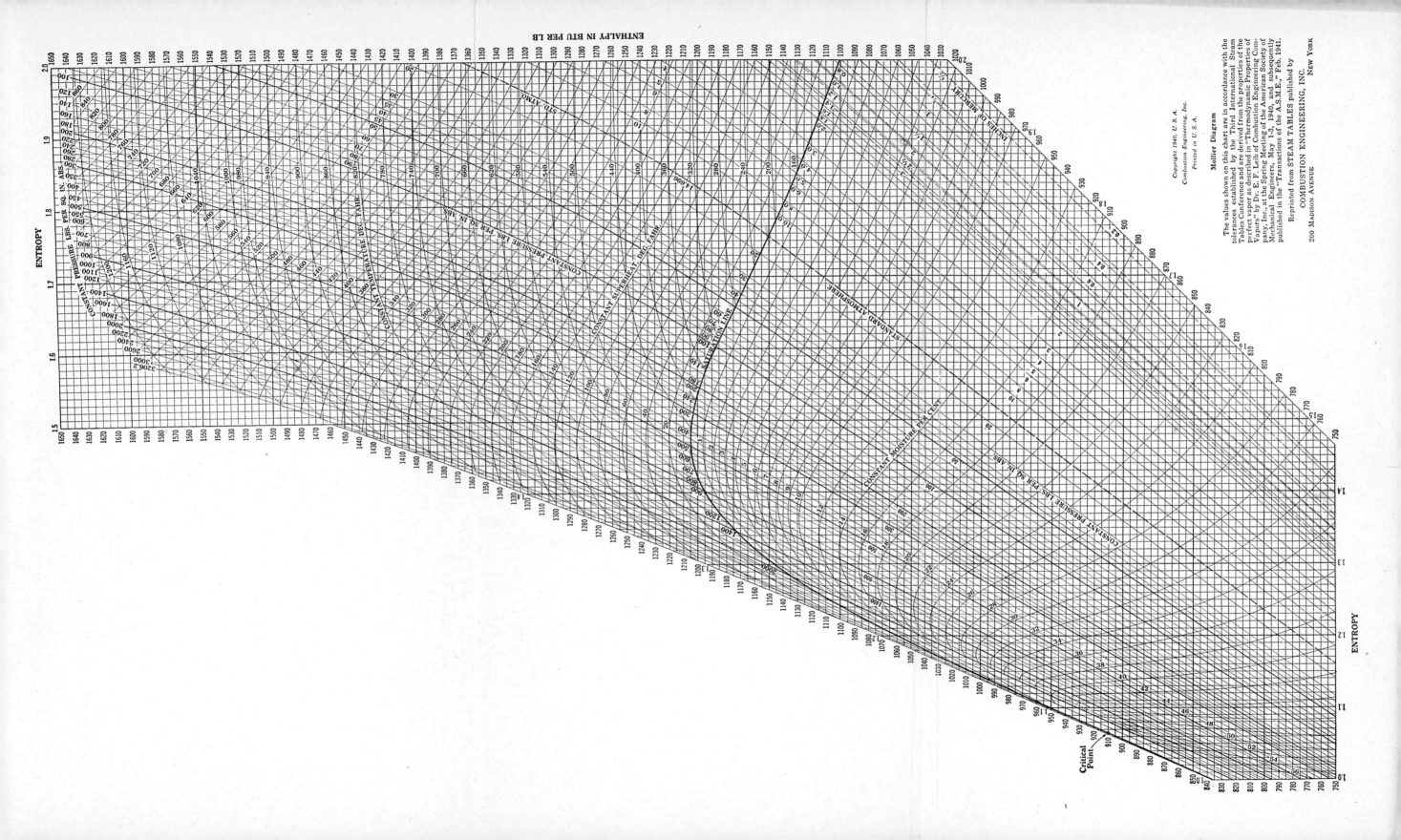

Mollier Diagram

The values shown on this chart are in accordance with the tolerances established by the Third International Steam Tables Conference and are derived from the properties of the perfect vapor as described in "Thermodynamic Properties of Vapors" by Dr. E. F. Leib of Combustion Engineering Company, Inc., at the Spring Meeting of the American Society of Mechanical Engineers, May 1-3, 1940, and subsequently published in the "Transactions of the A.S.M.E.," Feb. 1941.

Reprinted from STEAM TABLES published by
COMBUSTION ENGINEERING, INC.   NEW YORK
200 MADISON AVENUE

INDEX